D1539282

INTERNATIONAL SERIES IN PHYSICS

LEE A. DuBRIDGE, Consulting Editor

HIGH-FREQUENCY MEASUREMENTS

INTERNATIONAL SERIES IN PHYSICS

LEE A. DuBRIDGE, *Consulting Editor*

Dr. F. K. Richtmyer was consulting editor of the series from its inception in 1929 until his death in 1939.

HIGH-FREQUENCY MEASUREMENTS

BY

AUGUST HUND

Consulting Engineer, Fellow of the American Physical Society,
Institute of Radio Engineers, American Association
for the Advancement of Science

FIRST EDITION
EIGHTH IMPRESSION

McGRAW-HILL BOOK COMPANY, INC.

NEW YORK AND LONDON

1933

THE MAPLE PRESS COMPANY, YORK, PA.

PREFACE

Experimental work with high-frequency phenomena confronts us in many branches of natural philosophy. Therefore, familiarity with classical as well as modern science is of great advantage for successful research work. Consideration of this has been given in the following pages.

Unlike low-frequency measurements, the subject of this book deals with methods covering a very wide frequency band. What may be geometrically a coil and behave as an inductance in effect for the lower frequency range, may act in effect as a capacitance in the upper frequency band. Even simple devices, such as a voltmeter, may require a circuit and sometimes several circuits. A thorough knowledge of the frequency characteristic of the entire system is of importance. Generally speaking, it is not always possible to describe methods that are reliable for all kinds of experimental work. It is up to the investigator to use his judgment and to possess a certain degree of experimental skill. For this reason, many physical phenomena in direct application to high-frequency apparatus are described, and circuits as well as methods are critically discussed in order to show their limitations.

With respect to mathematical nomenclature and standard test circuits, whenever possible the rules of the Standardization Committee of the Institute of Radio Engineers are followed. Since many branches of science are here dealt with, duplication of symbols occurs in some cases. However, duplication is never found in any one formula. Thus among magnetic measurements μ is the conventional symbol for the magnetic permeability, and among tube measurements the same letter is found for the conventional amplification factor. Since the letter e is used to denote the instantaneous value of a voltage, it could not be employed to express the charge of an electron; therefore q is used. $\mathcal{E}$, a large printed epsilon, is used for the electric-field intensity so that it will not be confused with the voltage E which corresponds to it. There should be no confusion between ϵ used for the basis of the natural logarithm and the quantity $\mathcal{E}$. Since ϵ is used for 2.7183, the letter κ is employed for the dielectric constant. κ_e is used for the effective dielectric constant, since in some cases, for instance for the ionized layer of the upper atmosphere and the earth crust, one often has to deal with a complex value of the effective dielectric constant. The symbol κ is also used for the coupling factor.

v

The author has attempted to give references to reliable papers published in various countries and to present the subject matter in combination with his personal experience. Most of the references given in the footnotes are added to enable the reader to refer to other details. For this reason the author of each article referred to is listed in the Index, where a brief description of the contents of his article appears.

This treatise is not a translation of the second edition of the author's book "Hochfrequenzmesstechnik" but may be regarded as an up-to-date work on high-frequency phenomena applied to measurements. If, in addition to bringing many methods before the reader, the book also encourages research work in a most fascinating field of applied science, it fulfills its purpose. The author welcomes any corrections or suggestions for improvement.

The author is much indebted to his wife for her assistance in the preparation of the manuscript, and to Mr. F. Yeck for the many sketches.

AUGUST HUND.

WEST ORANGE, N. J.,
February, 1933.

CONTENTS

HIGH-FREQUENCY MEASUREMENTS

CHAPTER I

FUNDAMENTAL RELATIONS AND CIRCUIT PROPERTIES

In accurate scientific work, the ideal is to carry on measurements which are without error. Since this ideal cannot be attained, the methods used, as well as the values observed, must be studied critically in order to determine the most probable value of the quantity which is being measured. In every measurement, all conditions which may affect the correctness of the value sought must be considered. This requires a thorough knowledge of the underlying physical principles, and in many cases a careful theoretical analysis.

High-frequency currents deal with rapidly varying currents the instantaneous values of which show a definite recurrence in time. In addition, a certain recurrence in space also exists for electromagnetic waves passing through space or along wires. The recurrence is expressed in terms of the frequency of the exciting current. The number of complete periods per second denotes the frequency. The high-frequency band includes a frequency range from about 20 kc/sec to 600 Mc/sec, corresponding to a wave-length range in free space of 15 km to 50 cm. The wave length refers to the distance through which an electromagnetic wave is propagated through free space during one cycle of its exciting current. The velocity of propagation is about 3×10^{10} cm/sec. The above range includes about all the currents useful in present-day high-frequency work but does not include the much shorter waves studied by Hertz and Lodge, since their energy output is, so far, rather limited.

Maxwell's electrodynamic-field equations show that high-frequency fields include both electric and magnetic fields. They *cannot* be separated and are always in phase for waves traveling in empty space. Therefore, it would be incorrect to say that an antenna receives only the electric field and a loop aerial only the magnetic field, just as it would be incorrect to say that a parallel-wire connection supplying the high-frequency energy to a Hertzian rod radiator is a current feed, and a single-wire connection between the generator and a suitable point on the rod a voltage feed. It takes voltage and current to deliver energy.

1

1. Difference between High- and Low-frequency Measurements.—
In some respects, measurements at high frequencies do not differ essentially from those at low frequencies, while in other respects new methods
are necessary. For example, the modified arrangements of the Wheatstone bridge can be used at high frequencies in only a few cases, because
the inductance and capacitance effects of the different branches become
sufficiently pronounced to make close adjustment extremely difficult
and at best somewhat indefinite.

The dynamic constants must be distinguished from the static constants of a circuit. By dynamic constants are meant the effective values
of capacitance, inductance, resistance, etc., at a high frequency. The
static constants are measured at a low frequency and where possible with
direct current. The difference between the dynamic and the static
values may be due to a nonuniform distribution of electric charges along
the surface of a conductor or to a nonuniform distribution of current and
potential throughout the conductor. An ordinary aerial or antenna used
in radio work is an example. At a high frequency, electrically speaking,
such an antenna is a very long conductor, though it is practically a point
for a 60-cycle current. A voltmeter connected at different places between
the antenna and the ground would indicate quite different values at a
high frequency, whereas its indication for a 60-cycle current would be
practically constant along the entire length.

Radiation is mostly due to reflections of electromagnetic disturbances
traveling along a wire. The reflections generally occur either at the
respective ends or at some other place (transformer, etc.). The lines
of force are, one might say, snapped off at the end of the line, and electromagnetic waves detach themselves into space just as electrons, which
are either accelerated or decelerated, start to radiate energy because a
portion of the total field is correspondingly accelerated or decelerated.
The reflections at the ends of a line become a maximum where a stationary
wave system is developed on the wire. This happens when an antenna
is tuned since the electromagnetic disturbance traveling toward the open
end is reflected there and travels back to ground with the same velocity.
The radiation becomes more pronounced, the higher the frequency of the
exciting current. For commercial frequencies (for instance, 60 cycles/
sec) the longest power lines are about one-tenth of a wave length. It
can be shown that for a double line of length l of spacing a, the radiation
resistance is

$$R = 32\pi^2 \left[\frac{l}{\lambda}\right]^2 \left[\frac{2\pi a}{\lambda}\right]^2 \tag{1}$$

Therefore, when a transmission line is $l = 1000$ km long and has a spacing
$a = 2 \times 10^{-3}$ km, one has for a commercial frequency $f = 60$ cycles/sec
and a wave length $\lambda = 5000$ km, a radiation resistance

$$R = 32\pi^2 \left[\frac{1000}{5000}\right]^2 \left[\frac{6.28 \times 2 \times 10^{-3}}{5000}\right]^2 = 8 \times 10^{-11} \text{ ohm}$$

which is a negligibly small value. For instance, if the transmission line would carry even as much as 100-amp alternating current, the energy would be radiated at the rate of only

$$W = 8 \times 10^{-11} \times 10^4 = 8 \times 10^{-7} \text{ watt}$$

Comparing formula (1) with the formula for a straight antenna of height l excited in the quarter wave-length distribution (fundamental $\lambda = 4l$), the radiation resistance is as high as

$$R = 1579 \left[\frac{h_e}{\lambda}\right]^2 = 1579 \left[\frac{\frac{2}{\pi}l}{4l}\right]^2 \cong 40 \text{ ohm} \qquad (2)$$

if h_e denotes the effective height of the grounded vertical wire.

A condenser of even small capacitance offers an easy path for high-frequency currents, while an ordinary air-core coil may constitute a very high impedance in a high-frequency circuit. An injurious cross current may flow in a multilayer coil that is not properly designed. This is due to the capacitance effect of the coil, in spite of the fact that the inductance still exercises its choking effect. For frequencies above a certain critical frequency, the coil acts like a condenser and it would require a properly designed inductance in series with the ordinary multilayer coil to tune it again. The dynamic value of resistance is higher than its static value and is conveniently determined by direct measurement. For a properly designed air condenser, the dynamic capacitance is about equal to its static value. However, this does not apply where spacious layers (of cylindrical or other shape) are used as electrodes, or where the conditions are such as to make corona (glow discharge) appear. The dynamic capacitance C_1 and the static capacitance C_2 also differ when an imperfect dielectric is employed. The ratio C_1/C_2 is known as the frequency factor of a condenser. The dynamic inductance of a coil differs from its static inductance (low-frequency value). It is usually higher, but for a poorly designed inductance the effective inductance can with increasing frequency become at first somewhat smaller than the low-frequency value, since eddy-current losses of some of the turns within the other turns may act as a secondary of a transformer and decrease the effective lines of flux. Actual measurements are the only safe criterion for the effective inductance of a coil.

2. Wave Shape and Its Effect upon Measurements.—Since both continuous and damped electric waves can be used in high-frequency work, they may be conveniently classed as:

    a. Sustained waves, sinusoidal or any other form, produced by ferric and non-ferric generators.

  b. Discrete wave trains, damped sinusoidal, generally produced by spark and buzzer exciters.

  Sinusoidal high-frequency currents are conveniently obtained from an electron-tube generator. Sustained high-frequency currents with pronounced higher harmonics are generally due to the presence of iron (which causes a pronounced triple frequency) or are caused by working on a too long or an unsuitable portion of the internal characteristic of a tube generator (a pronounced double frequency). Sometimes such currents with a large harmonic content have good features for measurements since a tuning is possible for all frequencies. The current flowing into a condenser when distorted gives a higher effective reading, since currents of double, triple, and other harmonic frequency are less impeded by the condenser than its fundamental which is supposed to be measured.

  When a coil is used, the effective voltage produced across its terminals is higher when a distorted current wave exists, since the choking effect of an inductance is all the more pronounced for higher harmonics and produces corresponding harmonic voltages across the inductances.

  For sinusoidal cases, the ratio of maximum value A_m to corresponding effective value A is equal to $\sqrt{2}$. If the amplitudes of a distorted case are A_1, A_2, A_3, A_4, etc., for the fundamental and the successive higher harmonics, the measured effective value A is

$$A = \sqrt{0.5[A_1{}^2 + A_2{}^2 + A_3{}^2 + A_4{}^2 + \cdots]} \qquad (3)$$

The quantity A stands for either the current or the voltage. The harmonic content may give rise to errors in resonance measurements (page 21).

  For damped wave trains due to N discharges per second, the exact formula is

$$A = 0.5A_m\sqrt{\frac{4L - CR}{2R}N} \qquad (4)$$

where C, L, and R are the effective circuit constants for the capacitance, inductance, and resistance of an oscillator in farads, henries, and ohms, and A_m stands for the maximum value. For most of the work, the approximation

$$A = 0.5A_m\sqrt{\frac{N}{\delta f}} \qquad (4a)$$

can be used if δ denotes the logarithmic decrement $(R/2fL)$ per cycle, and f the number of cycles per second.

  3. Effect of Condensers and Coils in Measuring Circuits.—When a resistance R is connected in parallel with a condenser C, the effective capacitance C_e is greater (by the amount $1/(\omega CR)^2$) than without the shunt resistance. This means that a voltmeter of effective resistance R

would slightly increase the capacitance C to some effective value C_e when used for measuring the terminal voltage of the condenser (Fig. 1). The effective capacitance is

$$C_e = C\left[1 + \frac{1}{\omega^2 C^2 R^2}\right] \tag{5}$$

At the same time the effective resistance R_e of the combination becomes considerably smaller and is

$$R_e = \frac{R}{1 + \omega^2 C^2 R^2} \tag{6}$$

FIG. 1.—Actual and equivalent circuit if the voltage is measured across the condenser C.

The validity of these formulas can be proved as follows: Since the impedances of the parallel branches are $Z_1 = R$, $Z_2 = 1/(j\omega C)$, we have for the equivalent impedance

$$Z = \frac{Z_1 Z_2}{Z_1 + Z_2} = \frac{R}{1 + \omega^2 C^2 R^2} - \frac{j}{\frac{1 + \omega^2 C^2 R^2}{\omega C R^2}} = R_e - \frac{j}{\omega C_e}$$

giving (5) and (6). From (6) we obtain $\omega^2 C^2 R^2 = \dfrac{R}{R_e} - 1$ which gives another expression for the effective capacity, namely,

$$C_e = C\left[1 + \frac{R_e}{R - R_e}\right] \tag{5a}$$

Since, according to (6), the effective decrement due to the parallel combination of C and R is considerably smaller than for R alone, we can always cut down circuit losses by shunting a resistance with a biasing condenser. This is done with great advantage in tube circuits where high-frequency currents are passed around the various resistances supplying the energy. These results also have a bearing on the measurement of high resistances, since a low resistance R_e connected in series with a capacitance C_e can be substituted by a capacitance C of practically the same magnitude as C_e with a high resistance R in parallel. Since in this case the resistance to be determined is unknown and $R_x = R$, and the voltage E, current I, and phase displacement φ must have the same respective values for both the parallel and the series combination shown in Fig. 2,

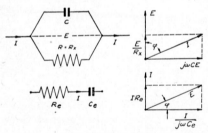

FIG. 2.—Phase angle φ of a condenser C whose loss resistance R_x is imagined to be in parallel and the equivalent series combination.

$$\tan \varphi = \omega C R_x = \frac{1}{\omega C_e R_e}$$

or

$$R_x = \frac{1}{\omega^2 C C_e R_e} \tag{7}$$

The case where the resistance R_x shows self-capacity effects is treated among the measurements on page 283. In a similar way it can be proved that an inductance L in parallel with a resistance[1] R has the equivalent constants

$$R_e = \frac{\omega^2 L^2}{R^2 + \omega^2 L^2} R \qquad L_e = \frac{R^2}{R^2 + \omega^2 L^2} L \tag{8}$$

These constants act again as though R_e and L_e were in series.

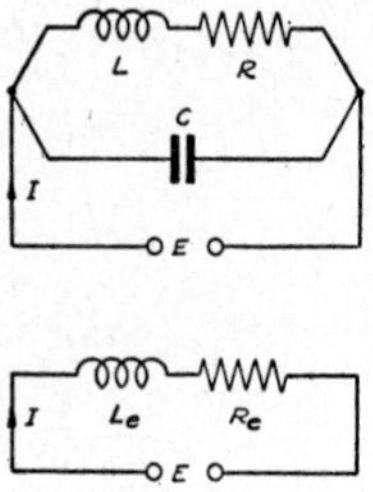

FIG. 3.—A coil with losses, in parallel with a perfect condenser and the equivalent series combination.

When a coil of inductance L and resistance R is shunted by a condenser of capacitance C as in Fig. 3, we find, for $Z_1 = R + j\omega L$ and $Z_2 = 1/j\omega C$, the equivalent impedance

$$Z = \frac{Z_1 Z_2}{Z_1 + Z_2} = \frac{R}{[1 - \omega^2 CL]^2 + \omega^2 C^2 R^2}$$
$$+ j\frac{\omega L[1 - \omega^2 CL] - \omega C R^2}{[1 - \omega^2 CL]^2 + \omega^2 C^2 R^2} = R_e + j\omega L_e$$

Therefore, the parallel condenser C changes the inductance L to an equivalent value

$$L_e = \frac{L[1 - \omega^2 CL] - CR^2}{[1 - \omega^2 CL]^2 + \omega^2 C^2 R^2} \cong \frac{L}{1 - \omega^2 CL} \tag{9}$$

and the resistance of it to a value

$$R_e = \frac{R}{[1 - \omega^2 CL]^2 + \omega^2 C^2 R^2} \cong \frac{R}{[1 - \omega^2 CL]} \tag{10}$$

For values of $\omega^2 CL$ smaller than unity, both the apparent inductance L_e and resistance R_e are larger than without a parallel condenser. Both are smaller for $\omega^2 CL > 1$.

An application of these results is the case of a coil with self-capacitance which can, as an approximation,[2] be imagined as being due to an inductance with a capacitance C in parallel. Hence the self-capacitance of a coil has the effect of increasing, at first, the inductance and the resistance with increasing frequency until from a certain frequency on

$$f_0 \cong \frac{1}{2\pi\sqrt{CL}}, \left(\text{exact formula Eq. (14)}\right) \text{ a decrease occurs. Since the}$$

displacement currents due to the self-capacitance C flow across the insulation of the coil, there exist dielectric losses and a resistance ρ must be

---

[1] R denotes the high-frequency resistance of the coil alone. If R_0 denotes the direct-current resistance, $R = R_0 + kf^2$; for details see under measurements on p. 278.

[2] Strictly, the self-capacitance is distributed in the coil.

assumed in series with C as in Fig. 4 in order to account for it. The effective resistance of the coil then becomes

$$R_e' = \frac{R + \omega^4 C^2 L^2 \rho + \omega^2 C^2 R \cdot \rho [R + \rho]}{[1 - \omega^2 CL]^2 + \omega^2 C^2 [R + \rho]^2} \simeq \frac{R + \omega^4 C^2 L^2 \rho}{[1 - \omega^2 CL]^2} \cdots \quad (11)$$

Comparing (10) and (11), we note that the coil capacitance C causes an increase[1] of the ordinary[2] high-frequency resistance according to the factor $1/[1 - \omega^2 CL]^2$, while the dielectric loss of the coil gives another increase $\omega^4 C^2 L^2 \rho / [1 - \omega^2 CL]^2$ where the term $\omega^4 C^2 L^2 \rho$ is the characteristic factor of the increase due to the loss in the fictitious resistance ρ in series with C and $1/[1 - \omega^2 CL]^2$ is the factor due to the ideal capacitance action on the dielectric effect.

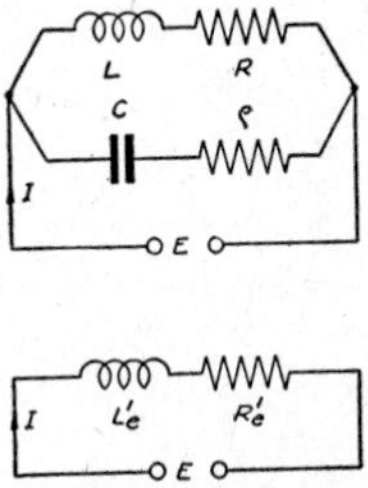

The equivalent inductance L_e' of the parallel combination shown in Fig. 4 is

FIG. 4.—A coil with losses, in parallel with a condenser with losses and the equivalent series combination.

$$L_e' = \frac{\frac{1}{\omega^2 C}\left[\frac{L}{C} - R^2\right] - L\left[\frac{L}{C} - \rho^2\right]}{[R + \rho]^2 + \left[\omega L - \frac{1}{\omega C}\right]^2} \quad (12)$$

since the equivalent series reactance $X = j\omega L_e'$. The resonance frequency $f_0 = \omega_0/2\pi$ occurs for the value of ω which makes the reactance $X = 0$, that is, which makes the numerator of L_e' vanish. It becomes

$$f_0 = \frac{1}{2\pi\sqrt{CL}}\sqrt{\frac{\frac{L}{C} - R^2}{\frac{L}{C} - \rho^2}} = \frac{1}{2\pi\sqrt{CL}}\sqrt{\frac{L - CR^2}{L - C\rho^2}} \quad (13)$$

which for the negligible dielectric loss ($\rho = 0$, Fig. 3) simplifies to

$$f_0 = \frac{1}{2\pi\sqrt{CL}}\sqrt{1 - \frac{CR^2}{L}} \quad (14)$$

Both results show that for current resonance the *resistance* affects the value of the resonance frequency to some extent. The total current I in Fig. 3 flowing to the parallel combination is

$$I = E\sqrt{\left[\frac{R}{R^2 + \omega^2 L^2}\right]^2 + \left[\omega C - \frac{\omega L}{R^2 + \omega^2 L^2}\right]^2} \quad (15)$$

The circuit is usually *tuned by varying* the setting of C which gives a minimum value

[1] The values for $\omega^2 CL < 1$ are of interest only because beyond the first natural coil resonance frequency, the coil is of no practical value anymore.

[2] According to footnote 1 on page 6, direct-current resistance plus increase due to the skin effect which is proportional to the square of the frequency.

$$I_{\min} = \frac{R}{R^2 + \omega^2 L^2} E \tag{16}$$

when E and I are in phase, that is, when $\omega C = \dfrac{\omega L}{R^2 + \omega^2 L^2}$. It is practically,[1] but *not exactly* the *same as when f is varied* until the value f_0 is reached. Equation (16) shows that for the apparent resonance setting (assuming for true resonance a frequency $\omega_0/2\pi$) the equivalent resistance of the combination has a value

$$R_e' = \frac{R^2 + \omega_0^2 L^2}{R} \tag{17}$$

[1] The rigid solution shows that the effective impedance of the parallel combination is

$$Z = \sqrt{\frac{R^2 + \omega^2 L^2}{(\omega R C)^2 + (\omega^2 C L - 1)^2}} \tag{I}$$

with a reactance

$$X = -\frac{\omega[L - C(\omega^2 L^2 + R^2)]}{(\omega R C)^2 + (\omega^2 C L - 1)^2} \tag{II}$$

By resonance is understood that the reactance vanishes, that is $X = 0$, or

$$L = C[R^2 + \omega^2 L^2] \tag{III}$$

This condition can be produced by varying either f, C, or L, respectively. When the frequency f is varied, the setting

$$f_r = \frac{1}{2\pi}\sqrt{\frac{1}{CL} - \left[\frac{R}{L}\right]^2}$$

will satisfy (III) and when this value is inserted in (I) we find the impedance $Z_r = L/CR$. When the capacitance C is varied the setting

$$C_r = \frac{L}{R^2 + \omega^2 L^2} \quad ,$$

will satisfy (III) and give the impedance $Z_r = \dfrac{R^2 + \omega^2 L^2}{R^2}$. When L is varied, we find for $A = \sqrt{1 - (2\omega CR)^2}$ the setting

$$L_r = \frac{1 + A}{2\omega^2 C}$$

which satisfies (III) and gives the impedance $Z_r = \dfrac{1 + A}{(\omega C)^2[1 - A]}$

In parallel circuits it is often customary to work with anti-resonance for which the impedance Z becomes a maximum. We have then again three cases, namely, dZ/df, dZ/dC or dZ/dL is zero for which $Z = Z_{\max}$ when

$$f_a = \frac{1}{2\pi}\sqrt{\frac{\sqrt{1 + 2R^2\frac{C}{L}}}{CL} - \left(\frac{R}{L}\right)^2}; \quad C_a = \frac{L}{\omega^2 L^2 + R^2}; \quad L_a = \frac{1 + \sqrt{1 + (2\omega CR)^2}}{2\omega^2 C}$$

If these values are introduced in (I) it will be found that for the setting C_a,

$$Z_{\max} = \frac{R^2 + \omega^2 L^2}{R}$$

gives the same value as Z_r which is the value for C_r in case of resonance. There exists, however, a difference for the other corresponding impedance values.

which is large compared with R_e at frequencies not near resonance. By neglecting R^2 in comparison with $\omega_0^2 L^2$, and by use of Eq. (14), in which we neglect CR^2/L in comparison with unity, we have the effective resistance R_e' at resonance

$$R_e' = \frac{L}{CR} \tag{17a}$$

which for $R = 0$ would give $I_{\min} = 0$, since $R_e' = \infty$. The current through the coil branch is $I_L = \dfrac{E}{\omega_0 L}$ that flowing to the parallel combination $I_{\min} = E/R_e'$ and the *current ratio at resonance* becomes,

$$\frac{I_L}{I_{\min}} = \frac{R_e'}{\omega_0 L} = \frac{L/CR}{1/\omega_0 C} = \frac{2Lf_0}{R}\pi = \frac{\pi}{\delta_0} \tag{18}$$

where $\delta = \delta_0$ denotes the logarithmic decrement of the parallel combination at resonance. The effective resistance at resonance is the reason why

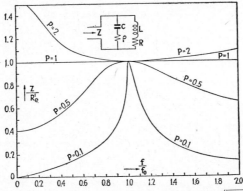

Fig. 5.—Shows that for $P = 1$ the circuit acts like a resistance $\sqrt{L/C}$ for all frequencies.

a parallel-resonance circuit can transfer energy from coil L (Fig. 5) to a secondary coil coupled to it. As is shown by Eq. (29), a secondary circuit will increase the effective resistance R_e corresponding to the energy transfer.

The circuit shown in Fig. 4 has another property of interest as can be seen from the curves given in Fig. 5. When the two resistances R and ρ have the value $\sqrt{L/C}$ we obtain the $P = 1$ line showing that the equivalent impedance of the parallel combination is *independent* of the *frequency* and for the entire frequency band equal to an ohmic resistance $Z = \sqrt{L/C}$. Such a parallel combination can therefore be used to match lines and recurrent networks of surge impedance $\sqrt{L/C}$. The proof is as follows: Putting $R = \rho$ simplifies Eq. (13) to $f_0 = 1/2\pi\sqrt{CL}$.

Putting $f/f_0 = Q$, and $R\sqrt{C/L} = P$, gives $R + j\omega L = R\left[1 + j\dfrac{Q}{P}\right]$;

$R - \dfrac{j}{\omega C} = R\left[1 - \dfrac{j}{PQ}\right]$ leading to the symbolic expression

$$Z = R\frac{[1 + P^2] + jP\left[Q - \dfrac{1}{Q}\right]}{2P^2 + jP\left[Q - \dfrac{1}{Q}\right]}$$

having an absolute value

$$Z = R\sqrt{\frac{[1 + P^2]^2 + P^2\left[Q - \dfrac{1}{Q}\right]^2}{4P^4 + P^2\left[Q - \dfrac{1}{Q}\right]^2}} \tag{19}$$

For $f = f_0$, we have $\omega = \omega_0$ and $Q = 1$, and the effective value of the resistance at resonance

$$Z_0 = R_e' = R\frac{1 + P^2}{2P^2} \tag{20}$$

which for $P = 1$ gives

$$R_e' = R = \sqrt{\frac{L}{C}} \tag{21}$$

Putting $P = 1$ in (19) shows that the impedance $Z = \sqrt{L/C} = R$ at any frequency.

The frequency gradient dX/df of any reactance combination is always positive. This means that a reactance between any two points of a network always has a positive increment for a positive increment of frequency. This is true because for an inductive reactance $X_1 = \omega L = kfL$ we have $dX_1/df = kL = 2\pi L$ and for a capacity reactance $X_2 = -1/\omega C = -1/kfC$ we obtain $dX_2/df = 1/kCf^2 = 1/\omega Cf$. Both derivatives come out positive. Hence, when X_1 and X_2 act in series, the sum of the derivations $\dfrac{dX_1}{df} + \dfrac{dX_2}{df}$ is again a positive quantity just as the case for a parallel connection for which $X_3 = \dfrac{X_1 X_2}{X_1 + X_2}$ leads to a positive value since

$$\frac{dX_3}{df} = \frac{X_1^2 \dfrac{dX_2}{df} + X_2^2 \dfrac{dX_1}{df}}{[X_1 + X_2]^2}$$

These results express the fact that an *increase in frequency always makes the reactance more positive.*

4. Energy Transfer between Circuits.—In order to transfer energy from one circuit to another, the circuits must be coupled. The fundamental types are shown in Fig. 6. The degree of coupling is expressed by the coupling coefficient κ which for the direct inductive, magnetic, and capacitive coupling is

$$\kappa = \frac{X_m}{\sqrt{X_1 X_2}} \tag{22}$$

when X_m denotes the mutual or transfer reactance common to either circuit, and X_1 and X_2 the total similar[1] reactances of the respective circuits when not affecting each other. For the direct coupling we then have

$$\kappa = \frac{j\omega L_\kappa}{\sqrt{j\omega[L_1 + L_\kappa]j\omega[L_2 + L_\kappa]}}$$

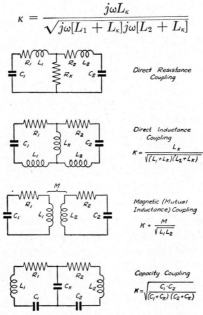

FIG. 6.—Different kinds of coupling.

which simplifies to the expression given in the figure. The small coupling due to the common resistance of L_κ is neglected. For the capacitive coupling $X_m = 1/j\omega C_\kappa$, $X_1 = 1/j\omega C_I$; $X_2 = 1/j\omega C_{II}$ where $C_I = \dfrac{C_1 C_\kappa}{C_1 + C_\kappa}$ and $C_{II} = \dfrac{C_2 C_\kappa}{C_2 + C_\kappa}$. We note that for $X_m^2 = X_1 X_2$ the coupling is 100 per cent.

In inductively coupled circuits as in Fig. 7, when the total primary impedance $Z_1 = Z_a + Z_b$ when not affected by the secondary, and the total secondary impedance $Z_2 = Z_c + Z_d$ when not affected by the primary, one has the vector equation

[1] Similar to that of coupling, magnetic when coupling is magnetic, capacitive when coupling is capacitive.

$$E_1 = Z_1 I_1 + Z_m I_2 \\ 0 = Z_2 I_2 + Z_m I_1 \Big\}$$

$$(23)$$

if Z_m denotes the transfer impedance. The equivalent impedance $Z = E_1/I_1$ when both circuits are acting on each other is obtained by elimination of I_2 and is

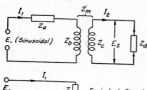

$$Z = Z_1 - \frac{Z_m{}^2}{Z_2}$$

$$(24)$$

Fig. 7.—The coupled circuit with impedance load.

which holds for any two coupled circuits. Elimination of I_1 gives the expression for the secondary current

$$I_2 = \frac{Z_m}{Z_1 Z_2 - Z_m{}^2} E_1$$

$$(25)$$

Applying these results to the circuit shown in Fig. 8 gives $Z_1 = R_1 + j\omega L_1$, $Z_2 = R_2 + j\omega L_2$, $Z_m = j\omega M$, and

$$Z = \left[R_1 + \frac{\omega^2 M^2}{R_2{}^2 + \omega^2 L_2{}^2} R_2 \right] + j\omega \left[L_1 - \frac{\omega^2 M^2}{R_2{}^2 + \omega^2 L_2{}^2} L_2 \right]$$
$$= R_e + j\omega L_e$$

$$(26)$$

showing that the effect of the secondary circuit is equivalent to an increase of resistance R_1 by the amount $A R_2$ and a decrease of the primary inductance L_1 by $A L_2$ where $A = \dfrac{\omega^2 M^2}{R_2{}^2 + \omega^2 L_2{}^2}$.

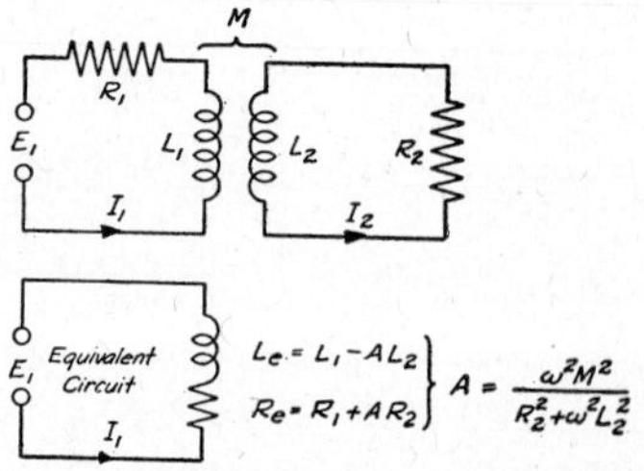

In the general circuit (Fig. 7), maximum energy transfer can be obtained by varying Z_1, Z_2, or Z_m. An inspection of (24) shows that, by varying the coupling between the two circuits, the secondary current I_2 passes through a maximum when

$$Z_m{}^2 = Z_1 Z_2 \qquad (27)$$

Fig. 8.—The coupled circuit with resistance load.

The maximum value of I_2 is increased to an optimum value when the total impedance Z_2 of the secondary is properly adjusted. This is usually done by varying the reactive component in the secondary which may be a tuning condenser or a tuning coil. Since $Z_1 = R_1 + jX_1$ and $Z_2 = R_2 + jX_2$, the maximum condition for varying the secondary reactance is obtained for

$$X_2 = \frac{Z_m{}^2}{Z_2} X_1$$

$$(28)$$

where $Z_m{}^2 = R_1 R_2 + X_1 X_2$.

The transformer with an impedance load is a common circuit in high-frequency work. There is then the simplified case of Fig. 7 since $Z_a = 0$ and

$$Z_b = R_1 + jX_1$$
$$Z_c = R_2 + jX_2$$
$$Z_d = R + jX$$

The impressed alternating voltage then works into an equivalent single circuit of an effective resistance R_e in series with an effective inductance L_e. They are

$$R_e = R_1 + \frac{X_m{}^2[R + R_2]}{[R + R_2]^2 + [X + X_2]^2} = R_1 + \frac{\kappa^2 X_1 X_2[R + R_2]}{[R + R_2]^2 + [X + X_2]^2}$$

$$X_e = X_1 - \frac{X_m{}^2[X + X_2]}{[R + R_2]^2 + [X + X_2]^2} = X_1 - \frac{\kappa^2 X_1 X_2[X + X_2]}{[R + R_2]^2 + [X + X_2]^2}$$

where for the coupling coefficient κ

$$X_m = \kappa\sqrt{X_1 X_2} \qquad \text{and} \qquad M = \kappa\sqrt{L_1 L_2}$$

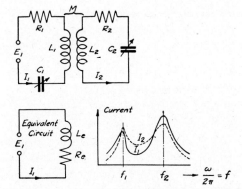

FIG. 9.—Tuned coupled circuit and the effective current variation in the respective circuits depending on the frequency f of the impressed voltage E, of constant amplitude.

Although this result looks rather complicated, the application to many practical cases is often simple. For instance when an audio transformer is used between two stages of tube amplification,

$$R_e \cong \frac{X_1}{X_2} R \qquad \text{and} \qquad X_e \cong \frac{X_1}{X_2} X$$

where X_2/X_1 is equal to the square of voltage transformation. The grid resistance $r_g = de_g/di_g = R$ is then high compared with R_2. For maximum power transfer from the plate of the first tube toward the transformer the internal plate resistance $r_p = R_e$ and

$$\frac{r_p}{r_g} = \frac{X_1}{X_2}$$

For the circuit shown in Fig. 9,

$$Z_1 = \sqrt{R_1{}^2 + \left[\omega L_1 - \frac{1}{\omega C_1}\right]^2} \quad \text{and} \quad Z_2 = \sqrt{R_2{}^2 + \left[\omega L_2 - \frac{1}{\omega C_2}\right]^2}$$

with a power factor $\cos \varphi = R_2/Z_2$.

Owing to the back action on the primary circuit

$$\left.\begin{aligned} R_e &= R_1 + A R_2 \\ L_e &= \left[L_1 - \frac{1}{\omega^2 C_1}\right] - A\left[L_2 - \frac{1}{\omega^2 C_2}\right] \\ A &= \frac{\omega^2 M^2}{Z_2{}^2} \end{aligned}\right\} \tag{29}$$

The effective values of the primary and secondary currents then become

$$\left.\begin{aligned} I_1 &= \frac{E_1}{\sqrt{R_e{}^2 + \omega^2 L_e{}^2}} \\ I_2 &= \frac{\omega M}{Z_2} I_1 \end{aligned}\right\} \tag{30}$$

I_1 and I_2 pass through two maxima when the effective reactance $X = \omega L_e$; that is, the value of L_e becomes zero. This is true because the relation for L_e is biquadratic with respect to the frequency $\omega/2\pi$. For

$$f_1 = \frac{1}{2\pi\sqrt{C_1 L_1}}; f_2 = \frac{1}{2\pi\sqrt{C_2 L_2}}; \kappa = \frac{M}{\sqrt{L_1 L_2}}; Z_2 \cong \omega L_2 - \frac{1}{\omega C_2}, \text{ we find}$$

$$f = \pm\sqrt{\frac{f_1{}^2 + f_2{}^2 \pm \sqrt{[f_1{}^2 - f_2{}^2]^2 + 4\kappa^2 f_1{}^2 f_2{}^2}}{2[1 - \kappa^2]}}$$

which for $C_1 L_1 = C_2 L_2 = CL$, that is, $f_1 = f_2 = f_0$, gives the frequencies

$f_1' = \dfrac{f_0}{\sqrt{1 + \kappa}}$ and $f_2' = \dfrac{f_0}{\sqrt{1 - \kappa}}$ where $f_0 = \dfrac{1}{2\pi\sqrt{CL}}$. In reality, the I_1 and I_2 curves are somewhat displaced with respect to each other since the resistance of the secondary R_2 has little effect upon the settings for maximum current effect. Although for couplings which are not very loose we obtain two maximum settings, a difference exists between the two maxima found here and those when a spark-gap oscillator acts on a resonator. In the latter case, the two coupling frequencies exist *simultaneously*, while, for sinusoidal excitation as here, each maximum setting occurs only when excited with the particular frequency. Equations (29) and (30) also explain the well-known resonance click (and grid dip) utilized when a frequency of a coupled circuit is determined with a heterodyne generator (Fig. 20). For a very loose coupling between both circuits, we have for resonance $\omega^2 CL = 1$ for each circuit, but near this setting one of the two possible frequencies f_1' or f_2' is responsible for the frequency of the tube generator. By slowly varying either the condenser C_1 of the primary or the condenser C_2 of the secondary near the true resonance setting, the oscillation for one frequency will break off and jump with a click to the oscillation of the other frequency. The click is nothing but the interference tone produced between the oscillation which is stopped (dies off) and the new oscillation which builds up, both occurrences taking place during a very short interval.   The most favorable coupling for which maximum energy is transferred between the tuned circuits occurs for $dI_2/dM = 0$ or

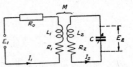

FIG. 10.—Coupled circuit with tuned secondary.

$$M = \frac{\sqrt{R_1R_2}}{\omega} \tag{31}$$

This result can also be directly obtained from Eq. (27), since for resonance $Z_m{}^2 = Z_1Z_2 = R_1R_2 + X_1X_2 = R_1R_2$ and $Z_m = j\omega M$.   Using this result in the general Eq. (25), where for the tuned coupled system $Z_1Z_2 = R_1R_2$, we find for the *maximum possible* secondary current

$$I_2 = \frac{\sqrt{R_1R_2}E_1}{R_1R_2 + R_1R_2} = \frac{E_1}{2\sqrt{R_1R_2}} \tag{32}$$

The circuit shown in Fig. 10 plays an important part in high-frequency work since it represents the equivalent network of a tuned amplifier. Since $Z_1 = R_0 + R_1 + j\omega L_1 = \rho + jX_1 ; Z_2 = R_2 + j\left[\omega L_2 - \dfrac{1}{\omega C} \right]$ and $Z_m = j\omega M$, the equivalent impedance, according to Eq. (24), is

$$Z = Z_1 - \frac{Z_m{}^2}{R_2}$$

since for tuned secondary $X_2 = 0$.   Assuming, further, that the resistance R_0 is large compared to R and L_1 only a few coupling turns, then $Z_1 \cong \rho \cong R_0$ and the equivalent impedance becomes

$$Z = \rho + \frac{\omega^2M^2}{R_2} = R_e$$

that is, it is pure resistive.   The primary and secondary currents are then

$$I_1 = \frac{E_1}{Z} = \frac{R_2E_1}{R_2 \cdot \rho + \omega^2M^2} \quad \text{and} \quad I_2 = \frac{\omega MI_1}{R_2} = \frac{\omega ME_1}{R_2 \cdot \rho + \omega^2M^2}$$

The voltage E_2 is

$$E_2 = \omega L_2I_2 = \frac{\omega^2L_2ME_1}{R_2\rho + \omega^2M^2}$$

and the voltage ratio of *circuit* transformation

$$\frac{E_2}{E_1} = \frac{\omega^2ML_2}{R_2\rho + \omega^2M^2}$$

when the secondary is tuned.   According to Eq. (27), this ratio can be still further increased by adjusting for the best coupling which for the above assumptions requires

$$\omega^2 M^2 = \rho\, R_2$$

and the possible maximum circuit transformation becomes

$$\frac{E_2}{E_1} = \frac{\omega L_2}{2\sqrt{R_2[R_0 + R_1]}} \tag{33}$$

Hence the maximum voltage step-up for fixed circuit resistances is directly proportional to the reactance of the secondary coil.

5. Resonance Curves.—For sustained high-frequency currents, the plot of the effective current against the exciting frequency is known as the "resonance curve."[1] Figure 11 gives such curves for a coil in series with a condenser and a coil in parallel with the condenser. The former is known as the voltage-resonance case, since for a constant applied e.m.f. and resonance ($\omega L = 1/\omega C$), the maximum current I flowing through the series combination produces very high voltages across the terminals of either coil or of the condenser. The other case is known as current resonance, since at resonance the current flowing to the parallel combination is practically zero, although very heavy antiphase currents flow in the respective parallel branches. There are also resonance curves which are based on a current decrease in a step-over resonator due to absorption. The resonance setting is then marked by a sharp current

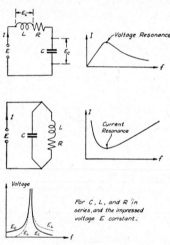

Fig. 11.—Voltage and current resonance.

minimum. Resonance curves due to the dynamometer effect between two circuits are dealt with on page 182 and in Fig. 142. Figure 9 gives the resonance curves for the coupled-circuit resonator.

For voltage resonance, the resonance curve is given by the relation

$$I = \frac{E}{\sqrt{R^2 + X^2}} \sin{[\omega t - \varphi]} \tag{34}$$

where

$$\varphi = \tan^{-1}\frac{X}{R} = \tan^{-1}\frac{\omega L - \dfrac{1}{\omega C}}{R} = \frac{\pi}{\delta}\left[\frac{f^2 - f_0{}^2}{f^2}\right]$$

$$\delta = \frac{R}{2Lf_0} \text{ and the resonance frequency } f_0 = \frac{1}{2\pi\sqrt{CL}} \tag{35}$$

[1] In some cases it is of advantage to call the plot of the square of the current against the frequency the resonance curve.

The resonance curve can also be expressed by means of the degree of detuning $\Delta\omega = \omega - \omega_1$ where ω denotes the angular velocity $2\pi f$ of the applied voltage $e = E_m \sin \omega t$ producing the resonance current $I_m \sin \omega t$ and $\omega_1 = 2\pi f_1$ the angular velocity of the circuit due to its natural frequency f_1. For the damping factor $\alpha = R/2L$ the equation of the resonance curve becomes

$$I_m = \frac{E_m}{R + j\omega L + \dfrac{1}{j\omega C}} = \frac{E_m/2L}{\dfrac{j\omega}{2}\left[1 - \dfrac{\omega_1{}^2}{\omega^2}\right] + \alpha} = \frac{E_m/2L}{j\Delta\omega\dfrac{\omega + \omega_1}{2\omega} + \alpha} \cong \frac{E_m/2L}{\alpha + j\Delta\omega}$$

Introducing the corresponding effective values, there is for the resonance curve

$$I = \frac{E}{2L\sqrt{a^2 + \Delta\omega^2}} \qquad (35a)$$

Figure 12 shows that the phase displacement φ changes very rapidly from a negative to a positive value, since near resonance $f \cong f_0$ and

$$\varphi = \frac{\pi}{\delta}\frac{[f + f_0][f - f_0]}{f_0{}^2} = \frac{2\pi}{\delta}\frac{f - f_0}{f_0}$$

Equation (34) shows that it is immaterial whether we change the frequency, capacity, or the inductance. All three variations give the same resonance curve, assuming that C, L, and R, are constant for the comparatively small frequency range near resonance. Since E/R denotes the resonance current, the resonance voltage across C or L is

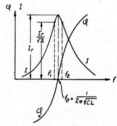

$$\frac{E}{R}\omega_0 L = E_r$$

and the voltage ratio at resonance becomes

$$\frac{E_r}{E} = \frac{\omega_0 L}{R} = \frac{2f_0 L}{R}\pi = \frac{\pi}{\delta} = S \qquad (36)$$

Fig. 12.—Resonance and phase curves.

giving exactly the same ratio as obtained for current resonance in Eq. (18). The voltage across the coil or the condenser is therefore very high and becomes higher as the logarithmic decrement $\delta = R/2Lf_0$ becomes smaller. The quantity δ therefore measures the sharpness S of tuning, since the resonance curve becomes more peaked as δ becomes smaller. A circuit with a large inductance and a small capacitance (for one and the same frequency) gives therefore a much sharper tuning, assuming that in each case the resistance R is of the same order.

In Fig. 11, the voltage curves across the inductance L and capacitance C show that more change is obtained by noting the voltage drop across the inductance for values just below the resonance frequency. The same is true for the voltage drop across the condenser for frequencies higher than the resonance frequency. This is of importance when harmonics are to be determined by means of a tube voltmeter, since, for instance, for a given voltage due to the second harmonic across either the inductance or the capacitance, the voltage across the inductance due to the fundamental will be only one-fourth of that across the capacitance. The effect due to the fundamental will therefore be all the less, the higher the order of the harmonic for which the voltage is to be determined. Hence, when the harmonic content of a current is to be determined by means of a tube voltmeter, the error in the measurement becomes less when the tube voltmeter is connected across the inductance.

The equation of the resonance curve for current resonance is given by Eq. (15), showing that there is not exactly the same resonance curve when f or C is varied. But for feebly damped circuits this is not the case, since we obtain the expression for the resonance curve as

$$I = E\sqrt{R^2\frac{C^2}{L^2} + \left[\frac{1}{\omega L} - \omega C\right]^2} \cos\left[\omega t - \varphi\right] \tag{37}$$

where

$$\varphi = \tan^{-1}\frac{\dfrac{1}{\omega L} - \omega C}{RC/L}$$

giving the resonance setting $I_r = \dfrac{CR}{L}E$, and the current ratio at resonance $I_L/I = \pi/\delta$ as already found in Eq. (18). The current through the condenser or through the coil branch is all the greater compared with the total current flowing to the parallel combination, the smaller the logarithmic decrement δ.

By means of the resonance curves it is possible to determine the effective resistance and efficiency of circuits as is shown among the measurements. It is then often of advantage to bring the expression for this curve in a more convenient form. For instance, for Eq. (34), for the *resonance curve* we find the expression

$$I = \frac{I_r}{\sqrt{1 + P^2}} \tag{38}$$

where $I_r = E/R$ and denotes the resonance current,[1] and $P = X/R$ gives

[1] When the impressed voltage is distorted and of the form:
$[E_1 \sin \omega t + E_2 \sin 2\omega t + E_3 \sin 3\omega t + E_4 \sin 4\omega t + \cdots]$ and the circuit is tuned to the fundamental frequency, the effective current is

$$I_r' = \frac{E_1}{R\sqrt{2}}\sqrt{1 + \frac{\delta^2}{\pi^2}\left[\left(\frac{2}{3}E_2\right)^2 + \left(\frac{3}{8}E_3\right)^2 + \left(\frac{4}{15}E_4\right)^2\right]\frac{1}{E_1{}^2}}$$

$$P = \frac{\omega L}{R} - \frac{1}{\omega CR} = \frac{\omega L}{R}\left[1 - \frac{1}{\omega^2 CL}\right] = \frac{\omega L}{R}\left[1 - \frac{\omega_0^2}{\omega^2}\right] = \frac{\omega}{2\delta f_0}\left[1 - \frac{\omega_0^2}{\omega^2}\right] =$$

$$\frac{\pi}{\delta}\frac{\omega}{\omega_0}\left[1 - \frac{\omega_0^2}{\omega^2}\right] = \frac{\pi}{\delta}\left[\frac{f}{f_0} - \frac{f_0}{f}\right] = S\left[\frac{f}{f_0} - \frac{f_0}{f}\right]$$

where S denotes the sharpness of resonance. For the value $P = 1$, the resonance current I_r is reduced to a value $0.71 I_r$ which corresponds to a small detuning if the decrement δ is not unreasonably large, and introducing the relative detuning

$$d = \frac{f - f_0}{f_0} \tag{39}$$

in the above expression, we obtain

$$\frac{f}{f_0} = 1 + d \text{ and } \frac{f}{f_0} - \frac{f_0}{f} \cong 1 + d - [1 - d] = 2d$$

since d is small compared with unity. Hence

$$P = 2Sd = 2S\left[\frac{f - f_0}{f_0}\right] \tag{40}$$

When the resonance current is reduced to a value $I = 0.71 I_r$ corresponding to a frequency f which may be either higher[1] or lower than the resonance frequency f_0, then $P = 1$, and Eq. (40) yields the formula for the sharpness of resonance

$$S = \frac{f_0}{2[f - f_0]} \tag{41}$$

and since $S = \pi/\delta$, the formula for the logarithmic decrement becomes

$$\delta = 2\pi\frac{f - f_0}{f_0} = \frac{\pi w}{f_0} \tag{42}$$

where w denotes practically the width $2(f - f_0)$ of the resonance curve when the square of the resonance current I_r is equal to twice the square of the current I corresponding to a frequency f. Calling f_1 and f_2 the smaller and larger frequencies on each side of the resonance curve corresponding to the same current reading $I = I_r/\sqrt{2}$ (Fig. 12), the logarithmic decrement can also be computed from the formula

---

since for such a tuning $\omega L = 1/\omega C$ and any higher harmonic of order $p\omega$ the reactance

$$X = p\omega L - \frac{\omega L}{p}$$

$$= \omega L\frac{p^2 - 1}{p}$$

and $I_p = E_p/X$ and $I_r' = \sqrt{I_r^2 + I_p^2}$

[1] Detuning can be obtained by changing to frequency values on either side of the resonance setting (Fig. 12).

$$\delta = \pi\frac{f_2 - f_1}{f_0} \tag{43}$$

When a square-law current detector (thermoelectric instrument as is usually the case) is used, it is only necessary to read off the resonance frequency f_0 and the frequencies f_1 and f_2, respectively, when the test circuit is detuned by increasing and decreasing its capacity setting so far as to produce the half deflection on the indicator as noted when the circuit was in resonance. These derivations[1] form the basis of many measurements, since for sustained oscillations the *power factor* of a circuit is *equal to* the *logarithmic decrement divided by* π. The power factor lies between zero and unity and is unity for an ideal circuit.

6. Resonance Curves Taken with a Frequency Meter with Special Reference to Currents of Large Harmonic Content.—A good frequency meter is an ordinary resonance circuit which exhibits very small circuit

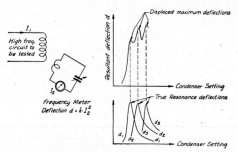

Fig. 13.—Resultant resonance curves for distorted currents.

losses. The decrement δ is therefore small and settings of maximum current response are sharp. The settings for maximum current response are usually noted with an indicator the deflections of which are proportional to the square of the current. The maximum reading corresponds to the condition of resonance and even to a high precision when only the few lower harmonics are picked out with a loosely coupled frequency meter. But if the current to be investigated has a large harmonic content and it is necessary to tune to frequencies which are of a high order with respect to the fundamental frequency, a step-over resonator should be interposed[2] between the test circuit and the frequency

---

[1] A knowledge of the logarithmic decrement δ of a circuit is just as important for undamped as for damped currents, although only in the latter case is it directly seen on the current wave. In each case the circuit losses produce the same decrement and decrease the efficiency of the system. Only for a negligible δ is the natural frequency of a circuit equal to $1/(2\pi\sqrt{CL})$ and a very sharp tuning possible.

[2] A good way is to use a tube circuit with a plate reactance tuned to the particular harmonic. The e.m.f. acting on the grid of the tube is due to the distorted harmonic current.

meter and be tuned to the particular harmonic current whose frequency is to be determined. If this is not done and the frequency meter is directly coupled to the test circuit as shown in Fig. 13, the resultant resonance curve due to successive harmonics which are relatively close together because of the high harmonic[1] order is as shown by d. The successive maxima do not exactly correspond to the true frequencies $(p - 1)f, f,$ and $(p + 1)f$, where p denotes the order of harmonics. The $d_1, d_2,$ and d_3 curves denote the resonance curves of the respective successive harmonic currents when acting independently. Hence, a loosely coupled step-over resonator tuned to the frequency to be measured will emphasize, more or less, only the particular resonance curve (d_2 curve, for instance) in a frequency meter which is loosely coupled to it because the effect of the deflection due to the neighboring harmonics ($(p - 1)f$ and $(p + 1)f$ in this case) are then negligible.

It can be shown that the effect of the frequency discrepancy, when such precautions are not taken into account, is proportional to the fourth power of the power factor of the circuit. The effect can therefore be reduced to a small amount when the decrement of the frequency meter is chosen small.

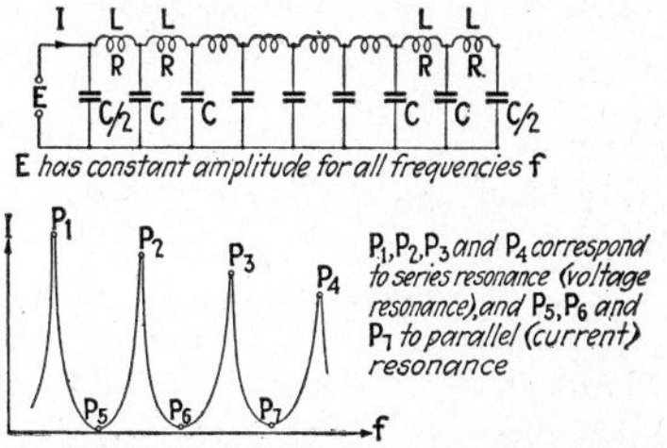

7. Resonance Curves of Distributed Circuit Elements.—When a parallel-wire system which is short-circuited at the far end is excited by a constant e.m.f. of variable frequency, the current in the line will vary as the frequency is changed. There is a series of frequencies for which the line behaves as an ohmic resistance, and a series of frequencies for which it acts as though having a very high reactance. Exactly the same thing happens for an open-ended double line and for an antenna.

FIG. 14.—Multiresonance curve of a recurrent network of inductances along and capacitances across the line.

This action is due to the distributed nature of capacitance, inductance, and resistance. The same thing occurs with a long coil which has distributed inductance and capacitance. Figure 14 shows the resonance curve of such a system where the points of maximum current I flowing into the network correspond to unity power factor in case of voltage resonance and the points of minimum current correspond to a condition of unity power factor for an equivalent current resonance. It can be shown that the sharpness of tuning is more marked than it would be for a single closed circuit with localized inductance, capacitance, and resistance. Such arrangements can be used to advantage for circuit tuning and for filters.

[1] The successive resonance settings on the variable condenser are very close together.

8. Summation and Multiplication of Sinusoidal Time Variations of Different Frequencies.—The *summation* of sinusoidal waves plays a part when voltages or currents, respectively, are superimposed upon each other in the same circuit. This means that it also exists for currents or the voltages of distorted wave form.

Suppose two alternating voltages $e_1 = E_1 \cos \omega t$ and $e_2 = E_2 \cos \omega_2 t$ are applied to the same circuit, and $\omega_1/2\pi$ and $\omega_2/2\pi$ have any value whatsoever, just as the amplitudes E_1 and E_2 are different. The instantaneous value of the resultant e.m.f. is then

$$
\begin{aligned}
e = e_1 + e_2 &= E_1 \cos \omega_1 t + E_2 \cos \omega_2 t \\
&= E_1 \cos \omega_1 t + E_2 \cos \omega_2 t + E_2 \cos \omega_1 t - E_2 \cos \omega_1 t \\
&= E_2[\cos \omega_1 t + \cos \omega_2 t] + [E_1 - E_2] \cos \omega_1 t \\
&= \left[2E_2 \cos \frac{\omega_1 - \omega_2}{2} \right] \cos \frac{\omega_1 + \omega_2}{2} + [E_1 - E_2] \cos \omega_1 t \\
&= E_I \cos \frac{\omega_1 + \omega_2}{2} + E_{II} \cos \omega_1 t \quad\quad (44)
\end{aligned}
$$

The resultant voltage consists therefore of a part of mean frequency $\frac{f_1 + f_2}{2}$, whose amplitude fluctuates in step with the difference frequency $f_1 - f_2$, and a purely cosinoidal part of frequency f_1, which disappears when the amplitudes E_1 and E_2 are equal. Therefore, these substitutions can be made:

$$
m = \frac{\omega_1 + \omega_2}{2}; \quad\quad d = \omega_1 - \omega_2 \quad\quad (45)
$$

and have

$$
\omega_1 = m + \frac{d}{2}; \quad\quad \omega_2 = m - \frac{d}{2}
$$

The resultant instantaneous voltage is given by

$$
\begin{aligned}
e &= E_1 \cos \left[m + \frac{d}{2} \right] t + E_2 \cos \left[m - \frac{d}{2} \right] t \\
&= [E_1 + E_2] \cos mt \cos \frac{d}{2}t + [E_1 - E_2] \sin mt \sin \frac{d}{2}t \\
&= [\cos mt - \varphi]\sqrt{[E_1 + E_2]^2 \cos^2 \frac{d}{2}t + [E_1 - E_2]^2 \sin^2 \frac{d}{2}t} \\
&= \left[\cos \frac{\omega_1 + \omega_2}{2}t - \varphi \right]\sqrt{E_1{}^2 + E_2{}^2 + 2E_1 E_2 \cos [\omega_1 - \omega_2]t} \quad (46)
\end{aligned}
$$

where

$$
\varphi = \tan^{-1} \frac{E_1 - E_2}{E_1 + E_2} \tan^{-1} \frac{\omega_1 - \omega_2}{2}t \quad\quad (47)
$$

The amplitude of the resultant wave varies therefore in rhythm with the difference frequency $\frac{\omega_1 - \omega_2}{2\pi} = f_1 - f_2$ and between the limits $E_1 + E_2$ and

$E_1 - E_2$. When the difference frequency is small compared to the mean frequency $\dfrac{f_1 + f_2}{2}$, the amplitude can be considered constant for the time of a cycle of the mean frequency.

Figure 15 shows the superposition graphically for a case where the amplitudes of the component waves are equal. It can be seen that at points P the phase jumps 180 deg. which explains why the mean frequency $\dfrac{f_1 + f_2}{2}$ cannot be detected with a frequency meter.

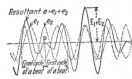

FIG. 15.—Showing the beat voltage e due to a voltage e_1 of frequency f_1 and a voltage e_2 of frequency f_2 (at P a phase change of 180 deg.).

The frequency of the amplitude variation which takes place between the limits $E_1 + E_2$ and $E_1 - E_2$, and with the difference frequency known as the beat frequency, can be detected when the resultant wave is rectified, since the resultant wave (Fig. 15) is not unsymmetrical enough. When $f_1 + f_2$ is a simple multiple of $f_1 - f_2$, the resultant beat wave is said to be "pure."

A distorted current can be imagined as the superposition of pure waves of the fundamental and higher harmonic frequencies. If one takes the case of the $(p - 1)$th and $(p + 1)$th higher harmonic, the resultant current for equal amplitudes becomes

$$i = i_{p-1} + i_{p+1} = I[\sin\{(p - 1)\omega t + \varphi_1\} + \sin\{(p + 1)\omega t + \varphi_2\}]$$
$$= 2I \sin\left[p\omega t + \frac{\varphi_1 + \varphi_2}{2}\right] \cos\left[\omega t - \frac{\varphi_1 - \varphi_2}{2}\right] \qquad (48)$$

which for $p = 4$ and $\varphi_1 = \varphi_2 = 0$ gives the resultant beat current shown in Fig. 16. For this example, $f_1 = 3f$ and $f_2 = 5f$ and the mean frequency of the resultant current is $\dfrac{f_1 + f_2}{2} = 4f$, and the beat frequency $f_2 - f_1 = 2f$. Therefore the mean frequency becomes higher compared with the fundamental frequency as the order of the interfering harmonics becomes higher. For unequal amplitudes of the interfering harmonics,

$$i = I_{p-1} \sin[(p - 1)\omega t + \varphi_1] + I_{p+1} \sin[(p + 1)\omega t + \varphi_2] \qquad (49)$$

For equal Amplitudes

For unequal Amplitudes

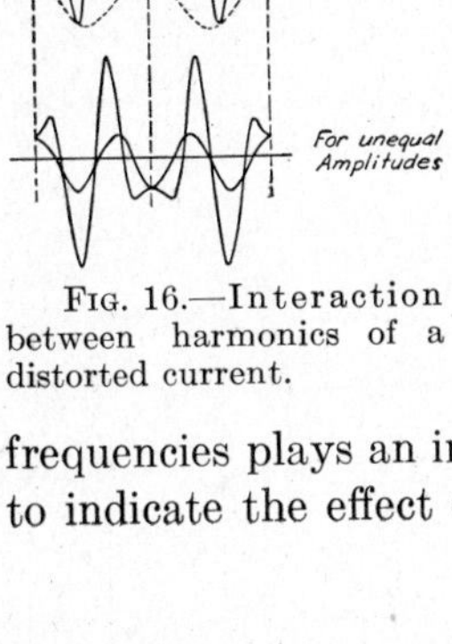

FIG. 16.—Interaction between harmonics of a distorted current.

the resultant current i is as shown in the lower representation of Fig. 16.

The superposition of two waves of unequal frequencies plays an important part since upon rectification it is possible to indicate the effect of two high-frequency currents by means of a current due to their difference or beat frequency. Since the beat frequency $f_1 - f_2$ is in many cases small compared with the mean frequency $\frac{1}{2}(f_1 + f_2)$, the rectified current can be computed from the relation

$$E = \frac{1}{2}\left[(E_1 + E_2)\cos\frac{\omega_1 - \omega_2}{2}t\right]^q \tag{50}$$

where $q = 2$ for a square-law detector, E denotes the effective value of the resultant voltage acting on the detector, and E_1 and E_2 are the amplitudes of the component waves which are assumed equal.

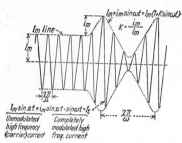

FIG. 17.—Symmetrical amplitude modulation of a high-frequency current of frequency $\Omega/2\pi$ by means of an audio current of frequency $\omega/2\pi$.

The *multiplication* of sinusoidal variations plays a part when high-frequency currents are to be modulated. Suppose a high-frequency current of instantaneous value $I_m \sin \Omega t$ is multiplied by the instantaneous value of a harmonic variation $K \sin \omega t$, where $K = i_m/I_m$ expresses the ratio of the amplitude of an audio current $i_m \sin \omega t$ to that of the high-frequency current, one obtains

$$KI_m \sin \Omega t \sin \omega t = \frac{KI_m}{2}\{\cos(\Omega - \omega)t - \cos(\Omega + \omega)t\} \tag{51}$$

showing that a term of lower frequency $\dfrac{\Omega - \omega}{2\pi}$ and a term of a higher frequency $\dfrac{\Omega + \omega}{2\pi}$ is obtained.

Figure 17 shows the application to a case where a high-frequency current is modulated by an audio current. The instantaneous value of the modulated high-frequency current is

$$i = \underbrace{I_m \sin \Omega t}_{\substack{\text{unmodulated} \\ \text{carrier current}}} + \underbrace{i_m \sin \Omega t \sin \omega t}_{\text{completely modulated}} = [I_m + KI_m \sin \omega t]\sin \Omega t$$

$$= I_m \sin \Omega t + \frac{i_m}{2}\cos(\Omega - \omega)t - \frac{i_m}{2}\cos(\Omega + \omega)t \tag{52}$$

showing that, in addition, to frequency $\Omega/2\pi$ of the circuit current, one also has the sum and difference frequencies $\dfrac{\Omega + \omega}{2\pi}$ and $\dfrac{\Omega - \omega}{2\pi}$. The factor $K = i_m/I_m$ denotes the *degree of modulation*. When the modulated current passes through a resistance R, the energy dissipated is

$$W = I^2R = \left[\frac{I_m^2}{2} + \frac{K^2I_m^2}{8} + \frac{K^2I_m^2}{8}\right]R = \frac{K^2 + 2}{4}I_m^2R \tag{53}$$

Hence if the carrier is suppressed, the energy required is only

$$W_1 = \frac{K^2}{4} I_m{}^2 R \tag{54}$$

For complete modulation ($K = 1$), the energy loss with all three frequencies is three times as much as when only the two side frequencies are present.

If a modulated voltage

$$e = [E_m + e_m \sin \omega t] \sin \Omega t \tag{55}$$

$$\underbrace{E_m + e_m \sin \omega t}_{\substack{\text{modulating} \\ \text{e.m.f.}}} \quad \underbrace{\sin \Omega t}_{\substack{\text{variation of} \\ \text{carrier}}}$$

is impressed on a detector with a current which varies according to $i = ae + be^2$, for the current in the detector,

$$i = \frac{b}{2}\left[E_m{}^2 + 2E_m e_m \sin \omega t + \frac{e_m{}^2}{2} + \frac{e_m{}^2}{2} \cos 2\omega t \right] + \text{radio-frequency terms}$$

$$= \frac{b\, e_m}{2}\underbrace{\left[2E_m \sin \omega t + \frac{e_m}{2} \cos 2\omega t \right]}_{\text{terms of single and double audio frequency}} + \text{terms which cannot affect a tele-}$$

$$\text{phone receiver} \tag{56}$$

The effective value of the telephone current is

$$I = \frac{b\, e_m}{2} \sqrt{2E_m{}^2 + \frac{e_m{}^2}{8}}$$

$$\cong \frac{b\, e_m}{2} \sqrt{2E_m{}^2} = \frac{b\, E_m e_m}{\sqrt{2}} = k E_m e_m \tag{57}$$

since the doubly periodic second term under the square root is small compared with the first term. Even for 100 per cent modulation, which is the most extreme condition, it is only 6.25 per cent of the fundamental since then $e_m = E_m$. Equation (57) shows that for the registered telephone current it is immaterial whether the amplitude of the carrier or that of the modulating wave is large as long as the product $E_m e_m$ is constant.

Since a modulated high-frequency current covers a frequency band twice the modulating frequency with the carrier frequency halfway between, a tuned circuit will produce more distortion the sharper it is tuned, that is, the smaller its decrement, since for an induced e.m.f. of modulation K per cent

$$e = [E_m + K E_m \sin \omega t] \sin \Omega t$$

The current i in a tuned circuit consisting of a coil (L, R) and a condenser (C) is

$$i = \frac{E_m}{R} \sin \Omega t + \frac{K E_m}{2Z_1} \cos\left[(\Omega - \omega)t - \varphi_1 \right] - \frac{K E_m}{2Z_2} \cos\left[(\Omega + \omega)t - \varphi_2 \right] \tag{58}$$

where $Z_1 = \sqrt{R^2 + X_1{}^2}$; $Z_2 = \sqrt{R^2 + X_2{}^2}$; $X_1 = [\Omega - \omega]L - \dfrac{1}{[\Omega - \omega]C}$;

$X_2 = [\Omega + \omega]L - \dfrac{1}{[\Omega + \omega]C}$; $\varphi_1 = \tan^{-1}\dfrac{R}{X_1}$ and $\varphi_2 = \tan^{-1}\dfrac{R}{X_2}$. The

reactances to currents of the two side-band frequencies, $\dfrac{\Omega + \omega}{2\pi}$ and

$\dfrac{\Omega - \omega}{2\pi}$ are for the circuit tuned to the carrier frequency $\Omega/2\pi$.

$$X_1 = [\Omega - \omega]L - \left[1 + \frac{\omega}{\Omega}\right]\Omega L = -2\omega L \doteq -\frac{\omega R}{f\,\delta} = -2\pi\frac{\omega}{\Omega}\frac{R}{\delta}$$

$$X_2 = +2\pi\frac{\omega}{\Omega}\frac{R}{\delta}$$

since $\Omega L = 1/\Omega C$ and for audio-frequency modulation ω/Ω is small

compared with unity, that is, $\dfrac{1}{\left(1 - \dfrac{\omega}{\Omega}\right)} \cong 1 + \dfrac{\omega}{\Omega}$. Hence $\varphi_1 = -\varphi_2 = $

φ and the effective current I flowing in the tuned circuit is, for the effective values $E = E_m/\sqrt{2}$ and $I = I_m/\sqrt{2}$,

$$I = \frac{E}{R}\sin\,\Omega t + \frac{K\,E}{2\sqrt{1 + \left[\dfrac{2\pi\omega}{\Omega\delta}\right]^2}}\{\cos\,[(\Omega-\omega)t-\varphi] - \cos\,[(\Omega+\omega)t+\varphi]\} \quad (59)$$

The amplitudes of the currents due to the side frequencies $\dfrac{\Omega - \omega}{2\pi}$

and $\dfrac{\Omega + \omega}{2\pi}$ are therefore more reduced as the decrement δ becomes smaller.
The distortion due to this amplitude effect, and the one due to the phase effect φ, can be avoided by suppressing the carrier current and tuning to only one side-band frequency.

Moreover, by modulating a high-frequency carrier current with a current of lower frequency, the phase angle of the carrier varies between 0 and 90 deg within one-half of the period of the modulating current. Hence the frequency of the carrier itself must vary within the period of the modulating current. This is the reason why stations receiving the same program from two stations of same carrier frequency may give rise to distortion. The same thing also happens when a transmission line is energized at different places with generators of exactly the same carrier frequency. When two generators are modulated, they undergo the frequency change mentioned above and beats occur in the line at points that are at different distances from the respective senders of source, owing to the finite velocity of wave propagation.

9. Negative Resistance.—An apparatus represents a negative resistance if a sudden *increase in voltage* produces a sudden *decrease in current*.

The differential quotient de/di is therefore a *negative* quantity, whereas for an ordinary resistance this ratio is positive. A negative resistance therefore has a falling volt-ampere characteristic, but otherwise it has the same properties as an ordinary resistance since it impedes a flow of a constant current.

A negative resistance is a conductor which has an internal source which either partially or entirely supplies the circuit losses and in some cases supplies a surplus of energy. In the first case, this is equivalent to reducing the effective resistance of the circuit, while for the second case the effective resistance disappears altogether. When the negative resistance supplies more energy to the circuit in which it is connected than it absorbs, it gives rise to a current increase and can in some cases produce oscillations. Examples are dynatron-tube generators and ordinary amplifiers with a back feed to the grid which produces self-oscillations, that is, any sort of tube oscillator. Also Poulsen arc oscillators are based upon the negative resistance action of the arc.

It can be shown that a series combination of an ohmic resistance R and a negative resistance $(-r)$ when connected across a variable source of voltage e will produce amplified voltage variations e_1 and e_2 across R and $(-r)$, and the voltage amplifications are

$$\frac{\delta e_1}{\delta e} = \frac{R}{R - r} \qquad \frac{\delta e_2}{\delta e} = -\frac{r}{R - r} \tag{60}$$

When the negative resistance $(-r)$ is connected in parallel to an ordinary resistance R and the parallel combination is energized by a variable current i, in R and r the current amplifications obtained are:

$$\frac{\delta i_1}{\delta i} = -\frac{r}{R - r} \qquad \frac{\delta i_2}{\delta i} = \frac{R}{R - r} \tag{61}$$

When a negative resistance $(-r)$ is connected in series with a coil of resistance R and inductance L and a constant voltage E is suddenly applied across the combination, the current increases according to the law

$$i = \frac{E}{R - r}\left[1 - \epsilon^{-\frac{R-r}{L}t}\right] \tag{62}$$

By a proper choice of $(-r)$, the current increase can be accelerated at will. When R is numerically equal to r, a short-circuit current flows. Fortunately such apparatus (dynatron, Poulsen arc, negatron, tungar with open filament) produces only a negative-resistance action over a limited portion of the volt-ampere characteristic, and any short-circuit currents would be automatically checked.

An important arrangement for the production of oscillations with a negative resistance $(-r)$ is given in Fig. 18, where a constant voltage E is suddenly impressed on the combination. Considering this voltage as a vector E revolving with zero angular velocity, we have

$$E = I(-r) + I\frac{\frac{1}{nC}[nL + R]}{nL + \frac{1}{nC} + R} =$$

$$I\left\{\frac{n^2CL(-r) + n[CR(-r) + L] + [R - r]}{n^2CL + nCR + 1}\right\} \quad (63)$$

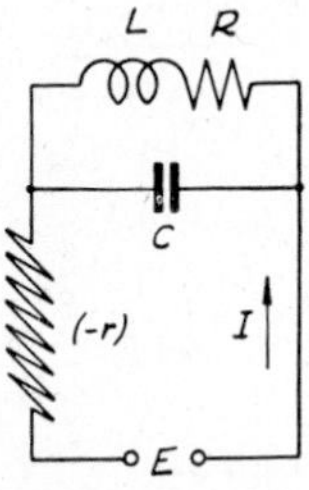

and a bisymbolic[1] multiplication with the respective angular velocities 0 and n yields

$$\left.\begin{array}{l} n^2CL(-r) + n[CR(-r) + L] + [R - r] = 0 \\[2mm] n_1 = -\left[\dfrac{R}{2L} - \dfrac{1}{2Cr}\right] + j\sqrt{\dfrac{1}{CL} - \alpha^2} = \alpha + j\omega \\[2mm] n_2 = \alpha - j\omega \end{array}\right\} \quad (64)$$

Fig. 18.—The negative resistance $(-r)$ gives rise to the production of oscillations.

showing that sustained oscillations are obtained for $R = \dfrac{L}{C\,r}$.

10. Electrostriction and Magnetostriction.—A change in shape and dimensions of a dielectric when acted upon by an electric field is known as "electrostriction." In the case of magnetostriction, certain materials change in shape and dimensions under the action of magnetic fields.

For electrostriction the change in shape and dimension becomes considerable when piezo-electric dielectrics are used, and under the action of an electric force with the same frequency as that of one of the natural frequencies of the piezo-electric substance.

The effect in Rochelle salt is very pronounced. However, since this substance is rather hygroscopic and has poor mechanical properties, crystal quartz is preferred for high-frequency work.

Steel and pure iron, although strongly magnetic, show only very weak magnetostrictive effects. But pure nickel, while it is only slightly magnetic, gives a strong magnetostrictive response. One gauss shortens a nickel rod about $\frac{1}{10^6}$ of its length. According to G. W. Pierce[2] alloys of 36 per cent nickel and 64 per cent iron, which is the approximate composition of invar and other stoic metal, is very magnetostrictive. Unfortunately this alloy has a large temperature coefficient. Monel metal, an alloy consisting of 68 per cent nickel, 28 per cent copper, and small percentages of iron, silicon, manganese, and carbon, is also very suitable. Alloys of chromium, nickel, and iron (nichrome) are very active when a magnetic field is applied. All of these materials are improved by annealing. If a rod of some magnetostrictive material forms the core of a coil through which an alternating current flows, the

---

[1] For details: *Elektrotech. u. Maschinenbau*, Heft 26, 34, 37, and 45, 1920.

[2] Pierce, G. W., *Proc. Am. Acad. Arts Sci.*, April, 1928; W. L. Webster, *Proc. Roy. Soc.* (*London*), December, 1925; A. Schulze, *Z. Physik.*, 448, 1928.

rod is magnetized at the peak of each half cycle and made to expand irrespective of the polarity of magnetization. The rod will therefore expand and contract longitudinally with twice the frequency of the exciting current. But when the rod is simultaneously subjected to a steady magnetization which is greater than the peak value of the alternating field, then the resultant magnetization will increase and decrease with the alternating field but will never reverse its polarity. In this case the frequency of longitudinal-rod vibration is the same as that of the alternating current.

Piezo-electric[1] and magnetostrictive substances play an important part in frequency standardization.

11. Electrons, Ions, and Ionization.—The atoms of all substances contain both positive and negative electricity, the latter existing in the form of minute corpuscles known as "electrons." The sum of the negative charges of the electrons in the outer part of the atom is assumed to be equal to the positive charge of the nucleus, so that in its normal condition the whole atom is neutral or uncharged. All electrons are identical, irrespective of the type of matter to which they belong. An electron is electricity. The kinetic energy of the electron is of purely electromagnetic origin, and, with this in mind, a so-called mass m can be ascribed to the electron which is due to the velocity v and which is inconceivably small since it is only about $m = 9 \times 10^{-28}$ g when moving with a velocity smaller than one-fifth that of light ($v < 60{,}000$ km/sec). The effective relativity[2] mass m_e is given by $m/(1 - \beta^2)^p$ if β denotes the ratio of the velocity v of the electron to the velocity c of light. For $p = 0.5$ we have the expression of the transverse and for $p = 1.5$ the expression for the longitudinal mass. The energy given to an electron of charge q falling through E volts of potential difference is

$$\frac{qE}{300} = \int^v vd(m_e v) = mc^2\left\{\frac{1}{[1 - \beta^2]^{1/2}} - 1\right\} \tag{65}$$

which for lower velocities approaches the non-relativistic value $0.5mv^2$. Both relations play an important part when dealing with electron tubes.

The combined mass of about 1800 electrons is the same as that of the lightest atom, which is hydrogen, and the number of electrons that would be required to make a gram is numerically the same as the number of cubic centimeters contained in the volume of earth. In e.s. c.g.s. units, the charge q carried by the electrons is 4.774×10^{-10} cm$\sqrt{\text{dynes}}$, corresponding to (-1.592×10^{-19}) international coulombs. Therefore, if two spheres each containing 1 g of electrons were placed 100 cm apart they would repel each other with a force equal to the weight of about

---

[1] References: W. G. CADY, Bibliography on Piezo-electricity, *Proc. I.R.E.*, **16**, 521, 1928.

[2] For details and examples, see tube measurements Chapter XIII.

3×10^{22} tons, thus exceeding the gravitational force by about 5×10^{42} times. A current of 1 amp is equivalent to a flow through a given cross section of 6.285×10^{18} electrons/sec.

When an electron is placed in an electric field at a point where the electric force ε in volts per centimeter acts, for the mechanical force on the electron we have

$$F_1 = q\varepsilon 10^7 \text{ dynes} \tag{66}$$

Because of the negative charge q, the force acts against the direction of the applied electric field. When the electron moves with a velocity v in a magnetic field of flux density B, a mechanical force F_2 is exerted on the electron, which is given by the expression

$$F_2 = \frac{I \, d}{10} B = \frac{-qvB}{10} \text{ dynes} \tag{67}$$

where F_2, v, and B are vectors since the mechanical force is perpendicular to the direction of the magnetic field intensity B and to the velocity v. The quantity d in centimeters denotes the distance through which the electron moves in 1 sec. The total force is therefore

$$F = F_1 + F_2 = q\left[\varepsilon 10^7 - \frac{1}{10}Bv\right] \tag{68}$$

when the electron is subjected to both an electric and magnetic field. Therefore when an electron is projected with the velocity v at an angle θ to the magnetic field H, the deflecting force is $Hqv \sin \theta$. If ρ is the radius of the curvature of the resulting path,

$$Hqv \sin \theta = \frac{mv^2}{\rho} \text{ or } \rho = \frac{mv}{Hq \sin \theta} \tag{69}$$

which is the equation of a helix. For $\sin \theta = 1$

$$\rho = \frac{mv}{Hq} \tag{69a}$$

one has a circle. These results have a bearing upon the cathode-ray oscillograph (page 65).

The current flow in a conductor is due to moving electrons which break away from the atoms and reenter the neighboring atoms. The electron theory assumes that in conductors there are many free electrons in addition to those which are bound. The free electrons are in constant motion and the velocity of motion changes with the temperature as for heat motions of molecules.[1] A current in a conductor is then due to a

---

[1] The reason metals are good conductors is because we have to deal with atoms only. They are closely crowded and can interchange electrons when only small electric forces act. For $(-273)°C.$, the resistance would be zero. For further details, see page 262.

transfer of electrons from one atom of the conductor to the other under the influence of an electric field. A conductor becomes positively charged when under such actions a deficiency of electrons occurs. It becomes negative when there is an excess of electrons. For insulators the electrons move only with extreme difficulty. An ideal insulator would be a body in which there are only bound electrons. Under the action of an electric field they can be displaced only somewhat from the equilibrium position.

Since an electron starting from rest and moving freely under the influence of an electric field ε through a distance d will acquire a velocity v given by

$$\varepsilon\, q\, d = \tfrac{1}{2}mv^2 \text{ (volt-energy relation)} \tag{70}$$

where $q/m = 1.765 \times 10^8$ international coulombs/gram, we have for a voltage drop $E = \varepsilon\, d$ along the distance through which the electron accelerates, the velocity

$$v = 6 \times 10^7 \sqrt{E^{\text{(volts)}}} \text{ cm/sec (volt-velocity relation for electrons)} \tag{70a}$$

Therefore, when a voltage $E = 100$ volts is impressed between the hot filament of an electron tube and its anode, the electrons emitted will strike the anode with a velocity of 6000 km/sec, and the velocity of 1 volt-electron is $v = 600 \times 10^5$ cm/sec. The electrons are suddenly stopped at the anode and the kinetic energy $\tfrac{1}{2}Nmv^2$ of N electrons produces heat in the anode. When the kinetic energy of the electrons is sufficiently great, they leave the electrodes again as *secondary* electrons. This is especially the case when the accelerating anode is perforated, as in the dynatron of A. W. Hull, so that many of the high-speed electrons can rush through the holes against another electrode which is less positive and there reflect backward several (up to 20) secondary electrons. Secondary electrons may come from either the free or the bound electrons in the target electrode, more energy being required for the emission of the latter than of the former. Probably both cases occur simultaneously. For the production of secondary electrons a certain energy is necessary. For electrodes usually employed in tubes the average work to be done corresponds to 10 volts. If, therefore, W denotes the energy of the primary electron in volts, the number P of the produced secondary electrons is about

$$P = \frac{W}{10} \tag{71}$$

Since one electron is the smallest electrical quantity,[1] secondary emission

---

[1] The atomic structure of electricity can give rise to limitations in tube measurements. The emission current in electron tubes is a quantum-like flow which (W. Schottky, Schrott effect, 1918) can be noticed when the amplification is high, 5000 fold and more. A telephone receiver will then also indicate noises due to this effect and, if they are louder than the sound to be detected, the effect gives rise to error

is possible only when W is at least 10. The number of the secondary emissions can therefore be increased when the velocity of the primary electron is made large.

Formula (70a) also gives a means of computing the "electron lag" in high-vacuum tubes. The same plays a part when dealing with Schrott or shot effects and also when tubes work in the very high frequency range such as amplifiers and oscillators, since only those electrons which have time to pass from the cathode to the anode of a thermionic tube during half a period $[= 1/(2f)]$ of the oscillation can contribute to the alternating component of the plate current. If t_ϵ denotes the time for an electron to reach the plate, the amplitude of the alternating component of the plate current is decreased by $t_\epsilon/(1/2f)$. Since v in formula (70a) stands for the maximum velocity which the electron has obtained when it is about to hit the anode of positive potential E volts with respect to the cathode (neglecting the small initial velocity of the electron), the value for the average velocity of the electron, during its passage from the cathode to the anode, is $0.5v$. But the distance d covered divided by the time t_ϵ of transit is equal to the average velocity; hence

$$t_\epsilon^{(\text{sec})} = \frac{2 \times \text{average distance between cathode and anode}}{v}$$

$$= \frac{2d^{(\text{cm})}}{6 \times 10^7 \sqrt{E^{(\text{volts})}}}$$

If the average distance d between the cathode and the anode is 1 cm and 100 volts anode potential are used, the time of electron transit is then 3.33×10^{-9} sec, while for $E = 900$ volts on the anode it is only 1.11×10^{-9} sec. For a high-frequency oscillation of 100 Mc/sec, half a period is equal to $1/(2f) = 5 \times 10^{-9}$ sec, showing that for 100 volt-electrons the current lost on account of electron lag is $2 ft_\epsilon = {}^{333}\!/_5 = 66.6$ per cent, while for 900 volt-electrons only ${}^{111}\!/_5 = 22.2$ per cent is lost. By loss is meant that these electrons swarm to and fro without producing any output power. This explains the fact that for very high frequency work sufficiently high plate voltage is to be provided if much output is expected.

Any carrier of positive or negative charges is known as an ion. Like an electron, it can be made to move when either electric or electric and magnetic fields act upon it. The positive ion has at least one positive elementary charge and appears to occur always with an *actual* mass, which for the case of a positive hydrogen ion is about eighteen hundred times the apparent mass of an electron not moving much faster than about one-fifth of the velocity of light. The negative ion is either a pure

---

or drowns out altogether the sound to be detected. The energy to be amplified must therefore be greater than that due to the Schrott effect and must be supplied at the rate of 10^{-16} watt at least.

electron or an electron bound to a neutral particle. The negative and positive ions produce currents in the opposite directions, since an electric field applied to two electrodes will attract negative ions to the anode and positive ions to the cathode. This is used in determining the quality of a vacuum of electron tubes. The volt energy of positive and negative ions for velocities which are not very high can be calculated according to (70) by means of

$$v = \sqrt{2 \times 10^7 \frac{q}{m} E} \text{ cm/sec} \text{ (volt-velocity relation for ions)} \qquad (72)$$

where q/m now denotes the charge to mass ratio of the ion, E the voltage, and v the velocity. In this formula q is in coulombs and would be -1.592×10^{-19}, for a negative ion containing one electron, m is the mass of the ion in grams, and E is in volts.

An understanding of ionization in gases is needed for the phenomena which take place inside electron tubes or which occur when electromagnetic waves pass through the ionized layer of the upper atmosphere. Electrons can move freely only in a gas where the pressure is low and the distance through which the electron passes is smaller than the mean free path. For such conditions the electron will not collide with gas molecules.

Ionization can be produced in several ways. In one method an incandescent cathode or some other source emits electrons—or causes an electron discharge—which after sufficient acceleration collide against gas molecules with a speed which produces positive and negative ions through impact. This is known as "electronic bombardment." To do this, a certain amount of work must be done at the expense of the kinetic energy $\frac{1}{2}mv^2 = E q$ of the electron. This work is expressed in "electron volts" by many physicists. For air it is about $E = 16$ volts, showing that for any anode voltages in electron tubes equal to and higher than 16 volts a certain amount[1] of ionization may be expected. This voltage is also known as "ionization voltage." The following table gives the

H	H_2	He	N_2	O_2	Ne	A	Hg
13.54	16.1	24.5	16.9	15	21.5	15.4	10.39

ionization voltage in volts for several substances. For most metal vapors the ionization voltage is between 4 and 10 volts. According to Eq. (70) the volt velocity requires, for a free path of d cm, an electric field strength ε which must be at least E/d or greater than this value.

[1] For work where the least current due to positive ions migrating toward the cathode is undesirable, as for tube galvanometers and direct-current amplification of thermoelectric current, the plate voltage of the tube connected to the input to be amplified should be less than 16 volts.

When the mean free path between gas molecules is very small, as, for instance, in the ordinary atmosphere near the surface of the earth, ionization can take place only when the electric-field strength is chosen correspondingly high. This is the reason why it requires a high voltage to produce a spark across an air gap, while for a neon lamp the glow due to ionization appears with ordinary voltages, sometimes as low as 90 volts between electrodes. Since, according to Eq. (70),

$$E = \frac{\frac{1}{2}m\,v^2}{q} \quad \text{ionization voltage (potential)} \tag{73}$$

the *ionization potential* is defined as the ratio of ionization energy to the charge of the electron. According to the above examples, its magnitude differs with the type of atom, some atoms requiring two to three times as much energy in the impact as others. The kinetic energy which an electron acquires in free passage between points with a difference of 1 volt is about 1.59×10^{-11} erg, and ionization potentials of 10 volts require about 1.59×10^{-10} erg to separate an electron from an atom. When the voltage applied is less than the ionization potential, the electron will be displaced in the atom to a location of higher potential energy. When it returns to its original position, the absorbed energy is used to liberate electromagnetic waves which are characteristic to the atom itself. For monatomic gases ionization takes place in such a way that the liberation of one electron leaves a positive ion behind and these positive ions and the free electrons may be regarded as the primary sources of the ionized gas. In addition to this, negative ions may be formed by the recombination of the electrons with neutral atoms. For multiatomic gases, for which the molecule is made up of several atoms, the molecules generally break up at first into atoms and the process of the latter is as above. But it can also happen that molecule ions are created, for which the entire molecule either loses or gains an electron. When electrodes are used to which higher voltages are applied the respective ions move toward the electrode of opposite polarity. During their motion they are accelerated and, when the distance between electrodes is more than the mean free path[1] (given by the pressure and kind of the gas), the ions must collide with neutral gas particles. If the impact is sufficiently violent, an electron is either knocked off entirely or moved to a larger orbit. For the latter case, it will return again and produce an electromagnetic radiation which is either visible or in the ultravisible band.

---

[1] For atmospheric pressure it is only 10^{-5} cm. If the distance between the cathode and the plate of an electron tube is 0.5 cm, the vacuum must be high. Assuming that only one out of every 1000 electrons passing to the plate collides with a molecule of the gas, the pressure necessary is $p = 10^{-5}/0.5 \times 10^3 = 2 \times 10^{-8}$ atm corresponding to 1.52×10^{-5} mm. of mercury. In the design of tubes the vacuum factor should be higher yet, about 10^{-5}, that is, only one electron collides for every 100,000 electrons flowing to the anode.

Ionization can also be brought about by electromagnetic waves of very high frequency, such as ultra-violet rays and X-rays. Calling W the energy received by a molecule or an atom when such ultra high-frequency waves affect it, one has, according to Planck's law

$$W = h f \text{ ergs} \tag{74}$$

where f denotes the frequency of the exciting vibration and $h = 6.55 \times 10^{-27}$ erg-sec is known as the Planck constant. Assuming that the whole energy of the incident light of frequency f is given to a single electron in the gas particle, the electron leaves the atom with the energy

$$\tfrac{1}{2} m v^2 = h f - W_0 \tag{75}$$

where W_0 denotes the energy[1] lost by the electron in order to escape from the atom. Hence, when E denotes the positive potential in e.s. c.g.s. units, which is just sufficient to prevent the discharge of the electron from the atom, the Einstein-Planck law (1905)

$$E q = \tfrac{1}{2} m v^2 = h f - W_0 \tag{76}$$

Now, if W_1 is the energy needed to release the first electron from the atom,

$$W_1 = h f \tag{77}$$

---

[1] Since we are, in the above case, interested only in the photoelectric effect, that is, in the effect of light especially in the ultra-violet range, the following may be said with respect to the classical theory of light. According to the classical theory, the energy of the absorbed light would not be $h f$ as in Eq. (75) but proportional to the square of the amplitude of the incident light and to the square of its frequency which cannot be checked experimentally. But the Einstein-Planck relation [Eq. (75)] has been experimentally confirmed and shows that the intensity of the incident light affects only the number of electrons liberated, not their velocity v.

When dealing with such effects the "dualism" in theoretical physics plays a part, since when dealing with frequencies of radiation it is convenient to use the wave theory but when dealing with the interaction of radiation and matter it seems better to assume the radiant energy constituted of photons. This means elementary quanta traveling in straight lines and obeying the laws of geometrical optics. If the mechanism of production of spectral lines would be an ordinary linear oscillator, the classical theory of electrodynamics would require that the frequencies of the lines follow the law of harmonics which is

$$f = p f_1$$

if f_1 denotes the fundamental frequency and p any integer. But spectroscopy shows that each line in the spectrum, for instance, of an element such as sodium, is represented as the difference between two terms given by the relation

$$f = a - \frac{b}{p^2} = \frac{W_i}{h} - \frac{W_f}{h}$$

The constants a and b/p^2 denote, therefore, energy levels, since W_i and W_f are the energies in the initial and final states. Cases of this type make use of the postulates of Bohr and more recent advances make use of the "matrix calculus" (Born, Jordan, Pauli, Heisenberg, and others).

Comparing this with (74) shows that W must be at least equal to or larger than W_1 in order to liberate an electron and produce ionization. For helium the ionization potential is about 25 volts, and the energy in joules $W_1 = qE = 1.592 \times 10^{-19} \times 25$ joules, since the charge of the electron is 1.592×10^{-19} coulomb. But 1 watt $= 10^7$ erg/sec; hence $W_1 = 4 \times 10^{-11}$ erg. Putting this in Eq. (77) gives a frequency of about

$$\frac{4 \times 10^{-11}}{6.55 \times 10^{-27}} = 61 \times 10^{14} \text{ cycles/sec}$$

Hence only ultra-violet light can liberate an electron from the helium atom and cause ionization. Roentgen rays correspond to a still higher frequency and can be used as a very active agent to ionize gases.

When an electron collides with a gas atom with insufficient speed to produce ionization, the electron of the atom is at first displaced to another orbit of energy level W_{II} instead of the orbit of the normal level W_I which it occupied before and, when falling back, gives off the energy in the form of electromagnetic radiation of frequency f according to

$$q E_r = h f = W_{II} - W_I \tag{78}$$

where E_r is known as the *radiation potential*. All atoms have many characteristic frequencies. These frequencies form the well-known line spectra of a gas and the blue glow of improperly exhausted electron tubes is due to it. If the corresponding wave length $\lambda = c/f$ is expressed in Ångström units, for the radiation potential,

$$E_r = \frac{12{,}344}{\lambda} \tag{78a}$$

where E_r is in volts. For the hydrogen atom it is 10.15 volts, for the H_2 molecule 11.57, for the helium atom 21.12, for the neon atom 16.6, for the argon atom 11.5, and for the mercury atom 4.66 volts. E_r denotes, therefore, the anode potential which is just sufficient to cause the atom to radiate a spectrum line. These resonance radiations, which may be due either to electronic bombardment of insufficient speed for ionization or to electromagnetic waves of very high frequency, can produce ionization indirectly. Thus, when a blue glow occurs due to this effect, some of the electrons may be far enough displaced from the atom to produce a convection current, or the ultra-violet rays may be sufficient to ionize any mercury vapor that is left in a vacuum tube.

According to Poisson's equation for the potential E at any point in space,

$$\frac{\partial^2 E}{\partial x^2} + \frac{\partial^2 E}{\partial y^2} + \frac{\partial^2 E}{\partial z^2} = -4\pi\rho = -4\pi(Q_1 - Q_2) \tag{79}$$

where $N_1 q_1 = Q_1$ denotes the positive and $N_2 q_2 = Q_2$ the negative space charges for N_1 positive ions and N_2 electrons per cubic centimeter. Strictly, Eq. (79) reads

$$\nabla^2 E - \frac{1}{c^2} \frac{\partial^2 E}{\partial t^2} = -4\pi\rho \qquad (79a)$$

where $\dfrac{1}{c^2} \dfrac{\partial^2 E}{\partial t^2}$ refers to the propagation of the potential with velocity c through the gap between the electrodes. But the square of the time for the electromagnetic wave motion is negligible to the time square taken for the electrons to pass across the space. For good electron tubes $\rho = -Q_2$. Now, when an electric field is produced between two parallel electrodes, the current I passing across the space between the electrodes increases at first as the voltage applied to the electrodes is increased, since the velocity of the ions increases. From a certain voltage on, no increase of current takes place for quite an increase of voltage, since the ions pass to the electrodes as fast as they are formed. If the ionizing agent is the hot cathode of an electron tube, the saturation current could be increased by increasing the temperature of the cathode. But there are always gas molecules present in a tube and it is necessary not to increase the supply of the primary source but to go up in applied voltage until the electrons attain such speed as to produce ionization through impact. The current will then increase again, usually with a slight blue glow present which may become very cloudy and is detrimental when the tube is not sufficiently exhausted, since it may happen that both the electrons of the primary source and the heavier ions formed may collide with gas molecules and increase the ionization. Now, when alternating voltages are applied to a tube with two cold electrodes, ionization occurs similar to discharges in Geissler tubes when the vacuum is not too high. As the frequency of the applied e.m.f. is increased, the free electrons, which are always present in any gas in addition to ions, may not be able to travel the entire distance between the internal electrodes during each half cycle. Hence, there will be no loss of charge. Most of the electrons then remain in the gas and can produce increased ionization through impact. For such high frequencies there can be no permanent separation of the charges and as many electrons will vibrate one way as the other. No space charge can then destroy the field and a cloud of both types of charge is formed, which gives the necessary condition for recombination and the emission of luminosity. It is therefore *easier* to produce glows in discharge tubes when a high-frequency e.m.f. is applied.

When we have two plane electrodes, each parallel to the YZ plane of a coordinate system, then according to Eq. (79) the quantity x denotes any distance along the X-axis for points between the electrodes for which the potential E is given by

$$
\left.
\begin{aligned}
\frac{\partial^2 E}{\partial x^2} &= -4\pi(Q_1 - Q_2) \text{ for positive ions and electrons} \\
&= \quad 4\pi Q_2 = -4\pi\rho \text{ for a pure electron discharge}
\end{aligned}
\right\} \tag{80}
$$

In this result it is assumed that each electrode is an equipotential surface. Applying this to a properly evacuated electron tube with plane electrodes, where one electrode has zero potential everywhere and emits N electrons per square centimeter with an initial velocity v_0 cm/sec, and the other electrode is again an equipotential plane but of higher potential, then one has, according to Eq. (70), the energy relation

$$
EQ_2 = ENq = \tfrac{1}{2}Nm[v^2 - v_0{}^2] \tag{81}
$$

if v denotes the velocity at any place x of potential E with respect to the electrode which emits the electrons of mass m and charge q. Because of the current density

$$
I = -\rho\, v
$$

since there is a flow of negative charge, from Eqs. (80) and (81),

$$
\frac{\partial^2 E}{\partial x^2} = \frac{4\pi I}{v} = \frac{4\pi I}{\sqrt{v_0{}^2 + \dfrac{2qE}{m}}} \tag{82}
$$

Neglecting the initial velocity of the electrons, one obtains for the current density of the electron current between the plates

$$
I = \frac{E^{1.5}}{q\pi\sqrt{\dfrac{m}{2q}d^2}} \tag{83}
$$

where d denotes the distance between the electrodes and E the positive potential applied to the plane electrode which receives the electrons from the other plate which is at zero potential.

With respect to the ionization of the upper atmosphere which may be due to the corpuscular electron emission of the sun—to its ultra-violet radiation as well as cosmic rays—the following is added. Electromagnetic waves passing through an ionized space cause ions to vibrate according to the frequency of the exciting current which produces the waves. The oscillating ions must therefore contribute to the electric current and the Maxwellian equation for the magnetic- and electric-field vectors H and $\mathcal{E}$ must be changed to the form

$$
\operatorname{Curl} H = \underbrace{\frac{\kappa}{c^2}\frac{\partial \mathcal{E}}{\partial t}}_{\substack{\text{Maxwellian}\\ \text{displacement}\\ \text{component}}} + \underbrace{4\pi Nq\frac{\partial s}{\partial t}}_{\substack{\text{due to ions of}\\ \text{charge } q}} \tag{84}
$$

if N denotes the number of ions per cubic centimeter, s the displacement of each ion from its original position, $c = 3 \times 10^{10}$ cm/sec = the velocity of light and κ the dielectric constant. The second term is therefore $4\pi q \Sigma v$ if v stands for the geometric sum of all field velocities per unit volume. The average effect of the motions of the ions due to thermal agitation cancels out. If the permeability μ is also taken into account,

$$\text{Curl } \mathcal{E} = -\mu \frac{\partial H}{\partial t} \qquad \text{Curl } H = \frac{\kappa}{c^2} \frac{\partial \mathcal{E}}{\partial t} + 4\pi q \Sigma v \qquad (85)$$

If therefore a plane electromagnetic wave moves in the x direction, the equation of motion is

$$\frac{\partial^2 \mathcal{E}_z}{\partial x^2} = \frac{\mu \kappa}{c^2} \frac{\partial^2 \mathcal{E}_z}{\partial t^2} + 4\pi \mu \frac{\partial}{\partial t}(q \Sigma v) \qquad (86)$$

From this expression it is evident that the phase velocity c' is different from the velocity c of light, since we deal with an effective dielectric constant κ_e instead of κ. If the effect of the earth's magnetic field or any other independent magnetic field is neglected, the effective dielectric constant κ_e of an ionized layer is smaller than for a perfect vacuum. If $\omega/(2\pi)$ denotes the frequency of the exciting current producing the electromagnetic wave, q the charge, and m the mass of an ion, the effective dielectric constant in the e.s. c.g.s. system is

$$\kappa_e = 1 - \frac{4\pi N q^2}{m \omega^2} \qquad (87)$$

if no collisions take place. But if the ions collide p times per second, this constant becomes

$$\kappa_e = 1 - \frac{4\pi N q^2}{m \omega \sqrt{\omega^2 + p^2}} \qquad (88)$$

if all collisions are assumed inelastic. Since the permeability of the ionized layer of the atmosphere remains unchanged and the dielectric constant κ_e alone changes, for the phase velocity one finds $c' = c/\sqrt{\kappa_e}$ since $\mu = 1$. The phase velocity c' is greater than the velocity c of light. The phase velocity c' must be distinguished from the group velocity c'', since c' is the speed at which an infinitely long sinusoidal wave train travels through an ionized medium. It can be shown that the group velocity with which the energy of the wave is transmitted through an ionized gas is $c'' = c\sqrt{\kappa_e}$, which means that it becomes zero when the value of the effective dielectric constant vanishes. Hence for $\kappa_e = 0$ the ionized layer cannot transmit the particular electromagnetic wave, since the ions are excited with their natural frequency and attain maximum amplitude of vibration. Under such conditions they will collide with molecules and give up the energy obtained from the electromagnetic wave. If it is assumed that electrons vibrate only (they are the easiest ones to be moved), for the case of no collisions one finds, for $\kappa_e = 0$, the resonance frequency of the electron to be $f_0 = q\sqrt{N/m\pi} = 8.98\sqrt{N}$ kc/sec, which for $N = 10^5$ electrons/cc gives 2840 kc/sec. Hence, when the frequency f_0 is found by means of the selective absorption of the corresponding electromagnetic wave, the number of electrons per cubic centimeter can be computed. When a magnetic field of H gauss also acts, assuming that the magnetic field of the wave is negligible in comparison to it, the resonance frequency is $f_0 = 53 \times 10^{-16} H \frac{q}{m}$ kc/sec if the charge q of the ion is expressed in e.s. c.g.s. units and its mass in grams. For an electromagnetic wave passing through an ionized gas of hydrogen ions and field strength of $H = 0.5$ gauss, there would be a resonance frequency of the ions of only 775 cycles/sec, while for electrons having a mass of about eighteen hundred times lighter it would be $f_0 = 1395$ kc/sec. The above field strength corresponds to about the magnitude of the earth's magnetic field.

12. Electron-tube Relations.—The modified Richardson equation for the saturation current i_s is

$$i_s = SAT^2\epsilon^{-\frac{q\Phi}{kT}} \tag{89}$$

where S denotes the surface of the hot cathode in square centimeters, the electronic charge $q = 1.592 \times 10^{-19}$ coulomb, the Boltzmann constant $k = 1.372 \times 10^{-16}$ erg/deg (also known as the "molecular gas constant"), T the absolute temperature of the hot cathode, and $\Phi = 8.62 \times 10^{-5}B$ volt, the volt equivalent of the work to free the electrons from the cathode. The quantity Φ is also known as "Richardson's work function" and as a rule its value is smaller, the larger the atomic number. The quantity B is known as the "electron affinity." For tungsten, $B = 52.6 \times 10^3$ and $\Phi = 4.53$ volts; for molybdenum, $B = 50 \times 10^3$ and $\Phi = 4.31$ volts; for thorium, $B = 34.1 \times 10^3$ and $\Phi = 2.94$ volts; while for platinum, $B = 62.7 \times 10^3$ and $\Phi = 5.4$ volts. If the above Richardson equation for the total electron emission for each square centimeter of hot-cathode surface is written in the logarithmic form,

$$\log_{10} i_s = \log_{10} A + 2 \log_{10} T - 5040\frac{\Phi}{T} \tag{90}$$

since $\frac{q\Phi}{kT} = 11,600\frac{\Phi}{T}$. This equation can be solved graphically by plotting the sloping T lines for a fixed absolute temperature against the work function.

According to C. D. Child, I. Langmuir, and W. Schottky, the space current i for electrodes of any form follows the three-halves-power law with respect to the voltage e; that is, $i = k_1 e^{1.5}$. Generally, it may be said that

$$i = Ke^m \tag{91}$$

expresses the current voltage relation for any portion of the characteristic. The value of m is about 2 for the lower portion, and 1 for the straight middle portion. For the upper region of certain tubes $m = 1.5$ if the effect of saturation is neglected. The *static* resistance R_p of a tube for a certain voltage e is e/i and, for a *variable* anode potential e, the *dynamic* resistance r_p becomes

$$r_p = \frac{de}{di} = \frac{R_p}{m}$$

The dynamic resistance r_p is therefore smaller than the direct-current resistance R_p as long as $m > 1$. The experiment shows that for zero cold-electrode potential ($e = 0$), a small space current still exists and that a small space current exists even for small negative values of e. The reason for this is that the electron evaporation from the surface of the hot cathode follows the Maxwellian velocity-distribution law. Hence, electrons with a temperature velocity greater than the velocity

$v = \sqrt{\dfrac{2q}{m}(-e)}$ due to the applied electric field $(-e/d)$, where d denotes

the electrode spacing, reach the cold electrode and constitute a space current $i_\epsilon = -i$. The emission current for negative cold-electrode potentials e then follows the equation

$$i = i_s \epsilon^{-\frac{qe}{kT}} = i_s \epsilon^{-\frac{e}{8.6 \times 10^{-5}T}} \tag{92}$$

since $q = 1.592 \times 10^{-19}$ coulomb, $k = 1.372 \times 10^{-16}$ erg/deg $= 1.372 \times 10^{-16} \times 10^{-7}$ watt. The quantity i_s again denotes the saturation current and T the absolute temperature of the hot cathode. The quantity $8.6 \times 10^{-5}T$ corresponds to the emission velocity in volts. For tungsten, T is about equal to $2300°$ K and the above expression reduces to $i = i_s[\frac{1}{150}]^e$. Hence, for a total emission current $i_s = 22.5$ ma for a negative plate potential $e = -2$ volts, we find $i = 10^{-3}$ ma.

If a grid is inserted between the hot cathode and the anode, for the grid current I_g, anode current I_p for E_g and E_p as grid and plate potentials, the relation is

$$I_g + I_p = K_1[\mu E_g + E_p]^m = K_1 E^m \tag{93}$$

where E may be considered as lumped tube potential with respect to the hot cathode. It is evident that K_1 then denotes practically the reciprocal of the static internal plate resistance of the tube, since the grid current of properly operating tubes is negligible.

When variable potentials act on the electrodes, the dynamic resistance r_p of the plate is given by $\partial e_p/\partial i_p$ if e_p and i_p stand for the variable plate potential and current, respectively. If e_g denotes the variable grid potential producing the variations i_p and e_p, respectively, the dynamic mutual conductance g_m over the grid is $\partial i_p/\partial e_g$, while its static value G_m is I_p/E_g.

A basic relation for amplifier measurements is

$$l_m \, r_p = \frac{\partial e_p}{\partial e_g} = \mu \tag{94}$$

where μ denotes the amplification factor of the tube.

Interelectrode capacitances play an important part. For an ordinary three-element electron tube there are the grid-plate capacitance C_{gp}, grid-filament capacitance C_{gf}, and the plate-filament capacitance C_{pf}, the last being the least important since it shunts the internal as well as the external plate circuit. The grid-plate capacitance is the most important one because by means of it any action in the external plate branch can be fed back into the grid branch, thus making the tube, to a certain extent, a reversible four-pole if the grid-filament terminals are considered the two input poles and the plate-filament terminals the output poles. The total capacitances

$$C_{gp} + C_{gf} = C_g; \; C_{gp} + C_{pf} = C_p; \; C_{gf} + C_{pf} = C_f$$

give the grid, plate, and filament capacitance, respectively. It is customary to measure the direct capacitances when the filament is not burning. If the filament were heated for the corresponding charges q and potentials e, one would have

$$C_g = \frac{\partial q_g}{\partial e_g}; \; C_p = \frac{\partial q_p}{\partial e_p}; \; C_{gp} = \frac{\partial q_p}{\partial e_g}; \; C_{pg} = \frac{\partial q_g}{\partial e_p}$$

One must then distinguish between a grid-plate and a plate-grid capacitance. If the filament is not heated, the direct capacitances for ordinary receiving tubes is only a few micromicrofarads. For a 201A tube or its equivalent, for instance, $C_{gf} = 5.8$, $C_{gp} = 10.1$, and $C_{pf} = 6.1$ $\mu\mu f$. The measurement can be carried on as follows. The grid and plate are connected together and the capacitance ($C_f = C_{gf} + C_{pf}$) measured from grid to plate. When the filament and grid are connected together and the capacitance between the filament and plate is measured, $C_p = C_{gp} + C_{gf}$. For the filament and plate connected, the capacitance measured between filament and grid yields $C_g = C_{gf} + C_{gp}$. From these measurements may be computed

$$C_{gf} = 0.5[C_f + C_g - C_p]; \; C_{gp} = 0.5[C_p + C_g - C_f];$$
$$C_{gp} = 0.5[C_f + C_p - C_g] \tag{95}$$

Other determinations are found among tube measurements.

13. Notes on Shielding.[1]—Amplifiers and other high-frequency apparatus require careful shielding as well as grounding. Thus the compartment in which careful high-frequency measurements are to be made should be completely surrounded by a copper screen which in a spacing of about 5 cm should be completely surrounded by another copper screen, grounded and connected at one point to the inside screen. This point can then be used to bring the grounded connection of the high-frequency source into the compartment. Metal walls with dimensions large compared with the wave length must be used to screen off electromagnetic waves. If ρ denotes the reflection ability of metals of specific conductivity σ, according to Planck at any frequency f,

$$\rho = 1 - \frac{2\sqrt{f/\sigma}}{c}$$

with c as the velocity of light. The absorption ability is then $\frac{2}{c}\sqrt{\frac{f}{c}}$, that is, equal to $(1 - \rho)$. A copper shield as thin as 0.01 mm acts toward electromagnetic waves in the megacycle range practically as a mirror, while for long electromagnetic waves corresponding to the audio-frequency range, the copper plate shield must be about 1 cm thick, since the thickness necessary to act as a screen decreases proportionally inversely as the square-root value of the frequency.

Since in a high-frequency laboratory there are pick-ups due to the electromagnetic wave directly and pick-ups due to electric and magnetic fields, respectively, it is important to distinguish between the action due to the association of the electric and magnetic fields constituting an electromagnetic wave and the effects of electric and magnetic fields themselves. In Gaussian units for $\mathcal{E}$ = electric field, H = magnetic field, I = current density, ρ = volume density of charge, c = velocity of light, v = velocity of electron, and F = the force acting on the electron, the Lorentzian equations

$$\left. 4\pi I + \frac{\partial \mathcal{E}}{\partial t} = c \text{ curl } H; \quad -\frac{\partial H}{\partial t} = c \text{ curl } \mathcal{E}; \text{ div } \mathcal{E} = 4\pi\rho; \text{ div } H = 0; \right\} \quad (96)$$

$$\text{and } F \quad = \quad \underbrace{\mathcal{E}}_{} \quad + \quad \underbrace{\frac{v \times H}{c}}_{}$$

| total force | electric driving force on electron in direction with $\mathcal{E}$ | magnetic driving force acts only when electron is in motion and is perpendicular to both the direction of motion and H |

From the force equation it is evident that for a thin vertical wire (antenna), the current, that is, the electron flow, occurs only along the wire (up and

---

[1] BARFIELD, R. H., *J. Inst. Elec. Eng.* (*London*), **12**, 249, 1924; J. H. MORECROFT and A. TURNER, *Proc. I.R.E.*, **13**, 477, 1925; G. W. O. HOWE, *Exptl. Wireless*, **7**, 57, 179, 1930; C. R. ENGLUND, *Exptl. Wireless*, **7**, 204, 1930.

down), since the vector product $v \times H/c$ has only an effect of crowding the electrons somewhat to one side of the wire. Therefore it may seem that the magnetic effect of the electromagnetic wave never produces a driving voltage in the vertical wire. Hence, a shielding with respect to the magnetic effect would, at first, not seem of value for some purposes. But from the other equations it is evident that the varying magnetic flux $-\partial H/\partial t$ must be associated with an electric field which acts in turn on the electrons. For an arriving e.m. wave the screening, therefore, *changes* the relation between $\mathcal{E}$ and H in the wave outside the screen only, since it is not possible to have $\mathcal{E}$ within the screen without H.

If $\int \mathcal{E}\, dl$ and $\int H\, ds$ denote the line and surface integrals of the electric- and magnetic-field vectors, respectively,

$$-\int \frac{\partial H}{\partial t} ds = c \int \operatorname{curl} \mathcal{E}\, ds = c \int \mathcal{E}\, dl \qquad (97)$$

since, according to the Stokes theorem the *line* integral $\int \mathcal{E} dl$ of a vector field around a closed curve is numerically the same as the *surface* integral $\int \operatorname{curl} \mathcal{E}\, ds$ of the curl of the same vector taken over *any* surface bounded by this curve. Therefore if the closed curve does not vary with time, from (97) the line integral $c\int \mathcal{E} dl$ around the fixed closed curve, that is, the entire induced voltage (in case of a receiver) is numerically equal to

$-\dfrac{\partial}{\partial t}\displaystyle\int H ds$, that is, to the negative rate of change of the total magnetic

flux passing through the surface. Hence it is immaterial whether the voltage induced in a conductor by an arriving e.m. wave is computed by means of the magnetic or by means of the electric field of the wave, since these two field vectors are *always associated* with each other.

What then happens in a screened space is as follows: Suppose copper wires or a mesh of such wires are arranged around a cage. There is then an electrostatic screen which must form a termination for every electric line component which is not closed on itself, that is, an electric line of force which can start out on a conductor and end on a conductor. But the screen cannot readily stop closed or rotary electric fields. They pass through the openings and cracks and affect an amplifier, etc., within the screen. The rotary electric fields which are *always associated* with the magnetic fields in the same numerical proportion can be kept away from an amplifier or some other apparatus only when they are surrounded by a *completely* closed envelope. It is thus essential that the metal envelope be not too thin; otherwise the eddy currents induced upon the outside of the envelope will penetrate to the inside of it and produce variable surface charges on the inside of the screen which again will produce electric fields within the screen.

A shielding between a coil A and B can be affected by placing either another coil, a wire mesh, or a metal plate between the two coils. For perfect shielding any current flow in A should not induce any voltage across coil B. If E_1 denotes the induced voltage across coil B if no shield is present, and E_2 the induced voltage with a shield interposed and the same current of unchanged frequency flows through coil A as without shield, then

$$S = \frac{E_1 - E_2}{E_1}100 \tag{98}$$

denotes the percentage shielding of coil B, since the mutual inductance between the two coils is proportional to the voltage induced across coil B. When an ordinary copper mesh is used, as a rule, very little shielding is obtained, while a copper mesh with a soldered border about 1 cm wide acts as a fairly good shield. A solid copper plate is best, since the resistance to the induced eddy currents is lowest. Therefore, it is *essential* that, when shielding is due to eddy currents, their flow should be along a low-resistance path. It is therefore of no advantage to cut narrow slits diametrically across the effective shielding area or use shielding material of low specific conductivity. Therefore, when different stages of amplifiers are to be shielded from each other, the covers of the boxes should make *good* contact with the rest of the box.

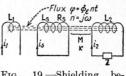

Fig. 19.—Shielding between two coils.

The shielding effect of a coil is shown in Fig. 19. Suppose coil L_1 carries a high-frequency current of instantaneous value i_1 producing the magnetic flux φ which passes perpendicularly to the planes of the turns of the shielding coil L_s and the coil L_2 to be shielded. Coil L_s has N_s turns, each one of area A_s, and coil L_2 is designated by N_2 and A_2. If each coil were in the magnetic field alone, the voltages $e_s = A_sN_sd\varphi/dt$ and $e_2 = A_2N_2d\varphi/dt$ would be induced in the respective coils. Coil L_2 is closed through a load impedance Z which also includes the effective resistance of L_2 and L_s short-circuited so that only the resistance R_s of the coil itself is effective. For the mutual inductance M acting between L_s and L_2 and $n = d/dt = j\omega$,

$$e_s = nL_si_s + R_si_s + nMi_2; \; e_2 = nL_2i_2 + Zi_2 + nMi_s$$

Eliminating i_s from these two relations, for $Z_s = nL_s + R_s$,

$$\frac{e_2 - nL_2i_2 - Z\,i_2}{nM} = \frac{e_s - nMi_2}{Z_s}$$

or

$$e_2 - \underbrace{\frac{nM}{Z_s}e_s}_{} = \underbrace{\left[nL_2 - \frac{n^2M^2}{Z_s}\right]}_{}i_2 + \underbrace{Z\,i_2}_{} \tag{99}$$

| induced voltage without shielding coil L_s | decrease in voltage across L_2 due to shielding coil L_s | effective impedance of coil L_2 when shielding coil is present | voltage drop across load |

From this result it can be seen that the shielding coil produces a *smaller* effective induced *e.m.f.* across coil L_2 and also *decreases* the *impedance* of the L_2 circuit, since a reduction n^2M^2/Z_s takes place.   Complete shielding occurs when no voltage is induced at all, that is, when

$$e_2 - \frac{nM}{Z_s}e_s = 0$$

or

$$\frac{nM}{Z_s} = \frac{A_2N_2}{A_sN_s} \tag{100}$$

Hence, for complete screening, the ratio of the transfer reactance nM to the total impedance of the closed shielding coil must be equal to the ratio of the turn-area product of the coil to be shielded to that of the shielding coil.   When for a short-circuited shielding coil the resistance R_s is neglected in comparison to the reactance nL_s and the coupling factor $\kappa = M/\sqrt{L_sL_2}$ between the shielding and the shielded coil is utilized in (100), the theoretical condition of the complete shielding becomes

$$\kappa = \frac{A_2N_2}{A_sN_s}\sqrt{\frac{L_s}{L_2}} \tag{100a}$$

Hence, as far as the driving voltage only is concerned, the degree of shielding can be obtained from (99) by taking the ratio of voltage reduction across L_2, due to shielding, to the voltage without shielding and expressed in percentage it becomes

$$S = \frac{100nMe_s}{Z_s\,e_2} \tag{101}$$

where S is in percentage.   Hence for a negligible resistance R_s of a short-circuited shielding coil L_s, $Z_s = nL_s$ and

$$S = \frac{100MA_sN_s}{L_sA_2N_2} = 100\kappa\sqrt{\frac{L_2}{L_s}}\frac{A_sN_s}{A_2N_2} \tag{101a}$$

where S is in percentage.   Therefore when L_s and L_2 are identical coils $(A_s = A_2, N_s = N_2, L_2 = L_s)$, the percentage shielding is proportional to the coupling coefficient between shielding coil and coil to be shielded. A complete shielding with coils side by side then seems practically impossible since κ would have to be unity; that is, $M = L_s = L_2$.   Now if L_s as well as L_2 each consist of a single turn of the same dimension and are placed so close to each other that $\kappa = 0.4$ which is practical, then $S = 40$ per cent.   Hence still 60 per cent of the voltage e_2 which would be induced across L_2 without shielding is still passed on toward this coil and would be effective across it if L_2 would remain constant.   But, according to (99), the shielding coil *also decreases* the effective coil *reactance* of L_2 by the amount

$$\frac{n^2M^2}{Z_s} \cong \frac{n^2M^2}{nL_s} = \frac{n\kappa^2L_sL_2}{L_s} = \omega\kappa^2L_2$$

since the j factor in $n = j\omega$ is of no concern in this analysis. Hence the effective coil reactance is only

$$X_e = \omega[1 - \kappa^2]L_2 \tag{102}$$

which in this particular example gives $0.84\omega L_2$. According to (99) and Fig. 19, Z denotes the load impedance, and the load current i_e of the circuit to be shielded, $i_e = 0.6e_2/Z$. The voltage effective across the reduced value of L_2 then becomes

$$e_e = i_e X_e = \frac{0.504\omega L_2 e_2}{Z}$$

For no shielding coil, load current and voltage are

$$i_2 = \frac{e_2}{Z} \text{ and } e_e' = i_2 X_2 = \frac{\omega L_2 e_2}{Z}$$

The *effective* shielding, taking both change in voltage and change in L_2 into account, is then

$$S_e = \frac{100[e_e' - e_e]}{e_e'} = 100[1 - 0.504] = 49.6\%$$

Hence the formula for the effective shielding becomes

$$\begin{aligned} S_e &= 100[1 - (1 - \kappa^2)(1 - \kappa)] \\ &= 100[1 - (1 + \kappa)(1 - \kappa)^2] \end{aligned} \tag{103}$$

where S_e is in percentage. Shieldings of this type may have desirable features in experiments with large loops such as frame antennas. When the single-turn shielding coil L_s consists of a copper tube enclosing the coil L_2, a considerable degree of shielding is possible.

For amplifiers, screening by means of coils is not customary, since a most effective shielding is required. Copper cylinders which surround the coil to be shielded are then convenient. The screening cylinder then has a diameter of about twice the diameter of the coil to be shielded and the length is somewhat longer than the coil. It is not well to choose the diameter much less than about 1.6 times the diameter of the coil; otherwise the coupling coefficient κ between the shield toward the coil causes too great an increase of the effective coil resistance and a decrease in effective coil inductance. This can be understood from the following analysis. The solid cylinder acts as a low-resistance secondary with respect to the enclosed coil. If R_1 and L_1 denote the constants of the enclosed coil when not shielded and if R_2 and L_2 the constants of the surrounding screen, the ordinary equivalent transformer equation (page 12) can be applied, and, for the coupling factor $\kappa = M/\sqrt{L_1 L_2}$ between shield and coil, the effective coil constants in the presence of shielding are

$$R_e = R_1 + AR_2$$
$$L_e = L_1 - AL_2 = L_1[1 - \kappa^2 \sin^2 \psi]$$

where

$$A = \frac{\omega^2 M^2}{R_2{}^2 + \omega^2 L_2{}^2} = \frac{\omega^2 \kappa^2 L_1 L_2}{R_2{}^2 + \omega^2 L_2{}^2} = \frac{L_1}{L_2} \kappa^2 \sin^2 \psi$$

$$\sin^2 \psi = \frac{\omega^2 L_2{}^2}{R_2{}^2 + \omega^2 L_2{}^2}$$

(104)

The enclosed coil L_1 usually denotes the tuning-interstage coil. Therefore it is not desirable to have a large reduction AL_2 so that the resonance setting with the shield is not very different from the resonance setting without it. To keep AL_2 small, either A, L_2, or both can be made small. The value of L_2 is made small by choosing a cylinder (a single turn only). Since A is proportional to the square of the coupling factor κ, it is essential that the shielding cylinder be large, and, for economy, of about the dimensions as given above. Since the logarithmic decrement $R_e/2L_e f$ increases with the effective resistance, that is, with the increase AR_2, it is also essential to keep this product low. This is also done by choosing a well-dimensioned shielding cylinder. R_2 denotes the effective resistance to the induced currents in the cylinder. There is no gain in choosing the thickness t of the cylinder walls unreasonably large, since for high-frequency work the induced currents can penetrate the inside wall of the cylinder only slightly. If t is chosen much beyond the penetration thickness at the particular frequency, the rest of the walls will act only as a dead mass, that is, not decrease at all the effective resistance R_2. Since the skin to which depth high-frequency currents penetrate is small compared with the diameter of the shielding cylinder or shielding boxes if rectangular enclosures are used for screening, the maximum useful thickness can be computed from the skin-effect ratio $\left(\dfrac{R_2}{R_0} = \dfrac{\text{high-frequency resistance}}{\text{direct-current resistance}}\right)$ of a plate which extends infinitely in all directions if it is assumed[1] that the magnetic-field strength H acts at the inside wall of the screen, while there is no flux whatsoever at the outside wall. For the thickness t in centimeters, the frequency f in cycles per second, the specific conductivity σ of the cylinder (for copper $\sigma = \frac{1}{1700}$ sec/cm^2), $k = 2\pi\sqrt{\sigma f}$ and $k\,t = \beta$, the skin-effect ratio becomes

$$\frac{R_2}{R_0} = \beta \frac{\sinh 2\beta + \sin 2\beta}{\cosh 2\beta - \cos 2\beta}$$

(105)

which leads to the approximations

$$\frac{R_2}{R_0} = \begin{cases} 1 + \frac{64}{45}\pi^4\sigma^2 f^2 t^4 \text{ for very small values of } \beta \\ \beta \text{ for large values of } \beta (\beta \geqq 2.5) \end{cases}$$

---

[1] JAEGER, B. W., "Elektrische Messtechnik," 2d. ed., 1922, p. 9; M. v. ARDENNE, "Verstärkertechnik," Julius Springer, Berlin 1929, p. 225.

Since β depends upon the frequency f and the thickness t of the cylinder for a given material which should have a high specific conductivity σ, it can be seen that for the high-frequency range for which f is large and thicknesses t which are not unreasonably small (t several millimeters), the approximation formula $R_2/R_0 = \beta$ holds ($\beta \geqq 2.5$). This is a linear law and, since the direct-current resistance increases proportionally inversely with the thickness, for a certain frequency the high-frequency resistance R_2 remains constant. Hence, by putting $\beta \geqq 2.5$, the minimum thickness t can be computed for any particular frequency. Using the value $\beta = 3$, one has $\beta = kt = 3$ and for $f = 1000$ kc/sec, and copper ($\sigma = 59 \times 10^{-5}$ sec/cm^2)

$$t = \frac{3}{2\pi\sqrt{\sigma f}} = \frac{3}{2\pi\sqrt{59 \times 10^{-5} \times 10^6}} = 0.0197 \text{ cm}$$

that is, about a thickness of 0.2 mm is sufficient.

It should be remembered that for the increase AR_2 due to the reflected portion of the high-frequency resistance of the shielding box, the phase angle ψ [Eq. (104)] enters in the form of $\sin^2 \psi$. Hence, when the dimensions and the material of the shielding cylinder are fixed, the increase in coil damping due to shielding is proportional to $R_2 \sin^2 \psi$ leading to a maximum increase if $R_2 = \omega L_2$. From (104) it can also be seen that this condition corresponds to a maximum reduction of the coil inductance. For this condition the shielding cylinder and the coil to be shielded are matched with respect to energy transfer as well as to shielding. When R_2 is increased by means of poor joints so that $R_2 > \omega L_2$, the back action of the cylinder on L_1 and R_1 is less pronounced. The effective coil resistance R_e decreases somewhat but with it also the shielding action. When the shielding cylinder of about the same length as the coil is cut along its length, R_2 becomes ∞, and no appreciable shielding exists.

When the coil to be shielded is completely enclosed (also at the end faces of the coil), the reflected resistance is much larger. The cylinder should then be made not much shorter than about 1.5 times the length of the coil.

CHAPTER II

HIGH-FREQUENCY SOURCES AND OTHER USEFUL LABORATORY APPARATUS

For satisfactory work the unmodulated high-frequency current of a source should have a good wave form, except for frequency tests where a high harmonic content is of advantage. The high-frequency source should be properly shielded and grounded and so designed that the load current flowing into the measuring system cannot react back to produce changes in supply voltage and frequency. It is best to design a high-frequency source to meet the needs of a particular test and frequency range, although for many measurements simple tube generators of the type described in the next section seem satisfactory. For receiver tests, signal generators are now commercially available. The testing equipment consists essentially of six parts. An audio-frequency generator (1) feeds into a high-frequency generator (2) to bring about the desired degree of modulation. The modulated high-frequency current works through an attenuator into an artificial antenna (3), into the test receiver (4), output meter (5), and a speaker (6). The output impedance of the generator should not exceed 2 ohms and the output voltage should be adjustable from about 1 to 200,000 μv. Very careful shielding is essential.

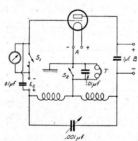

FIG. 20.—Calibrated tube generator.

14. Useful Laboratory Generators.—(For normal frequency, 25 to 2000 kc/sec and output range.) An oscillator of the Hartley type, as a rule, is satisfactory for laboratory work. A pure wave form is then obtained by tuning a step-over resonator (*C-L* circuit) loosely coupled to the oscillator or employing a shield-grid amplifier and an output tube with a plate circuit which is tuned to the fundamental frequency. The circuit shown in Fig. 20 holds for fixed-supply voltages and the frequency calibration is constant within a small percentage. A frequency range from the audio-frequency end up to 5000 kc/sec can be readily covered by using interchangeable coils and a straight-line frequency condenser of about 0.001 μf to change the frequency within the range. If a 0.001-μf condenser is not available, a 0.0005-μf condenser will do. It is then of advantage to have a calibration sheet with the rough frequency values for various condenser settings right on the coil. The grid-current meter can be shunted by means of switch S_1 and when used is a ready

50

means of indicating when another circuit is tuned to the generator. A grid-current dip is then noted when the coupling is not too close and not too loose. Too close a coupling produces the "drawing" effect which is not desirable in measurement work. When a frequency meter is then coupled to the oscillator instead of the circuit, the accurate frequency is found for the same grid-dip indication. The rough calibration is therefore satisfactory for locating the setting approximately and the frequency meter gives the frequency accurately. It will be found that the grid dip can still be noted even when the frequency meter is coupled so loosely to the generator that the indicator of the frequency meter hardly registers. The reaction between the oscillator and frequency meter is therefore very small. The phones in the filament returns can also be used to note the resonance setting of a coupled resonator by means of a click. This type of indication is still more sensitive than the grid-dip method. This is followed up in detail on page 173. A parallel-plate feed is not advisable when covering a very wide range, since the high-frequency

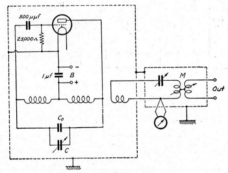

Fig. 21.—Laboratory generator.

choke will act unsatisfactorily for the extremes of the range. However, when an oscillator is to be used for the broadcast range only (500 to 1500 kc/sec), a fixed parallel-plate feed can be used without any difficulty.

Figure 21 shows a laboratory oscillator with a somewhat better frequency constancy. The values for the grid leak and grid condenser indicated in the figure and a small fixed condenser C_0 of about 50 $\mu\mu$f make the frequency but little dependent on the supply voltages (of A and B batteries). C denotes a straight-line frequency condenser of about 0.001 μf maximum setting. The coil across the grid and the plate of the tube is of about 85 μh when the frequency band of the broadcast range is to be covered.

Figure 22 shows a circuit by means of which the high frequency can be modulated to any degree by means of an audio-frequency source of adjustable voltage and frequency. Such expedients are required when testing receiving sets and the like. It is then best to work with small B voltages (not much higher than 90 volts) in order to keep the radio-frequency voltages low. The modulated high-frequency current is then connected to either a potentiometer, a mutual inductance, or a suitable attenuation box in order to produce the small voltage needed for the input terminals of the set. The attenuator which is indicated is a constant-impedance type with attenuation ratios 1, 10, 100, 1000, and 10,000, and a potentiometer tap on the last shunt branch to give inter-mediate voltage values. For many measurements it may be of advantage to go to still more complicated circuits, where the audio generator affects a modulator tube and this tube, in turn, affects a tube which generates the high-frequency current. The best way, although most complicated, is to obtain the modulated high-frequency current by means of the

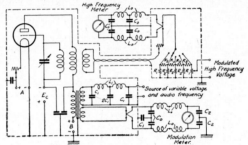

Fig. 22.—Generator for receiver tests, external modulation.
$$C_0 = 0.5\mu f; \ C_1 = 1000\mu\mu f; \ C_2 = 0.01\mu f$$
$$L_0 = 300 mh; \ L_1 = 30 mh$$
$$R_1 = 55\Omega; \ R_2 = 6.11\Omega; \ R_3 = 495\Omega.$$

modulation of a separately excited amplifier. It is then possible to find a design for which practically no frequency modulation occurs, that is, for which the carrier frequency remains fixed even though amplitude modulation is applied.[1]

15. Relaxation Oscillators (Glow-discharge Tube Oscillator, Multi-vibrator, Grid-leak Oscillator, Double-grid Oscillator).—By relaxation oscillators are meant generators of distorted currents for which the varia-tions are due to condenser charges and discharges over a resistance. As in the case of the second type of arc oscillations, the fundamental fre-quency cannot be found from the abridged Thomson formula since no inductance[2] is effective. The capacitance-resistance product is then a measure for the frequency and it should be remembered that the periods

---

[1] For circuits used in certain testing laboratories, the reader is referred to the following articles: L. Bergman, *Telefunkenztg.*, **7**, 32, 1925; C. Kuhlmann, *Jahrb. d. drahtl.*, **25**, 43, 1925; F. Gabriel, *E.N.T.*, **4**, 426, 1927; G. Rodwin and T. A. Smith, *Proc. I.R.E.*, **16**, 155, 1928; A. F. Van Dyck and E. T. Dickey, *Proc. I.R.E.*, **16**, 1507, 1928; K. W. Jarvis, *Proc. I.R.E.*, **17**, 664, 1929; C. R. Burke, *Gen. Radio Experimenter*, **4**, No. 10, March, 1930; C. J. Franks and Malcolm Ferris, *Radio Eng.*, **11**, 37, 1931.

[2] For the second type of arc oscillations the inductance of the shunt branch is not effective for that portion of the cycle for which the current is essentially constant.

for positive and negative loops are not necessarily of the same duration. Generally speaking, the frequency is all the higher the smaller the capacitance and the smaller the resistance over which the respective condenser charges and discharges occur. The resultant wave shape is therefore, for the general case, unsymmetrically distorted and very rich in harmonics, which is a valuable feature when the harmonic generator is used for frequency measurements. Unlike ordinary harmonic generators, not only multiples of the fundamental relaxation frequency but also submultiples[1] of a known impressed frequency f can be utilized in connection with the fundamental relaxation frequency, since integer submultiples, such as $f/2, f/3, f/4, f/5$, can be readily stabilized by means of a very small e.m.f. induced anywhere in the relaxation oscillator (for details, see Chap. V). The constants of the circuit can then be varied over a wide range without affecting the stabilized frequency of the relaxation oscillations.

Figure 23 indicates the simplest type of a relaxation oscillator. A glow-discharge tube is employed. A certain critical voltage exists below which no discharge current through the tube can flow. Suppose the starting voltage to be 100 volts. A current I begins to flow as soon as the battery reaches a voltage E of 100 volts, and by means of a protective resistance R a certain current value will be reached.

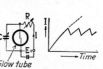

FIG. 23.—Glow-discharge relaxation oscillator.

Because of the persistency of the ionization, the voltage can now be lowered somewhat below the 100 volts without stopping the current flow. If the value of R is chosen sufficiently high and the condenser C at first dispensed with, a current begins to flow again when a voltage of 100 volts is reached. But, if because of the IR drop the voltage across the tube falls below the lower critical voltage, the tube theoretically again turns into an infinite resistance and the current I becomes zero. Hereafter the upper critical tube voltage of 100 volts is again effective and ignition takes place again, and so on. The rate of the continuous flashes can be readily varied by connecting a variable capacitance C parallel to the tube and a current I will take place as indicated in the figure. When the value of C is large, flashes of a very low rate can be produced, one every minute and the like. By making C very small or omitting it altogether (tube capacitance only effective), a frequency in the high audio range (about 10 kc/sec) and, with special tubes, up into the short wave range can be produced. The saw-shaped current variation is very rich in harmonics but of comparatively small amplitude. It can be increased by inserting a coil in parallel with a variable condenser in the R branch and tuning to the desired frequency. For submultiple-frequency work the oscillator can be used as it is or with only a stage[2] of amplification

[1] VAN DER POL, B., *Z. Hochfreq.*, **31**, 178, 1926; **32**, 114, 1927.
[2] *Proc. I.R.E.*, **16**, 1076, 1928.

A much better relaxation oscillator is the multivibrator[1] shown in Fig. 24. Fundamental frequencies as high as 50 kc/sec and as low as about 1 cycle/min can be readily obtained. With a frequency of such a low order, the current and voltage variations in the different branches can be followed by ordinary direct-current meter readings. The circuit is nothing but a two-stage capacity resistance-coupled amplifier which feeds back upon itself. R_1 and R_2 are the respective grid leaks, C_1 and

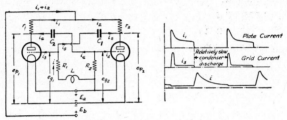

Fig. 24.—Multivibration and its action.

C_2 the coupling condensers from tube 2 to tube 1 and *vice versa*, and r_1 and r_2 the external plate resistors. A small coupling coil L is inserted for delivery of the oscillations to other circuits. The values of R_1 and R_2, for instance, may be 75,000 ohms each, and r_1 and r_2 about 50,000 ohms each. They should be noninductive. The capacitances C_1 and C_2 are variable, each having steps of 500, 1000, 2000, 3000, and 4000 $\mu\mu f$,

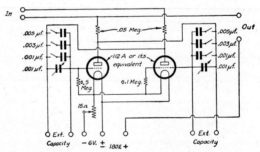

Fig. 25.—Laboratory multivibrator.

which may be connected singly or in parallel and a variable-air condenser of 500 $\mu\mu f$ capacitance. The range is then from 0.5 to 30 kc/sec. Figure 25 shows a multivibrator as a harmonic generator for fundamental frequencies of from a few cycles per minute to about 50 kc/sec, and for frequency submultiple work. It can also be used to produce a linear time axis for the cathode-ray oscillograph (Fig. 45) if the grid leak of one tube is substituted by the plate resistance of a saturated two-element tube. The terminals marked "in" and "out" are for frequency sub-

[1] ABRAHAM, H., and E. BLOCH, *Compt. rend.*, **168**, 1105, 1919; *Ann. physik.*, **12**, 237, 1919; see *Proc. I.R.E.*, **13**, 207, 1925.

multiple work when a small voltage taken from a constant frequency (f) source (piezo oscillator) is impressed across the "in" terminals and controls the fundamental frequency of the multivibrator as an exact integer submultiple of f. The output terminals give the corresponding output of frequency f/m where $m = 1, 2, 3, \cdots$ up to 40. For all other work the "in" and "out" terminals are short-circuited.

For the performance of the multivibrator, reference is made to Fig. 24. For simplicity, $R_1 = R_2 = R$, $r_1 = r_2 = r$, and $C_1 = C_2 = C$ is assumed. When the circuit is closed, it would seem that the plate currents i_1 and i_2 were equal. But experiment as well as theory proves that unstable equilibrium exists and one tube circuit, so to speak, "pumps" against the other and *vice versa*. The current curves shown in Fig. 24 indicate what happens. The directions of the various currents show a positive flow. If the effect of the small output coil used to couple to another circuit is neglected, the grid voltage e_{g_1} and e_{g_2} of the respective tubes are

$$e_{g_1} = E_a - R\,i = E_a - R[i_3 + i_5]; \ e_{g_2} = E_a - R[i_4 + i_6]$$

The corresponding plate potentials are

$$e_{p_1} = E_b - r[i_1 - i_6]; \ e_{p_2} = E_b - r[i_2 - i_5]$$

The corresponding condenser charges are therefore

$$q_1 = C[e_{p_2} - e_{g_1}]; \ q_2 = C[e_{p_1} - e_{g_2}]$$

Hence, if any variations take place, the six currents can be found from the following equations

$$i_1 = \varphi(e_{g_1}, e_{p_1}); \ i_2 = \varphi(e_{g_2}, e_{p_2}); \ i_3 = \psi(e_{g_1}, e_{p_1}); \ i_4 = \psi(e_{g_2}, e_{p_2});$$

$$i_5 = -\frac{dq_1}{dt} = C\left[\frac{de_{g_1}}{dt} - \frac{de_{p_2}}{dt}\right]; \ i_6 = -\frac{dq_2}{dt} = C\left[\frac{de_{g_2}}{dt} - \frac{de_{p_1}}{dt}\right]$$

(i_5 and i_6 are the condenser charge and discharge currents). Now, suppose that at a certain moment the plate current i_2 increases by a small amount. Because of the voltage drop in r_2, the plate voltage e_{p_2} becomes smaller. This change in plate potential acting through C_1 reduces the grid voltage e_{g_1} of the other tube. This in turn *decreases*, because of amplification, the plate current i_1 several times as much as the stimulating *increase* in plate current i_2. Because of the reduced voltage drop $i_1\,r_1$, the plate potential e_{p_1} becomes higher and is propagated to the grid of the other tube by means of C_2, thereby increasing the grid potential e_{g_2}. This will cause a further increase in the plate current i_2 which is many times larger than the initial or stimulating increase. This process will almost suddenly assert itself, at the same time reducing

i_1 as i_2 increases until the grid potential e_{g_1} becomes so negative that the left tube ($i_1 = 0$) is blocked, and the grid potential e_{g_2} becomes very positive so that a large plate current i_2 is produced. Therefore it can be seen that any increase in plate current in one of the tubes will be rapidly accelerated, and one of the condensers will be charged while the other is discharged. The growing plate current is limited by the saturation value of the particular tube and the corresponding grid potential becomes constant. But such an unsymmetrical current equilibrium (for which one tube delivers full emission and the other acts as an open circuit) cannot exist, for the assumed symmetrical network and the condenser charges tend to become equalized and current variations are produced in the opposite direction as expressed by the above equations. The discharge takes place rather slowly, depending upon the CR product. Hence, when the grid of the left tube has become so negative that the tube is blocked ($i_1 = 0$), the discharge path for the particular condenser is then from the negative grid through R_1, through the small coupling coil to filament, through the other tube to plate, and back to the positive side of the condenser C_1. The current, of course, flows around this path from positive to negative polarity. During this discharge, the negative grid potential e_{g_1} becomes smaller and smaller until, from a certain value on, a plate current i_1 is possible. As soon as this happens, instability is again produced and the current i_1 increases almost suddenly to the saturation value, while i_2 becomes zero. The grid leak R_2 then begins to discharge C_2 and the time constant $C_2 R_2$ determines when the next current reversal takes place. Hence, the alternate discharges of C_1 and C_2 determine the time between successive reversals and these periods are equal only when $C_1 R_1 = C_2 R_2$ and the time can be increased by increasing either the capacitance or the resistance or both. When $C_1 = C_2 = 3 \ \mu f$ and $R_1 = R_2 = 2$ megohms, the time between reversals is about 10 sec and a direct-current meter can be used to note the current changes.

An ordinary tube oscillator with a properly chosen grid leak and grid condenser can be used to produce relaxation oscillations. The high-frequency oscillations are then intermittent and the envelope curve is due to the relaxation oscillations. The high-frequency oscillations generated build up the grid-condenser charge until the tube becomes blocked and a discharge takes place over the grid leak and high-frequency oscillations build up again. The high-frequency oscillations are then responsible for maintaining the relaxation oscillation and only one tube is needed instead of two as for the multivibrator. The disadvantage is that high-frequency oscillations are present. A double-grid tube can also be used to produce relaxation oscillations.

16. Notes on Air- and Iron-core Transformers.—Such transformers are of importance when currents are to be measured by means of a step-down transformer, and small signal voltages of known strength are to be produced. It is then essential to know to what extent the ratio of transformation depends upon the turn ratio and how to design such normal mutual inductances.[1] Suppose there is an air transformer of primary inductance L_1 and resistance R_1, feeding into a secondary system of inductance L_2 and total resistance R_2. A practical design for an instrument of this type as used in measuring large currents is shown in Fig. 26. The secondary coil L_2 is wound uniformly around a ring-shaped core (bakelite, for instance) with a small diameter which is about 2 to 8 cm and with the outside diameter from 5 to 12 cm. The primary coil L_1 is made up of either one turn or only a few turns. The ends of the primary are brought in and out in opposite directions to avoid any inductive effect of the lead-in wires. Since the resistance of the primary can often be neglected,

Fig. 26.—Current transformer for measuring large high-frequency currents.

$$\frac{I_1}{I_2} = \frac{\sqrt{R_2{}^2 + \omega^2 L_2{}^2}}{\omega M} \simeq \frac{L_2}{M}\left[1 + \frac{R_2{}^2}{2\omega^2 L_2{}^2}\right] \qquad (1)$$

and for negligible R_2

$$\frac{I_1}{I_2} = \frac{L_2}{M} = \frac{N_2}{N_1} \qquad (1a)$$

that is, equal to the ratio of secondary to primary turns. For the upper frequency range it is not advisable to use a very large turn ratio; otherwise the natural frequency of the secondary can give rise to errors. It is better then to employ a smaller turn ratio and a series resistance with the I_2 indicator.

When an iron core is used, the reactance of the secondary winding must be small. Toroids of silicon-steel laminations (10 mil or 0.0254 cm) which are packed about 1.43 cm thick with an outside diameter of about 2-in (5.08 cm) and 1-in (2.54 cm) inside diameter are then used. The core is covered with insulating oiled silk and about one hundred secondary turns are uniformly spaced over the core. The primary turn is looped through the hole in the toroid as in Fig. 26. The current ratio is then

$$\frac{I_1}{I_2} = \frac{N_2}{N_1}\left[1 + \frac{KR_2}{\omega L_2}\right] \qquad (2)$$

[1] CAMPBELL, A., and D. W. DYE, *Proc. Roy. Soc. (London)*, **90**, 621, 1914; R. LINDEMANN, *Z. Instrumentenk* **35**, 143, 1915; *Jahrb. d. drahtl.*, **11**, 62, 1916; N. W. McLACHLAN, *Electrician*, **78**, 382, 1916; G. KEINATH, *Jahrb. d. drahtl.*, **11**, 43, 1916; G. MOELLER and E. SCHRADER, *Jahrb. d. drahtl.*, **22**, 56, 1923; D. W. DYE, *J. Inst. Elec. Eng. (London)*, **63**, 597, 1925; G. ANDERS, *Proc. I.R.E.*, **15**, 297, 1927; V. G. SMITH, *Proc. I.R.E.*, **15**, 525, 1927; G. RODWIN and T. A. SMITH, *Proc. I.R.E.*, **16**, 155, 1928; R. S. GLASGOW, *J. Am. Inst. Elec. Eng.*, **47**, 327, 1928; H. DIAMOND and E. Z. STOWELL, *Proc. I.R.E.*, **16**, 1194, 1928; H. D. OAKLEY, *Radio Eng.*, **10**, 42, 1930; L. COHEN, *Electronics*, **1**, 21, 1930.

The coefficient K depends upon the iron losses and is slightly smaller than unity. When $KR_2/\omega L_2$ is small compared to unity, one has again

$$\frac{I_1}{I_2} = \frac{N_2}{N_1} = \frac{L_2}{M} \tag{3}$$

When ordinary air transformers are used for receiver-calibration work, one again has for a low-loss secondary ($R^2 << [\omega L_2]^2$), so that the ratio of transformation is, as above,

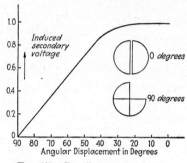

FIG. 27.—D-coil mutual inductor.

$$\rho = \frac{L_2}{M} \tag{4}$$

But at higher frequencies a dependence of ρ on the frequency may occur, because of the capacity effects between the primary and secondary turns. They produce a decrease of ρ, giving a value

$$\rho_1 = \frac{\rho}{1 + \omega^2 A} \tag{5}$$

The constant A depending upon the magnitude of the intercapacity effect between primary and secondary coils can be found experimentally from two measurements ρ_1 and ρ_2 at frequencies $\omega_1/2\pi$ and $\omega_2/2\pi$, respectively, and is then given by

$$A = \frac{\rho_1 - \rho_2}{\rho_2\omega_2{}^2 - \rho_1\omega_1{}^2} \tag{5a}$$

For standard mutual inductances for receiver testing, D coils can be used to advantage (Fig. 27). When the primary voltage is kept constant, the calibration curve for the secondary induced voltage is practically constant to about 20-deg angular displacement.

17. Tuned Air Transformers.—Considering the case of the secondary coil L_2, R_2 tuned by a condenser C_2 across it, the relations (31), (32), and (33) as given on pages 15 and 16 are obtained. Since, according to formula (31) on page 15, the secondary current I_2 has a maximum value when

$$\omega M = \sqrt{R_1 R_2} \tag{6}$$

the proper adjustment of the mutual inductance is the determining factor because R_1 and R_2 are more or less fixed. Since $\omega = 1/\sqrt{C_2 L_2}$, the inductance L_2 of the secondary can be computed when C_2 is known. Referring to the calculation of the primary inductance L_1 from the relation

$$\kappa = \frac{M}{\sqrt{L_1 L_2}}$$

for the coefficient of coupling, the relation $\omega^2 M^2 = R_1 R_2$ and the condition that the apparent impedance of the tuned transformer must be equal to the effective resistance R_1 to which the primary is connected,

$$Z = \frac{\omega^2 M^2}{R_2} = \frac{\kappa^2 \omega^2 L_1 L_2}{R_2} \qquad (7)$$

The ratio of the transformer is then given by

$$\rho = \frac{1}{\kappa}\sqrt{\frac{L_2}{L_1}} \qquad (8)$$

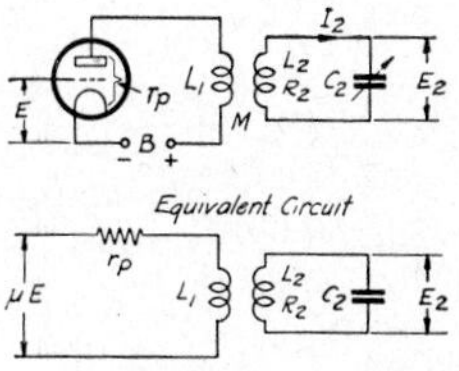

Therefore the ratio of transformation is larger as the time constant L/R of the coils becomes larger.

FIG. 28.—Tuned transformer in tube circuit.

18. Resonance Transformer in Tube Circuits.—Figure 28 gives the case for a tuned high-frequency amplifier where μE denotes the effective grid voltage acting in the plate circuit of the internal dynamic tube resistance r_p. The secondary current for any C_2 setting is then

$$I_2 = \frac{c}{a + jb} \qquad (9)$$

for

$$
\left.
\begin{aligned}
a &= r_p R_2 + \frac{L_1}{C_2} + [M^2 - L_1 L_2]\omega^2 \\
b &= r_p\left[\omega L_2 + \frac{R_2}{r_p}\omega L_1 - \frac{1}{\omega C_2}\right] \\
c &= -j\omega M \mu E
\end{aligned}
\right\} \qquad (9a)
$$

Therefore maximum secondary current flows when the reactance jb disappears, that is, for

$$\omega = \frac{1}{\sqrt{C_2\left[L_2 + \frac{R_2}{r_p}L_1\right]}} \cong \frac{1}{\sqrt{C_2 L_2}} \qquad (10)$$

since the plate resistance r_p of a tube is large compared with the coil resistance R_2. The condenser current I_2 for frequencies materially different from resonance frequency is given by the approximation

$$I_2 = \frac{c}{r_p\left[\omega L_2 - \frac{1}{\omega C_2}\right]}$$

while for resonance the condenser current becomes

$$I_r = \frac{c}{r_p R_2 + \omega^2 M^2}$$

leading to a selectivity

$$\frac{I_r}{I_2} = \frac{r_p\left[\omega L_2 - \dfrac{1}{\omega C_2}\right]}{r_p R_2 + \omega^2 M^2} \tag{11}$$

and a voltage amplification

$$\frac{E_2}{E} = \frac{I_r/j\omega C_2}{E} = \frac{-\mu M}{C_2[r_p R_2 + \omega^2 M^2]} \tag{12}$$

The voltage amplification per stage can also be computed by using the ordinary formulas for the tuned air transformer and relations (6), (7), and (8). Therefore assuming that the time constant of the secondary air coil is about $L_2/R_2 = 30 \times 10^{-6}$ sec, a tube with an internal dynamic plate resistance $r_p = 10^4$ ohms, and an amplification factor $\mu = 8$, there is for a frequency of 10^6 cycles/sec, that is, $\omega = 6.28 \times 10^6$ for $C_2 = 0.000\ 1\mu f$ from $\omega = 1/\sqrt{C_2 L_2}$, the secondary inductance $L_2 = 2.535 \times 10^{-4}$ henry. The secondary-coil resistance then becomes

$$R_2 = \frac{2.535 \times 10^{-4}}{30 \times 10^{-6}} = 8.45 \text{ ohms}$$

Assuming a coupling coefficient $\kappa = 40$ per cent, we find from the condition $r_p R_2 = \omega^2 M^2$ or

$$r_p R_2 = \kappa^2 \omega^2 L_1 L_2$$

the primary inductance $L_1 = 5.3 \times 10^{-5}$ henry. The ratio of transformation due to the transformer is then

$$\rho = \frac{1}{\kappa}\sqrt{\frac{L_2}{L_1}} = \frac{1}{0.4}\sqrt{\frac{25.35 \times 10^{-5}}{5.3 \times 10^{-5}}}$$

that is, 5.47 times. The voltage amplification per stage is

$$A_e = 0.5 \ \mu\rho = 21.9 \text{ times}$$

19. Autotransformer in Tube Circuits.—A voltage change can also be brought about by means of autotransformers as indicated in Fig. 29, where ρ denotes the ratio of partial turns to entire turns applied to the next tube. For the upper circuit of Fig. 29 this ratio is 1 and the tuned external plate circuit acts as a resistance L/RC, while for the lower circuit it acts as a resistance $L/\rho^2 RC$. If E is again called the effective alternating voltage acting between grid and the filament of the first tube and I the corresponding alternating current in the plate branch, for the straight position of the tube characteristic,

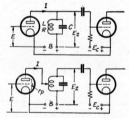

Fig. 29.—Tuned autotransformer in tube circuits.

$$I = \frac{\mu E}{r_p + \dfrac{L}{\rho^2 RC}} \tag{13}$$

where $\rho = 1$ for the circuit without a coil tap to the plate. The effective alternating voltage drop due to the external plate load is

$$E_p = -I\frac{L}{\rho^2 RC}$$

$$= -\mu E \frac{L/\rho^2 RC}{r_p + \dfrac{L}{\rho^2 RC}} \qquad (14)$$

and this voltage multiplied by ρ must give the effective voltage E_2 applied toward the second tube. Hence

$$E_2 = \mu E \frac{L/\rho RC}{r_p + \dfrac{L}{\rho^2 RC}} \qquad (15)$$

Hence voltage amplification due to the first tube and plate circuit

$$\frac{E_2}{E} = \mu \frac{L/\rho RC}{r_p + \dfrac{L}{\rho^2 RC}} \qquad (16)$$

When $L/\rho^2 RC = r_p$, the optimum maximum voltage is transferred to the next grid, while for $L/\rho^2 RC < r_p$, the resonance maximum becomes sharper (circuit more selective) but the voltage passed on to the next grid is smaller. This can be verified by evaluating $dE_2/d\rho$ and equating the result equal to zero. From this result it is evident that for maximum amplification the anode tap should be chosen so that r_p and ρ match and L is high. The upper limit of L is given by the self-resonance of coil L.

20. Notes on High-frequency Oscillographs.—The oscillograph is an apparatus for recording the wave form of a variable voltage or current. In order to record the true wave shape, the natural frequency and the damping of the movable agency of the oscillograph must be as large as possible. For this reason the vibrating loop of an ordinary electromagnetic oscillograph is designed so that its natural vibration is from 6000 to 10,000 cycles/sec and the loop with a small mirror is submerged in oil. An oscillograph of this type is, however, unsuitable for high-frequency work, since the inertia of the movable system is altogether too large to follow the fast oscillations and the damping too small. It then becomes necessary to use instruments whose movable parts show practically no inertia effect as is the case for the cathode-ray (Braun tube) and the glow-discharge (Gehrke tube) oscillograph. Nevertheless, the ordinary oscillograph can be used in high-frequency work, for instance, when certain phenomena are studied by means of beat notes in the audio-frequency band or by means of audible modulations. The degree of modulation of a high-frequency carrier can also be recorded with an ordinary electromagnetic oscillograph if the high frequency is first rectified. For no modulations, the image of the vibrator mirror will then trace a line parallel to the time axis and any audio-frequency modulations will be indicated by displacements from this parallel line.

21. Helmholtz Pendulum for the Plotting of Discharge Phenomena by the Point-by-point Method.—In 1869 Helmholtz suggested a pendulum which during its half swing strikes and operates two contacts. The time interval between the moments for which the contacts are affected by a falling pendulum can be adjusted by means of a micrometer screw. Thus with the arrangement in Fig. 30, discharges occurring in single circuit, as well as in coupled circuits, can be studied if the frequency does

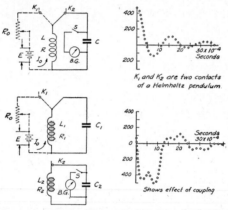

FIG. 30.—Helmholtz pendulum contacts K_1 and K_2 for plotting discharge curves.

not exceed 20 kc/sec. The pendulum then consists of two independent contact switches K_1 and K_2, respectively, which can be opened by means of a falling pendulum in rapid and calculable succession. If the two contacts are lined up (line perpendicular to direction of the swing of the pendulum), K_1 and K_2 will open simultaneously, while for any other relative displacement there will be a time interval.

When both contacts are closed, the condenser C of the oscillation circuit CL is charged and, when the pendulum opens K_1, the condenser C begins to discharge until K_2 is also opened by the pendulum. The switch S is thereafter closed by hand and the first throw on the ballistic galvanometer BG is noted. The throw is proportional to the remaining condenser charge. The contact points are then somewhat displaced with respect to each other and another point of the discharge is observed until the entire discharge characteristic

$$q = I_0 \sqrt{CL} \sqrt{\frac{\dfrac{1}{CL} - 8\alpha^2}{\dfrac{1}{CL} - \alpha^2}}\, \epsilon^{-\alpha t} \sin\left(\omega t + \varphi\right)$$

$$\cong \frac{I_0 T}{2\pi} \epsilon^{-\alpha t} \sin\left(\frac{2\pi}{T}t + \varphi\right)$$

for $\alpha = R/2L$ is found by plotting the maximum throws against the time. The constant of the pendulum is as a rule between 10^{-6} and 2×10^{-6} sec for one turn on the micrometer screw which displaces K_2 with respect to K_1.

22. The Braun Cathode-ray Tube.—The cathode-ray tube of the late F. Braun[1] produces cathode rays by means of bombardment. The cathode-ray tube indicated in Fig. 31 consists of a *cold* cathode and a circular anode with a small hole at its center. When the air in the bulb is exhausted to about 0.006 mm of mercury, a *positive* accelerating voltage from 10 to 20 kv on the anode with respect to the cathode by bombardment will cause the cathode to give off cathode rays perpendicular to its surface. The rays which fall through the hole of the anode or through the opening of another grounded metal shield, which is also metallically

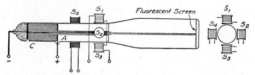

FIG. 31.—Cold-cathode-ray tube using deflection coils $S_1 S_3$, $S_2 S_4$ and a coil S_5 for striction field which focuses the fluorescent spot.

connected to the anode, then form a pencil-like bundle of negatively charged particles which can be deflected by an electric[2] as well as by a magnetic[3] field. Therefore, if a revolving field (which may be electric or magnetic) of constant intensity is applied to the cathode ray, it will describe a conical surface. Since cathode rays produce luminescence where they strike the glass walls and very pronounced luminescent spots when the inside of the glass wall is covered with chalk, zinc sulfide,

[1] BRAUN, F., *Wied. Ann.*, **60**, 552, 1897 (cold-cathode-ray tube); A. WEHNELT, *Physik. Z.*, **6**, 732, 1905, first hot-cathode-ray tube; E. L. CHAFFEE, *Jeff. Phys. Lab. Contr.*, p. 287, 1911; *Proc. Am. Acad. Arts Sci.*, **47**, Nov. 9, 1911; A. DUFOUR, *Compt. rend.*, **158**, 1339, 1914 (tube with photographic plate inside the tube); H. HAUSRATH, "Apparate und Verfahren zur Aufnahme und Darstellung von Wechselstrom kurven und elektrischen Schwingungea" (footnote 1, detailed description of the cold-cathode-ray tube); J. B. JOHNSON, *Phys. Rev.*, **17**, 420, 1921; *Bell System Tech. J.*, **1**, 142, 1922, and *Western Electric Instruction Bull.* 176 (describes the hot-cathode-ray tube in detail and gives a rather complete list of references); W. ROGOWSKI and W. GROESSER, *Arch. Elektrotech.*, **15**, 377, 1925 (describes improved hot-cathode-ray tubes); M. KNOLL, *J. Am. Inst. Elec. Eng.*, **49**, 463, 1930 (describes a method whereby a Lenard window and Lenard ray oscillograms can be photographically recorded in air in a considerably shorter time than with high-vacuum photography—A. Dufour).

[2] H. EBERT. See also Kaufmann and Aschkinass, *Wied. Ann.*, **62**, 588, 1897 (theoretical electrostatic sensitivity charge per mass).

[3] THOMSON, J. J., *Phil. Mag.*, **44**, 293, 1897 (theoretical electromagnetic sensitivity charge per mass of particles).

calcium tungstate, zinc sulfate, their motion can be observed. Calcium tungstate ($CaWO_4$) gives rise to a bluish fluorescent spot which is very suitable for photographic work, while zinc sulfide and zinc silicate produce a yellow-greenish effect convenient for visual observations. Therefore it is customary to coat the inside of the end face of the tube with such a substance. A mixture of calcium tungstate and zinc sulfide (in equal amounts by weight) in water glass (sodium silicate) seems satisfactory for experimental work. A thin coating is then obtained by means of a spray.

23. Notes on the Design of Cathode-ray Tubes.—Two types of tubes can be distinguished. For one type the cathode is cold and the electron beam is produced by ionic bombardment, and for the other type thermionic electron emission (hot cathode) occurs.

The cathode rays in a cold tube are produced by the fact that a few gas molecules, a few positive ions, and free electrons are always contained within the tube. Therefore, if a strong electric field is applied between the cathode and the anode, the positive ions are attracted toward the cathode and the positive space current would be stopped after all positive ions are collected at this electrode. But on the path to the cathode the positive ions dislodge, after colliding with neutral gas molecules, other electrons leaving behind other positive ions which when striking the cathode with sufficient speed liberate electrons at the cathode which constitute the cathode beam toward the anode. A rather high voltage (10 to 20 kv) is therefore required for the cold-cathode tube and the cathode beam becomes accordingly "stiff" so that stronger deflecting fields (although still weak) are required than when electrons leave the cathode freely. The hot-cathode-ray tube, for which electrons leave freely, requires accelerating voltages only, and anode voltages ranging from 300 to 2000 volts are then sufficient to produce very brilliant spots on the screen and a beam which is not so stiff. For cold-cathode-ray tubes the brilliancy (density) of the spot depends upon the anode voltage and the degree of vacuum. Therefore, if the condition of the vacuum changes, the density of the spot must also vary. Many of the cold-cathode-ray tubes become harder (better vacuum) and it is necessary to admit traces of air by some means. Another difficulty is that, because of working with a pressure as high as about 0.006 mm of mercury, the tube characteristic is not very stable. Any negative charges which collect on the inside of the glass walls may give rise to spurious deflections. Much of this trouble can be overcome by using highly polished electrodes from which the gases are excluded by heating them under a high vacuum by means of eddy currents produced by a strong high-frequency field applied outside the tube. The glass walls should also be baked to almost the collapsing temperature of the glass. After the glass walls and the electrodes are again at normal temperature, traces of air are gradually admitted while the pump is kept in motion. The tube should be sealed off for a pressure which requires a voltage of about between 10 to 15 kv in order to produce a bright spot. With a treatment of this kind, little trouble should be found even though the tube is operated for one thousand or more hours. As far as the brilliancy of the spot is concerned, it can be greatly increased (for cold- and hot-cathode-ray tubes by applying a magnetic striction field).[1] This field is produced by means of a coil S_5 in Fig. 31. About 500 amp-turns are needed and, when excited with an adjustable direct current, the spot can be readily focused, since a sufficiently strong magnetic field along the axis of the coil will cause the cathode rays to crowd into a tight bundle. The action of the striction field H_s is as follows: The magnetic lines of force due to the striction turns S_5 (Fig. 34) are parallel with the axis of the tube and cause the electrons which are traveling toward the fluorescent screen of the tube to move along helical paths tangent to the line of magnetic force through the point of the cathode which gives off the electrons. The helixes are formed because the electrons are accelerated along the tube by means of the electric field due to the anode potential E. There exists also a velocity perpendicular to the length of the tube due to the H_s lines. For a distance l between the cathode (may be hot or cold) and the fluorescent screen, a certain average velocity $v_l = \sqrt{2Eq/m}$ of the electrons due to E, definite magnetic-field intensities H_s can be found for which a sharp fluorescent spot occurs on the screen. One value of H_s produces a condition for which all electrons rotate once about the axis while passing through the length l. The spot is then magnetically focused. A focusing also occurs when the electrons describe two complete helical paths around the axis when passing from the cathode to the screen and so on. Hence if T is the time for one rotation (one complete helical path described), it must be also equal to the time for the component propagation along the l direction with the velocity v_l. If α denotes the angle between the electrons emerging and the axis, $v \sin \alpha$ is the component velocity perpendicular to the H_s lines of force and the electrons will be thrown around a circle of radius r when the motion along l is at first ignored. Then for the charge q and the mass m of one electron and for $v = v_l$,

$$\underbrace{\frac{m(v \sin \alpha)^2}{r}}_{\text{centrifugal force}} = \underbrace{H_s q v \sin \alpha}_{\text{magnetic force}}$$

For the angular velocity,

$$\omega = \frac{2\pi}{T} = \frac{v \sin \alpha}{r} = \frac{q}{m} H_s.$$

[1] Ryan, H. J., *Electrician*, **51**, 770, 1903; *Trans. A.I.E.E.*, **20**, 1417, 1903; *Proc. A.I.E.E.*, **30**, 511, 1911.

For the time T of one complete rotation about the axis,

$$T = \frac{2\pi}{H_s q/m}$$

Taking now the linear uniform velocity along l one has for it $v \cos \alpha$ and the distance between the cathode and screen becomes

$$l = [v \cos \alpha]T$$

Solving for T and equating the result to the expression obtained for T before gives the magnetic field intensity

$$H_s = \frac{2\pi v \cos \alpha}{q/m}$$

required for producing the first focus. In this expression $q/m = 1.769 \times 10^7$ e.m.u./gram and $v = 6 \times 10^7 \sqrt{E^{(\text{volts})}}$ cm/sec. The angle α which produces the blur of the fluorescent spot without a proper H_s field is found by estimating the diameter d of the blurred spot when the H_s field does not act and evaluating $\alpha = \tan^{-1} \frac{d}{2l}$. If a long single-layer coil of N_0 turns per centimeter is used for producing the striction field, $H_s = 0.4\pi N_0 I$ gauss when the direct current I is in amperes.

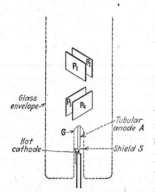

There are two kinds of constructions for the design of the hot-cathode-ray tube. For one (Western Electric type, Fig. 32), the electrons are produced by a dull point emitter (oxide-coated filament). The cathode is then so shaped as to protect the coating of the active part of the filament by placing it out of the direct path of the positive ions from the anode. A metal shield with a small aperture is between the anode A and the cathode. This shield is at the same potential as the negative end of the low-voltage filament (about 2 volts). These elements are sealed into a small bottle-shaped glass tube G, in the neck of which is mounted a narrow platinum tube A serving as the anode.

Fig. 32.—Hot-cathode-ray tube of Western Electric Company. ($P_1 P_2$ and $P_3 P_4$ are deflection condensers. $P_1 P_3$ and A are connected to ground. S and negative end of filament are connected together.)

Hence only electrons which sweep inside this tube are responsible for the fluorescent spot on the screen. After the tube is evacuated to a high degree, a small amount of argon gas is admitted in order to further tighten the electron-stream bundle. This gas also serves to prevent the accumulation of charges within the tube. With this construction the cathode is protected from injurious effects of positive-ion bombardment, since the volume of the gas to which both the anode and the hot cathode are exposed is not sufficient to produce ionization for an arc. Since the time of electron flight toward the fluorescent screen is longer for such low accelerating potentials than is the case with the high voltages used in cold-cathode-ray tubes, there is much more tendency for the beam to spread along its path. This tendency is counteracted by the argon gas which is at a very low pressure and the action is about as follows: As the thermionic electrons are accelerated by the positive-anode potential at a velocity of many thousand kilometers per second and when one of them collides with one of the gas molecules which move at a velocity of only a fraction of a kilometer per second, the force of the collision knocks off one or more electrons from the molecule. The remaining nucleus then becomes a positive ion which attracts free electrons. But these positive ions are heavy compared with the electrons. Therefore they move with comparatively low speeds and are only knocked around by the electrons traveling at a high speed and stay practi-cally in the line of the cathode-ray pencil where they are formed. Hence the entire length of the cathode beam forms a stream of positive ions which must attract the free electrons and also keep them in straight lines. The electrons would otherwise have a tendency to spread because of their mutual repulsion. The current to the anode in this type of tube is only ½ ma. In series with the B battery supplying the anode voltage, a protective resistance of about 2000Ω is inserted, so that if an arc is formed the tube cannot be destroyed.

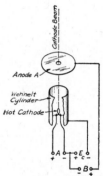

Fig. 33.—Hot-cathode-ray tube with a Wehnelt retarding electrode.

The other type of hot-cathode-ray tube is as indicated in Fig. 33. Its construction is simpler as far as the work of the glass blower is concerned, but accelerating voltages from 600 to about 2500 volts on the anode are required to produce a dense and well-focused spot. The brilliancy of the spot is then exceedingly good and of the order observed with cold-cathode-ray tubes when properly functioning. Since the source of electrons is a hot cathode, the brilliancy of the spot can be increased by changing the filament temperature, while for a cold tube, after being sealed off, the density of the spot can be increased for a focused beam only by means of the anode potential, that is, at the expense of the deflec-tion sensitivity. The tube shown in Fig. 33 uses a Wehnelt cylinder at whose center is a dull emitter (oxide-coated filament). The Wehnelt cylinder uses a retarding potential which is about 10 per cent of the value of the accelerating anode potential. The negative cylinder potential prevents the disintegration of the filament. The anode consists of a circular disk about 3 mm from the front edge of the Wehnelt cylinder. A small hole of about 2 mm in diameter at the center of A passes the electron stream responsible for the fluorescent spot. A commercial tube of this type is due to M. von Ardenne.[1]   An inert gas at a very low pressure is again used to produce a very concentrated beam.

For the deflection of the cathode ray, deflection coils or deflection condensers or both can be used.   They have the same action for the cold- as for the hot-cathode-ray tube.   Figure 31 illustrates the case

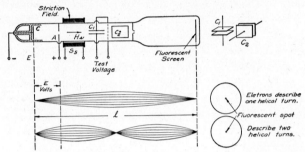

FIG. 34.—Cathode-ray tube with deflection condensers C_1 C_2, and striction field H_s for focusing the fluorescent spot.

where the cathode beam is deflected magnetically, while Fig. 34 indicates the case where an electric field is effective.   The deflection condensers C_1 and C_2 can also be outside the tube if no static deflections are of interest.   When locating the spot of a tube, it is convenient to connect all terminals of the two deflection condensers together; otherwise the cathode-ray stream may not strike the fluorescent screen.   If the spot even with this condition is much off the center of the screen, an ordinary horseshoe magnet properly turned against the tube will bring the spot to a suitable point.   In some tube designs (Western Electric) the location of the spot is stabilized by connecting one plate of each deflecting condenser to the grounded anode and leaks of 1 to 2 megohms across the deflection

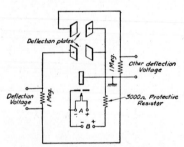

FIG. 35.—Circuit for the Western Electric cathode-ray tube.

plates.   The circuit is then as in Fig. 35.   Any charges which would otherwise collect on the internal deflection plates can then leak off instead of producing a biasing effect on the cathode beam.   Although this avoids a false superimposed deflection of the beam, it is a disadvantage when studying the conditions of two circuits which should *not* have common leads (for instance, when the frequency relation between two independent generators is compared by Lissajous figures; the interconnection within the tube may give rise to automatic synchronization).   It would then seem better to employ external deflection electrodes, or internal deflection quadrants the leads of which come out through the

[1] *E.N.T.*, **7**, 80, 1930.

glass walls right behind the quadrant plates, rather than through a common tube base. Deflection coils and one set of deflection plates can also be used. The capacitance of the plates can then be kept very small (smaller than 10 c.g.s. units) and a much higher voltage sensitivity will be obtained when working in the higher-frequency range.

24. Static Voltage and Current Sensitivity of Cathode-ray Tubes.— With reference to Fig. 36, the undisturbed electron of mass m and charge q travels along the X-axis until it strikes the fluorescent screen producing a luminescent spot at P. When an electric field $\mathcal{E} = E/a$ due to the voltage E across the indicated deflection condenser acts, the path of the cathode ray is towards P_1, producing a deviation PP_1 of the fluorescent spot along the same direction as $\mathcal{E}$, that is, along the Z-axis. When a current I flows through the deflection coils which are in series so that a magnetic field of intensity H acts, the fluorescent spot moves from P to P_2, that is, a deflection along the Y-axis.

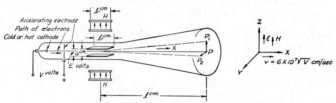

Fig. 36.—Deflections P-P_1 and P-P_2 of the fluorescent spot due to an electric field $\mathcal{E} = E/a$ and magnetic field H, respectively.

The electrons traveling in the X direction have a velocity $v = dx/dt$. If a magnetic field H acts as indicated in the figure, the electrons experience a deflecting force Hqv along the Y direction. But mass times acceleration is equal to this force or

$$m\frac{d^2y}{dt^2} = qH\frac{dx}{dt}$$

or

$$\frac{d^2y}{dt^2} = \frac{q}{m}H\frac{dx}{dt} = \frac{v^2}{2V}H\frac{dx}{dt}$$

since

$$\tfrac{1}{2}mv^2 = qV$$

Integrating yields

$$\frac{dy}{dt} = \frac{v^2}{2V}\int_0^t H\frac{dx}{dt} = \frac{v^2}{2V}\int_0^b H\,dx = \frac{v^2}{2V}Hb$$

But

$$\frac{dy}{dt} = \frac{dy}{dx}\frac{dx}{dt} = v\frac{dy}{dx}; \text{ therefore } \frac{dy}{dx} = \frac{v}{2V}Hb$$

giving upon integration over the entire length l, the deflection

$$y = PP_2 = \frac{v}{2V}H\,b\,l$$

But, according to (3) $v = 6 \times 10^7 \sqrt{V}$ and when the deflection PP_2 as well as the dimensions of b and l are in centimeters and the driving voltage between anode and cathode in volts, then

$$PP_2 = \frac{0.3H \, b \, l}{\sqrt{V}} \qquad (17)$$

Therefore it can be seen that the magnetic deflection, that is, the current sensitivity, is more pronounced when the distance l from the deflection coil to the fluorescent screen is large and when the width b through which the magnetic intensity H acts on the cathode ray is also large. Formula (4) was derived on the assumption that H acts uniformly over the length b which is not exactly true. In reality

$$PP_2 = \frac{0.3H}{\sqrt{V}}F \qquad (17a)$$

if F depends upon the distribution of the H field and path of electrons in the field. When hot-cathode-ray tubes are used for which the cathode beam is not very stiff (V only 300 to 2000 volts) and the deflection turns are arranged as Helmholtz coils, it is possible to obtain a current sensitivity of about 1 cm/10 amp-turns. The pair of deflection coils should have a narrow rectangular cross section so that the deflecting magnetic field acts on a good portion of the cathode beam.

With respect to electric deflections by means of a deflection condenser of width b along the X-axis, a more rigid formula can be obtained. Then the force $\mathcal{E} q$ must be equal to $m\dfrac{d^2z}{dt^2}$, since the deflection now takes place along the Z direction. Since

$$\frac{dz}{dt} = \frac{dz}{dx}\frac{dx}{dt} = v\frac{dz}{dx}$$

$$\frac{d^2z}{dt^2} = \frac{vd^2z}{dx^2}\frac{dx}{dt} + \frac{dv}{dt}\frac{dz}{dx} \simeq v^2\frac{d^2z}{dx^2}$$

because the acceleration dv/dt can be neglected for small displacements. Hence

$$v^2\frac{d^2z}{dx^2} = \frac{q}{m}\mathcal{E} = \frac{v^2}{2V}\mathcal{E}$$

and

$$\frac{dz}{dx} = \frac{1}{2V}\int_0^b \mathcal{E}dx = \frac{b\mathcal{E}}{2V} = \frac{b\dfrac{E}{a}}{2V} \qquad (18)$$

$$z = PP_1 = \frac{blE}{2aV}$$

with the anode as well as the deflection voltages in volts and the dimensions as well as the deflection again in centimeters. It can be seen again that the voltage sensitivity can be made larger by increasing the length b of the deflection condenser, by increasing the distance between the deflection plates to the fluorescent screen, by making the gap a between the deflection plates smaller, and by choosing a smaller anode potential V. The latter is more or less fixed for a given tube when a cold cathode is employed, while for a hot-cathode-ray tube V can be chosen comparatively low, down to 300 volts, since thermionic electron emission occurs. Therefore when $V = 300$ volts, $l = 20$ cm, $b = 1$ cm, and $a = 0.5$ cm, the voltage sensitivity E/PP_1, according to (18) becomes equal to 15 volts/cm deflection.

When internal deflection condensers are used, the capacitance is still very small and of the order of ordinary tube capacitance, about 10 $\mu\mu$f. But, on account of being internal electrodes, some of the electrons striking the fluorescent screen are reflected back and may be accumulated on these electrodes. Since there exists also a heavy cloud of ions between the electrodes, spurious voltages may be superimposed and give rise to errors in the deflection when only small voltages (smaller than about 3 volts) are applied to the deflection condenser. These spurious voltages can be avoided by a proper bias. The charges collected in this way cause the deflection plates to act like a unilateral device when the internal tube connection is used as indicated in Fig. 35. With a static deflection voltage of 30 volts about 25-μa flow across the space and for the polarity reversed, that is, with -30 volts, only about 2 μa can be observed for a particular case.

25. Dynamic Deflections Due to Variable Magnetic and Electric Fields and Lissajous Figures.—If, in a tube with deflection coils (Fig. 31), a high-frequency current flows through the series coils S_1, S_3 only, the fluorescent spot on the screen describes a straight line whose length is proportional to the maximum value of the exciting current, since the spot is linearly polarized and moves to and fro in synchronism with the variable magnetizing current. The same holds for the current which flows through S_2, S_4 only, except that the luminous line is now perpendicular to the one obtained above, since the exciting field acts in space quadrature. Hence, when magnetizing currents $i_1 = I_1 \sin \omega t$ and $i_2 = I_2 \sin \omega t$ with the same frequency and phase ($\varphi = 0$) flow through the respective pairs of coils simultaneously, the resulting deflecting force which deflects the cathode beam is again linearly polarized, but under an angle $\alpha = \tan^{-1} \dfrac{I_1}{I_2}$. However, when the condition of equal phase does not exist (phase φ), the fluorescent spot circumscribes an area. For sinusoidal current one then generally has the case of an elliptically polarized magnetic field which for a proper phase-amplitude relation may give a circularly polarized field. Such closed characteristics (Fig. 37) can also be produced by using deflection condensers (Fig. 34) which also act in space quadrature, since, according to the formulas derived in the previous section, the component deflections are here proportional to the voltage across the deflection condenser, just as for the coil deflection they are practically proportional to the magnetizing force as long as they are not too intense. In Fig. 37 the amplitudes as well as the frequencies of the impressed voltages are the same. The general Lissajous figure is then an ellipse with its major axis forming the diagonal of the two component directions. For the phase difference $\varphi = 0$, the ellipse degenerates into a 45-deg line, while for $\varphi = 90$ deg one obtains a circular trace. When the respective component amplitudes

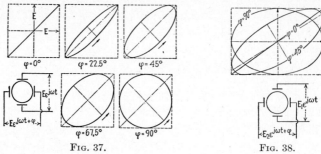

FIG. 37.

FIG. 38.

FIG. 37.—Lissajous diagrams for equal amplitudes and frequencies but different phase angles.

FIG. 38.—Lissajous diagrams for equal frequencies but different amplitudes and phase angles.

are no longer equal, the general trace of the fluorescent spot is still an ellipse, but with increasing phase angle φ not only the eccentricity of the ellipse changes but also the major axis turns as can be seen from Fig. 38.

26. Equation and Application of Lissajous Figures.—The simplest cases of such figures are illustrated in Figs. 37 and 38. The cathode ray is then affected by two harmonic forces which act at 90 space degrees, that is, in quadrature. For $\theta = \omega t$ there are the component deflections $x = E_1 \sin \theta$ and $y = E_2 \sin (\theta + \varphi)$. Since

$$\sin \theta = \frac{x}{E_1} \text{ and } \cos \theta = \frac{\sqrt{E_1{}^2 - x^2}}{E_1}$$

one has

$$y = \frac{E_2\{x \cos \varphi + \sqrt{E_1{}^2 - x^2} \sin \varphi\}}{E_1} \tag{19}$$

for the equation of the *general* ellipse. For

$$\varphi = 0° \quad y = \frac{E_2}{E_1} x \text{ a line of inclination } \alpha = \tan^{-1} \frac{E_2}{E_1}$$

$$\varphi = 90° \quad y = \frac{E_2}{E_1}\sqrt{E_1{}^2 - x^2} \text{ or } \left(\frac{x}{E_1}\right)^2 + \left(\frac{y}{E_2}\right)^2 = 1 \text{ an ellipse}$$

which for equality of the amplitudes ($E_1 = E_2$) gives the circle of Fig. 37. For

$$\varphi = 180° \quad y = -\frac{E_2}{E_1} x \text{ a straight line}$$
$$\varphi = 270° \text{ as for } \varphi = 90°$$
$$\varphi = 360° \text{ as for } \varphi = 0°$$

All possible ellipses are inscribed in the right-angled parallelogram of Fig. 38. The sides of the rectangle are $2E_1$ and $2E_2$, since one component deflection varies between $\pm E_1$ and the other between $\pm E_2$. Therefore it is evident that the fluorescent spot in the general case, for unequal amplitudes E_1 and E_2 and somewhat unequal frequencies $\omega_1/2\pi$ and $\omega_2/2\pi$, must produce a *rectangular luminous area* on the fluorescent screen, since the inscribed ellipse changes continuously (φ is not constant), while simultaneously the main axes of the ellipse undergo a rotation. This conclusion is of importance when Lissajous figures are used for frequency-standarization work, where, for instance, the voltage E_1 across one deflection condenser comes from a generator of known frequency and the voltage E_2 across the other deflection condenser is taken from a source whose frequency is to be determined. At the beginning of the measurements, the frequencies cannot be equal and, no doubt, the amplitudes are also of different magnitude. But, according to the above conclusion, this does not matter at all since the two sides of the rectangular figure indicate to what extent the amplitudes are off, even though the frequencies are not exactly adjusted. Hence, as the frequency of one source is gradually adjusted toward a stationary Lissajous figure, an indistinct rectangular area will first appear indicating that the frequency is about correct. Then one of the amplitudes is varied until the rectangular figure becomes of square shape. Next the frequency is somewhat varied until a stationary Lissajous figure appears. This is followed up on page 192 under frequency measurements.

Moreover, stationary Lissajous figures do not require that the component frequencies f_1 and f_2 be equal. They are also possible for any value of f_1/f_2, which makes this a ratio of two integer numbers, such as ½, ⅓, ⅔, etc. The Lissajous figures are then more complicated, as can be seen from Fig. 39. The two upper representations hold for the cases where f_1/f_2 are either exactly or only approximately equal to the ratio 2:1. In the former case a parabola is obtained, while in the second case the parabola continuously moves and turns but always so that it touches the circumscribed rectangle which is formed by the double values of the respective component amplitudes. The rotation and its direction are very useful since they can be used to compute the frequency difference. For instance, if the Lissajous figure makes half a rotation per second, then $f_1 - f_2 = 0.5$ cycle/sec. For such complicated figures, where rotations take place, one cannot speak in a true sense of phase displacement, since one vector rotates faster than the other. This means that, even though both sinusoidal variations start with equal phase, immediately afterwards one variation falls behind the other. The phase at the beginning then characterizes the shape of the stationary pattern as can be seen from the lower representation of Fig. 39. There is a simple rule for recognizing the frequency ratio f_1/f_2. For instance, if the lower row of representations touches the circumscribed rectangle twice vertically and three times horizontally, then the frequency ratio 2:3 exists. Other Lissajous figures which are of importance are shown in Fig. 40. If equal phases exist for the indicated frequency ratios, the

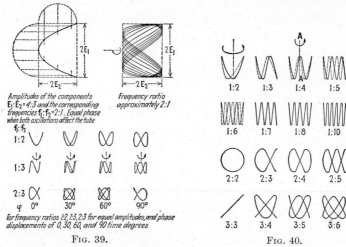

Amplitudes of the components $E_1:E_2=4:3$ and the corresponding frequencies $f_1:f_2=2:1$. Equal phase when both oscillations affect the tube $f_1:f_2$

Frequency ratio approximately 2:1

For frequency ratios 1:2, 1:3, 2:3 for equal amplitudes, and phase displacements of 0, 30, 60, and 90 time degrees

Fig. 39.

Fig. 40.

Fig. 39.—Lissajous diagrams for sinusoids of different frequencies.
Fig. 40.—Lissajous diagrams which are useful in frequency calibration work.

heavily drawn portions of the figures appear, while for all other conditions the figure revolves. There is no particular difficulty in holding the figures stationary if the sources are properly coupled to the deflection elements of the cathode-ray tube. This method can be used, for instance, to calibrate a beat oscillator with an ordinary house current (60 cycles/sec). The zero beat point is obtained by either a plate-current indicator in one of the high-frequency generators, or by means of the cathode-ray tube. The output of the beat oscillator is connected to one deflection condenser and, as zero frequency is obtained, the spot will be seen to move slowly to and fro until it becomes stationary. The same can also be noted on the plate meter. This requires, of course, that no automatic synchronization takes place between the constituent frequencies of the beat oscillator. In order to find the 60-cycle position, a stationary ellipse is generally obtained if the other deflection condenser is connected across a 60-cycle source of appropriate amplitude. The dial of the beat oscillator is then turned until the heavily drawn figure corresponding to the ratio 1:2 is obtained which gives the 120-cycle setting. Then the setting 1:3 corresponding to 180 cycles is found, and so on. There are no difficulties in carrying on the calibration up to about 4000 cycles in this way, depending, of course, upon the spread of the scale. For frequencies still higher, the calibration points come closer and closer and it is better to set an auxiliary generator to some calibration point, for instance, $10 \times 60 = 600$ cycles/sec, and find the calibration points for consecutive integer multiples of 600 in the same way. An application to high-frequency standardization is described on page 193.

For gear-shaped closed figures produced by superimposed variable voltages on the anode of the cathode-ray tube, see Sec. 86, where their application to the calibration of frequency meters is described.

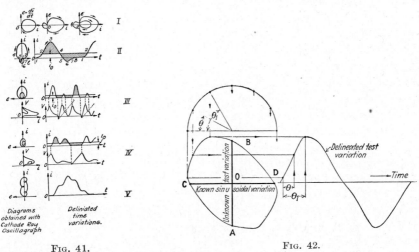

Diagrams obtained with Cathode Ray Oscillagraph   Deliniated time variations.

Fig. 41.   Fig. 42.

Fig. 41.—High-frequency oscillograms (cyclic and dynamic arc characteristics, v voltage across and i current through an oscillating arc).

Fig. 42.—Delineation of a Lissajous-Ryan diagram.

27. Construction of the Curve Shape from a Lissajous Figure.—

Figure 41 shows closed figures and other stationary patterns as obtained with cathode-ray tubes. For closed diagrams it is often desirable to construct the variation with the time, that is, in the simplest case, to construct a sine curve from the corresponding circle.

Unless a special time axis as described in the succeeding section is used, it is convenient to produce a Lissajous-Ryan diagram as illustrated in Fig. 42, since for high-frequency work it is easier to obtain a good stationary closed figure than an oscillogram (time variation of voltage or current) as obtained by ordinary electromagnetic oscillographs. This method is of value especially when a distorted current wave is to be investigated. The experiment then consists of applying a portion of the voltage of the unknown wave to one deflection element of the tube giving the fluorescent line (*AB* in Fig. 42). Next, a sinusoidal wave is applied to the deflection element in quadrature to it and the linear trace *CD* is obtained. Hereafter, both voltages are impressed simultaneously on the respective deflection elements and the indicated closed Lissajous-Ryan diagram is obtained. Since the known sinusoidal variation corresponds to a circle, it is possible to construct the time variation of the unknown voltage by means of the semicircle shown in the figure. It is then customary to use a known sinusoidal variation which has the same frequency as the fundamental of the distorted wave to be investigated. This is necessary because a stationary closed pattern can be obtained only either when the frequency of the auxiliary sinusoidal variation is equal to the fundamental frequency of the variation to be studied or the ratio between them is a whole number. If the time variation of the amplitude curve of a modulated high-frequency carrier is to be studied, the frequency of the known sinusoidal variation need only be equal to the modulation frequency. In the Lissajous-Ryan figure, *OC* and *OD* represent positive and negative maximum amplitudes of the known sinusoidal variation. The circumference of the semicircle is divided into equal portions. The same number of equal portions corresponds to them along the time axis *t*. The construction is as shown in the figure.

Since this method is applicable only when one variation is known, other expedients must be used in addition to delineate complicated Lissajous figures. In cases of this type where neither the vertical nor the horizontal deflection is known, one deflection is made proportional to the differential quotient[1] (with respect to the time) of the other which acts in space quadrature. For instance, this is the case in the delineation of cyclic and dynamic arc characteristics[2] obtained on Poulsen circuits. The constructed time variations are shown in Fig. 41. The time axis in diagrams I to V of Fig. 41 is then found by producing equal shaded areas, since the condenser of the oscillator must take up just as much energy during the charge as during the discharge. Diagram II indicates the development of the *i*, *t* curve from the corresponding cyclic diagram. The quantity *e* signifies the instantaneous value of the voltage across the few turns which carry the oscillation current and whose terminals are connected to the deflection condenser of the tube. The vertical deflection is proportional to di/dt, since *L* in

$$e = -\frac{L\,di}{dt}$$ is a constant. The value i_0 denotes the constant current

taken from the direct-current source in case of arc oscillations. The *i*, *t* curve is constructed as illustrated in Fig. 42. For di/dt = max, the maximum steepness of the *i*, *t* curve is found. The length of

[1] MARTENS, F. F., *Verh. Phys. Ges.*, **21**, 65, 1919.
[2] YAGI, H., *Proc. I.R.E.*, **4**, 371, 1916.

the time axis between the points 2-4-2 can not be found directly from the cyclic diagram but by means of the shaded areas. Diagrams III and IV indicate the delineated i, t and v, t curves constructed from the cyclic and dynamic characteristics.[1] Diagram V is a case with harmonics present (cyclic diagram contains small loops).

For the theory of the above method where the auxiliary deflection is proportional to the differential quotient of the time variation to be found, for the vertical component deflection one has the function

$$y = F(t) \tag{20}$$

and for the horizontal component

$$x = k\frac{d[F(t)]}{dt} \tag{21}$$

k is a constant. Then

$$\frac{dt}{k} = \frac{dy}{x}$$

Since the constant k is generally known (in the above example $k = L$), the time dt during which the fluorescent spot describes a curve element on the closed trace can be computed. The average distance of the curve element towards the Y-axis is x and the projection on the Y-axis is dy. As in ordinary Fourier wave analysis, a number of successive close points 1, 2, 3, 4, . . . N are chosen on the closed trace described by the fluorescent spot. Their coordinates are $x_1, x_2, \ldots x_N$ and $y_1, y_2, \ldots y_N$. The time t_N at which the fluorescent spot just sweeps across point N can then be computed from

$$t_N = k\sum_{2}^{N}\frac{y_N - y_{N-1}}{0.5[x_N + x_{N-1}]} \tag{22}$$

if point x_1, y_1 corresponds to $t = 0$. When the sum $\sum_{2}^{N}$ is taken over the entire fluorescent trace, the value T/k is obtained, since once around the closed figure corresponds to the fundamental period.

28. Linear Time Axis for Obtaining Time Variation Directly on the Fluorescent Screen.—Instead of producing Lissajous or some other closed diagrams, time variations can be directly produced on the fluorescent screen. The auxiliary condenser and coil deflection, respectively, can then be produced by sinusoidal voltages and currents near their zero values.[2] When deflection coils are used, the auxiliary sinusoidal current (which can be a low-frequency current) is chosen so large that only the portion of the

[1] H. Plendl (*Z. Hochfreq.*, **31**, 153, 1926) has given a still more simple graphical solution. See also G. Joos and E. Mauz, *Z. Hochfreq.*, **19**, 2, 1922.

[2] ZENNECK, J., *Physik. Z.*, **14**, 226, 1913; W. ROGOWSKY, *Arch. Elektrotech.*, **9**, 115, 1920.

cycle next to the intersection with the time axis (zero line) falls on the screen. Since a sine variation is practically linear while passing through the time axis, the component deflection due to this current must also be linear with the time. Another method for producing a linear time axis is due to L. Mandelstam.[1] The production of the time axis depends upon the charging and discharging of a condenser. Suppose a condenser of capacitance C is charged at regular intervals by some means, say some sort of automatic switching arrangement, and allowed to discharge gradually through a pure resistance R, then the CR product determines the speed at which the discharge takes place. Hence when the resistance is formed by the plate resistance r_p of a two-element electron tube or an ordinary three-element tube with the grid and plate connected together and an underrated filament current (plate current limited by filament temperature, temperature saturation), the current through r_p is independent of the voltage and a uniform time axis can be produced with the linear condenser discharge since the deflection is practically proportional to the time, because r_p is proportional to the voltage across it. Therefore, the automatic charging device consists conveniently of a relaxation oscillator (page 52) because, in such an oscillator, the current as well as the voltage variation is produced by an automatic charging and discharging of a condenser over a resistance. An ordinary tube oscillator with a grid condenser and leak also produces such variations. Therefore, one can distinguish between three types of linear time-axis devices, namely, (*a*) multivibrator, (*b*) glow-discharge tube, and (*c*) tube oscillator with grid leak and grid condenser.

The pattern obtained in all three cases is as indicated in Fig. 43 if a sinusoidal variation is made directly visible on the fluorescent screen. The condenser of the time-axis apparatus then charges during the intervals t_1 and t_2, while during the linear discharge period t_3 the full-line portion of the sinusoid is traced out. For this case the entire relaxation period $(t_1 + t_3 + t_2)$ is chosen about twice as long as the period $T = 1/f$ of the sinusoidal variation to be studied. During the time that the condenser charges, the fluorescent spot sweeps back from B to A which by no means interferes with the forward trace of the sinusoidal variation if the entire time $(t_1 + t_2 + t_3)$ is made exactly an integer multiple of the fundamental period $T = 1/f$ of the test wave. The back-sweep trace BA will look fainter, since the charging epoch of the condenser is usually considerably smaller than the time of discharge. Only for a condition of this kind does the fluorescent spot sweep over and

[1] *Jahrb. d. drahtl.*, **1**, 124, 1907; see also improvement of the method by W. Rogowsky, *Arch. Elektr.*, **9**, 115, 1920; application of this process with glow-discharge tubes are due to F. Bedell and H. J. Reich, *J. Am. Inst. Elec. Eng.*, **46**, 563, 1927; H. A. Thomas, *Exptl. Wireless*, **4**, 15, 1927 (describes time-axis scheme due to E. V. Appleton, Watson Watt, and J. F. Herd).

over the same trace. Since the total time, that is, the period of the relaxation oscillations, is always chosen greater, relaxation frequencies must be used which are integer submultiples of the fundamental frequency of the test wave. This is a very simple matter, since a relaxation oscillator when only somewhat affected by a small portion of a sinusoidal voltage of the test wave will automatically produce frequencies which are submultiples (page 203).

Figure 44 indicates a system whereby a glow-discharge tube with a variable capacitance C in multiple is used to produce relaxation oscillations. By varying C for fixed resistance R of the time constant CR, the frequency can be set from a very low value (a few cycles per minute) to about 3000 cycles/sec, if ordinary glow-discharge tubes are used. A very high frequency can be obtained with special tubes. The funda-

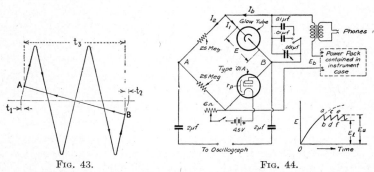

FIG. 43.   FIG. 44.

FIG. 43.—Pattern on the fluorescent screen with a linear time axis. ($t_1 + t_2$ is the time during which the condenser is charged; t_3 is the time of condenser discharge.)

FIG. 44.—Linear time axis circuit using a glow-tube oscillator.

mental frequency of the relaxation oscillation increases as C is decreased. Since the discharge tube can pass a starting current only above a certain critical voltage E_u, the saw-shaped charge and discharge characteristic indicated in the figure is obtained. The supply battery is connected across the series combination of the discharge tube and an electron tube with temperature saturation, while the output of the bridge is taken off across terminals A and B and passed through large condensers ($2\mu f$) towards the deflection condenser of the cathode-ray tube which is to produce the linear time axis. The action of the glow-discharge bridge with the tube resistance r_p is then as follows: When the supply voltage E_b of proper voltage is impressed, the total current I_b splits itself into currents I_1 and I_2 which flow over the respective parallel branches. The capacitance C formed by the glow-discharge tube and any parallel condenser will therefore be charged through the plate resistance r_p of the tube along Oa until at a point a the voltage across the discharge tube reaches the upper critical value E_u for which ignition takes place and a glow discharge sets in and the capacitance C begins to discharge at a rapid rate until the lower critical voltage E_l corresponding to point b is reached for which the discharge stops. After this, the voltage across the glow discharge increases again almost linearly until at point c another glow discharge takes place, and so on. As shown on page 52 in connection with a relaxation oscillator of this type, the frequency of the saw-shaped ripples $abcde$, etc., is a function of the time constant, that is, of the capacitance-resistance product. This frequency in turn determines the difference of $E_u - E_l$. The characteristic of the voltage variation across points A and B is therefore of the same nature, since only a series resistance of 0.25 megohm is added. Hence, during the relaxation oscillation, the short falling portions ab, cd, etc., correspond to the discharges of the condenser C and the back sweep of the cathode-ray spot is so rapid that only a faint trace of it can be seen across the stationary pattern of the delineated time variation on the screen. In this apparatus the almost straight portions bc, de, etc., are responsible for the useful cathode-ray trace. As mentioned above, the frequency of the relaxation oscillation must have a relation to the fundamental frequency f to be investigated so that the cathode ray sweeps back *once* during every *half* cycle of f or some multiple of it. Since a much lower relaxation frequency than the frequency of the test wave (for several cycles delineated) is then used, the method just described in the case of customary glow-discharge tubes can be readily applied to delineating unknown waves up to about 30 kc/sec.

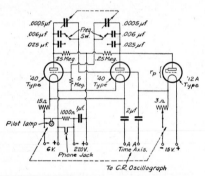

Fig. 45.—Linear time axis circuit using a multivibrator.

For still higher frequencies the multivibrator shown in Fig. 45 with 240 and 112 tubes, or their equivalent, can be used. This type of relaxation oscillator is capable of producing a fundamental frequency at least up to 50 kc/sec, and it is therefore possible to draw out unknown time variations up to almost the broadcast range (about 500 kc). A UX 112-A tube, or its equivalent, is used to produce the resistance r_p so that the current is independent of the voltage and the rate of the condenser discharge becomes practically uniform and a linear time axis is produced. The two adjustable condensers are again alternately and very rapidly charged up to full voltage, while the corresponding discharges leak out slowly over the respective resistances. The voltage of the condenser which leaks off through the UX 112-A tube, whose space current is limited by the filament temperature, is applied through 2 μ condensers to the deflection condenser producing the time axis. The relaxation frequency can be varied from a very low value up to about 50 kc/sec, by varying the capacitance. It is then convenient to have about the same condenser setting for both (UX 240) tubes of the multi-vibrator. By means of the filament rheostat of the UX 112-A tube, a finer variation of the relaxation frequency is possible.

For the delineation of time variations of a still higher frequency, the intermittent tube oscillator shown in Fig. 46 is useful. It can be employed to depict time variations up to 1000 kc/sec. The tube T_1 serves as a high-frequency oscillator. The circuit uses a grid condenser $(C_1 + C_2)$ which is adjustable by means of the setting of C_2. An adjustable discharge leak is again formed by the plate resistance r_p of tube T_2

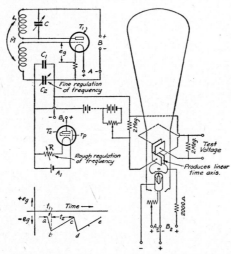

Fig. 46.—Intermittent tube oscillator as a linear time axis device (a b, c d, etc., condenser charge; b c, d e condenser discharge.)

with the space current limited by filament temperature. This resistance can also be varied by the filament rheostat R. The voltage across the grid condenser is applied over a suitable potentiometer to the deflection condenser of the cathode-ray tube. Because of the grid condenser and its leak r_p, the condenser $C_1 + C_2$ becomes charged as the high-frequency oscillations due to CL branch build up, and the grid potential e_g becomes more negative (decrease a to b) during the charging time t_1. For a condition corresponding to point b, the grid potential is so negative that the tube becomes blocked (no plate current) and the high-frequency oscillation must also stop. The accumulated negative grid charge now begins to leak out slowly over r_p until, after a time t_2 corresponding to point c, the high-frequency oscillation can again build up, and so on. Therefore there are again comparatively rapid charge periods t_1 of $C_1 + C_2$ which include, besides, high-frequency potentials due to the oscillation constant CL. The shortness of t_1 can therefore be adjusted by the CL setting. The potential variation during this time again constitutes the back sweep of the cathode-ray beam (line BA in Fig. 43), the trace of which is normally only faint because of its high speed and is readily distinguishable from the desired time variation. The discharge periods t_2 (Fig. 46) will produce the desired trace of the time variation because they are much slower. The grid-potential variations bc, de, etc., during the discharge are again due to a relaxation oscillation whose frequency can be adjusted by means of the setting of the grid condenser or by means of the setting of the rheostat R which controls the filament current of the tube T_2, that is, the resistance r_p over which the discharge occurs. Hence when two complete cycles of the test wave are to be shown, the time-scale frequency must again be half of the value of the fundamental frequency of the test wave.

29. Visualization of Very Fast Transients.—The deflection arrangement of Fig. 47 deflects the cathode ray by means of one electric and two magnetic fields. The magnetic fields are produced by means of the deflection coils 1-1 and 2-2 which are mounted perpendicular to each other, while the deflection condenser 3-3 causes the transient time variation to act in the same direction on the ray as the auxiliary current passing through deflection coils 1-1. When high-frequency transients of very short duration are to be recorded, the cathode ray is made to trace a carrier sine wave of comparatively low frequency and the transient variation is superimposed upon this wave. The deflection coils 1-1 carry a discharge current which acts as the linear time axis (α). Its purpose is to draw out the component to-and-fro motion (β) due to a known high-frequency current flowing through coil 2-2 as in diagram γ. Therefore when the rapid-transient variation is impressed on the deflection condenser 3-3, it will show up as in diagram δ. A portion of the sine wave shown in γ and δ then acts as time axis for the transient. It is therefore possible to photograph very rapid transients which can be done conveniently only under a vacuum or by means of a Lenard window (see the next section). When the oscillator frequency is 50 kc/sec, and the effective width of the linear trace is 100 mm, the average distance corresponding to 1 μsec is 10 mm. The cathode ray is held off the film or photographic plate at the top until all is set for the exposure, so that the

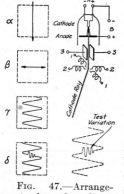

FIG. 47.—Arrangement for the direct visualization of fast transients.

---

[1] This method is due to A. Dufour, *Compt. rend.*, **158**, 1339, 1914; *L'onde élec.*, **1**, 638, 1922. It was applied by K. B. McEachron and E. I. Wade (*Trans. A.I.E.E.*, **44**, 832, 1925) for the investigation of transients.

transient will not be missed. In order to start the linear time axis and the rapid transient to be pictured, a revolving-contact apparatus is provided and so timed that the transient phenomenon takes place while the 50-kc wave is being traced.

30. Notes on Visual Observations and Photographing Cathode-ray Patterns.—For visual observations the cold- and hot-cathode-ray oscillograph as described in the previous sections is sufficient, while for photographic work with very high recording speeds (very brief transients), of the order of microseconds, either the photographic film is placed in the same vacuum chamber with the cathode-ray particles[1] or a Lenard window at the end of the tube is used so that for very high anode potentials (about 75 kv) Lenard rays[2] affect the film in free air. This latter achievelment is much simpler than vacuum photography. For both visua-observations on the fluorescent screen and photographic work, a stationary pattern is of advantage since it is traced over and over by the fluorescent spot and each repetition of the trace adds to the brightness. In the discussion in the previous sections it was shown that Lissajous figures and drawn-out time variations by means of a linear time axis give stationary patterns. For closed patterns the brightness of the trace is then independent of the frequency and the speed if the latter does not change too much along different portions of the cycle; otherwise brighter portions will be noticed at places where the linear speed is less. Visual observation as well as photographic work becomes more difficult when the trace is due to a single sweep of the fluorescent spot only. This happens when transient phenomena are to be investigated. For velocities of the spot much higher than about 10,000 cm/sec, only faint traces are seen and any variations along the trace are practically lost. For photographic work of transients, unless they occur very slowly, vacuum photography or outside photography with Lenard rays only are of use. For vacuum photography the cathode rays affect the photographic film of the plate directly and photographing up to a few millions per second is possible. The same happens for photographic rays with Lenard rays. When stationary patterns are to be photographed, the trace on the fluorescent screen of ordinary cathode-ray tubes is sufficient and the time of exposure is a few seconds to several minutes, and a screen which is rich in blue is used. Ordinary fast plates are equally good as color-sensitized plates or films. When only a rough record of the pattern is desired, it can be drawn over in pencil on transparent paper or be obtained without a camera by placing a photographic film in direct contact with

[1] DUFOUR, A., *loc. cit.*

[2] KNOLL, M., *Z. tech. Physik*, **10**, 28, 1929; *Rev. Sci. Instruments*, **1**, 507, 1930; *J. Am. Inst. Elec. Eng.*, **49**, 463, 1930; C. M. SLACK, *J. Optical Soc. Am.* and *Rev. Sci. Instruments*, **18**, 123, 1929.

the end face of the cathode-ray tube. The developed product will then not be so distinct as when photographed with a camera.

Open-air high-speed photography is carried on by Lenard[1] rays up to recording speeds of 500 km/sec, and details up to one-millionth of a second can be followed on the photographed trace. When a thin electron window (Lenard window) is mounted in the end face of the tube, the electron stream constituting the cathode ray passes through it from the vacuum into free air, and luminosity can be produced for a distance of as much as 5 cm. Some Lenard windows consist of aluminum about 0.0026 mm thick. In order to stand the pressure of the atmosphere against the vacuum, the thin aluminum foil is sealed over a very small opening (1.7-mm hole) or, as in the Coolidge cathode-ray tube,[2] a nickel foil 0.0127 mm thick and 7.5 cm in diameter is reinforced by a honeycomb

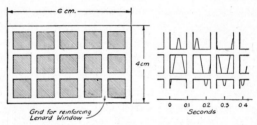

Fig. 48.—Oscilligrams with a Lenard window and high-speed electrons (shaded areas aluminum foils down to 7μ or cellon foils down to 16μ).

structure of molybdenum. Ordinary blueprint paper can then be used to locate the spot. C. M. Slack[3] constructed a Lenard tube in which a hollow bottle-shaped glass window with a thickness of 5 or 10 μ was used to admit the cathode ray into the free air. A much more convenient construction of a Lenard window is the *large plane* window by M. Knoll,[4] shown in Fig. 48. Aluminum or cellon foils are used for the window which can be as large as 6 by 4 cm. The supporting grid consists of upright steel ribbons placed at right angles to each other and having a cross section of 0.3 by 4.0 mm and a distance of 10 mm from each other. For the further support of the foil, a very fine wire mesh of phosphor-bronze (10 wires per millimeter, each 0.04 mm thick) is stretched over the steel ribbons. The reinforced network with the window is cemented vacuum tight to the end of the tube. As indicated in Fig. 48, the close-knit wirework remains imperceptible to the eye and only the steel skeleton is noticeable in the photograph. It can be used as a coordinate system.

[1] Lenard, P., *Ann. Physik.* **51**, 225, 1894; see also W. D. Coolidge, J. *Franklin Inst.*, **202**, 693, 1926.
[2] *Loc. cit.*
[3] *Loc. cit.*
[4] *Loc. cit.*

Not only photographic plates and films can be used but also ordinary bromide paper, as employed in ordinary electromagnetic oscillographs.

31. Notes on Differential Systems.—In many high-frequency measurements, a certain quantity is determined by comparing its action with a standard quantity of the same kind. In order to reduce the number of branches and avoid undesirable mutual actions between many branches, differential systems with only two branches are often employed. Thus the Wheatstone bridge arrangements with four branches and their modifications for alternating-current measurements can be reduced to only two parallel branches if a differential or balanced transformer is used. The test sample and the standards are then compared *simultaneously*, that is, under the same conditions. Another example is the differential calorimeter and the adaptation as a differential thermal measuring device without the use of the calorimeter.

32. Simple and Differential-calorimeter Systems.—Calorimetric methods, although slow, are among the most reliable methods when osses or other determinations are to be made with distorted voltages and currents and any combination of frequencies. The heat delivered to a system is always a measure of the losses and it is independent of the direction of current flow. Such methods are especially useful when the iron losses and the effective resistance of coils are to be found.

The simple calorimeter is a well-known device. It may consist of two cylindrical vessels, which are insulated from each other by air and arranged in such a way that one container completely encloses the other, Containers with polished nickel surfaces seem suitable. The double container is submerged in kerosene which is kept in circulation by a small paddle wheel. A heater keeps the liquid at a fixed temperature which may be controlled thermostatically. The constancy is checked by a thermometer or some other means. The calorimetric liquid which fills the inside container is at first at the same temperature as the liquid surrounding the entire calorimeter. A thermoelement is suspended in the inside liquid through a small opening of the cover. It is connected to a suitable galvanometer in order to observe the temperature increase due to the heat given off by the test sample submerged in the inside liquid. A calibration of the galvanometer is not required when an auxiliary small heating coil is also submerged in the inside liquid. It may consist of a constantan wire (about No. 30) which is wound on ebonite or some other suitable substance. The heat loss of the test sample is then found by producing, by a known direct current I and terminal voltage E across the auxiliary coil, the same galvanometer deflection as is obtained when the desired high-frequency current passes through the test sample. The heat loss is then $W = E I$. This method has the disadvantage that the known direct-current test must be carried on at a different time from that of the test with the sample to be examined.

The differential system which carries on the determination simultaneously consists of two simple calorimeters as described above, for which the two thermoelements are connected against each other through a suitable galvanometer. One calorimeter contains the test sample and the other the auxiliary coil heated with direct current. In order to have a well-balanced indicator system, the inside calorimetric liquids are at first held at the same temperature, that is, neither high-frequency current flows through the test sample nor is there a flow of the auxiliary direct current. Resistances are connected to the respective thermoelements and varied until a zero current passes through the galvanometer. Hereafter, the test sample is excited with the desired high-frequency current of effective value I_1 and the direct voltage E across the auxiliary heating coil varied until, for a direct current I, zero balance is again obtained. The relation

$$W = I_1{}^2 R_x = EI$$

then gives the expression for the coil loss W and its effective resistance R_x.

33. Simple and Differential Thermic Indicator.—When less accuracy but more speed is desirable, the calorimeter may be dispensed with.

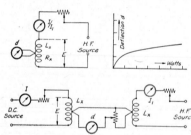

FIG. 49.—Simple and differential thermal indicator.

The thermocouple for the simple thermal indicator is then connected to the test coil as indicated in Fig. 49. Care must be taken that no high-frequency currents pass over the thermocouple to the galvanometer and that the coil L_x does not radiate heat appreciably. For this circuit, the system is at first calibrated with direct current and the voltage drop E across the coil multiplied by the direct current I plotted against the deflection d of the galvanometer. The desired high-frequency current of effective value I_1 which is measured by a thermoelectric indicator is sent through the test coil L_x and the wattage W is read from the calibration curve for the deflection d obtained. Again there is the relation $W = I_1{}^2 R_x$ from which the total loss as well as the high-frequency resistance R_x can be computed. This method is useful only when measurements are carried on with air coils. The differential thermal indicator consists of two circuits. Two equal test coils L_x are used, and two thermocouples attached to each coil are balanced before the measurement is carried on, that is, for zero current through the galvanometer. The desired high-frequency current I_1 is then passed through one test coil, and the direct current I flowing through the other equal coil is varied until, for a terminal voltage E, zero current again passes through the galvanometer. The same relation as above gives watts dissipated and the dynamic coil resistance R_x.

A hot-wire thermometer can also be arranged to give a differential action.

34. Differential Transformer Which Can Be Used to Determine Impedance, Resistance, Inductance, Coupling, Capacitance, Phase Displacement, and Power.—The differential or balanced transformer indicated in Fig. 50 consists of two equal primary coils P_1 and P_2, wound in opposition and symmetrically placed with reference to the secondary coil S. When the currents in the two coils are equal in effective value and are in phase, their inductive effects on the secondary coil neutralize each other exactly, and no voltage is induced in the secondary. If audio-frequency currents flow to the differential system, an ordinary telephone receiver connected across the secondary can be used to indicate the balance (zero current). If the wave shape is distorted, the zero current is tuned to the fundamental frequency. If high-frequency

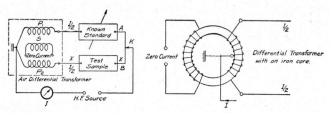

Fig. 50.—Differential (balanced) transformers for high-frequency and audio-currents.

currents flow to the system, sensitive thermoelectric indicators, regenerative tube detectors, and a crystal rectifier in series with a galvanometer (crystal detector) can be used. Since at the beginning of a measurement the system is very unbalanced, it is of advantage to use a double-pole double-throw switch for which the middle terminals lead to the secondary coil of the balanced transformer, one pair of outside terminals of the switch to a thermoelectric milliammeter (about 100 ma, full-scale deflection) and the other pair of outside terminals to the crystal detector. The secondary is at first connected to the thermoelectric indicator and a rough balance obtained. Hereafter the switch is thrown and the crystal detector works through a wall galvanometer for the final adjustment. For very high frequency it is of advantage to tune the secondary. The system then becomes extremely sensitive. But when working in the lower frequency range (25 to 50 kc) more secondary turns are needed and the tuning is not so sharp. A regenerative detector partially neutralizes the resistance. A dynatron connected across the tuned secondary will also accomplish the same effect. If a thermocross bridge (Fig. 59) is used as a zero-current detector, the indications are proportional to the secondary current and it is possible by a proper phase shifter (page 235) to adjust for the phase only or for the amplitude balance only.   This is of great advantage when measuring condenser losses, since the reactive component at high frequencies for any slight off-balance may outweigh the off-balance due to the dielectric loss considerably.

In the application of the differential transformer, the test sample is connected in one primary branch and the standard in the other.   The phase balances with reference to lagging and leading current are accomplished by variometers and variable-air condensers, while any amplitude differences are balanced out by properly chosen high-frequency resistances.   Ordinary decade boxes with an Ayrton Perry winding are satisfactory up to 1500 kc/sec.   Any slight unbalance due to the resisteance of the differential transformer can be balanced out by means of a traveling contact along a slide wire AB of constantan or manganin wire.

As far as the design of the differential transformer is concerned, one must distinguish between high, middle, and lower high-frequency ranges. When a wooden core of about 15-cm diameter is used, an air transformer with 18 turns of litz for each primary winding, and about 300 turns for the secondary which is wound in a groove of 12-cm average diameter, works satisfactorily for the range of 25 to 60 kc/sec.   For the range 60 to 200 kc/sec, 18 turns for each primary and 125 secondary turns can be used.   For the range of 200 to 1500 kc/sec, 6 turns for each primary and 9 secondary turns work very well.   In the construction of the high-frequency differential transformer it is important that an electrostatic shield on each side of the primary be provided so that no capacity coupling exists with the secondary turns.

Reference is made to Fig. 51 for the construction of the audio-frequency differential transformer.   It indicates an iron core built up of

Fig. 51.—Core for a balanced transformer used in the audio-frequency range.

fine iron wire in the form of a toroid.   Before winding the coils, the iron core is thoroughly insulated.   Three layers of enameled copper wire (about No. 36 A.W.G.) are wound uniformly on it.   Each layer is composed of about 1200 turns and insulated from the other layer by friction tape.   The two primary coils of about 300 turns are wound on top of it.   A middle tap leaves 150 turns for each primary coil.

A symmetrical arrangement of all apparatus and careful shielding are of great importance for the entire differential system.

35. Modified Differential Bridge.—The disadvantage of the differential system just described is that the test sample and standard must be of the same magnitude unless "difference" measurements are carried on, which are by no means always accurate.   Although it is possible to build transformers with transformation values up to 8:1 (between the two primaries) for the audible frequency range, a different turn ratio for the two primaries is not of much use in the high-frequency range.   A ratio of transformation between the two primary branches can be obtained, however, by using the scheme shown in Fig. 52. The ratio of transformation is then equal to C_2/C_1, for the test impedance X to the standard impedance S. The same differential transformer as described above can be used in this bridge arrangement by ignoring the center tap 1 of the

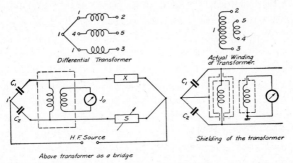

Differential Transformer

Actual Winding of Transformer.

H.F Source

Shielding of the transformer

Above transformer as a bridge

FIG. 52.—Differential bridge.

two primaries and connecting the outside terminals by means of C_1 and C_2 to the ratio tap $1'$.

36. Notes on the Symmetrical and Unsymmetrical Attenuation Box, Transmission Units, and Power Levels.—An attenuation box is a device which produces a known damping if inserted in a network with proper terminations. Figure 53 shows a single symmetrical T-section of pure resistances R_1 and R_2 designed for a termination R_0 which is also a pure resistance. For $R_0 = 600\,\Omega$ the curves shown in the figure are obtained

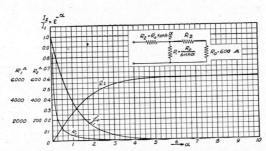

FIG. 53.—Attenuation box with symmetrical T-sections. Curves shown for $R_0 = 600\,\Omega$.

with an output current $I_2 = I_1 \epsilon^{-\alpha}$ where α denotes the damping of the section. Thus, if $R_1 = 100\,\Omega$, $R_2 = 508\,\Omega$, one has $\alpha = 2.5$ and I_2 only $0.082 I_1$, while for $R_1 = 1.105\,\Omega$ and $R_2 = 600\,\Omega$ the attenuation in radians is as high as $\alpha = 7$ and only $0.000912 I_1$ is available at the output end. A large reduction of the current can be obtained by using either a single section with a relatively small shunt resistance R_1 and a comparatively large series resistance R_2 (which can never become greater than R_0) or several sections in series. For instance, for $R_1 = 15.32\,\Omega$ and $R_2 =$

584.9 Ω, the current at the end of the section is only 1/78.33 of the value at the beginning of it. Using two sections in series makes the entering current I_1 about 6140 times greater than the current leaving the second section, because the reduction of current is $(1/78.33)^2$. Therefore it is only necessary to measure the input current if a very small load current through R_0 is to be found. This plays an important part in field-intensity measurements when a very small artificial voltage is generally to be produced by means of a correspondingly small high-frequency current, whose magnitude can be determined by means of α of the attenuation box, and the input current I_1, which is measured with customary thermoelectric meters. In such a measurement the load resistance R_0 consists of a straight wire resistor of 1 ohm inserted in the aerial or at the center portion of a loop in series with a pure resistance which is $(R_0 - 1)$ ohm. Amplification can also be measured by means of the damping effect of an attenuation box (see under measurements).

It has become customary to use transmission units to express ratios of voltage, current, and power. A decimal logarithmic unit called the "bel" is in use in the United States, and in Europe a Napierian unit called the "neper." Both units are of about the same order since 1 bel = 1.15 neper. A submultiple which is one-tenth of the bel, the "decibel," is of greater practical importance and is known as "the transmission unit" or the "TU."

$$1 \text{ TU} = 0.115 \text{ neper}; 1 \text{ neper} = 8.686 \text{ TU} = 8.686 \text{ db.}$$

The number of units of transmission for a ratio of two powers P_1 and P_2 is

$$\log_{10} \frac{P_1}{P_2} \text{ in the American system}$$

$$\frac{1}{2} \log_\epsilon \frac{P_1}{P_2} \text{ in the European system}$$

The number of units of transmission for a ratio of two voltages E_1 and E_2 and of two currents I_1 and I_2, if the squares of these ratios are equal[1] to the power ratio, is

---

[1] When current and voltage ratios are associated with equal impedances, then I and E are proportional to $\sqrt{P}$. This can be seen from the following derivation where for the impedance Z, voltage E across it, current I through it, effective resistance R of Z and power factor $\cos \varphi$, the energy dissipated in Z is $P = \dfrac{E^2 \cos \varphi}{Z}$ for the voltage relation and $P = I^2 Z \cos \varphi = I^2 R$ for the current relation. Hence $N_{TU} = 10 \log_{10} \left(\dfrac{P_1}{P_2}\right) = 10 \log_{10} \dfrac{I_1^2 R_1}{I_2^2 R_2} = 20 \log_{10} \left(\dfrac{I_1}{I_2}\right) + 10 \log_{10} \left(\dfrac{R_1}{R_2}\right)$ for the current relation and $N_{TU} = 10 \log_{10} \dfrac{E_1^2 Z_2 \cos \varphi_1}{E_2^2 Z_1 \cos \varphi_2} = 20 \log_{10} \left(\dfrac{E_1}{E_2}\right) + 10 \log_{10} \dfrac{Z_2}{Z_1} + 10 \log_{10} \dfrac{\cos \varphi_1}{\cos \varphi_2}$ Hence for equal impedances $Z_1 = Z_2 = Z$ and $\cos \varphi_1 = \cos \varphi_2 = \cos \varphi$.

$$2 \log_{10} \frac{E_1}{E_2} \text{ or } 2 \log_{10} \frac{I_1}{I_2} \text{ in the American system}$$

$$\log_\epsilon \frac{E_1}{E_2} \text{ or } \log_\epsilon \frac{I_1}{I_2} \text{ in the European system}$$

Hence the number of transmission units is

$$N_{TU} = 10 \log_{10} \frac{P_1}{P_2}$$

and

$$N_{TU} = 20 \log_{10} \frac{I_1}{I_2} \text{ or } = 20 \log_{10} \frac{E_1}{E_2}$$

(23)

Hence the TU is ten times the logarithmic ratio of any two powers and N_{TU} denotes the number of transmission units by which the two powers P_1 and P_2 differ. For instance, from Table XV at the end of the book it can be seen that a transmission system has a loss of 3.5 TU when its power ratio is 0.447, and that an amplifier has a gain of 3.5 TU when its power ratio is 2.24. It is also evident that 1 TU corresponds to a change of 11 per cent decrease or 12 per cent increase in voltage or current. Tables XVI and XVII at the end of the book give the voltage and current ratios as well as the power ratio. These tables were arranged by members of the technical staff of Wired Radio, Inc.

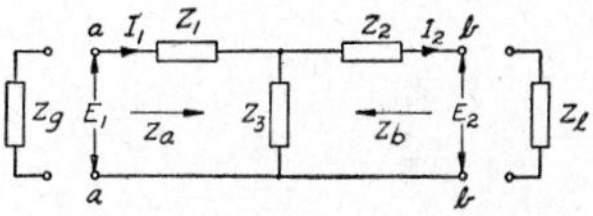

Fig. 54.—Unsymmetrical impedance T-section (Z_g internal impedance of supply; Z_l load impedance).

Figure 54 shows an unsymmetrical network Z_1, Z_2, Z_3 which can be used to advantage in amplifier and other measurements. With it, terminations of lines and circuit branches of *different* characteristic impedances can be coupled without reflections at the joints. Looking into the open terminals a, a toward the Z_l loaded unsymmetrical network, one has the impedance $Z_a = Z_1 + \dfrac{Z_3[Z_2 + Z_l]}{Z_2 + Z_3 + Z_l}$ and

$$Z_l = 0.5\{\sqrt{PQ} + S\}$$

if $P = Z_1 + Z_2$; $Q = Z_1 + Z_2 + 4Z_3$; $S = Z_1 - Z_2$ and $Z_l = Z_a$. With terminals b, b open and looking into the network toward impedance Z_g connected across terminals a, a, one finds $Z_b = Z_2 + \dfrac{Z_3[J_1 + Z_g]}{Z_1 + Z_3 + Z_g}$ which for $Z_g = Z_b$ yields

$$Z_g = 0.5\{\sqrt{PQ} - S\}$$

With such terminations no reflections will take place on either end (a, a or b, b). Hence if Z_g denotes the characteristic impedance of the system to the left of a, a and Z_l the characteristic or any load impedance of the system connected to terminals b, b, the unsymmetrical network will match for no reflections at a, a and b, b and the transmission loss of the unsymmetrical network which interlinks the two circuits can be readily computed from the propagation constant n, since for no reflections $E_2 = E_1\epsilon^{-n}$ and $I_2 = I_1\epsilon^{-n}$. Hence $\epsilon^{2n} = \dfrac{E_1 I_1}{E_2 I_2}$ or $n = 0.5 \log_\epsilon \dfrac{E_1 I_1}{E_2 I_2}$; that is,

$$n = \log_\epsilon \sqrt{\frac{E_1 I_1}{E_2 I_2}} \text{ nepers} \qquad (24)$$

TABLE I

8.686α decibel loss	$\tanh \dfrac{\alpha}{2}$	$\sinh \alpha$	8.686α decibel loss	$\tanh \dfrac{\alpha}{2}$	$\sinh \alpha$
1	0.05754	0.11525	26	0.90460	9.97768
2	0.11450	0.23203	27	0.91461	11.1882
3	0.17129	0.35295	28	0.92331	12.4941
4	0.22603	0.47750	29	0.93155	14.0918
5	0.28029	0.60955	30	0.93870	15.7343
6	0.33193	0.74732	31	0.94523	17.7442
7	0.38251	0.89749	32	0.95099	19.8106
8	0.43008	1.05539	33	0.95624	22.3394
9	0.47615	1.23311	34	0.96086	24.9395
10	0.51902	1.42252	35	0.96528	28.1216
11	0.56080	1.63426	36	0.96878	31.3934
12	0.59862	1.86378	37	0.97215	35.3979
13	0.63455	2.12223	38	0.97511	39.5155
14	0.66738	2.40406	39	0.97803	44.5551
15	0.69780	2.72007	40	0.98018	50.2371
16	0.72637	3.07532	41	0.98229	56.0797
17	0.75263	3.46839	42	0.98425	63.2307
18	0.77630	3.90738	43	0.98590	70.5839
19	0.79833	4.39810	44	0.98741	78.7921
20	0.81809	4.95210	45	0.98883	88.8386
21	0.83548	5.55584	46	0.99005	100.1659
22	0.85298	6.26224	47	0.99111	111.8136
23	0.86753	7.01330	48	0.99207	126.0700
24	0.88095	7.86828	49	0.99292	140.7296
25	0.89370	8.87014	50	0.99369	158.6726

α is the attenuation constant in nepers and 8.686α the decibel loss of the unsymmetrical T network of Fig. 55. $R_1 = 0.5 \left[p \tanh \dfrac{\alpha}{2} + q \right]$; $R_2 = 0.5 \left[p \tanh \dfrac{\alpha}{2} - q \right]$; $R_3 = p/(2 \sinh \alpha)$; $p = R_g + R_l$; $q = R_g - R_l$.

It is not always convenient to find n from voltage and current measurements. Besides, it is to be realized that the propagation constant for an unsymmetrical network has different values from the left to the right and from the right to the left. For the propagation constant from left to the right,

$$\overrightarrow{n} = \log_\epsilon \frac{I_1}{I_2} = \log_\epsilon \frac{Z_2 + Z_3 + Z_l}{Z_3}$$

while from right to the left it is

$$\overleftarrow{n} = \log_\epsilon \frac{Z_1 + Z_3 + Z_g}{Z_3}$$

because for $\overrightarrow{n}$, according to Kirchhoff's laws, $I_2 = I_1 \dfrac{Z_3}{Z_3 + Z_2 + Z_l}$ and $\dfrac{I_1}{I_2} = \dfrac{Z_2 + Z_3 + Z_l}{Z_3} = \epsilon^n$. This result and the expressions for Z_g and Z_l give a means for finding the values of Z_1, Z_2, and Z_3 as well as of the propagation constant n, since the terminations Z_l and Z_g are given. One finds

$$\left. \begin{aligned} & Z_1 = 0.5 \left\{ p \tanh \frac{n}{2} + q \right\}; \; Z_2 = 0.5 \left\{ p \tanh \frac{n}{2} - q \right\}; \\ & Z_3 = \frac{p}{2 \sinh n}; \qquad n = \cosh^{-1}\left[\frac{Z_1 + Z_2 + 2Z_3}{2Z_3} \right] \\ & p = Z_g + Z_l \text{ and } q = Z_g - Z_l \end{aligned} \right\} \quad (25)$$

The propagation constant n in above formulas stands for $\overrightarrow{n}$, that is, the direction from Z_g toward Z_l. If therefore an unsymmetrical network with resistances R_1, R_2, and R_3 is used in order to couple with no reflections two different resistances R_g and R_l, the solutions are as given in Fig. 55. This arrangement can be used in amplification measurements (Secs. 54, 55 and Figs. 79, 82) where the output resistance of an attenuation box (say 600 ohms) has to be matched for no reflection against the input impedance of an amplifier. Then $Z_g = R_g = 600$ ohms and Z_1 is equal to the input impedance of the amplifier. Suppose all impedances are resistances and $R_g = 600\Omega$ and $R_1 = 200\Omega$ are fixed and known. Let R_g be the characteristic resistance of an attenuation box, whose transmission loss is known, either in nepers or in decibels (1 db = 0.115 neper and 1 neper = 8.686 db). The propagation constant $n = \alpha + j\beta = \alpha$ nepers giving 8.686α db. The values of R_1, R_2, and R_3 can be computed if a suitable transmission loss for the network of Fig. 55 is assumed. The magnitude of the loss is a matter of compromise since, if 8.686α is taken too small, R_2 may come out negative and lead to an impossible network. For too large values of 8.686α, unnecessary attenuation is inserted into the system. In many cases values from 10 to 20 db for 8.686α are suitable. Hence assuming for this particular case

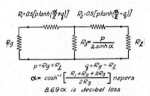

$R_1 = 0.5[p\tanh(\frac{\alpha}{2}+q)]$ $R_2 = 0.5[p\tanh(\frac{\alpha}{2}-q)]$

R_g $R_3 = \dfrac{p}{2.\sinh\alpha}$ R_L

$p = Rg + R_L$
$q = Rg - R_L$
$\alpha = \cosh^{-1}\left[\dfrac{R_1 + R_2 + 2R_3}{2R_3} \right]$ nepers
8.69α is decibel loss

Fig. 55.—Unsymmetrical attenuator for coupling a resistance R_g with a resistance R_l.

20 decibels, one finds from Table I, $\tanh \dfrac{\alpha}{2} = 0.81809$ and $\sinh \alpha = 4.9521$. From Fig. 55, $p = 600 + 200 = 800\Omega$; $q = 600 - 200 = 400\Omega$; $R_1 =$

$0.5(654 + 400) = 527\,\Omega$; $R_2 = 0.5(654 - 400) = 127\,\Omega$; and R_3 $400/4.9521 = 80.8\,\Omega$. From the R_2 expression it is seen that a smaller decibel loss could have been selected, since R_2 is well above zero value. To check this result, the neper formula of Fig. 55 can be used; hence

$$\alpha = \cosh^{-1}\left[\frac{527 + 127 + 2 \times 80.8}{2 \times 80.8}\right] = \cosh^{-1} 5.052 = 2.303$$

and 8.686×2.303 gives the 20 db assumed above.

CHAPTER III

APPARATUS AND SYSTEMS FOR MEASURING HIGH-FREQUENCY MINUTE TUBE AND IONIZATION CURRENTS

If high-frequency currents are measured by their heat effects, the meters can be built to work over a wide frequency range. Hot-wire instruments were the early common indicators, but in recent years thermoelectric indicators have come more into use because their losses are comparatively small, their calibrations are more reliable, and instruments measuring down to 1 ma can be built without difficulty. With more sensitive direct-current indicators, the microampere range can also be covered. For larger currents, apparatus based on the repulsion between two current-carrying conductors can be used. Current transformers (page 57) covering a certain frequency range with meters in the secondary and the Hartman and Braun meter are customary meters for the measurement of larger currents. For the latter, a large high-frequency current is split into different branches so as to produce in the hot wire (whose dimensional change due to heat effects produces the indication) current sections along it which are made up by the smaller fractional branch currents but not by one and the same shunt current, as would be the case in the usual shunted ammeter. The bolometer arrangements and the thermocross bridge are useful devices if small currents are to be indicated, and if properly designed are desirable zero-current indicators. Extremely small currents can be determined with certain tubes (high grid insulation) and tube circuits.

37. Aperiodic and Oscillatory Detector Circuits.—An oscillatory detector circuit is an indicator which is tuned. It is selective and therefore has great sensitivity at one frequency. The sensitivity can be further increased if the effective circuit resistance is kept low. It can be made practically zero if an apparatus with a negative resistance reaction is used. A regenerative tube detector is one example and a dynatron is another. Such expedients are of special use if the disappearance of currents is to be indicated very exactly. This is the case for differential transformer and bridge circuits. An aperiodic detector is one which is not tuned to the frequency of the measuring circuit. It is usually loosely coupled to the measuring circuit in order to reflect practically no resistance and reaction into the measuring system. Although an aperiodic detector is not so sensitive as the tuned detector, it has the

95

advantage of a broad frequency response and does not require an adjustment. Figure 56 shows the simplest kind of oscillatory and aperiodic detectors. A crystal rectifier K is used in conjunction with a galvanometer G of suitable sensitivity. These detectors work for damped and sustained time variations, and up to the highest frequencies. They are good zero-current indicators, that is, useful for apparatus where only the disappearance of a current is of interest. The induced current which is rectified always charges the block condenser C_0 in the same direction and the indicator is affected by unipolar current impulses. For damped sinusoids of the audible group frequency, a telephone receiver can be substituted for the galvanometer. This is also possible for sustained variable currents when modulated in the [audio-frequency range or when two high-frequency currents produce audible amplitude variations.

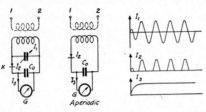

Fig. 56.—Oscillatory and aperiodic detector system. (1–2 denotes measuring circuit.)

Circuits of this type can be connected directly to a branch of the measuring circuit or are coupled to it as is shown in the figure. Tube detectors can be of the grid-condenser grid-leak type or may employ an appropriate grid bias. When a plate meter is used, the change in plate current is utilized. A very sensitive arrangement can be obtained if the normal plate current I_b through the meter in a parallel branch is balanced out, inasmuch as a much more sensitive instrument can then be used to note the effects of the changes in the plate current. An ordinary two-element tube or an ordinary three-element tube with the grid and plate interconnected can also be used instead of the crystal detector of Fig. 56. The plate voltage is then due to the induced e.m.f., and the small electron current due to the initial velocity of the electrons can be balanced out. When using a three-element tube, one must distinguish between square-law and linear detectors. The linear detector is a tube system to which a modulated high-frequency voltage of from one to several (25 and more) volts is applied, while for a square-law detector the upper limit of the applied high-frequency voltage is about half a volt. With the linear detector a great deal of the dynamic tube characteristic is used and the work characteristic is almost linear; that is, proportionality exists between the output in the plate branch with respect to the input voltage across the grid and filament. Besides this, a linear detector theoretically does not produce distortion and is just as sensitive for comparatively small input voltages (unless too small, for which the curved portion of the tube characteristic is operative). It is also possible to suppress a weak signal when a strong signal is present simultaneously.

38. The Bolometer Arrangement for Indicating Small Currents.—
The system shown in Fig. 57 is a bridge circuit balanced by a direct current I. A baretter consisting of a fine platinum wire (Wollastan wire) is located in one branch of the bridge. This wire is exceedingly thin[1] and therefore its resistance will change considerably with any change in current flow. A balance of the direct-current bridge is then possible only for a certain current kI passing through the thin baretter wire. Therefore even if only a small high-frequency current I_1 is superimposed, the galvanometer G will produce a deflection. A certain small range for the direct-current excitation exists, for which the deflection of the galvanometer becomes largest for one and the same small high-frequency current I_1. An arrangement of this type is very sensitive and must be well protected from air currents so that direct-current balance may be kept constant.

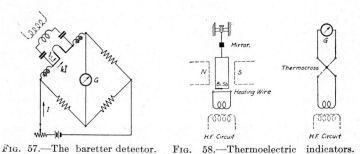

Fig. 57.—The baretter detector.   Fig. 58.—Thermoelectric indicators.

39. Simple Thermocross Arrangements and the Thermogalvanometer.—In the simple thermocross arrangements as indicated in Fig. 58, a low-resistance galvanometer is used as one indicator. It is then connected across one thermoelement of the cross, while the remaining thermocouple serves for the high-frequency current path. A special heating wire can also be used and the thermocouple connected to the direct-current indicator is welded with the common joint against the heating wire or suspended in fixed and close proximity to the heating wire. Commercial thermoelements are in a vacuum and are sensitive and keep their calibration well. They are far superior to homemade thermocouples and if available should be used. For rough work, thermocouples of tellurium and constantan or tellurium and platinum are satisfactory. If such materials are not available, a couple of iron and constantan wire can also be used. For thermoelectric force, reference is made to Table II where metals and alloys are arranged according to their thermoelectric

---

[1] A thin silvered wire with a thin platinum core is drawn out to a still smaller diameter and soldered across two copper terminals. The much thicker silver coating is then removed by dipping the small loop of the baretter into a solution of nitric acid (HNO_3). Wires from 0.001- to 0.0005-mm diameter can be obtained in this way.

property. This table gives the thermoelectric force of two metals when the joint of one metal is at 0°C and that of the other at 100°C. The numbers are in millivolts. The thermoelectric force of an iron

TABLE II

Bismuth	0	Brass	7.1
Constantan	3.0	Gold	7.2
Nickel	5.1	Silver	7.4
Platinum	6.6	Copper	7.4
Mercury	6.7	Cadmium	7.6
Aluminum	7.1	Iron	8.3
Lead	7.1	Antimony	10.

constantan couple for a temperature difference of 100°C is then 8.3 − 3 = 5.3 mv. The thermogalvanometer indicated in the same figure is due to W. Duddell.[1] It should not be confused with commercial thermogalvanometers for which a thermoelement is usually connected to a portable table millivolt or microvolt meter with the thermocouple within the instrument. The Duddell galvanometer is much more sensitive than the ordinary thermocross arrangement shown in the same circuit. It uses two dissimilar metals (antimony-bismuth element) of high thermoelectric e.m.f. and the heating wire which carries the high-frequency current affects the couple by heat radiation only. The thermoelectric current which flows in the rectangular conductor produces a magnetic field which, by interaction with the stationary magnetic flux of the magnet, causes the rectangular conductor to turn. The deflection is proportional to the square of the current.

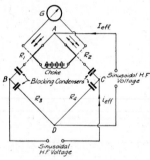

Fig. 59.—The thermocross bridge.

40. The Thermocross Bridge as a Current Indicator.—All instruments with indications which are produced *directly* by the Joulean heat effects of the current follow a square law. The same is true of the ordinary thermoelectric indicator. This is an inherent disadvantage when small currents are to be indicated. A linear deflection law is then the most desirable. The bridge arrangement shown in Fig. 59 satisfies the straight-line law even when the resistances R_1 and R_2 of the two thermoelements are different, although equality gives greater sensitivity.[2] The direct current which flows through the galvanometer is due to the difference of the currents which are produced in both thermoelements connected against each other through the galvanometer. It is an easy matter to prove that

$$i_{galv} = k T_{eff} i_{eff} \cos \varphi \qquad (1)$$

[1] *Electrician*, **56**, 559, 1906.
[2] *Gen. Elec. Rev.*, **17**, 987, 1914.

Therefore if I_{eff} denotes the larger auxiliary current and is kept constant, the galvanometer deflection is directly proportional to the effective value of the small high-frequency current, since the power factor $\cos \varphi$ is constant and cuts down the constant of proportionality only.

A vacuum-tube bridge with two tubes instead of the two thermocrosses can be used in the same way.

41. Calibration of a Thermocross System.—In the circuit of Fig. 60 if the voltage V is connected by contacts 1 and 2 and the galvanometer G by contacts 5 and 6, the deflection d_1 is proportional to the voltage $E = E_1$ across the couple; that is,

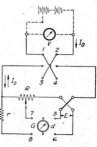

Fig. 60.—Calibration of a thermocross system.

$$E_1 = k_G d_1 = \underbrace{k_1 I_0{}^2}_{\text{thermo effect}} + \underbrace{k_2 I_0}_{\text{Peltier effect}}$$

if k_G is the constant of the galvanometer and k_1 and k_2 factors for the thermoelectric and Peltier effects, respectively. When the polarity of the battery is reversed by connecting contacts 3 and 4, the Peltier effect becomes negative and smaller value $E = E_2$ across the thermo-element produces the deflection d_2 according to

$$E_2 = k_G d_2 = k_1 I_0{}^2 - k_2 I_0$$

The average value of the voltage is then

$$\frac{E_1 + E_2}{2} = k_G \frac{d_1 + d_2}{2} = k_1 I_0{}^2$$

and the heating current of the joint

$$I_0 = \sqrt{\frac{k_G}{k_1}} \sqrt{\frac{d_1 + d_2}{2}} = k_T \sqrt{\frac{d_1 + d_2}{2}}$$

if k_T is the constant of the thermocross system. If R denotes the entire resistance of the input circuit, the calibration constant is

$$k_T = \frac{V}{R \sqrt{\dfrac{d_1 + d_2}{2}}}$$

since $I_0 = V/R$.

42. Calibration of a Bolometer System.—The baretter circuit shown in Fig. 61 can be conveniently calibrated by a thermocross whose constant k_T is known. At first the baretter current kI is set for the greatest sensitivity of the bolometer. The deflection d_B increases with the square of the high-frequency current I_1 and since the square law also holds for the thermovoltage,

$$I_1{}^2 = k_T d_T = k_B d_B$$

or

$$k_B = k_T \frac{d_T}{d_B} \tag{2}$$

43. Calibration of Hot-wire and Thermoelectric-current Meters.—
By a thermoelectric-current meter is meant an apparatus which uses a
direct-current indicator with a self-contained thermocouple. Its calibration, therefore, is obtained in the same fashion as that of a hot-wire
instrument. The simplest way is by connecting the test instrument in
series with a standard high-frequency meter.

Another way is by connecting the test meter I_x in the calibrated circuit indicated in Fig. 62. I_s is a standard current indicator. By means

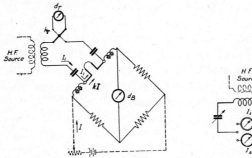

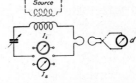

Fig. 61.—Calibration of a bolometer.   Fig.   62.—Calibration of hot-wire
                                              and thermoelectric-current meters.

of a tube generator, suitable high-frequency currents are produced in the
measuring system and the constant k of the circuit is determined from

$$k = \frac{I_s}{\sqrt{d_s}} \tag{3}$$

where I_s denotes a current reading of the standard instrument in the
circuit producing the corresponding deflection d_s for the desired frequency
band in the coupled thermoelectric indicator. The current meter to be
calibrated is then inserted in the circuit and the calibration curve I_x
obtained from the corresponding deflections d_x by means of the formula

$$I_x = k\sqrt{d_x} \tag{4}$$

If a current changer is used with a current indicator, the calibration is
carried on by the secondary current I_2 (Fig. 26) because the current ratio
is known.

44. Notes on Current Transformers for Measuring Instruments.—
It is evident from the discussion in Sec. 16 that both an air and an iron-
core step-down transformer can be used to measure large high-frequency
currents by means of measuring only secondary currents with a thermo-

electric or other meter of comparatively low current-carrying capacity. In order to avoid inductive effects of the incoming and outgoing leads, the few primary turns are looped through the opening of the core as indicated in Fig. 26. The secondary turns go straight to the indicator. The step-down current transformer must be astatic and have a large time constant for the secondary branch so that the inductive reactance is large compared with the resistance component. The astatic condition is approached by using a toroid-shaped transformer.

45. The Eddy-current Galvanometer for High-frequency Currents.— This device also follows the square law. It consists of a circular copper disk that is suspended on a thread of quartz. The current to be measured flows through a coil whose high-frequency magnetic field causes the disk to turn out of the 45-deg position. The disk is at the center of the coil with about six turns on a diameter of 2.5 cm. The deflection is observed by means of a telescope and a small mirror on the movable disk.

46. The Short-circuit Ring Galvanometer for the Measurement of Small High-frequency Currents and Phase Angles.—This apparatus[1] follows a linear law. It consists of two stationary coils at right angles to each other. They are of square shape (2.5 cm^2) and with about five turns of litz wire. A copper ring of 1-cm diameter is suspended by a thread of quartz in such a way that its plane coincides with the plane of one of the stationary coils. When high-frequency currents I_1 and I_2 of the same frequency pass through the respective stationary coils, with the use of a telescope and a small mirror attached to the ring the deflection reads

$$d = KI_1I_2 \qquad (5)$$

If I_1 denotes a constant auxiliary high-frequency current of the same frequency as I_2, any changes in I_2 must produce deflections which are directly proportional to the changes in I_2. A galvanometer of this kind measures very small high-frequency currents and their phase, since for a phase displacement φ

$$d = KI_1I_2 \cos \varphi \qquad (6)$$

47. The Hot-wire Thermometer as a Current Meter.—An instrument of this type cannot claim great accuracy. It consists of a glass tube with a hot wire at the lower end. An alcohol manometer is attached to the upper end. When a current passes through the hot wire, the air above it expands because of the heat, and the increase of pressure indicated by the manometer is a measure of the current. This apparatus can also be changed to a differential thermometer. A U-shaped tube is used, and two hot wires are suspended in the upper ends of the U. The air expands downward on each side when the current flows through the respective hot wires and pushes a liquid to the center of the lower straight arm of the U-shaped tube when the currents produce the same heat

[1] MANDELSTAM, L., and N. PAPALEXI, *Ann. Physik*, **33**, 490, 1910.

effects.   For a difference in current the indicating liquid will be to one side.

48. Circuits for Measuring Small High-frequency Currents.—Small high-frequency currents are conveniently measured by small potential drops produced by them.   It is possible to use a Wheatstone-bridge circuit which contains either one electron tube in one branch (Fig. 63) or two tubes (Fig. 64) similar to the thermocross bridge.   If a single tube

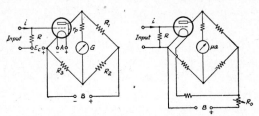

Fig. 63.—Bridge systems as current meters.

is used, one can use either the circuit to the left of Fig. 63 or the scheme to the right due to S. C. Hoare if a low-current filament tube such as the 199 type or its equivalent is available.   In the latter circuit the filament battery is dispensed with and a low-voltage B battery (6 to 22.5 volts) is used to excite both the filament and the plate.   In each Wheatstone bridge system the grid resistance R is used to produce a voltage drop across the grid and the filament.   The bridge is balanced for short-circuited input terminals.   A galvanometer G which may be a micro-ammeter μa indicates the condition of zero current.   For this case the resistances are such that $r_p:R_1 = R_3:R_2$.   Therefore if a direct current or a high-frequency current flows over a suitable resistance R, the zero-current indicator gives a deflection.   When ordinary receiving tubes and low-voltage B supply are used for this circuit, the resistances in all four branches, for a balanced system, are in the neighborhood of ten to twenty thousand ohms, while R may have

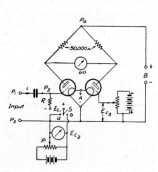

Fig. 64.—Two-tube bridge as a current meter.

values from 50,000 Ω up to about 5 megohms depending upon the frequency used.   Figure 64 shows a double-tube bridge where, for high-frequency work, P_1P_2 denote the input terminals.   The high-frequency current then passes through the condenser C of negligible impedance and down the grid-leak resistance R. For direct-current amplifications P_2P_3 are the input terminals.   The tube to the left has a fixed grid bias E_{c_1} and a variable bias E_{c_2}.   The single-pole double-throw switch is at first connected with a, and the grid

bias E_{c_3} of the other tube is varied until the microammeter μa indicates
zero current. When the unknown current i flows, the switch S is
thrown toward b and the slider of the E_{c_2} potentiometer to some point P,
for which condition zero current is again obtained. The reading E_{c_2} on
the voltmeter is then a measure of the current i.

Another way of measuring small currents is by means of the tube
galvanometer[1] shown in Fig. 65. A double-grid tube is used here for
reasons explained in connection with
Fig. 71. Very small currents i_1 can be
measured by this circuit since a direct-
current back feed is employed. The
circuit is so adjusted that the sum of
the space-charge current i_3 and the plate
current i_2 is equal to the saturation current, that is, constant. Hence, i_2 can
increase only at the expense of i_3 and

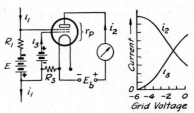

Fig. 65.—Tube galvanometer.

vice versa. Since i_3 passes through the back-feed resistance R_3, this current
must cause a decrease of the space-charge grid potential, while the current
i_1 to be measured produces the opposite effect. The resulting grid voltage
is therefore

$$e_g = i_1 R_1 - i_2 R_3 + E$$

where E can be negative or positive. When working along the straight
portion of the tube characteristic, the plate current is

$$i_2 = \frac{e_g + \alpha E_b}{r_p}$$

and

$$\frac{de_g}{di_1} = \frac{R_1}{1 - \dfrac{R_3}{r_p}}$$

that means, for $R_3 = r_p$ the amplification becomes infinitely large and
for $R_3 < r_p$ it decreases hyperbolically with decreasing values of R_3.
The amplification is as follows: The unknown current i_1 increases the
potential of the outer grid. This causes an increase of the plate current
i_2. But, since the inner grid is so positive that its current i_3 together
with i_2 is equal to the constant emission current of the filament, an
increase of plate current must cause a decrease of i_3. But this gives a
reduced voltage drop across R_3. This increases the potential of the
outer grid still further and the whole cycle is gone through again and
again, the effects being additive. The effect of the back-feed resistance
R_3 is therefore equivalent to an increase of the steepness of the work
characteristic of the tube. The tube used in this circuit must use a

[1] JAEGER, W., and H. SCHEFFERS, *Wiss. Veröffentl. a.d. Siemens Konzern*, **2**, 325,
1927.

highly insulated grid.   For this reason it is brought out at the top of the glass envelope through a highly insulated seal.   Currents as low as 10^{-14} amp can then be indicated.

49. Notes on the Amplification and Measurement of Very Small Currents.—Generally speaking, the amplification of exceedingly small currents is very difficult.   This is all the more true when very small direct currents delivered from a low-resistance source (thermoelement, for instance) are to be amplified.   When small currents taken from a photoelectric cell are to be amplified, there is not so much difficulty if the grid insulation is high, that is, if the control grid comes out at the top of the tube.   In some cases it is possible to pass the small current through a suitable known resistance.   The potential drop across the resistance is then used for the plate excitation of an ordinary three-element tube. The grid of the tube connecting through a microammeter to the positive end of the filament will indicate a small grid current.   Any positive plate potentials decrease the grid current.

For ordinary three-element tubes it is of advantage to use only small plate voltages (6 to 15 volts), since for much higher voltages positive ionization is present.   The reason is because even for well-exhausted tubes enough gas molecules are present for customary positive plate potentials (say 45 to 90 volts) to cause ion currents.   The positive ions, which are produced by collision with electrons, partially discharge the grid, so that a very small grid potential due to small currents to be determined becomes still more insignificant.   Therefore the plate potential must be chosen below the ionization potential.

For ordinary receiving tubes the grid current can be 1 μa, while with specially designed tubes[1] currents up to 10^{-17} amp (that is, about 63 electrons/sec) can be determined and this is better than the electrometer method with a sensitivity of 10^{-10} to 10^{-15} amp.   Besides the effect of leakage in ordinary tube-socket connections (resistance across grid and filament not much higher than 10 megohms) and the positive ionization due to collision as mentioned above, the following agencies can produce a grid current: (*a*) electrons from the filament; (*b*) electrons emitted by the grid due to its temperature; (*c*) positive ions given off by the filament; (*d*) photoelectric electrons given off by the grid and due to the light of the filament; (*e*) electrons emitted from the grid due to soft X-rays given off by the plate because of the bombardment of the plate by the plate current.

With ordinary tubes any grid electrons due to the thermionic emission of the filament can be avoided by a high enough negative grid bias (2.5

[1] THOMPSON, B. J., *Electronics*, **1**, 290, 1930; for other contributions along this line: H. NELSON, *Rev. Sci. Instruments*, **1**, 281, 1930; R. D. BENNETT, *Rev. Sci. Instruments*, **1**, 466, 1930 (with a list of references); G. F. METCALF and B. J. THOMPSON, *Phys. Rev.*, **36**, 1489, 1930.

to 4 volts). When low-powered hot cathodes (thoriated tungsten filaments, dull emitter) are used, the grid next to them will be heated but little. If, besides, they are of a suitable metal, they can be made to give off only a negligible amount of thermions. The positive ions given off to some extent by any hot cathode constitute a grid current (grid negative) and this flow can be greatly diminished by placing a positively charged space-charge grid between the hot cathode and the control grid so that any positive ions from the filament are bent around and driven back to the filament. A dull emitter for the filament will cut down the photons from the grid, and plate voltages below 6 volts will also avoid even the softest X-rays.

50. Methods for Measuring Exceedingly Small Currents.—The methods described are especially suitable for the most difficult task of

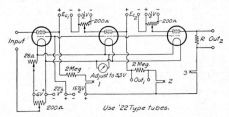

Fig. 66.—Amplification of direct voltages (microammeter inserted at 1, 2, and 3 in order to note successive amplification effects by means of the current change and the external plate resistance).

determining small direct currents. Figure 66 shows an arrangement by which small thermoelectric current can be detected. If, for instance, a Coblentz pile with about 20 elements in series is located at the focus of a parabolic mirror, radiation heat from a bucket of hot water placed about 300 ft away will produce a variation in plate current of 20 μa in the last tube (microammeter inserted at 3). Although this circuit is very sensitive, it avoids practically all precautions necessary (last section) for stable operation. This circuit, although sensitive, is fickle and does not keep good calibration. It is useful, however, when only indications are required.

The vacuum-tube electrometer of Fig. 67 due to H. Nelson[1] can be used to measure current down to 10^{-15} amp. This tube has an input resistance as high as 10^{16} ohms across the grid (control cylinder) and the

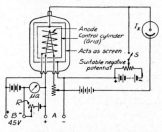

Fig. 67.—Tube electrometer.

other electrode. The grid-shaped anode of this tube is next to the hot cathode (oxide coated), and at a positive potential of only 4.5 volts. It is made of nickel. A control cylinder of nickel with a lead-in wire through the top of the tube surrounds the anode, while the exterior

[1] *Loc. cit.*

nickel envelope acts as a screen.   Because of the high input resistance, the microammeter (μa), whose reading is brought to a suitable point by means of R and the shunt battery E, can be used to determine the rate at which a small current builds up a charge on the control cylinder, since a direct relation exists between the change in the current noted by the microammeter and the charge building up on the grid.   This therefore is the same case as with the quadrant electrometer, where the insulated quadrants take the place of the control cylinder and the deflection of the needle corresponds to the deflection of the pointer of the microammeter. In the above circuit the control cylinder is kept at a suitable negative potential.   Placing the anode between the hot cathode and the control cylinder keeps any positive ions given off by the filament from reaching the control cylinder.   A space-charge grid is therefore unnecessary. The anode potential is as low as 4.5 volts, thus preventing any positive ionization by collision.   Therefore when the active tube is enclosed in an airtight container, the input resistance is practically that due to the glass leakance only.   If a small photoelectric current I_x is to be measured, the voltage on the control cylinder will remain practically constant if the shunt switch S is closed.   But when S is opened the current I_x will pass toward the control cylinder and charge it up, thus producing a change in the reading of the microammeter.   From this, the rate change of potential of the control cylinder is obtained.   Hence, if the effective capacitance with all the connections is known, the magnitude of I_x may be computed.   For much of the work it is more convenient to connect a high resistance across the open switch S and determine the voltage drop caused by the current passing through the high resistance.

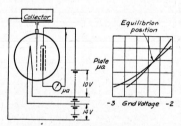

Fig. 68.—Tube galvanometer.

The circuit (Fig. 68) due to R. D. Bennett[1] is again a single-stage unit and employs an ordinary double-grid tube (222 type or its equivalent).   All positive operating potentials are chosen below about 15 volts in order to avoid positive ionization. The grid assumes a potential which is determined by its leakance resistance and the relative abundance of positive and negative ions.   Therefore it is evident that the effective input resistance is asymmetric for a relatively greater number of electrons than positive ions.   The leak resistance is then much higher for a negative than for a positive grid charge.   Figure 68 illustrates a circuit used to measure ionization currents supplied by an ionization chamber.   The speed of the deflections in the plate meter can be increased at the expense of the sensitivity if a grid leak is used.   A much more steady operation is then obtained and the sensitivity can be regained by further amplifica-

[1] *Loc. cit.*

tion. The effective grid resistance r_g is obtained by noting the time for a definite charge to leak away. It is very high in this case and about $4 \times 10^{12}\,\Omega$. From the grid-voltage plate current characteristic it is noted that a large current amplification exists when the equilibrium position falls on the steep portion of this characteristic. This position can be varied somewhat by changing the relative values of the screen-grid and plate potentials. Suppose the steepness g_m of this characteristic is about $\delta I_p/\delta E_g = 2 \times 10^{-5}$ amp/volt and the total plate current at the equilibrium position 11.7 μa, then a meter with 15-μa maximum deflection can give directly an indication of 0.1 μa which in this particular case is due to a change in grid potential of

$$\frac{10^{-7}}{2 \times 10^{-5}} = 5 \times 10^{-3} \text{ volt}$$

and a grid current of

$$\frac{5 \times 10^{-3}}{r_g} = \frac{5 \times 10^{-3}}{4 \times 10^{12}} = 1.25 \times 10^{-15} \text{ amp}$$

which is a very small current. By using a sensitive galvanometer (10^{-10}) in the plate circuit, and again compensating the plate current as in Fig. 67 by a battery in shunt and a resistance R, the sensitivity of the system can be increased to about 10^{-18} amp. The plate current in this case can also be balanced out by a potentiometer across a portion of the plate battery.

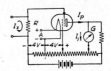

Fig. 69.—Tube galvanometer. ($g_m = 25 \times 10^{-6}$ amp/ volt; $r_p = 40,000\,\Omega$; $\mu = 1$.)

Figure 69 shows the circuit due to B. J. Thompson[1] for which a special tube meets practically all the requirements for producing a very high input resistance (r_g about $10^{16}\,\Omega$). The grid current is then of the order of 10^{-15} amp. Although this tube is not useful as a voltage amplifier ($\mu = 1$), it may be used as a very powerful current amplifier. If R denotes a very high leak resistance and I_1 the change in plate current flowing through a sensitive galvanometer (sensitive to 10^{-10} amp) and whose current flow is at first balanced out when I_x does not act, any value of the unknown current I_x can be computed from

$$I_x = \frac{I_1}{g_m R} \tag{7}$$

For $R = 4 \times 10^{11}\,\Omega$, a current as low as $\dfrac{10^{-10}}{4 \times 10^{11} \times 25 \times 10^{-6}} = 10^{-17}$ can be measured. When taking the entire circuit into consideration, the current amplification is 10^7 fold.

51. Methods for Measuring the Effects of Photoelectric Currents.— The tubes and circuits just described can all be used for this work.

[1] *Loc. cit.*

Figure 67 illustrates, for instance, the case of a photoelectric cell in the circuit. Figure 70 shows a fundamental single-tube arrangement using an ordinary receiving tube of the three-element type. In order to have a sensitive system it is convenient to measure only the variation of the plate current I_p when any photoelectric currents are acting. The current through the milliammeter M. A. is then balanced out by a coarse (R) and a fine (r) variable resistor and a suitable voltage tap T, when the cathode of the cell is not affected by light. A linear response in the reading of the milliammeter is obtained when the voltage acting on the cell is much above saturation and a vacuum type of cell is employed. The amplification of a photoelectric current i with an ordinary three-element tube is usually inappreciable in the first stage. This can be understood from Fig. 71. Suppose the dotted shield grid connected to some suitable positive potential B_1 is not present. One then has to deal with the interelectrode capacitances of the tube as well as the interelectrode capacitance C_p of the photoelectric cell. In this case, the effective grid to ground capacitance is

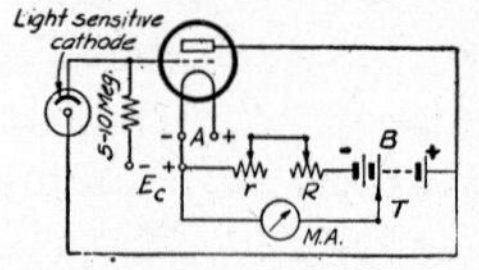

Fig. 70.—Ordinary three-element tube for measuring photoelectric currents.

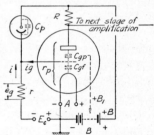

$$C = C_p + C_{gf} + \underbrace{A_e C_{gp}}_{\substack{\text{effective grid-}\\\text{plate capacitance}}} \tag{8}$$

Fig. 71.—Effects of interelectrode capacitances.

if A_e denotes the voltage amplification per stage. The leak resistance r is made as large as possible in order to give a very high grid voltage e_g due to the photoelectric current. But the maximum value of r is limited for any frequency by the value of C, since it is in parallel with r which is supposed to carry the current i only. We deal here with the relation,

$$e_g = i \, r \left[1 - \epsilon^{-\frac{t}{C r}} \right] \tag{9}$$

Hence if t is given, the maximum allowable value of the leak resistance is

$$r_{\max} = \frac{t}{C} \tag{10}$$

since

$$e_g = i \, r_{\max} \left[1 - \frac{1}{\epsilon} \right] = 0.63 i \, r_{\max}$$

Assuming that the load resistance R is several times the internal tube resistance r_p, the voltage amplification A_e is obtained approximately equal to the amplification factor μ and, by assuming further that C_p, C_{gf}, and C_{gp} are about equal, from (8)

$$C = [2 + \mu]C_p \tag{11}$$

which combined with (10) results in

$$r_{max} = \frac{t}{[2 + \mu]C_p} \qquad (12)$$

This outcome combined with the relation $e_g = 0.63\, i\, r_{max}$ leads to

$$e_g = \frac{0.63i\, t}{[2 + \mu]C_p} \qquad (13)$$

The corresponding plate potential e_p is μe_g and

$$e_p = 0.63 \frac{\mu}{2 + \mu} \frac{i\, t}{C_p} \qquad (14)$$

Since the ratio $\mu/(2 + \mu)$ varies with μ but little and is about unity with large values of μ, the first amplifier stage using an ordinary three-element tube cannot amplify the current i much. However, by using a shield grid (dotted branch of Fig. 71) with the proper positive potential B_1, Eq. (8) gives

$$C \cong C_p + C_{gf}$$

which gives

$$e_p = 0.63\, \mu \frac{i\, t}{C_p + C_{gf}} \qquad (15)$$

Hence a decided amplification is possible with a shield-grid tube because μ may have values of 60 and higher. The multistage shield-grid photo-electric amplifier with an ordinary three-element tube for the final stage is then as shown in Fig. 72, where for variable photoelectric currents grid condensers and grid leaks can be used instead of the negative grid biases. From the above analysis in connection with Fig. 71, it is

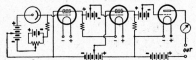

FIG. 72.—Cascade amplifier for measuring small photoelectric currents.

evident that current rather than voltage amplification must be dealt with. It can be shown that the current amplification A_i is larger the smaller the external impedance of the plate circuit. Hence, when dealing with an ordinary three-element tube (Fig. 71 without dotted shield grid), the effective amplification for one tube is equal to the change in plate current to the change in photoelectric current, that is,

$$A_{i|_{R=0}} = \frac{\partial i_p}{\partial i} = \frac{\partial i_p}{\partial i_g} \qquad (16)$$

This requires that $R = 0$. The kind of tube used therefore plays an important part. Hence from the plot of i_p against the grid current i_g, the useful amplification A_i can be obtained by the slope along this curve at a certain operating point. Equation (16) assumes that the leak resistance r is infinitely high. The cathode of the photoelectric cell and the grid of the tube are floating. Hence when no light affects the photoelectric cell, the floating-electrode combination will collect by means of the grid those few electrons which are not passed on to the plate or returned to the filament. The negative potential, being built up finally on the floating-grid and photoelectric cathode combination, will stop any further accumulation of electrons. But as soon as the cell is influenced by light, its cathode will carry off the electrons across the cell to its anode and the grid potential will become more positive until the rate at which electrons come from the filament is the same as the rate at which they leave the photoelectric cell. Then the grid current i_g is equal to the photoelectric current i. Since

$$\frac{\partial i_p}{\partial i_g} = \frac{\partial i_p / \partial e_g}{\partial i_g / \partial e_g} = g_m \, r_g \tag{17}$$

that is, equal to the product of the mutual conductance and internal grid resistance of the tube, the useful amplification A_i would also be equal to this product. However, if it is assumed that no grid current i_g flows and an external leak resistance r acts, then $e_g = ir$ and

$$A_{i_{|ig=0}} = \frac{g_m}{\partial i / \partial e_g} = g_m \, r \tag{18}$$

But under actual conditions both grid current i_g and the current through a finite external leakage resistance r exist, and one finds from (16), (17), and (18) the useful amplification

$$A_i = g_m \frac{r \, r_g}{r + r_g} \tag{19}$$

showing that the external leak resistance is very high. If a comparatively strong light affects the photoelectric cell, an ordinary three-element tube (112 type or its equivalent) can be used to operate a relay as in Fig. 73. Both plate voltage and grid bias are applied across the photoelectric cell. Hence, if light affects the cathode of the cell, a current flows from the positive terminal of the B battery through the plate meter, relay coil to the amplifier,

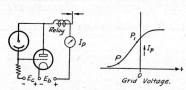

FIG. 73.—Circuit for large photoelectric currents.

and to the cell, respectively. The current flow through the cell produces a voltage drop across r such that the grid becomes more positive with respect to the filament. The operating point P of the tube is therefore moved to some point P_1 and produces a correspondingly higher plate current.

The bridge circuit of Fig. 64 can also be used[1] for photoelectric work. The cathode of the photoelectric cell is then connected to the grid, that is, to terminal P_3 and the anode of the cell through the positive pole of an additional battery to terminal P_4. The zero balance is first made

[1] A system of this type is described by C. H. Sharp, *Electronics*, **1**, 244, 1930.

when the photoelectric cell is not illuminated by connecting the single-pole switch on *a* and varying E_{c3}.   When the cathode of the cell receives light the off-balance is compensated as before by the voltage E_{c2} if the switch is closed on *b*.   This voltage is then again a measure of the photo-electric emission.

52. Notes on the Indication of Currents Due to Unmodulated and Modulated Infra-red and Other Rays.—For certain sound-reproduction

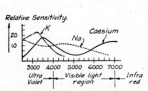

Fig. 74.—Relative color sensitivity of photoelectric cells.

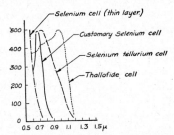

Fig. 75.—Spectral sensitivity distribution in the infra-red range.

and television work, rays covering the very high frequency spectrum are used.   Therefore frequencies far beyond Hertzian oscillations are dealt with.   If no modulations exist or are to be indicated, integrating detectors such as the bolometer, thermopiles, radiometers, which cover the spectrum up to 2.4 μ, can be used.   However, they are of no value if variations are to be indicated, since their action is sluggish even for very low frequencies.   Photoelectric effects must then be used.   Figure 74, for instance, gives the relative color sensitivity of potassium, sodium, and caesium photoelectric cells, while Fig. 75 gives the results for the spectral response distribution of different cells in the infra-red region. Like the Elster and Geitel photoelectric cells, the alkali metals with increasing atomic weight give a displacement of the limiting frequency of the selective photoelectric effect toward the long wave lengths.   According to Fig. 75, the same holds true if about 10 per cent tellurium is added to a selenium cell, since its spectral sensitivity is then displaced toward the infra-red, which shows, therefore, the effect of the added heavier atoms of an element of the same group.   The electric conductivity is, however, increased.   Therefore it is customary to produce very thin films by means of cathode sputtering.   In case of the thallium sulfide (thal-

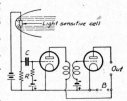

Fig. 76.—Amplification of the effects of modulated infra-red radiation.

lofide) cell, transparent films can be obtained by evaporation.   Such cells work in the audio-frequency band with a falling frequency characteristic in the upper frequency end of the band.   Other substances which respond to the photoelectric effect in the infra-red and are suitable for audio-frequency modulations are crystalline matter such as antimonite, molybdenite.   Elster and Geitel photoelectric cells work up to very high frequencies.   The limit of the photoelectric effect for all substances is somewhat above 1.1 μ.   In Fig. 76 a tellurium-selenium cell picks up infrared rays which are modulated with audio frequency.

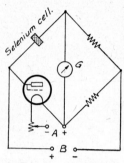

The condenser C is used to prevent the direct current passing through the selenium cell from reaching the grid. According to the frequency of the modulation, the value of C is somewhere between 0.01 and 1 μf.   The resistance R should be about equal to the resistance of the cell.   Figure 77 shows the cell in a bridge circuit with a tube with filament-temperature saturation acting as a constant resistance in the other branch.   The voltage of the B battery is then such that about 10 to 20 volts acts in series with the selenium cell.   Circuits with photoelectric cells are as described in the previous section.

Fig. 77.—Bridge circuit for studying the effects on a selenium cell.

53. Measurement of Very Small Grid Currents.—Grid currents as low as 10^{-3} μa can be determined with an ordinary microammeter in the plate circuit by the method indicated in Fig. 78.   The method is based on the fact that an external grid R has no effect on the plate current I_p when no grid current flows.   But with a grid current I_g a voltage drop occurs along R, resulting in a corresponding decrease i in the plate current.   The measurement then consists in closing the short-circuiting switch S of the leak and varying the resistance r for fixed E_c and E_b voltages until the current of the microammeter in the plate branch is just balanced out.   Points P_1P_2 of the respective characteristics for a grid leak and $R = 0$ produce the same plate current; that is, P_2P_1 must be the voltage drop I_gR along R and P_2P_3 the indicated current i in the microammeter when S is opened.   From

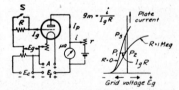

Fig. 78.—Determination of minute grid currents.

the relation of the steepness g_m of the work characteristic for $R = 0$ the grid current can be computed from

$$I_g = \frac{i}{g_m R} \tag{20}$$

54. Production of Very Small Currents and Their Determination.— Since it is difficult to measure small currents directly, it is customary to produce small alternating currents (1) by potentiometer arrangements, (2) with transformers, and (3) by attenuation networks.   It is then an easy matter to compute an unmeasurably small current from a larger current reading.   Potentiometer arrangements are well-known.   Customary attenuation boxes employ pure resistors connected along and across a line as indicated in Fig. 53 and described in detail in Sec. 36. For symmetrical sections, the input and output terminals of the attenuation box are interchangeable, but it is essential that the output terminals work into the load resistance R_0 for which the sections are designed. The comparatively large input current I_1 is measured with an ordinary thermoelectric indicator and the output current computed from $I_2 = I_1\epsilon^{-\alpha}$ if α denotes the attenuation. Attenuation boxes are usually calibrated in transmission units (decibels) in order to facilitate the computation. They are useful when very small currents are to be produced in order to match their effects against an unknown current to be determined. An example for the case of a small telephone current is given in the next section. Another application is illustrated in Fig. 79. A source passes a current I_1 into

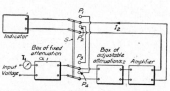

FIG. 79.—Determination of current amplification by means of fixed and variable attenuators.

an attenuation box of fixed attenuation α_1 which is in series with another attenuation box of adjustable attenuation α_2 and a current amplifier whose output current I_2 affects an indicator. The output current I_2 is then

$$I_2 = A_i I_1 \epsilon^{-(\alpha_1+\alpha_2)} \tag{21}$$

if A_i stands for the current amplification of the amplifier. The quantity I_2 denotes the effective alternating-current value which is due to the harmonic input voltage. When the switch S is now thrown toward P_1 P_2 P_3 P_4, the indicator is connected through the box of fixed attenuation α_1 to the source and the indicated output current is

$$I_2' = I_1 \epsilon^{-\alpha_1} \tag{22}$$

Therefore, if for the first connection the variable attenuation α_2 is changed until the same output current is obtained as for the second connection $(I_2 = I_2')$, all currents cancel out when comparing both equations and $A_i = \varepsilon^{+\alpha_2}$ is obtained. Hence, the current amplification can be computed from this relation which is conveniently written in the form $\log_{10} A_i = \alpha_2/2.303$. For an attenuation $\alpha_2 = 1$, a current amplification of 22×10^3 is obtained. When audio-frequency amplifications are performed, this procedure is especially simple, since the equality of the output currents I_2 and I_2' can be noted by means of a telephone receiver.

It can be seen that there are manifold applications of apparatus which produce attenuated currents.

55. Methods for Measuring Small Telephone Currents.—Figure 80 shows two circuits by means of which the audibility characteristic of a telephone receiver T can be approximately obtained. In the circuit to the left a sinusoidal audio current I of desired frequency f is passed through a potentiometer of resistance R and the sliding contacts K_1 and K_2 moved until the sound in T just disappears. When Z_t denotes the effective impedance of the telephone receiver and r the portion of the resistance of the potentiometer which is in parallel with T, the smallest response current I_t at a particular frequency is given by

$$I_t = \frac{r}{r + Z_t} I \tag{23}$$

The term $S = \dfrac{r}{r + Z_t}$ is known as the "sensitivity factor" and its reciprocal $A = 1/S$ as the "audibility factor." It is approximately proportional to the square of the high-frequency current if the system

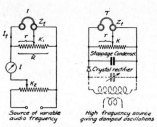

shown to the right is used in the test. The slider K is then moved until there is no difference noticed between dot and dash signals. The impedance Z_t of the receiver can be measured with one of the methods described in this text. Suppose the measurement gives the effective value of the inductance as $L_t = 0.5$ henry and the effective resistance $r_t = 2000\,\Omega$, then $Z_t = \sqrt{\omega^2 L_t{}^2 + r_t{}^2}$ which at 1000 cycles/sec gives $Z_t = 3730\,\Omega$.

Fig. 80.—Determination of sensitivity of telephone receivers.

If further the sound in the telephone receiver just disappears when for $I = 1$ ma for a setting $r = 1\,\Omega$ of the total resistance $R = 5000\,\Omega$, the telephone current becomes $I_t = \frac{1}{3731} = 0.268$ μa. When several telephone receivers are to be compared with each other, it is unnecessary to evaluate the minimum response current I_t. It is only necessary to keep the input current I constant for a certain frequency and move the slider K_1 until the sound just disappears. The best

receiver then has the smallest value of $S = \dfrac{r}{r + Z_t}$.

Figure 81 is a method used in the laboratory of L. W. Austin to determine telephone currents in receiving sets by means of a calibration circuit. Signals picked up in the head set of a receiving apparatus can then be used to find the field intensity of the arriving electromagnetic wave. When continuous signals arrive, a tube voltmeter can be employed, but with dot and dash signals the telephone-current method seems the most useful one. The method consists of comparing the received signal with similar tones coming from the calibrated network shown in the figure. An audio-frequency voltage of suitable frequency is applied to the resistance r_1. By means of the sliding contact along r_1, the current I_1 is brought to a suitable value. The

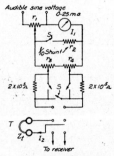

Fig. 81.—Comparator for the determination of small telephone currents. ($r_3 + r_4 = 100\,\Omega$; r_3 in steps of $10\,\Omega$; r_4 in steps of $1\,\Omega$.)

resistances $(r_3 + r_4)$ serve as a voltage divider. If $I_1 = 10^{-2}$ amp, then 1 volt is obtained across the terminals of $(r_3 + r_4)$. The current flows to the telephone receiver T over a resistance of $4 \times 10^5 \Omega$ so that the telephone current I_2 can be computed without the exact knowledge of the impedance Z_t of the receiver. The carrier current of the incoming wave is made audible by means of a heterodyne beat note or an autodyne detector (oscillating detector) and the beat note chosen (about 1000 cycles/sec) is equal to the frequency of the audio current impressed on the comparator. The sliding contacts along r_3 and r_4 are then moved until the current from the receiving set has about the same effect in the telephone as the current from the comparator. A better comparison can be obtained if the head set is slipped somewhat behind the ears and the telephone alternately connected to the comparator and to the receiving set.

Example.—Suppose the impedance of the telephone receiver is about $30,000 \Omega$ and that the sounds in the telephone are equally weak for 17Ω taken off by means of the sliding contacts along $(r_3 + r_4)$. For $I_1 = 10^{-2}$ amp, 0.17 volt is impressed on the telephone circuit. The telephone current is then approximately $I = \dfrac{0.17}{430,000} = 3.95 \times 10^{-7}$ amp. For the measurement of still smaller telephone currents the switch S_1 is closed in order to connect the $\frac{1}{10}$ shunt.

A method was described in connection with Fig. 79 which can be used to determine a small current I_2 by the use of two attenuation boxes of fixed and variable attenuation, respectively. Therefore when the indicator is a telephone receiver, the current I_2 flowing through the telephone receiver can be computed from $I_2 = A_i I_1 \epsilon^{-(\alpha_1 + \alpha_2)}$ where α_1 denotes the fixed attenuation, α_2 the variable attenuation, and A_i the current amplification of the amplifier. When all these quantities are known and the input current I_1 is measured with a thermoelectric meter, the telephone current I_2 can be computed. For the determination of I_2 it is then

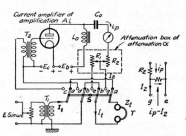

Fig. 82.—Attenuation-box current-amplifier method for the determination of a small current I_t.

unnecessary to use two attenuation boxes but one variable attenuation network as in Fig. 82 is sufficient. This circuit is an adaptation of a method originally suggested by H. J. Van der Bijl.[1] By means of the four-blade switch S the audio-frequency voltage $E \sin \omega t$ can be made to act through the transformer T_1 directly on the telephone receiver T so that $I_1 = I_t$. It is for the position of S shown in the figure, since I_1 flows "in" over terminals a, b and "out" over a, b to the right, to T. When the switch S is turned to the left, the current I_1 flows first over terminals cd toward transformer T_2 whose effective primary impedance

[1] *Phys. Rev.*, **24**, 311, 1919.

is equal to Z_t of the telephone receiver. After amplification in the tube circuit, the current i_p is obtained which can be decreased again by the variable attenuation α to some value I_2 which flows over terminals e and g to the telephone receiver. Hence, when I_2 is again made equal to I_1, that is, to the telephone current I_t when the switch S is turned toward the right, the gain A_i in current amplification is just compensated by the loss $\epsilon^{-\alpha}$ in the attenuation box, since the alternating current in the plate branch is then $i_p = A_i I_1$ and the output current becomes $I_2 = i_p \epsilon^{-\alpha}$. Hence, if the telephone for a certain frequency gives the same response when S is to the left as when it is to the right,

$$I_t = I_2 = i_p \epsilon^{-\alpha} = A_i I_1 \epsilon^{-\alpha} = I_1 \qquad (24)$$

Therefore, when the much larger current i_p is measured, the telephone current can be computed from

$$I_t = i_p \epsilon^{-\alpha} \qquad (25)$$

since α of the attenuation network is known. If α is unknown for a known current amplification A_i, there is for the above adjustment

$$A_i \epsilon^{-\alpha} = 1,$$

and I_t can be calculated from

$$I_t = \frac{i_p}{A_i} \qquad (26)$$

The variable attenuation network in Fig. 82 should not be confused with the shunt method indicated in Fig. 80, since the variable resistance R_1 acts across the outgoing line and the variable resistance R_2 along the outgoing line (L-shaped filter network as indicated in the figure) but in such a way that it always produces the *same* load resistance in the i_p branch.

56. Determination of the Harmonic-current Content of a Distorted Current.—With distorted alternating currents of commercial power frequencies, the current wave is usually photographed with an oscillograph and the oscillogram obtained analyzed by means of Fourier's series, unless the harmonic-resonance method of M. J. Pupin[1] is used. This method is greatly improved if the distorted current heterodynes with a

---

[1] Pupin, M. J., *Trans. A.I.E.E.*, **11**, 523, 1894; *Am. J. Sci.*, **48**, 379, 473, 1894; M. Pupin and Armagnat, *J. Phys.*, **1**, 345, 1902; For further developments see R. L. Wegel and C. R. Moore, *Bell System Tech. J.*, **3**, April, 1924; C. R. Moore and A. S. Curtis, *Bell System Tech. J.*, **6**, 217, 1927; A. G. Landeen, *Bell System Tech. J.*, **6**, 230, 1927; J. W. Horton, *Trans. A.I.E.E.*, **46**, 535, 1927 (gives a clear exposition of empirical analysis of couplex electric waves); M. Gruetzmacher, *E.N.T.*, **4**, 533, 1927 (describes an improved method for sound analysis by means of the heterodyne method similar to the one described by A. G. Landeen). For simplified harmonic analyzers see C. G. Suits, *Proc. I.R.E.*, **18**, 178, 1930; A. W. Barber, *Electronics*, **1**, 374, 1930; for a simplified method of measuring harmonic microphone currents, E. Meyer, *E.N.T.*, **5**, 398, 1928.

sinusoidal search current of variable frequency. The amplitudes of the harmonics are then detected by low-frequency beat currents produced between the particular harmonic and the sinusoidal search current. The heterodyne method which makes use of the selectivity at a frequency below that of the test current is readily applicable to the accurate measurement of any individual harmonic, even if small compared with the presence of other larger harmonic components.

Reference is made to the vector diagram of Fig. 83 for the original resonance method. When a sinusoidal current I of frequency $\omega/2\pi$ passes through an inductance L and condenser C, for resonance one has the equal reactances OP_1 and OP_2 perpendicular to the effective circuit resistance $OP = R$. When a second harmonic is also present, the impedance $Z_2 = PP_5$ is obtained for this harmonic, since twice the inductive reactance and half of the capacity reactance are effective. Therefore the tuned-out fundamental current is little affected by the presence of the

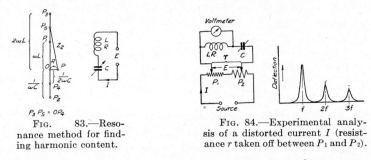

Fig. 83.—Resonance method for finding harmonic content.

Fig. 84.—Experimental analysis of a distorted current I (resistance r taken off between P_1 and P_2).

second harmonic, since I is nearly E/R. This can also be understood from the expression

$$I = \frac{E}{\sqrt{R^2 + \left[m\omega L - \dfrac{1}{m\omega C} \right]^2}} = \frac{E}{\sqrt{R^2 + m^2\omega^2 L^2 \left[1 - \dfrac{1}{m^2\omega^2 CL} \right]^2}}$$

which holds for any harmonic component ($m = 1, 2, 3, 4, 5, \cdots$). If C is so adjusted that resonance exists for the pth harmonic ($m = p$), one has $p\omega L = 1/(p\omega C)$; that is, $\omega^2 CL = 1/p^2$. For any other harmonic component, the intensity

$$I = \frac{E}{\sqrt{R^2 + m^2\omega^2 L^2 \left[1 - \dfrac{p^2}{m^2} \right]^2}} \tag{27}$$

can be used to determine to what extent any of the other harmonic components affects the resonance setting $m = p$ of a certain harmonic. Therefore, when a distorted current is to be analyzed, it can be done by the corresponding voltage drop across a noninductive resistance through which I flows. The circuit is then as in Fig. 84 if a resistance r of a few ohms is branched off from a low-resistance potentiometer P_1P_2 with a rough and finer adjustment in order to apply a suitable voltage E toward a low-resistance shunt circuit consisting of a coil L, R and a variable condenser C. This branch is tuned to resonance for the harmonics and the resonance voltage measured by a suitable high-impedance voltmeter. Most of the tube voltmeters described in the next chapter will do. The deflection of the voltmeter is then a measure for the harmonic intensity. A cathode-ray tube can also be used if either L or a portion of it acts as the deflection coil. If a magnetic deflection is inconvenient, one deflection condenser of the cathode ray may be connected

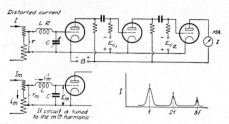

Fig. 85.—Current analysis using a two-stage tube voltmeter.

in multiple with the tuning capacitance C. In each case, the magnetic and electric deflection, respectively, is a measure of the harmonic-current intensity. The voltage step-ups across the coil and the condenser for resonance are $m\omega L/R$ and $1/(m\omega CR)$ for any harmonic and can be from 50 to 300 fold when the effective branch resistance R is low. Although at resonance for a low value of R the resonance voltage across L, R is essentially the same as across C, it is not immaterial whether the voltmeter is connected across the inductance or the capacitance. When more discrimination is required against harmonic components of lower frequency, the voltage should be measured across L, while against harmonic components of higher frequency the voltage across C should be used. The reason for this is that, for a constant impressed voltage E, the voltage drop across L below resonance (frequency of current less than

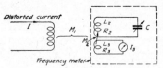

Fig. 86.—Frequency-meter method for finding harmonic content.

natural resonance frequency of circuit) is less than across C. The opposite is true for frequencies above the resonance frequency. With a fixed input resistance r this method is of use only for the harmonics which are comparatively strong. It would be impossible, for instance, to indicate harmonics which are only a few per cent—and especially when less than 1 per cent—less than the fundamental. For this reason either the double-tap potentiometers shown in Fig. 84 and Fig. 85, or a variable mutual inductance M_1 as in Fig. 86 can be used. For the circuit of Fig. 85 the grid bias E_{c2} is so high that for no distorted current I flowing toward the multistage tube voltmeter, the milliammeter just registers zero. The advantage of using a mutual inductance as in Fig. 86 is then the following. Suppose the frequency meter (wave meter) is of the simple type where the current indicator is directly inserted in the resonator (L_2, C_2 circuit). If the frequency meter is tuned to the mth harmonic, the harmonic resonance current is then

$$I_r = \frac{m\omega M_1 I_m}{R_e} \tag{28}$$

if R_e denotes the effective circuit resistance R_2 plus the resistance of the indicator and I_m the intensity of the mth harmonic of I. Since the order m of the harmonic is in the numerator, the method for the higher harmonic is relatively more sensitive, while for a pure resistance-drop voltage supply due to I the resonance current would be $I_m r / R_e$. Therefore, when the coupling M_1 of the frequency meter to the coil carrying the current I to be analyzed is kept constant, the resonance indicator I_r in the CL_2 branch indicates the correct relative values of the harmonic components. This presupposes that the effective circuit resistance R_2 is constant over the entire frequency range. Since, for great sensitivity, the frequency meter should be very selective, it is of advantage to reduce the effective circuit resistance of the resonance branch (CL_2) by coupling the resonance indicator I_3 loosely as in Fig. 86 and keeping M_2 constant (L_3 in a fixed position to the L_2 coil of the frequency meter). Since for this case the effective circuit resistance of the CL_2 branch is

$$R_e = R_2 + \frac{m^2\omega^2 M_3^2}{R_3^2 + m^2\omega^2 L_3^2} R_3 \tag{29}$$

where R_3 denotes the entire resistance of the tertiary aperiodic indicator circuit. If I_m again denotes the intensity of the mth harmonic of the test current I and M_1 is chosen so small that the frequency meter does not react appreciably on the coil which carries the distorted current I, one finds for the resonance current I_3 if tuned to the mth harmonic that

$$I_m = -\frac{R_e}{m^2\omega^2} \frac{R_3 + jm\omega L_3}{M_1 M_2} I_3 = A_m I_3 \tag{30}$$

that is, a value proportional to I_3. If $m\omega L_3$ is chosen small compared to R_3, then

$$I_m \cong -\frac{R_e R_3}{m^2\omega^2 M_1 M_2} I_3 = \frac{k R_e}{m^2 f^2} I_3 \tag{30a}$$

where $k = R_3 / 4\pi^2 M_1 M_2$ may be taken as the constant of proportionality and f denotes the fundamental frequency. The assumption of Eq. (30a) holds only for the middle- and lower-frequency range. The effective resistance R_e is at first obtained experimentally for a constant coupling M_1 with the differential method (page 268) as a function of the frequency.

From this, the value $R_e/(mf)^2$ for consecutive harmonics is computed which gives, according to (30a), the factor to be multiplied with the measured resonance current I_3, since k is a constant.

For the higher-frequency range where ωL_3 of Eq. (30) is generally very large compared with R_3, the equation simplifies to

$$I_m \cong K\frac{R_e}{mf}I_3 \tag{30b}$$

if the constant is now

$$K = \frac{L_3}{2\pi M_1 M_2}$$

since the minus sign and the j term can be ignored for numerical calculations. The values of R_e at different harmonic frequencies mf then must be divided by f, $2f$, $3f$, etc., only, for the fundamental, second harmonic, third harmonic, etc. If comparatively small harmonic intensities I_m with respect to amplitude of the fundamental of I are to be measured, a tighter coupling M_1 (but not too tight) is chosen in such a way that, when the frequency meter for normal coupling is detuned with respect to the fundamental frequency f, the deflection of the indicator is only $1/q$th of the resonance deflection. The coupling M_1 is then tightened up until for resonance with the fundamental again $1/q$th of the maximum deflection is obtained. Hence, when the frequency meter is tuned to any higher harmonic frequency mf for this tighter coupling M_1, the resonance indications come out q times larger with respect to the fundamental, and much smaller intensities can be measured. The deflections are then to be divided by q.

Similar increase of the sensitivity can be accomplished with the circuits shown in Figs. 84 and 85. Such resistances r are then taken from the low-resistance potentiometer carrying the distorted test current for the various harmonics to which the CL branch is tuned so that the resonance indicator (which is a tube voltmeter for Fig. 84 and the milliammeter for Fig. 85) always gives the same deflection. In the case of Fig. 85, the distorted current I consists of the harmonic intensities I_1, I_2, I_3, etc., of frequencies f, $2f$, $3f$, etc. Therefore, when the circuit is tuned to the mth harmonic and the galvanic coupling $r = r_m$ is chosen in order to produce sufficient voltage E_m between the grid and the filament to give a good deflection d on the milliammeter of the instrument, the current intensity I_m will divide itself into a portion i_m which flows over r_m and a portion i_m' which flows through the LC branch of the effective resistance R. Hence, $i_m r_m = i_m' R$ and, since the voltage applied to the tube is $E_m = i_m'/2\pi mfC$,

$$E_m = \frac{i_m r_m}{2\pi mfCR} \tag{31}$$

Since the fundamental current $I_m = I_1$ which flows to the parallel combination has normally the greatest intensity, the resistance coupling must be changed to some value $r = r_1$ in order to produce the same deflection d on the plate meter ($E_1 = E_m$), and

$$E_m = \frac{i_1 r_1}{2\pi f C R} \tag{32}$$

is obtained, since I_1 divides itself again into a current i_1 through r_1 and i_1' through the tuned CL branch. Comparing these expressions, one finds the harmonic intensity ratio

$$\frac{I_m}{I_1} = \frac{i_m}{i_1} = m\frac{r_1}{r_m} \tag{33}$$

and when multiplied by 100, Eq. (33) gives the intensity of the mth harmonic current in percentage of the fundamental current intensity. This analysis neglects the effect of the neighboring harmonics upon the plate-meter reading. As far as deflection d for the fundamental frequency f is concerned, it may be said that, for higher harmonics of comparatively small intensities, it is due practically to the fundamental component only. But, for the deflections d due to any of the upper harmonics, this is not quite true as may be understood from Eq. (27) and the experimental fact that, after detuning from the fundamental current setting toward the second harmonic setting, the plate meter generally passes through a minimum only but not an absolute zero reading until the deflection increases again in order to produce at resonance for $2f$ another maximum value. Neglecting the resistance R of the coil, for resonance of the second harmonic and a resistance $r = r_2$ in order to produce the same deflection d, the fundamental current produces a contribution

$$i_1' = \frac{r_2 i_1}{\omega L - \dfrac{1}{\omega C}} = \frac{\omega C r_2 i_1}{\omega^2 C L - 1} \tag{34}$$

which superimposes the grid-filament voltage

$$\frac{i_1'}{\omega C} = E_1'$$

on the desired voltage

$$E_2 = \frac{i_2'}{2\omega C} \tag{35}$$

where

$$i_2' = \frac{r_2 i_2}{R} \tag{35a}$$

since the second harmonic current I_2 which is tuned out splits into i_2 through r_2 and i_2' through the CL branch. But for this tuning $\omega^2 C L = 0.25$ $\left(\text{since } 2\omega L - \dfrac{1}{(2\omega C)}\right) = 0$ and the superimposed voltage due to the fundamental becomes

$$E_1' = \frac{r_2 i_1}{\omega^2 CL - 1} = -\frac{4}{3} r_2 i_1 \qquad (36)$$

Neglecting the effect of all other harmonic currents (which in most cases is small), the effective voltage applied to the grid and filament is

$$E_g = \sqrt{E_2^2 + E_1'^2} \qquad (37)$$

For the same plate-meter deflection d as for the fundamental resonance setting, the measured second-harmonic current comes out somewhat too large as can be computed from Eqs. 35, 36, and 37. The effect of the voltage E_1' can be found experimentally by noting the minimum deflection of the plate meter when changing the C setting from fundamental- to double-frequency resonance. This deflection may then be balanced out by increasing the grid bias E_{c_2} of the last tube in Fig. 85, until the plate meter reads just zero. The resonance setting for the second harmonic then gives the correct reading, since for a circuit which is not unreasonably damped the minimum deflection occurs not far from the $2f$ setting. Of course, the minimum deflection due to the fundamental becomes less when determining the third-harmonic content and in many cases can be neglected for this setting, or at least from this harmonic upward. The exact values of the disturbing fundamental-harmonic voltage E_1' can be found by applying a sinusoidal current of the same magnitude and frequency to the measuring system and noting the deflections at frequency $2f$, $3f$ when the corresponding resistances r_2, r_3, etc., are branched off on the potentiometer.

A more convenient way of determining small harmonic components is by the heterodyne method. A local generator (heterodyne) of variable frequency, of sinusoidal wave shape, and conveniently of constant-output amplitude feeds a search current into the detector circuit which is also used to indicate the effect of the distorted test current. As the frequency f of the sinusoidal search current is adjusted to about the frequency f_m of the harmonic component of the test current, the indicator of the detector circuit will slowly swing to and fro, in synchronism with the difference frequency $(f - f_m)$. Therefore, when this difference is about 1 cycle/sec or somewhat less, the amplitude of swing can be read directly on the indicator. From this reading and the amplitude of the search current, one can compute the amplitude of the particular harmonic. To obtain the value of another harmonic, the frequency of the search current is varied until it is about equal to the frequency of the harmonic. By adjusting the difference frequency which may be, for instance, 100 cycles/sec, and working into a vibration galvanometer tuned to 100 cycles/sec, a very small harmonic amplitude can be indicated. This can also be done by using a tuned audio-frequency amplifier with an indicator.

Generally when the search current and test current act in the grid branch of a vacuum tube (which has a bias such that its plate current just disappears without variable voltages on the grid) a direct-current meter in the plate branch registers a direct current, since plate currents flow which contain components of zero frequency (direct currents) and currents with the sum and differences of the frequencies of the harmonic components acting on the grid. The difference frequencies are utilized in the above schemes. Figure 87 shows a scheme where an ordinary tube voltmeter whose plate current I_p varies about the operating point P between P_1 and P_2 with the square of the applied grid potential. The beat amplitude due to the low-difference frequency $(f - f_m)$ between the frequency f of the sinusoidal search current I and the mth harmonic of

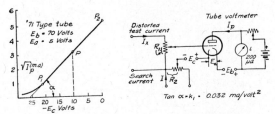

Fig. 87.—Simplified-tube voltmeter method.

frequency f_m of the test current I_x is noted with this voltmeter. This method is the simplest heterodyne method and accurate enough for much of the work. Since the useful tube characteristic P_1P_2 follows a square law, the current fluctuation i in the plate current I_p is

$$i = KI_mI \qquad (38)$$

because the voltage amplitude $E_m = I_mR_1$ of the mth harmonic of I_x acts across R_1 and is a measure of I_m and the voltage $E = IR_2$ across R_2 is proportional to the amplitude I of the sinusoidal search current. The constant in the above equation is therefore

$$K = kR_1R_2 \qquad (38a)$$

where the factor k can be computed from the work characteristic, if $k = 4k_1$ and k_1 denotes the plate milliamperes per volt input squared. Since R_1 and R_2 are also constants, it is more convenient to find K experimentally, that is, directly by applying two known sinusoidal currents I_m and I through R_1 and R_2, respectively, and noting the difference i in milliamperes between the maximum and minimum deflection of the plate meter. After having found the constant K from $i/(I_mI)$, the search current I of known intensity is varied in frequency in order to produce a difference $i = i_1$ between the maximum and minimum deflection of the plate meter when slow-beat swings occur for the search frequency almost equal to the fundamental frequency of the distorted current I_x. The amplitude of the fundamental component is then computed from

$$I_1 = \frac{i_1}{KI} \tag{39}$$

The frequency of I is then varied until again slow swings are obtained and the second-harmonic content is computed by means of the difference $i = i_2$ from

$$I_2 = \frac{i_2}{KI} \tag{40}$$

and so forth. The above formulas are based upon the fact that for a square-law tube voltmeter, a variable grid voltage of maximum value $e_g = E + E_x = IR_2 + I_x R_1$ will produce a variation i_p in the plate current I_p according to

$$i_p = k_2 e_g + k_1 e_g{}^2$$

which for the instantaneous value $E \sin \theta$ and $E_1 \sin \theta + E_2 \sin 2\theta +$ $\cdots + E_m \sin m\theta$ for the search voltage and voltage components due to the distorted current I_x gives for the search frequency $\theta/2\pi = f$ near a certain harmonic frequency $f + f_b$ (when the beat frequency f_b is about 1 cycle) of the test current I_x, an average current value equal to

$$k_1 \left\{ k_3 + av \left[\frac{EE_m}{2}(\cos 2\pi f_b t - \cos 2\pi(2f + f_b)) \right] \right\}$$

The constant term k_3 stands for the components of zero frequency and the constant k_1 for the curvature $(d^2 I_p / d^2 E_g)$ of the work characteristic $(I_p$ against $E_g)$. The term $k_1 k_3$ produces the steady minimum deflection in the plate-current meter if in this particular case the needle of the instrument swings in synchronism with the 1 cycle/sec beat frequency f_b. The average values of both cosine terms vanish, but, because of the smallness of the beat frequency f_b, the first term affects the plate meter and the needle swings to and fro, the swing being proportional to EE_m, that is, also proportional to the product of the amplitude of the search current I and the amplitude I_m of the harmonic of I_x, confirming Eq. (38). The value E of the grid voltage due to the search current can be readily measured by this circuit since it is a tube voltmeter. The search current I is then only applied and the tap along the

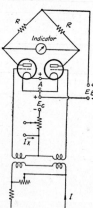

Fig. 88.—Bridge method as current analyzer (I, search current; I_x, distorted test current).

potentiometer varied until, for a certain value of R_2, a suitable deflection i is obtained. To this deflection corresponds a certain voltage on the calibration chart of the tube voltmeter. Hence, when the frequency of the search current I is varied and if the supply voltage of the I source should undergo a change, it is only necessary to readjust R_2 somewhat until for each near-harmonic frequency of the measurement the same deflection i exists when only the search voltage affects the tube voltmeter. If

such an adjustment becomes impossible, R_2 is not varied and the voltage
due to the search current is measured with the tube voltmeter for each
near-harmonic setting from the corresponding i reading.

Figure 88 shows a bridge circuit for which a direct-current balance
of the two plate currents exists. A sensitive indicator can then be used
to detect very weak harmonic currents. This indicator can be of the
vibration-galvanometer[1] type. A fixed tuned audio-frequency output
branch can be used instead of the indicator which works into a stage of
audio-frequency amplification and then through a rectifier into a direct-
current indicator. The circuit of Fig. 89 uses such a scheme. The

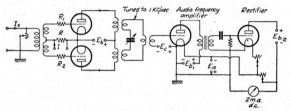

Fig. 89.—Harmonic analyzer.

sinusoidal search current I is then applied through a suitable resistance
R in the common input lead of the two tubes in push pull. R_1 denotes
high resistances and no grid bias is used. Under such conditions the
output modulation is proportional to the *smaller* of the respective input
currents and not affected by the larger input current. The amplitude
in the output can then be determined entirely by the amplitude of the
small harmonic content to be measured.

Figure 90 shows an arrangement in which the sinusoidal search
current I of variable frequency again produces, with any consecutive

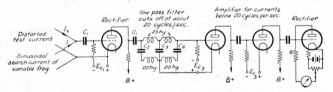

Fig. 90.—Harmonic analyzer. ($C_1 = 0.25\mu f$; $C_2 = 15\mu f$; $C_3 = 30\mu f$.)

harmonics of the distorted test current I_x in the first rectifier circuit, a
slow beat proportional to I and the amplitude of the particular harmonic.
The filter passes only currents below 20 cycles/sec, in order to make
the analysis also fit in the audio-frequency band. The slow-beat variation is then amplified and again rectified to affect a galvanometer.

Figure 91 shows an arrangement by means of which distortions in
carbon microphone transmitters can be studied. A constant sinusoidal

[1] For instance, as used in the General Radio oscillograph, since then the natural
period of the vibrating string can be readily adjusted to the beat frequency.

search current I is passed into the bridge circuit when a *pure* tone of frequency f affects the microphone. If I denotes the microphone current of constant resistance R_0 and variable resistance component R, for a search frequency f_s near the frequency f, the voltage across the microphone is

$$E = [R_0 + R \sin 2\pi ft]I \sin 2\pi f_s t$$
$$= IR_0 \sin 2\pi f_s t + \frac{IR}{2} \cos 2\pi(f_s - f)t - \frac{IR}{2} \cos 2\pi(f_s + f)t \quad (41)$$

If G is an alternating-current galvanometer with a natural vibration of about 50 cycles/sec, it will respond to the difference voltage of frequency $f_s - f = 50$. For distortion in the microphone, responses will also be registered by this instrument if f_s sweeps over the multiple-harmonic range, while for no distortion the galvanometer will only respond for the fundamental frequency.

Generally if a distorted test current

$$i_x = I_0 + I_1 \sin(\omega t - \varphi_1) + I_2 \sin(2\omega t - \varphi_2) + \cdots I_m \sin(m\omega t - \varphi_m)$$

acts in one branch of a dynamometric instrument (for instance, the fixed coil of an audio-frequency wattmeter) and the sinusoidal search current

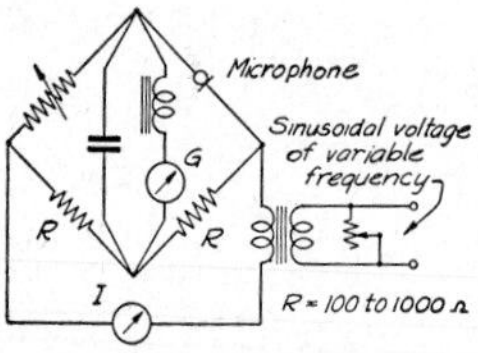

FIG. 91.—Acoustic harmonic analyzer.

$$i = I \sin(m\omega t - \varphi_m')$$

in the other branch (movable coil, for instance), their interaction gives rise to the dynamometer product $ki_x i$. The period of the movable coil is then much larger than that of the current. The deflection then is

$$d = \frac{k\pi}{2m} \int_0^{\frac{2m}{\omega}} ii_x = \frac{1}{2}kI \cdot I_m \cos(\varphi_m - \varphi_m') \quad (42)$$

Hence, when φ_m' changes, the deflection d changes also and maximum deflection takes place for $\varphi_m' = \varphi_m$ for which condition

$$d_{\max} = \frac{kI_m I}{2} \quad (43)$$

Since the dynamometer constant k can be found experimentally, and I from direct measurement, the intensity I_m of the harmonic current can be computed.

57. The Moullin Repulsion Ammeter.—An instrument of this type[1] can be made to work up to 30 Mc/sec, and 25 amp. The meter consists of two parallel copper cylinders one for the go and the other for the return of the high-frequency current to be measured. One cylinder is

[1] MOULLIN, E. B., *Proc. Roy. Soc. (London)*, A, **241**, 41, 1928; *J. Inst. Elec. Eng. (London)*, **68**, 544, 1930; see discussion also by M. F. Dunton and E. B. Moullin, *J. Inst. Elec. Eng. (London)*, **68**, 1173, 1930.

fixed in position and the other mounted so that the repulsive force between both conductors can be observed with a microscope and by the movement of a thin quartz pointer attached to the middle of the elastically mounted cylinder. In order to exclude the effects of the external magnetic fields, the two cylinders are surrounded by a heavy copper tube. Since the geometry of this arrangement is comparatively simple, the correction term due to the skin effect can be computed. It can be shown that the correction term approaches a limiting value and does not increase indefinitely as with ordinary thermal meters. If D denotes the spacing between the two copper cylinders of diameter d, the repulsive force F at any frequency $\omega/2\pi$ which causes the deflection can be computed from the series

$$F = \frac{2I^2}{D}\left\{1 + \frac{1}{2}\frac{d^2}{D^2} + \frac{3}{8}\frac{d^4}{D^4} - \frac{1}{\sqrt{2z}}\frac{d^2}{D^2}\left(1 + \frac{d^2}{D^2}\right) + \cdots\right\} \qquad (44)$$

if for a specific resistance ρ of the two conductors $z = \pi\omega d^2/\rho$ is larger than 3.5. At very low frequencies the effective value of an alternating current I produces the force

$$F = \frac{2I^2}{D} \qquad (45)$$

while for perfect conductivity and an infinite frequency, the force becomes

$$F = \frac{2I^2}{\sqrt{D^2 - d^2}} \qquad (46)$$

since within the two conductors there can no longer be any lines of force and each envelope of the cylinders must coincide with the lines of magnetic force. From this formula it can be seen that the increase of force is small as long as the spacing is much larger than d. Thus for $z > 10$ and $D/d = 1.5$, the ratio of the force at frequency $\omega/2\pi$ to the force at zero frequency is as small as 1.032, while for $D/d = 4$ it is only 1.005.

58. The Hot-cathode Ammeter.—Any of the tube-voltmeter circuits described in the following sections can be used to measure currents by passing the current through a low-resistance branch (so as not to affect the current too much) and applying the voltage developed to a tube voltmeter. A thermionic tube can also be used as shown in Fig. 92, where the unknown high-

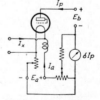

Fig. 92.—Hot-cathode ammeter.

frequency current I_x partially heats the filament and changes the space current I_p whose reading is a measure for I_x, if I_a is kept constant. The inserted choke coil prevents the high-frequency current from passing over the A battery. The method can be made more sensitive by using an indicator which measures only the changes δI_p due to I_x and using a filament which has a low electron affinity. The choice of the steady filament current I_a plays an important part in this instrument.

CHAPTER IV

DETERMINATION OF VOLTAGE

A voltage indicator must be such that its current consumption is small and the indicator does not appreciably affect the portion of the circuit across which the voltage is to be determined. The requirement of a *constant* small current may give difficulties in high-frequency systems, since skin effect may give rise to other resistance values of the indicator and any capacity and inductive effects of the indicator produce another frequency factor. Thus electrostatic voltmeters unless of special design may draw with increasing frequency such a displacement current that their use may become prohibitive. This is especially true in the case of such high frequencies where the capacity effect of the indicator may change the tuning of the circuit. Tube voltmeters of ordinary design may also give trouble within the range of very high frequencies and a calibration is always to be taken for the range for which they are used. Hot-wire voltmeters will require more current for their operation than thermoelectric voltmeters. They have, however, a place as switchboard instruments where great accuracy is not required and the frequency band over which they have to work is generally limited.

59. Reactance and Resistance Potentiometers.—Pure resistors in series may be used to extend the voltage range of a certain indicator by being affected by only a known fraction of the voltage to be indicated. The same can be done with suitable condensers and with an inductive reactance voltage divider. The electrostatic voltage divider consists of several good condensers C_1, C_2, C_3, C_4, etc., in series, one of which is conveniently variable. Since the resultant capacitance C which acts across the terminals between which the voltage is to be measured is given by

$$\frac{1}{C} = \frac{1}{C_1} + \frac{1}{C_2} + \frac{1}{C_3} + \frac{1}{C_4} + \cdots$$

it is convenient to connect a voltage indicator across C_1 whose value is varied until a suitable voltage E is indicated. The much higher unknown voltage is then

$$E_x = \frac{C_1}{C}E \tag{1}$$

For negligible ohmic resistances, the inductive-reactance potentiometer with sections L_1, L_2, L_3, L_4 in series gives a resultant inductance $L = L_1 + L_2 + L_3 + L_4$. If a tube voltmeter or other suitable type of meter is

128

connected across L_1, and L_1 is varied until a voltage E is indicated, the result is

$$E_x = \frac{L}{L_1} E \tag{2}$$

A potentiometer of this type is inferior in many respects to the condenser voltage divider and therefore hardly ever used. However, it becomes a good expedient when very small voltages E with respect to E_x are to be taken off. Thus, A. W. Hull[1] and N. H. Williams used the inductive potentiometer shown in Fig. 93 to measure the "shot effect." The requirement was a voltage divider which worked up to 750 kc/sec, and gave small calibration voltages from 5 to 150 μ volts. This demands a lumped variable inductance L_0 in series with a very small distributed inductance L_1, of which a still smaller inductance L is branched off to produce the very small reactive voltage drops. This is accomplished by

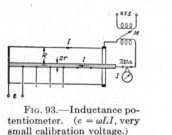

Fig. 93.—Inductance potentiometer. ($e = \omega LI$, very small calibration voltage.)

Fig. 94.— Ayrton Perry winding of resistors.

having a high-frequency source induce a current I in the secondary circuit of a variable mutual inductance M. The value of M can be either computed or measured (for instance, with the method shown in Fig. 206). The current I is read off with a thermoelectric-current indicator and the small desired voltage $e = \omega LI$ consists of the drop across a portion of a concentric copper cylinder which forms the inductance L_1. A hollow cylinder carries the current I at a certain instant in one direction, while a copper wire along its axis acts as return for the current. If this concentric-conductor system is imagined infinitely long, the inductance per unit length can be computed from

$$L = 0.0046 \log_{10} \left(\frac{R}{r} \right) \mu \text{ henries/cm} \tag{3}$$

A convenient ratio for R/r is 6 for a diameter $2r = 0.25''$ for the axial return. The correctness for the smaller voltage range given above is about 5 per cent, while for values of $e = 20$ and more microvolts an accuracy of about 1 per cent is obtainable.

In the case of resistance potentiometers, decade boxes wound in the Ayrton Perry type (Fig. 94) can be used for frequencies reaching

[1] *Phys. Rev.*, **25**, 160, 1925.

up into the broadcast range. Such resistances have very low inductive and capacity effects and are commercially available. They consist of two resistance wires in multiple, wound around a flat strip of insulation. Theoretically bare resistance wire (constantan and manganin because of their low temperature coefficient for working temperatures) can be used, since places where the wires cross should be points of equal potential on each parallel wire. When decade boxes are connected in series with a slider wire, a small voltage can be readily taken off by means of the sliding contact and one end of the slide wire. The slide wire consists of thin constantan wire (to make it more or less independent of skin effect), and a direct-current calibration of the wire can be used to obtain accuracies of about 1 per cent even for frequencies as high as 1500 kc/sec. If R, denoting the total series resistance, and r, the value taken off on the slider wire, are connected to a suitable voltage indicator (reading E), the unknown voltage E_x across R is

$$E_x = \frac{R}{r}E \qquad (4)$$

60. Notes on Hot-wire Voltmeters and Thermovoltmeters.—Hot-wire voltmeters like ammeters of the same type are not very efficient but are useful switchboard meters for high-frequency power work. Volt-

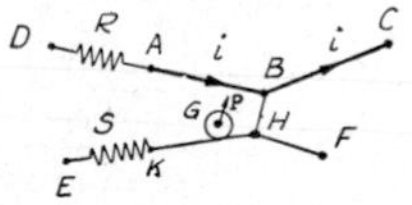

FIG. 95.—Hot-wire voltmeter. (R, resistance; S, spring; P, pointer).

meters of this type are constructed as in Fig. 95. ABC denotes the wire which carries the current i operating the meter. R is a pure series resistance and the voltage is applied to terminals D and C. $ACDEF$ are fixed points, while G is fixed as to location and denotes the projection of the shaft of the pointer of the voltmeter. S is a spring which pulls the pointer to the zero setting when no current i expands the hot wire ABC. The wire BH is a connecting lead to translate the expansion of the hot wire by means of cocon filament to the pointer and with a mechanical advantage sometimes as high as thirty. The hot wire which is a characteristic agency in this type of meter must be such that its coefficient of expansion is large and its melting point high so that under all conditions it is of good mechanical strength. As far as the electrical properties are concerned, it should heat quickly, have negligible skin effects, and no magnetic effects. Although some of these conditions can be only partially satisfied without conflicting with the others, it is customary to use alloys of platinum and silver (10 to 30 per cent platinum) and platinum iridium. For 30 per cent platinum in platinum-silver alloy the temperature coefficient of resistance is 24×10^{-5}, the linear expansion coefficient 15×10^{-6}, while for platinum-iridium wire with 30 per cent iridium, the temperature coefficient of resistance is 6×10^{-4} and the expansion coefficient 9×10^{-6}. The specific conductivity of the first alloy is 3.2 and that of platinum iridium 2.7. When nickel steel with 25 per cent nickel is used, the conductivity is 1.2, the temperature coefficient of resistance 13×10^{-4}, and the expansion coefficient 15×10^{-6}. Hence when a platinum-silver hot wire carries a current which changes its temperature by 80° C, above room temperature, the wire will increase by 0.2 mm if its original length were 160 mm, showing that the elongation of wire must be magnified by such mechanical means as illustrated in the figure. For hot-wire voltmeters thin wires must be used so that as much of the entire voltmeter resistance can be made operative as possible. Wire of from 0.02- to 0.05-mm diameter are customary in good commercial designs. The current i necessary for full deflection then goes up to 0.25 amp for platinum-silver alloy, about 0.2 for platinum iridium, and about 0.1 for nickel steel. Therefore, if a platinum-iridium wire is used with a resistance of 4Ω, a series resistance $R = 621\Omega$ is required if the voltmeter is to be read up to 125 volts. Up to about 20 kc/sec, hot-wire voltmeters are little affected by the frequency, and the direct-current calibration holds. For voltmeters reading up to 300 volts, a suitable series resistance R is usually mounted inside the meter. Instead of using a series resistance, a good air condenser of capacitance C can be used. If R_h denotes the resistance of the hot wire, for sinusoidal voltages, the voltage to be measured is

$$E_x = i\sqrt{R_h{}^2 + \left(\frac{1}{\omega C}\right)^2}.$$

Choosing C of such a value that R_h is negligible with respect to $1/\omega C$

$$E_x = \frac{i}{\omega C} \tag{5}$$

The voltmeter is then independent of the frequency $\omega/(2\pi)$ since i increases proportionally with $\omega/(2\pi)$. For a known value of C, it is then necessary to measure only i (in this case with the hot-wire instrument) in order to obtain the unknown voltage E_x.

Fig. 96.—Thermoelectric voltmeter.

The thermoelectric voltmeter of Fig. 96 was developed by L. T. Wilson.[1] It is built up symmetrically with respect to the thermocouple, multiplier resistances $R/2$, heater resistances $R_h/2$, as well as the shielding. The displacement current through the fictitious condenser C_1 toward the left-side screen and binding post P_1 is balanced by the displacement current C_2 toward the right-side screen and the binding post P_2. The instrument works up to 1 Mc with an error of about 1 per cent. A commercial design (Weston) of this type has a voltage range up to 20 volts. The full-scale deflection requires 2 ma. Unless a symmetrical design

[1] *J. Am. Inst. Elec. Eng.*, **48**, 446, 1924.

of this kind and no half-split screen is used, the meter will work satisfactorily only up to about 3 kc/sec. In the high-frequency range it would give certain deflections if the voltmeter terminals P_1P_2 are short-circuited, a certain deflection with only P_1 connected, and some other disturbing deflection with only P_2 connected.

61. Notes on Electrometers.—Such instruments work on the electro-static-repulsion principle and act like condensers. It is therefore necessary that electrometers with small effective capacitance be used. The quadrant electrometer consists of two fixed quadrants and a suspended needle. The latter is usually charged to a steady potential of 100 volts and the voltage to be determined is connected across the fixed quadrants. The needle is attracted toward one of the quadrants and repelled by the other and the final deflection is a measure of the difference of the applied voltage. The rate at which the needle moves is a measure of the current. As shown in Sec. 50, special electron tubes can be used today to measure minute currents which exceed the sensitivity of electrometers. The Dolezalek electrometer is shown to the left of Fig. 97. A light figure-eight-shaped vane is suspended by phosphor bronze or a platinumized quartz fiber between the quadrants. The last consists of a cylindrical brass chamber which is split into four parts. Opposite quadrants are electrically interconnected and act as the two fixed conductors. A small

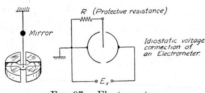

FIG. 97.—Electrometer.

mirror on the suspension registers the rotation of the vane and is observed by means of a scale and a telescope which is directed toward the mirror. The electrometer is surrounded by a grounded metal case. Only the *idiostatic* connection of the customary three connections of the quadrant electrometer plays a part in alternating voltages. This connection is indicated to the right of Fig. 97. The needle and one fixed conductor are connected to the same potential with respect to the other fixed conductor. Then the applied voltage can be either direct or alternating, since the vane is turned in the same direction. The deflection is approximately proportional to the square of the applied voltage. The well-known Compton electrometer differs from the Dolezalek type inasmuch as the floating needle is slightly tilted along its axis and one quadrant is moved somewhat above or below the plane of the three other quadrants. A much greater sensitivity is then obtained. Since for the measurement of alternating voltages the idiostatic connection is used, a variable condenser-shaped electrometer can be used. It is then known as the Kelvin multicell electrometer. The needle consists of several thin figure-eight-shaped aluminum plates which float between two sets of fixed plates. One set of the fixed plates and the floating system are connected to one voltage terminal, while the other set of fixed plates leads to the other voltage terminal. This instrument measures from about twenty-five up to several thousand volts. However, the large period of oscillation and its effective capacitance is a drawback in high-frequency work. It is then customary to use a B. Szilard[1] electrometer. The movable system consists of a thin but stiff needle and a wire of circular shape which can turn into a quadrant. The effective capacitance is then as low as 3 $\mu\mu$f, while with instruments of the above types it may be as high as 100 $\mu\mu$f. Another suitable type of high-frequency electrometer is the string electrometer of C. W. Lutz[2] (Fig. 98). A Wollastan wire about 0.001 to 0.002 mm in diameter and about 5 cm in length is stretched

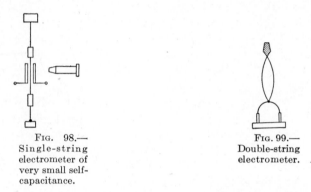

Fig. 98.—
Single-string
electrometer of
very small self-
capacitance.

Fig. 99.—
Double-string
electrometer.

vertically. On each side of the thin string are electrodes whose sidewise relative position is adjustable. The idiostatic connection is used again and the deflection curvature of the stretched string is observed by means of a microscope and ocular micrometer. The self-capacitance is again as low as 2 $\mu\mu$f. The double[3]-string electrometer in Fig. 99 consists of two platinized quartz filaments connected at the lower end to an elastic arc-shaped quartz mounting. If the two filaments are charged to the same potential, they will spread as indicated. The spread is read by means of an ocular scale. Although the sensitivity of the Lutz galvanometer for a proper tension of the string can be so adjusted that steady voltages from 0.001 volt to about 100 volts can be measured, this is not true for high-frequency voltages, since the square law prevails and no auxiliary direct voltages for increasing the sensitivity can be of use for alternating voltages. But high-frequency voltages from a few volts to about one hundred volts can be readily measured. This is also the case for the Wulf electrometer.

[1] *Physik. Z.*, **15**, 209, 1914.

[2] *Physik. Z.*, **13**, 924, 1912.

[3] WULF, T., *Physik. Z.*, **15**, 250, 1914; W. F. G. SWANN, *J. Am. Optical Soc.*, **11,** 375, 1925.

In order to increase the voltage range to still higher values, suitable air condensers in series with the electrometer can be used or the electrostatic voltage divider described on page 128 can be employed.

The calibration of such high-frequency electrometers can be done with steady voltages taken from a direct-current source. However, it should be remembered that the instrument when acted upon by alternating voltages measures the arithmetic-mean value and not the peak or the effective value. Therefore, if the form factor of the voltage is known, the effective value can be computed by multiplying the measured value by the form factor. For sinusoidal voltages the reading is multiplied by 1.565 to obtain the peak value, since this is the product of the form factor 1.11 and peak factor 1.41.

62. Notes on Spark-gap Voltmeters.—Very high peak voltages may also be determined by the sphere-gap voltmeter. The spheres between which the spark takes place should be polished to prevent premature ionization and producing a breakdown at somewhat lower voltages. Although the spark-gap voltmeter for a known peak factor (for instance, for sinusoidal voltages) can be calibrated in effective values, it seems more accurate to work with peak values for high-frequency work. The sparking distance is adjusted so that a spark can just not exist and the voltage corresponding to the spacing is taken from a calibration chart. It is best never to work with a spacing l between the spheres which is larger than about three times the diameter D of the sphere. The size of the spheres for still higher voltages is then chosen larger. Glow discharges must be prevented, and the lead-in wires should never have a diameter larger than about $0.2D$. The spark gap should be built up symmetrically. A sphere spark-gap voltmeter has the advantage over the spark-gap voltmeters with electrodes of other shapes because the breakdown voltage changes but little up to 25 kc/sec. For frequencies as high as 100 kc/sec, the calibrations taken at commercial power frequencies are about 10 per cent too high. Therefore it is customary to use the low-frequency calibration only as a rough guide. For a symmetrical sphere-gap voltmeter of sparking distance l and sphere diameter D both in centimeters, the peak value in kilovolts can be computed approximately from

$$E = \sqrt{2}\,\varepsilon\frac{l}{m} \tag{6}$$

where ε is in kilovolts per centimeter and given by

$$\varepsilon = 19.3\rho\left[1 + \frac{0.76}{\sqrt{pD}}\right] \tag{6a}$$

for the relative air density

$$\rho = \frac{3.92p}{T} \tag{6b}$$

if p is the atmospheric pressure in centimeters of the mercury column and T the absolute temperature in Kelvin degrees ($273 +$ centigrade). The quantity m in (6) is given by

$$m = 0.25\left[\frac{2l}{D} + 1 + \sqrt{\left[\frac{2l}{D} + 1\right]^2 + 8}\right] \qquad (6c)$$

Therefore it can be seen that for a constant room temperature a linear law exists between the atmospheric pressure p and the relative air density. Table III gives a low-frequency calibration for the peak values of a spark gap which may be used as a rough guide.

TABLE III

Length of spark, centimeter	Peak voltage, volts	
	For $D = 1$ cm	2 cm
0.02	1,560	1,530
0.04	2,460	2,430
0.06	3,300	3,240
0.08	4,050	3,990
0.1	4,800	4,800
0.2	8,400	8,400
0.3	11,400	11,400
0.4	14,400	14,400
0.5	17,100	17,100
0.6	19,500	19,800
0.7	21,600	22,500
1.0	23,400	24,900
1.1	24,600	27,300
1.2	25,500	29,100

63. The Corona[1] Voltmeter.—This method employs a perforated cylindrical electrode which is surrounded by a somewhat larger cylindrical electrode and well insulated from it, while a test wire whose corona voltage is to be measured lies along the axis. The perforated electrode is connected to ground and to the positive terminal of a battery (about 100 volts), while the negative pole of the direct-current source is connected through a sensitive galvanometer to the external cylinder. The galvanometer is in multiple with a resistance and uses a series resistance besides. If a sufficiently high voltage is applied between the axial test wire and the ground, a certain conductivity will set in between the cylindrical electrodes to start ionization in air. It is more convenient to

---

[1] WHITEHEAD, J. B., and N. INOUYE, *J. Am. Inst. Elec. Eng.*, **41**, 1, 1922; a more detailed description, J. B. Whitehead and T. Isshiki, *J. Am. Inst. Elec. Eng.*, **39**, May, 1920; in 1904 (*Am. Inst. Elec. Eng.*, **101**) H. J. Ryan indicated the possibility of using corona for measuring high voltages.

connect the *positive* pole on the external cylinder, since at the beginning of the corona discharge ionization takes place because of the motion of the electrons and because the corona discharge gives a peaked-shape wave form with more pronounced positive half waves. Since the galvanometer indicates the differential effect of the corona-discharge waves, it is evident that a rectification of the discharge gives more pronounced deflections. A two-element electron tube is then connected in the galvanometer branch so that the anode of the rectifier is connected with the external cylinder. The indications become still more pronounced if a three-element tube is used so that the grid connects to the external cylinder and the filament connects the corona circuit to ground. The indicator is then in the plate branch of the tube. The corona voltmeter can be used to determine voltages, since the corona discharge sets in at a well-defined voltage which changes with the air pressure. If $\mathcal{E}$ denotes the voltage gradient in kilovolts per centimeters, at the surface of the axial wire of radius r in centimeters, and ρ the relative air density defined by Eq. (6b), a linear relation

$$\frac{\mathcal{E}}{\rho} = k_1 + \frac{k_2}{\sqrt{r\,\rho}} \tag{7}$$

exists between $\mathcal{E}/\rho$ and $1/\sqrt{r\rho}$. This law holds for commercial power frequencies and an empirical law for high-frequency voltages is still an open problem. Nevertheless, it appears as if for a short axial wire (short compared to the wave length) only the constants k_1 and k_2 are different in the high-frequency range.

64. The Glow-discharge Voltmeter.—A suitable glow-discharge tube (Fig. 100) is connected across a potentiometer and the traveling contact

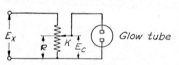

Glow tube

Fig. 100.—Glow-discharge-tube voltmeter.

K varied until the glow discharge just sets in. This happens when the peak value of the voltage across R is just equal to the upper critical voltage (flash voltage) E_c of the tube. A condenser potentiometer can also be used for which a fixed known capacitance is in series with a variable-air condenser which is shunted by the glow-discharge tube. The setting of the variable condenser is then decreased until the discharge just begins. If an ordinary high-frequency voltmeter measuring the effective voltage E is also connected in multiple with the glow-discharge tube, the ratio E_c/E gives the peak factor of the voltage wave. A. Palm[1] has developed such a device which can be used up to 1 Mc/sec, and for peak voltages up to about 15 kv. The self-capacitance of the tube has an average value of about 15 $\mu\mu$f. It is then advantageous to use a low pressure of neon or helium gas which will bring it close to the optimum of the voltage-pressure curve, because then the

[1] *Z. tech. Physik*, **4**, 233 and 258, 1923.

temperature effect will become small. If the shapes of the electrodes are properly chosen, the frequency factor also becomes small.

65. The Cathode-ray Tube as a Voltmeter.—The cathode-ray tube described in Chap. II forms a very convenient means for measuring peak voltages up to very high values. For low voltages a hot-cathode-ray tube with a comparatively small accelerating voltage (300 to 500 volts on the anode) is used to obtain a beam which is not too stiff and having a very high voltage sensitivity. One deflection condenser is used to measure the peak value by means of the half of the length of the linear trace of the fluorescent spot. A voltage sensitivity of about 1 volt/mm deflection is possible. For very high voltages either the deflection condenser is connected in series with several condensers in order to have an electrostatic volt divider or an external deflection condenser is used in connection with the voltage divider. The voltage sensitivity of the tube is then cut down by increasing the gap of the external deflection condenser and by using a stiffer beam. With this method it is essential that only the electric field of the deflection condenser be effective in producing the deflection of the fluorescent spot. Careful shielding is also necessary. Since the capacitance of the *external* deflection condenser can be made very small and the leakance negligible, this type of peak voltmeter practically does the work of a true electrostatic device.

66. Notes on Tube Voltmeters.—Fundamentally most tube voltmeters respond to positive peak voltages, since there is always an effect on the plate current as long as some instantaneous value of the applied variable voltage to be detected is positive. Hence, when an ordinary two-element thermionic tube is used and an unknown voltage is applied between the plate and hot cathode, space current will flow whenever the plate goes positive.[1] To annul the plate current, it is necessary to apply such a steady negative potential to the plate that its magnitude is equal to the positive peak value of the variable voltage to be measured. This is followed up in more detail in the next section. Where the voltage to be measured has a simple known wave shape, the effective value can be found by the peak factor. Thus, for a sinusoidal voltage, the direct-current potential which just compensates the plate current is divided by 1.41 in order to obtain the effective value of the test voltage. The two-element tube can also be used without an auxiliary steady voltage, since the plate current produced by the test voltage is a measure for it. The tube then acts as a rectifier and sinusoidal test voltages can be calibrated directly in effective volts. Although this direct-reading (by means of a calibration curve) tube voltmeter has the advantage of

---

[1] This assumes that the initial velocity of the electrons is zero which is not quite true, since a small current will flow even with an equipotential cathode connected directly to the plate without a B source. This small current due to electron pressure, however, can be balanced out.

simplicity, it cannot be used to measure voltages on systems which have a high internal impedance compared to that of the tube voltmeter or for voltages on open circuits since the current which produces the indication is taken from the test circuit. But for many purposes the rectifier type of two-element tube voltmeter has advantages, since its range can be greatly increased by inserting suitable resistances in series with the tube. The two-element peak voltmeter with the auxiliary steady voltage to compensate the plate current, of course, also has a very wide voltage range, without the need of a more sensitive plate indicator as required for the higher voltage range of the rectifier type with a high series resistance. However, the peak voltmeter also has its drawbacks. The auxiliary voltage must be carefully adjusted at a region of the tube characteristic when it gradually approaches its zero value. Hence, the peak voltmeter cannot be of much use for the determination of small peak voltages. But this can be partially remedied by using a three-element tube utilizing the amplification factor of a tube. It is then known as the "slide-back voltmeter" because the test voltage is connected in series to a direct voltage taken from a potentiometer and the series combination connected across the grid and filament of the voltmeter. As with the two-element tube, the potentiometer slider is moved to negative voltages until the plate current *just* disappears. Hence, like the two-element peak voltmeter no current is drawn from the test circuit. Like the two-element tube, the three-element tube with a grid can also be used with a calibration curve to read the effective values of sinusoidal voltages directly by noting the change in the plate current when a test voltage is applied. So that no grid current will be taken, that is, current from the test circuit delivering the voltage to be measured, the grid circuit uses a fixed negative bias for which there is no grid current. The three-element tube then acts as a detector and is known as the "Moullin[1] tube voltmeter." As shown in Sec. 69 these voltmeters can be operated either by the plate-current grid-potential curvature or by the curvature of the grid-current grid-potential characteristic, since in each case the three-element tube gives rectification action without absorbing power from the test circuit and possesses a comparatively small input capacitance. When only the changes in the plate current are indicated by a meter, the sensitivity of the voltmeter can be greatly increased for a constant curvature $\partial^2 i_p / \partial^2 e_g$, but only to a limit which is determined by the Maxwellian velocity distribution. Therefore it is customary to choose a plate potential so that the change in the average plate current for a given test voltage gives a maximum ratio to the current produced by the plate battery. For plate rectification (employing

[1] MOULLIN, E. B., and L. B. TURNER, *J. Inst. Elec. Eng.* (*London*), **60**, 706, 1922. E. B. MOULLIN, *J. Inst. Elec. Eng.* (*London*), **61**, 295, 1923; *Wireless World*, **10**, 1, 1922; H. G. MOELLER, *Z. Femmeldetechnik*, **5**, 96, 1924.

plate-current grid-voltage characteristic) this maximum condition usually occurs when no B battery at all is used, that is, when the plate is connected through the indicator to the positive end of the filament. This is also borne out in experiments with the Hohage[1] voltmeter which likewise uses the curvature of the plate-current plate-potential characteristic.

The tube voltmeters which measure the peak voltage with the slideback method do not depend upon the shape of the work characteristic, since at the time of reading the plate current just disappears and the effect of the auxiliary voltage just balances the peak value. However, all tube parameters play a part where direct-reading tube voltmeters (with calibration curve) using the rectification action of the tube are concerned. Although in the case of the determination of sinusoidal voltages, the alternating-voltage calibration always holds, it may be of interest to see what happens in the case of distorted voltage waves with such voltmeters.

Suppose a tube voltmeter with a grid working on the lower curvature of the grid-voltage plate-current work characteristic is used. When a distorted voltage e_g is impressed, for a negative grid bias E_c the effective grid to filament voltage is of the form

$$E_g = E_c + \underbrace{E_1 \sin \theta + E_2 \sin 2\theta + \cdots E_m \sin m\theta}_{e_g}$$

where $\theta = \omega t$ and E_c such that no grid current flows. Since, according to the rectification law, only the average value of the change i_p in the plate current I_p due to e_g is of primary interest, for an external load resistance R and the abbreviation $\rho = \mu e_g - i_p R$, the characteristic *work equation* is

$$i_p = \rho \frac{\partial I_p}{\partial E} + \frac{\rho^2}{2} \frac{\partial^2 I}{\partial E^2} + \frac{\rho^3}{6} \frac{\partial^3 I_p}{\partial E^3} + \frac{\rho^4}{24} \frac{\partial^4 I_p}{\partial E^4} + \cdots \tag{8}$$

for the function

$$F(E) = I_p = F[\underbrace{E_b - I_p R + \mu E_g}_{\text{available plate voltage}}]$$

if E_b denotes the voltage of the plate supply and the small effect due to the initial velocity of the electrons is ignored. This effect would require a small term added under the function sign F to the right. Equation (8) is to be evaluated to find what a tube voltmeter of the detector type actually measures. When ρ is small, Eq. (8) simplifies to a straight-line law, since only the well-known linear amplifier relation

$$i_p = \rho \frac{\partial I_p}{\partial E} = \frac{\mu e_g - i_p R}{r_p}$$

[1] HOHAGE, K., "Technische Mitteilungen der Versuchstkompagnie Tafern," No. 2, p. 21, 1917; *Helios*, **25**, 193, 201, 1919; K. HOEPFNER, *F.F.T.*, 4 Sonderh., p. 128, 1919.

remains. This does not apply to this case, since this is a curvature of the work characteristic. Therefore at least the terms of Eq. (8) up to the second derivative must be taken into account. Doing this for a sinusoidal test voltage $e_g = E_1 \sin \theta$ and a milliammeter of negligible load resistance R in the plate branch gives

$$\rho = \frac{\mu}{r_p} e_g = g_m e_g$$

and the corresponding variation

$$i_p = g_m e_g \frac{\partial I_p}{\partial E} + \frac{g_m{}^2 e_g{}^2}{2} \frac{\partial^2 I_p}{\partial E^2}$$

in the plate current I_p (Fig. 101). Since the plate meter indicates only direct currents, the change in the direct current must be produced by the average value i_{av} of i_p, that is, by

$$i_{av} = \frac{g_m E_1}{2\pi} \frac{\partial I_p}{\partial E} \int_0^{2\pi} \sin \theta d\theta + \frac{g_m{}^2 E_1{}^2}{4\pi} \frac{\partial^2 I_p}{\partial E^2} \int_0^{2\pi} \sin^2 \theta d\theta$$

$$= 0 + \frac{g_m{}^2 E_1{}^2}{4} \frac{\partial^2 I_p}{\partial E^2} = A E_1{}^2 \quad (9)$$

since for a given operating region the curvature $\partial^2 I_p/\partial E^2$ may be taken constant and A may also be taken as a factor of proportionality. That

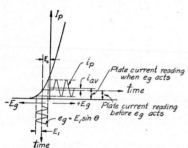

such an assumption is justified with a properly designed tube voltmeter of this type can be seen from the work characteristic shown in Fig. 87 where the square law holds over the straight-line portion of the E_c, $\sqrt{I_p}$ characteristic extending over a grid-voltage range as much as 20 volts, half of which corresponds to the maximum grid swing of a sinusoidal test voltage. This experimental curve confirms the theoretical result of Eq. (9) which states that the increase of current indicated by the plate meter is directly proportional to the square of the amplitude E_1 of the sinusoidal test voltage. The same result for the rectification effect i_{av} is also given by the rectification law. For a distorted test voltage

Fig. 101.—Showing why the plate-current reading changes by an amount i_{av}.

$$e_g = E_1 \sin \theta + E_2 \sin 2\theta + E_3 \sin 3\theta + \cdots E_m \sin m\theta$$

the increase in the plate-current reading when e_g acts is

$$i_{av} = \frac{g_m{}^2}{4} [E_1{}^2 + E_2{}^2 + E_3{}^2 + \cdots E_m{}^2] \frac{\partial^2 I_p}{\partial E^2}$$

$$= A[E_1{}^2 + E_2{}^2 + E_3{}^2 + \cdots E_m{}^2] \quad (10)$$

if it is again assumed that the derivatives $\partial^3 I_p/\partial E^3$, $\partial^4 I_p/\partial E^4$, etc., are negligibly small compared to the curvature $\partial^2 I_p/\partial E^2$ of the lumped tube characteristic which for a plate meter of negligible resistance is practically the same as the curvature $\partial^2 I_p / \partial E_g^2$ of the operating portion of the plate-current grid-voltage characteristic. It is known from ordinary alternating-current theory that the harmonic voltages act in quadrature to each other since they are of different frequency. Therefore if E_I, E_II, etc., denote the corresponding effective values which are obtained by dividing the peak values E_1, E_2, etc., by $\sqrt{2}$,

$$i_\text{av} = 2A[E_\text{I}^2 + E_\text{II}^2 + E_\text{III}^2 + \cdots] \tag{10a}$$

where $\sqrt{E_\text{I}^2 + E_\text{II}^2 + E_\text{III}^2}$ denotes the resultant voltage. Hence, with the above assumptions which are readily satisfied (for instance, by experimental characteristic in Fig. 87) a detector-type tube voltmeter with a calibration curve for the effective current values will also give the correct readings for the resultant effective value of a distorted test voltage. A more detailed analysis gives

$$E_g = E_c + \underbrace{E_1 \sin\theta + E_2 \sin 2\theta}_{e_g}$$

and the fluctuating plate current

$$
\begin{aligned}
I_p = F(E_g) = {}& F(E_c) + F''(E_c)\frac{E_1^2 + E_2^2}{4} \\
& + F'(E_c)[E_1 \sin\theta + E_2 \sin 2\theta] \\
& + F''(E_c)\frac{E_1^2 \cos 2\theta + E_2^2 \cos 4\theta}{4} \\
& + F''(E_c)E_1 E_2 \sin\theta \sin 2\theta \\
& + \text{terms due to higher derivatives}
\end{aligned}
\tag{11}
$$

where F', F'' stand for the first and the second derivatives. The plate current I_av indicated by the plate meter is therefore

$$I_\text{av} = \underbrace{F(E_c)}_{\substack{\text{when variable} \\ \text{does not act}}} + \underbrace{F''(E_c)\frac{E_1^2 + E_2^2}{4}}_{\substack{\text{increase } i_\text{av} \text{ of plate current} \\ \text{due to } e_g}} \tag{12}$$

which is superimposed by two currents of single and double frequency as the grid components as well as two currents of twice the frequencies of the two components of e_g. The last term evaluated in (11) yields the product of $\sin\theta$ and $\sin 2\theta$, that is, gives a modulated current because its amplitude $F''(E_c)E_1 E_2 \sin\theta$ waxes and wanes in synchronism with the double frequency. This current can then be decomposed as in

$$F''(E_c)E_1 E_2 \sin\theta \cos\theta = -F''(E_c)\frac{E_1 E_2}{2}[\cos(2\theta + \theta) - \cos(2\theta - \theta)]$$

$$= -F''(E_c)\frac{E_1 E_2}{2}[\cos 3\theta - \cos\theta] \tag{13}$$

where $\theta/\pi t$ may be imagined as the carrier frequency and $\theta/2\pi t$ as the frequency of the modulation component. The degree of modulation depends on the curvature $F''(E_c)$ of the static characteristic and has nothing to do with the indication of the direct-current meter in the plate circuit unless the mechanical or electrical system of the plate meter goes in resonance which can be avoided by using a large by-pass condenser across the meter. From this analysis it can also be seen that for no curvature, that is, a linear portion of the work characteristic, neither rectification nor modulation is possible. The first part is of interest here because under such conditions the plate meter could not detect test voltages.

If the Taylor's series in Eq. (11) were extended to the third and fourth derivatives, the change i_{av} noted in the direct-current meter of the plate circuit would not respond to the actual effective value of an impressed voltage.

67. Tube Voltmeters for Measuring Peak Voltages.—Such voltmeters make use of the fact that the thermionic plate current in an electron tube due to a variable accelerating voltage can be made zero by applying a suitable negative potential to the system in order to balance

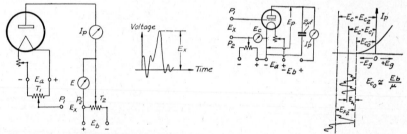

FIG. 102.—Peak voltmeter using a two-element tube.

FIG. 103.—Peak voltmeter using a three-element tube.

out the peak value of the variable accelerating voltage. Figure 102 gives the case of an ordinary two-element tube which can also be a three-element tube with the grid and plate connected together. P_1P_2 denotes the input terminals which can be bridged with a suitable resistance or coil to give a closed circuit (according to the measurement to be carried out). The tap T_1 of the potentiometer across the filament battery for the tap T_2 connected to the positive terminal of the B battery and P_1P_2 short-circuited is moved until the direct-current meter in the plate branch *just* does not indicate a plate current I_p. The test voltage is applied to the P_1P_2 terminals and T_2 moved to the right until the plate current I_p again *just* disappears. The indicated steady voltage E is then equal to the peak value. The voltage range of this meter is large as long as a direct-current source of a voltage at least as high as the peak voltage E_x to be measured is available. Tube voltmeters of this type and that indicated in Fig. 103 are perhaps the earliest applications of tubes to measurements because such circuits were used in some laboratories as far back as 1913. For the three-element tube of Fig. 103, an adjustable negative grid bias E_c is used to balance out the plate current resulting when a variable voltage of positive peak value E_x is applied between the grid and the filament. The measurement is as follows: For terminals $P_1 P_2$ connected together and no test voltage E_x acting, the slider along the grid potentiometer is moved to the left until the plate current *just* disappears for a setting $E_c = E_{c_0}$. When $E_x = E_{x_1}$ is applied, the plate meter registers again. The slider of the grid bias is then moved still further to the left until the plate current again *just* disappears corresponding to the indicated setting $E_c = E_{c_1}$. The difference $E_{c_1} - E_{c_0}$ then measures directly the positive peak voltage. For still larger positive peak voltages E_{x_2}, a much larger negative bias E_{c_2} is required to compensate the effect of the most positive peak voltage. The peak voltage is therefore determined by an ordinary voltmeter working on direct current. Since the resistance of the plate meter is negligibly small compared to the tube resistance, the grid bias E_{c_0} is practically equal to the voltage of the B battery divided by the amplification factor of the tube.

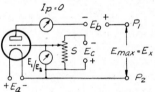

The circuits just described have the disadvantage that high-biasing batteries are required in order to balance out any plate currents if high peak voltages are to be measured. The scheme in Fig. 104 overcomes this difficulty, because the amplification factor μ of the tube is utilized to multiply the effect

Fig. 104.—Three-element-tube voltmeter for the determination of high peak voltages (uses a tube of a high amplification factor μ).

of the balancing bias, since the unknown peak voltage E_x acts in the *plate* circuit. The measuring process is then as follows: (1) The grid slider S for short-circuited input terminals P_1P_2 is moved to a position until I_p *just* disappears. This gives the reading E_1 on the voltmeter operating on direct current, and satisfies the expression

$$I_p = k[E_b + \mu E_1 + m]^q = 0$$

for the plate current of the tube anywhere on the useful portion of the work characteristic, if m denotes the contribution due to the initial velocity of the electrons, and q depends on the shape of the work portion. It need not be known here. (2) The test voltage of peak value E_x is applied across P_1P_2, so that a closed plate circuit is formed and the grid slider again moved until the plate meter *just* registers $I_p = 0$. This happens for a setting E_2 of the voltmeter giving the expression

$$[E_b + E_x + \mu E_2 + m]^q = 0$$

From these two equations

$$E_x = \mu[E_1 - E_2] = \frac{E_b}{E_1}[E_2 - E_1] = E_b\left[\frac{E_2}{E_1}\right] - 1 \tag{14}$$

This method can be still further extended in voltage range by applying the unknown large peak voltage E_x across a potentiometer and applying only a portion e_x toward the plate.

Figure 105 shows a scheme due to L. W. Chubb and C. L. Fortescue[1] where the peak voltage can be measured by the rectification of a condenser current. This method is applicable only in cases where the wave shape of the positive peak value does not differ from the negative peak value and there is not more than one peak in each half cycle. The method can therefore be used in cases where because of saturation limitation or some other causes either peaked or somewhat flattened half waves are produced. In this method two two-element thermionic tubes T_1 and T_2 are connected in multiple but so that one of them carries the positive and the other the negative portion of the current. A direct-current meter which is of the galvanometer type measures the rectified current flowing to either of the tubes. The switch can be closed to either terminal of the indicator which is of the microampere order. If a capacitance C is so chosen that the plate impedance of each tube is small compared to $1/(\omega C)$, then one has for the instantaneous values of condenser voltage and current $i = C\,de/dt$, and for one complete period $(1/f$ sec) the total charge passing through each rectifier is $\int i\,dt = C\int de$. The integration must be carried out over that portion of the cycle for which de/dt is positive for one tube and negative for the other tube. Hence, when a sinusoidal test voltage $E \sin \omega t$ is impressed, each rectifier carries per cycle the charge

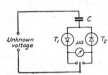

Fig. 105.—Determination of the peak voltage by means of two rectifiers T_1 and T_2.

$$\omega C E \int_{\frac{3}{4f}}^{\frac{1}{4f}} \cos 2\pi ft\,dt = 2CE$$

and, for f cycles/sec, the average current is $2fCE$. The indication of the microammeter is therefore proportional to the peak value of the impressed sinusoidal test voltage. The above derivation assumes that each rectifier passes currents only when the applied plate potential is positive. Because of the electron pressure a small current flows also against negative plate voltages down to about -1.5 volts. Hence each tube rectifier will pass a quantity of charge greater than that passed by C. This can be avoided by using the compensating connection for which the plate returns of the tubes are connected to about -1.5 volts below the negative end of the filament. This scheme like all rectifier methods consumes a certain amount of current from the branch across which the voltage is to be meas-

[1] *Trans. A.I.E.E.*, **32**, 739, 1913; a detailed discussion on the same subject R. Davis, G. W. Bowdler, and W. G. Standring, *J. Inst. Elec. Eng.* (*London*), **68**, 1222, 1930.

ured, and for this reason a proper slide-back method as in Fig. 104 is preferable. A three-element tube can also be used and in such a way that the plate is returned to the filament without a B battery, and the average grid current is noted by a microammeter. Next to the grid is a grid condenser C of large value in multiple with a high resistance R (to 2 megohms). The test voltage is connected to the other terminal of the grid condenser and to the filament. The average value of the rectified grid current flowing through R will charge C to some average value depending on the maximum value of the applied sinusoidal test voltage. This charge will act exactly as though a negative grid bias were applied. The grid current noted with the microammeter multiplied by R gives the average grid potential and is approximately equal to the maximum value of the applied test voltage. When a higher test voltage is applied, more average current will flow through R and a more negative bias is produced. The peak value is again found from the grid current reading and the value of R.

68. The Rectifier Type of Tube Voltmeter.—Any type of rectifier can be used to measure voltages. In the earlier days of radio, ordinary crystal rectifiers were used to compare small voltages. With the advent of the electron tube, it was more convenient to use such devices for the rectification because they have a high internal impedance which is practically resistive for quite a high frequency range. Figure 106 shows a convenient rectifier voltmeter for work where great accuracy is not of primary importance, but a large voltmeter range is required. For a sinusoidal test voltage, the deflection d of the microammeter μa is practically proportional to the average value of the applied test voltage, since for an effective circuit resistance R (practically equal to $R_1 + r_p$)

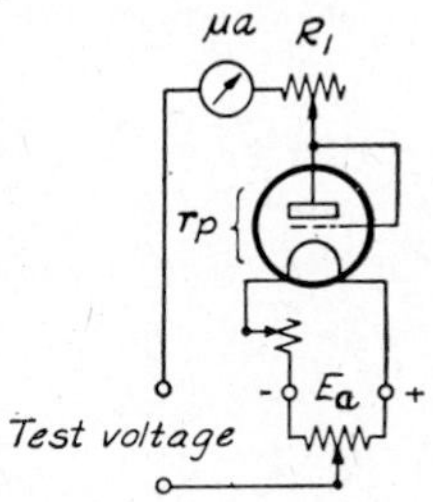

Fig. 106.—Two-element-tube voltmeter.

$$d = kI = k\frac{E_{av}}{2R} = KE_{av} \tag{15}$$

since only every other half wave of the test voltage produces a current flow. Since the effective value E of the test voltage is equal to the form factor k_1 times the average value E_{av}, the deflection d must also be proportional to the effective value; that is,

$$d = K_1E_e \tag{16}$$

where $K_1 = K/k_1$. The deflections of the microammeter can therefore be expressed in effective values of the impressed test voltage. For sinusoidal voltages $k_1 = \pi/(2\sqrt{2}) = 1.11$.

The calibration of this instrument can be carried on with a known sinusoidal voltage or with voltages taken from a direct-current source.

If the latter is done and E denotes the direct voltage, it must produce
a deflection

$$d = \frac{kE}{R} \tag{17}$$

Suppose the microammeter has a scale with 100 equally spaced divisions
and that the full-scale deflection 100 for a certain R_1 setting is produced
by $E = 50$ volts. The effective alternating voltage which also produces
the full-scale deflection, according to (16), is equal to $K_1 E_e$ and, by equating the right sides of (16) and (17) and using (15),

$$E_e = 2k_1 E = 111 \text{ volts}$$

Hence if an effective alternating-voltage scale is required, the setting of
R_1, for a direct voltage $E = 111{:}2 = 55$ volts, is varied until full-scale
deflection is again obtained. The deflection 100 then gives the effective
voltage $E_e = 100$ volts for the sinusoidal e.m.f. calibration. All other
divisions of the scale are proportional with the scale, since a linear law
exists according to (16). This is an inherent advantage of this meter.
To obtain an idea of the useful range of the meter, a practical illustration
is added. When a 199 type tube or its equivalent is used with a Weston
portable table galvanometer of 200-μa full-scale deflection, the effective
voltage range for $R_1 = 0$ is from 0.4 to 3 volts; for $R_1 = 20,000\,\Omega$, a
range of from 0.8 to 12 volts; for $R_1 = 70,000\,\Omega$, a range from 2.3 to 35
volts; for $R_1 = 170,000\,\Omega$, a range from 5.6 to 84 volts; for $R_1 = 670,000\,\Omega$,
a range from 22 to 300 volts; and for $R_1 = 1,170,000\,\Omega$, a range from 36
to 470 volts. A meter of this type with a high resistance R_1 in series

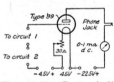

will not draw much current when working with small
deflections only and can be readily used as a
resonance indicator and for observing zero-beat condition as the frequencies of the two currents are
brought to the same value. The pointer of the
meter from about 25 cycles on downward will start
to vibrate with the beat frequency until for a 1-cycle

Fig. 107.—Beat indi-
cator.

beat, a very slow to and fro motion is observed. At zero beat, the pointer
will again stand still. Automatic synchronization is apt to take place
and care must be taken to have a very loose coupling and a true resonance
setting. For such work the current taken by the indicating system
should not be appreciable. This can be done by working with the
three-element detector of Fig. 107. The entire circuit can work on dry
cells containing the sources in the box which holds the meter. The
meter is for observing as above the slow-beat effects while the phone
jack can be used to note the approach of a beat note.

69. The Detector Type of Tube Voltmeter.—The commercial types of
Moullin[1] meters belong to this class and those due to K. Hohage.[1]   Grid

[1] *Loc. cit.*

rectification or plate rectification can be used. In some cases both can happen which is, however, not a desirable feature, since then the calibration curve may become multivalued. Fortunately, this happens, if at all, only for the lower end of the voltage scale near zero. This portion should not be used for any instrument of this type. Tube voltmeters of this type can be made direct reading and the sensitivity greatly increased by using the indicator so that only the change in the plate current produces the deflection. Such meters then work by means of rectification effects without drawing appreciable current from the source whose voltage is to be measured, and sensitive direct-current meters can be used as indicators.

Figure 108 gives the simplest kind of direct-reading Moullin voltmeter which works along the curvature of the grid-potential plate-current characteristic. The plate and grid voltages are obtained from the voltage drop along the filament and the drop along the filament rheostat. The only source needed is a 6-volt filament battery. The 1-μf condenser serves to by-pass the alternating-current component of the plate current. The meter is calibrated in effective volts, and for customary receiving tubes the range is approximately from 0.25 to 1.5 volts. A calibrated meter of this type is used as follows: The terminals for the test voltage E_x are at first short-circuited

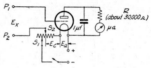

Fig. 108.—Tube voltmeter for range from about 0.25 to 1.5 volts.

and the filament slider S_1 moved until the sensitive direct-current meter just reads zero. In some cases it seems convenient to use an arbitrary zero for which there is a small current flow because such a point can be more easily established at the beginning of the measurement. The test voltage E_x is then applied to terminals P_1P_2 and in such a way that a conducting path exists between these terminals, and the plate meter gives the effective value of E_x directly or by means of a curve. The calibration is as follows: The filament switch is closed and the filament slider moved until normal filament current flows. This requires the insertion of a filament meter. The filament meter is then removed and the grid bias slider S_2 moved until the microammeter μa just reads absolute or arbitrary zero. This is done with the P_1P_2 terminals short-circuited. The setting of S_2 can be fastened permanently. A resistance of about $r = 10\,\Omega$ is connected across the P_1P_2 terminals and a sinusoidal current I passed through it. A thermoelectric current indicator measures I and, by varying I or by varying r, different effective voltages rI are applied to the tube and the corresponding deflections in the μa noted. The accuracy is about 2 per cent.

The bridge circuits shown in Fig. 63 can also be used as a direct-indicating tube voltmeter. The circuit to the right is the Hoare type

meter using only one source which can be placed inside the instrument
as in the commercial design of the General Radio Company. A range
from 0 to 3 volts and somewhat higher can be obtained if a B battery
of about 22.5 volts is used in connection with a 199 type tube or its
equivalent. For short-circuited input terminals, the bridge is balanced
by securing a zero deflection on the microammeter. This meter works
up to very high frequencies for direct and alternating voltages. The
upper limit is determined by the input impedance. The frequency
error of the commercial voltmeter is about 2 per cent for full-scale deflection at 20 kc/sec and about 3 per cent at frequencies as high as 300 kc/sec.
For very accurate work, the meter is therefore not dependable enough

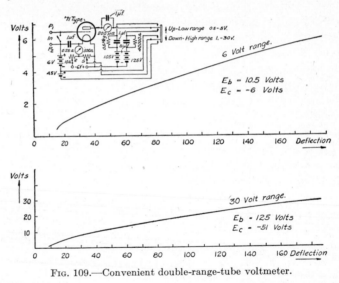

Fig. 109.—Convenient double-range-tube voltmeter.

for frequencies as high as met in the upper broadcast range but it should
prove satisfactory for most of the work even in this range when only
deflections are concerned as in the case of field-intensity measurements
and certain receiver tests, where one and the same deflection is used for
the standard and signal voltage. The second-harmonic error of this
meter can be almost eliminated by reversing the leads to the voltmeter
and averaging the readings obtained.

Figure 109 shows a tube voltmeter for measuring effective voltages.
A 171 tube or its equivalent is used and a double range provided. The
larger range from 1 to 30 effective volts has the switch in such a position
that 125 volts are applied to the plate and (45 + 6) volts act as negative
grid bias. For the lower range, 0.5 to 6 volts, 10.5 volts act as B battery
and 6 volts as negative grid bias. This is a most useful voltmeter.
Before using the meter, the input terminals P_1P_2 are short-circuited
the filament resistance R varied until 0.25 A is read and the arbitrary

zero deflection of the 200-μa meter set by means of the slider S of the filament potentiometer. Figure 110 shows a tube voltmeter described by E. T. Dickey[1] which is especially designed for testing audio-frequency amplifiers. A vacuum tube such as the 171 type with a comparatively low plate resistance and high grid bias is again used to cover a wider voltage range. A very high plate resistance ($2.4 \times 10^6\Omega$ for the 250 B battery supply for the 0- to 70-volt range) and ($0.2 \times 10^6\Omega$ for the 22.5-volt B battery supply for the 0- to 7-volt range) are used in order to obtain an almost linear deflection on the microammeter with respect to the effective value of the impressed voltage E_x. This is basic for this type of voltmeter and its action is the same as for the high plate-resistance amplifier. The range switch is thrown to the right for the $E_x = 0$ to

7-volt range and, for the higher range $E_x = 0$ to 70 volts, to the left. For voltage measurements in amplifiers with no direct current flowing, the grid switch S is connected toward the terminal 1. The grid choke L and grid condenser C are then not used. But, when direct currents also flow over the branch across which the effective value of the alternating voltage is to be measured, the input switch is thrown toward 2. An inductance L is used instead of a grid leak, since any disturbing voltage surges affecting the apparatus will bring the meter to its normal deflection sooner. With the values indicated, the coil L must have the lowest natural period outside the audio-

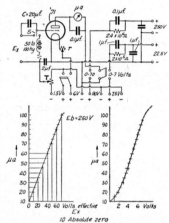

Fig. 110.—Double-range-tube voltmeter.

frequency range for which this tube voltmeter was designed. If the voltmeter is used for measuring voltages across a relatively high resistance R, the dotted resistance with a value of about 20 Ω is used in series with L. The plate current passing through the microammeter is small and the filament current can therefore be made smaller than the rated value. The filament resistance r is varied until only 4.5 volts exists across the filament and the potentiometer tap T is moved until the meter just registers the arbitrary zero setting which is 10 μa in this particular instrument.

Figure 111 shows a tube voltmeter which works along the curvature of the grid-potential grid-current characteristic. Using ordinary receiving tubes, an effective voltage range from about $\frac{1}{2}$ to 10 volts is possible if about $Eb = 90$ volts are used. Since a grid condenser C and grid leak R are used, this meter can be used for measuring alternating voltages in the presence of superimposed steady voltages. The meter is also of service when voltages across open systems (condensers) are to be meas-

[1] *Proc. I.R.E.*, **15**, 687, 1927.

ured. It should be noted, however, that the plate potential must be at least 50 volts or the test voltage to be measured must have a large amplitude in order to produce a change in plate current by means of the curvature of the grid-voltage grid-current characteristic. Therefore, some commercial designs (Siemens and Halske) employ amplification first by means of a space-charge grid tube as in Fig. 112 and use the second tube in shield-grid fashion in connection with grid rectification. The plate supply can then be made as low as 20 volts. Reference is made to Fig. 113 for the action of such voltmeters. The grid condenser acts as

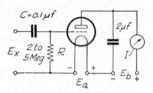

Fig. 111.—Direct-indicating-tube voltmeter which cannot be affected by a superimposed direct voltage.

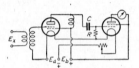

Fig. 112.—Double-grid-tube voltmeter.

a negligible impedance for any high-frequency fluctuations, while the high leak resistance R acts as an agency for the automatic building up of a negative grid bias by means of the rectification effect δI_g. Before E_x is applied, the automatic grid bias is close to zero potential, say at some slightly negative value E_c. But when E_x is applied, similar voltage variations will act on the grid and build up to a sustained variation $e_g = e_0 \sin \theta$ after the gradual increase in negative grid bias has reached

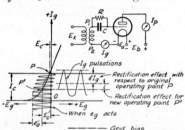

Fig. 113.—Explaining operation (portion of $I_g - E_g$ characteristic for negative values of E_g follows the law $I_g = I_0 \epsilon^{-pE_g}$; I_c grid current when e_g does not act).

the final value E_c'. The increase $E_c' - E_c$ depends on the grid-current characteristic and the value of the leak resistance R. Since the operation occurs along the lower curved portion of the I_g, E_g characterististic, a positive rectification effect i is produced with respect to the new operating point P'. But before E_x is applied, the grid current has a value I_c and it is the change from I_c to the grid-current value when E_x is applied that is of importance. The indicated value δI_g denotes the actual rectification effect in the grid current. This effect could be indicated directly by a sensitive instrument, but in this circuit it is amplified by the corresponding voltage change $R\, \delta I_g$ acting in the grid circuit. This gives the change

$$\delta I_p = g_m R\, \delta I_g \qquad (18)$$

in the plate current I_p if the amplitude of the test voltage E_x is small and the voltage of the B battery sufficient to operate along a linear portion of the grid-voltage plate-current characteristic. The rectification effect in the grid branch is then amplified into the plate branch by direct-current amplification, while for the tube voltmeter, in which the rectification effect is caused by the grid-voltage plate-current curvature, the test voltage is first amplified into the plate branch before its effect is rectified. The sensitivity for grid rectification is greater than for plate rectification. For small test voltages the decrease δI_p in the plate current measured by the direct-current meter is given by Eq. (18). If, for larger test voltages or insufficient B voltage, the change δI_p in the plate current also occurs along the lower bend of the grid-potential plate-current characteristic, there is in addition plate detection (plate-rectification action). The change δI_p noted in the plate-current reading is then

$$\delta I_p = \underbrace{\frac{g_m{}^2 e_0{}^2}{4} \frac{\partial^2 I_p}{\partial E_g{}^2}}_{\substack{\text{due to plate-}\\\text{rectification effect}}} - \underbrace{g_m R \; \delta I_g}_{\substack{\text{due to grid}\\\text{rectification}}} = \delta I_1 - \delta I_2 \qquad (19)$$

The first part, which can be understood from Eq. (19), is proportional to the square of the amplitude e_0 of the impressed grid voltage $e_g = e_0 \sin \theta$ and *increases* the normal plate current, since the lower bend of the I_p, E_g characteristic is operative. The second term, which is normally more effective, produces a *decrease* in the plate current. Hence when both grid-current and plate-current curvature with respect to the grid potential exist, the change in plate current is normally smaller. As the applied test voltage E_x increases for fixed B battery voltage, the first term of Eq. (19) increases rapidly, since it is proportional to the square of the amplitude e_0. For a certain amplitude e_0 there is a condition for which the increase δI_1 just balances the decrease δI_2 and the reading of the indicator in the plate branch is zero again, although a voltage E_x is impressed. For values of e_0 which are still larger, the pointer of the indicator will deflect beyond the arbitrary zero setting (giving negative indications), since the first term of Eq. (19) is more operative. Such a change from grid- into operative-plate rectification is by no means desirable and can be avoided with a properly designed tube voltmeter. Unlike instruments working with plate detection only, the operating grid voltage $R \; \delta I_g$ is unknown for the circuit of Figs. 111, 112, and 113, but it can be computed by the grid-rectification effect δI_g since the leak resistance R is known. The portion of the grid-current grid-voltage characteristic (I_g, E_g in Fig. 113) for which positive grid currents exist for negative grid potentials ($-E_g$ portion in the figure) can be computed. The kinetic energy of the electrons, when leaving the hot cathode without an external accelerating field, is responsible for the passing of some electrons against a small decelerating field of about 1 volt. According to Eq. (92) on page 41, for a pure electron emission of saturation value I_s and for negative cold-electrode potentials E, the space current I passing from the hot emitter toward the cold electrode can be computed from the exponential law.

$$I = I_s \epsilon^{-pE} \tag{20}$$

where $p = 1/(8.6 \times 10^{-5}T)$ and T is the absolute temperature (273 plus degrees centigrade) in Kelvin degrees. For negative grid potentials E_g the grid current becomes

$$I_g = \beta I_s \epsilon^{-pE_g} \tag{21}$$

if according to H. G. Moeller[1] the distribution factor $D = \dfrac{d(I_g/I)}{d(E_g/E_p)}$ is used. The electrons with a temperature velocity v_T can then be treated as though they were to leave the hot cathode of absolute temperature T with *zero* initial velocity, but so that the cathode has the potential $(-E_T) = \dfrac{1m}{2q}v_T^2$. According to (20) the current contribution dI of such electrons is

$$dI = pI_s \epsilon^{+pE_T}dE_T \tag{22}$$

But this electron current distributes itself in the three-element tube of the voltmeter partly toward the grid of potential E_g and toward the plate of potential E_p. The distribution function for small values of E_g/E_p increases linearly. We have

$$\frac{dI_g}{dI} = D\frac{E_g - E_T}{E_p}$$

and the grid current

$$I_g = \int_{-\infty}^{-E_g} \frac{pD[E_g - E_T]}{E_p}I_s \epsilon^{+pE_T}dE_T = \frac{D}{pE_p}I_s \epsilon^{-pE_g} \tag{23}$$

which for $D/pE_p = \beta$ confirms (22). Putting $\beta I_s = \alpha$ for the grid current,

$$I_g = \alpha \epsilon^{-p[E_c-e_g]} \tag{24}$$

where $e_g = e_0 \sin \theta$. The average value of the grid current then becomes

$$I_{av} = \frac{1}{T}\int_0^T I_g dt = \alpha \epsilon^{-pE_c}\frac{1}{2\pi}\int_0^{2\pi} \epsilon^{pe_0 \sin \theta}d\theta \tag{25}$$

The steady grid current without the variable test voltage acting ($e_g = 0$), according to (24), is

$$I_g = \alpha \epsilon^{-pE_c} \tag{26}$$

[1] "Die Elektronenröhren," F. Vieweg and Sohn, Braunschweig, 1929, p. 223; see also K. Strecker, "Hilfsbuch für Elektrotechnik," Schwachstrom ausgabe, J. Springer, Berlin 1928, p. 335.

and the rectification effect in the grid current can be computed from

$$\delta I_g = I_{\mathrm{av}} - I_g = \alpha \epsilon^{-pE_e} \left\{ \frac{1}{2\pi} \int_0^{2\pi} \epsilon^{pe_0 \sin \theta} - 1 \right\}$$

$$= \alpha \epsilon^{-pE_e} \left\{ \frac{1}{2\pi} \int_0^{2\pi} \sum_{m=1}^{m=\infty} (pe_0)^m \sin^m \theta d\theta \right\}$$

$$= \alpha \epsilon^{-pE_e} \left[\frac{p^2 e_0{}^2}{4} + \frac{p^4 e_0{}^4}{64} + \frac{p^6 e_0{}^6}{2304} + \cdots + \frac{(pe_0/2)^{2m}}{(m!)^2} \right] \quad (27)$$

$$= S \, \alpha \epsilon^{-E_e}$$

where S stands for the series in the parenthesis. Both the normal grid current I_g for no test voltage applied and the grid current I_{av}, when the test voltage with its final effect $e_g = e_0 \sin \omega t$ acts, can be measured with a sensitive instrument and their difference δI_g are then given. Eliminating the term $\alpha \epsilon^{-pE_e}$ between (26) and (27), for the ratio of the grid rectification effect to original steady grid current, one obtains the value S. Hence, when the test voltage is removed and the input terminals $P_1 P_2$ are electrically connected, for instance, as in Fig. 113, for a measured grid current I_g the grid-rectification effect is

$$\delta I_g = S \, I_g = \left[\frac{p^2 e_0{}^2}{4} + \frac{p^4 e_0{}^4}{64} + \frac{p^6 e_0{}^6}{2304} + \cdots \right] I_g \quad (28)$$

where, according to (20),

$$p = \frac{1}{8.6 \times 10^{-5} [273 + C^\circ]} \quad (28a)$$

C° being the centigrade temperature of the filament and e_0 the maximum value of the final variable grid voltage when the test voltage is applied. But, since in (18) the quantity $R\delta I_g$ denotes the voltage change produced in the grid branch by the rectification effect, the change δI_p in the plate-meter reading can be computed from

$$\delta I_p = g_m R I_g S \simeq \frac{g_m p^2 R I_g}{4} e_0{}^2 \quad (29)$$

as long as the change δI_p occurs along the straight portion of the I_p, E_g characteristic of steepness g_m. It can be seen that the change in current noted on the plate meter of the tube voltmeter is proportional to the square of the amplitude of the sinusoidal test voltage, that is, also to the square of its effective value. The change δI_p becomes larger the steeper the plate-current grid-voltage work characteristic, the higher the leak resistance R, and the higher the normal grid current I_g without test voltage. The last two factors depend, however, on each other, since as R increases I_g decreases and an optimum condition must exist. It can be shown that there is a maximum effect if δI_p occurs close to the lower bend of the I_p, E_g characteristic, but still along the straight-line portion.

70. Tube Voltmeters with Increased and Decreased Sensitivity.—
The sensitivity of tube voltmeters can be increased (1) by using very
sensitive instruments the deflections of which indicate only the change
in current; (2) by using additional amplification, and (3) by means of
special tubes.   The sensitivity is limited by the stability of the reading,
and for direct reading tube voltmeters cannot be too high if any accuracy
is expected.   Figure 114 shows a direct-reading tube voltmeter which
uses a microammeter μa to read the effective test voltages E_x directly

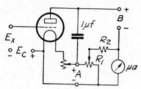

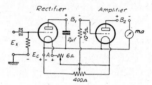

Fig. 114.—Direct-indicat-
ing-tube   voltmeter   with
steady   plate   current   compensated.

Fig.   115.—Two-tube   voltmeter.

by means of the difference current passing through the meter.   The
resistances R_1 and R_2 are chosen so that, for a suitable negative grid
bias E_c, the microammeter does just not register if the E_x terminals are
short-circuited.   For the average receiver tube, the resistance values
are about $R_1 = 400$ to 500Ω, and $R_2 = 3000$ to 5000Ω.   This circuit is
most convenient for amplification measurements, especially if the con-
stant-deflection method is used.   Figure 115 shows a two-stage tube
voltmeter.   If the dotted input condenser is used, this voltmeter can
also be used to determine alternating voltages with a superimposed
direct voltage.   If 199 tubes or their equivalent are used, the first tube

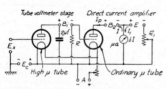

Fig. 116.—Millivoltmeter for
audio- and high-frequency
voltages.

with $B_1 = 20$ to 30 volts works as a detector,
and the second tube with $B_2 = 50$ to 90 volts
as an amplifier.   The negative grid bias E_c
of the first tube is chosen of such a magnitude
that the plate current falls to zero.   The
slider along the 400Ω potential is then
moved until the milliammeter ma reads
about 1.5 ma (about full deflection).   If the
test voltage E_x is impressed, the potential of the grid of the last tube
becomes more negative.   The reading on the plate meter will therefore
decrease.   The decrease depends on the resistance in the first tube, the
value of E_x, and the amplification factor of the second tube.   Figure 116
shows a similar two-tube voltmeter.   The only difference is that the
sensitivity is so increased that it acts as a reliable millivoltmeter.   For
increased sensitivity, the detector tube (first tube) uses a high mu tube
(a double grid can also be used) with a rated amplification factor of
about 30.   A high plate voltage is unnecessary, since the lower bend is

to be used for an efficient plate-rectification effect. B_1 is then about 45 volts and the voltage of the output tube about $B_2 = 45$ to 70 volts. The output tube is a receiving tube of $\mu = 6$ to 8. A microammeter μa can be used to measure the portion δI of the entire change δI_p in the plate current I_p of the last tube when E_x is applied. To do this, a current I_1 is made to flow in opposition to the portion I of the plate current, so that it just produces zero deflection when E_x is not impressed. This is accomplished by an auxiliary source E, conveniently of the same magnitude as the B_2 voltage so as to adjust the zero-current indication by means of a large resistance R_1. An adjustment is then much easier than when only a few volts are used for E and a small variable resistance R_1. The coupling resistance R is anywhere between 50,000 and 100,000Ω. If the voltages are properly chosen, the calibration curve of the deflection of the μa with respect to E_x is essentially linear for almost the entire range and voltage. A voltmeter of similar design has also been described by K. W. Jarvis.[1] He uses a 240 type tube for the tube-voltmeter stage and a 201 tube for the amplification stage with $B_1 = 45$ and $B_2 = 67$ volts, and a coupling resistance $R = 50,000\Omega$. A multirange milliammeter with the full-scale readings 20, 2.0, 0.2, and 0.02 ma acted as indicator. With the 0.02 scale, the effective voltage range for E_x is 20 to 100 mv. The maximum reading for the 2-ma scale is 1 volt. A voltage range of 50 to 1 volts can therefore be covered.

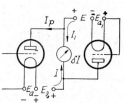

Fig. 117.—Plate-current compensation by means of another tube (deflection due to $\delta I = I_1 - I$).

This voltmeter works over the entire frequency range including all broadcast frequencies.

The compensation of the normal plate current can also be accomplished by the scheme shown in Fig. 117. In some cases a comparatively small balancing voltage E (Fig. 116) and low variable resistance R_1 are used. The disadvantage, besides a difficult balance adjustment, is that a large portion of the current change δI_p passes through the compensating branch and not through the indicator. This disadvantage is greater the lower R_1. This can be avoided if another tube of the same kind is connected as in Fig. 117. Such a scheme increases the sensitivity greatly, since the internal resistance r_p of the tube is high compared with that of the microammeter and can be readily changed by means of the filament current.

Figure 118 shows a multirange tube voltmeter for which 201-A, and 112-A tubes or their equivalent are used. Plate compensating is again provided for the last tube in order to use a microammeter for the readings. The switch S is closed only when the meter is in use. This tube voltmeter acts as a voltmeter and a millivoltmeter. It can be used up to fre-

[1] *Proc. I.R.E.*, **17**, 679, 1929.

quencies in the broadcast range. Since 0.5-μf coupling condensers and the grid leaks are properly chosen, a 60-cycle calibration will hold over practically the entire useful frequency range. Plate rectification is used again and the first two tubes work on 90 volts, while the final tube works on 45 volts. If the switch 1 only is closed, the tube voltmeter is most sensitive. Medium sensitivity exists if only 2 is closed, while an ordinary tube-voltmeter sensitivity exists if 3 only is closed. The range can also be changed by applying the potential variation at point P either directly toward the grid of the last tube or through 0.5, 2.5, 5, 10, or 20 megohms. As with most of the multirange tube voltmeters, the calibration can be relied upon only when it is made at the time of the measurement. Such a meter, however, has the advantage that for rough work, or work where only equal deflections are used, a very wide voltage range exists. Figure 134 shows another multirange tube voltmeter

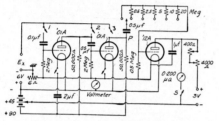

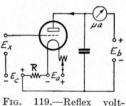

FIG. 118.—Multirange voltmeter.　　　FIG. 119.—Reflex voltmeter.

indicating directly the effective voltage. The last tube using the shield-grid connection acts as the tube voltmeter, while the first two stages serve for amplification. Figure 133 shows another type of tube voltmeter which can also be calibrated in effective values since a semipower tube with a thermoelectric indicator is used in the last stage. Both tube voltmeters (Figs. 133 and 134) are most suitable for measuring audio-frequency voltages, since the frequency characteristic is flat in this band.

The reflex voltmeter shown in Fig. 119 is due to W. B. Medlam and U. A. Oschwald.[1] Unless used in combination with a stage of direct-current or some other amplification, it will work only in the volt range about 0 to 20 volts, for E_b = 67.5 volts and a grid bias E_c depending on the receiver tube used but over a wider range of voltage than the ordinary tube voltmeter. The plate current passes over the load resistance R which is high (a few hundred thousand ohms) so that a microammeter can be used to read the effective voltage E_x directly or by means of a calibration curve. Plate rectification is used again and the voltage drop along R produces an additional negative grid bias which increases with I_p and consequently also with E_x. Figure 120 extends the voltage cali-

[1] *Exptl. Wireless*, **3**, 670, 1926.

bration still farther so that, for instance, with a 222 type tube or its equivalent,[1] a range 0.1 to 10 effective volts can be readily covered. Therefore, the grid-leak shield-grid tube voltmeter is still more sensitive than the grid-leak three-element tube voltmeter. This circuit is very suitable as a resonance indicator in the upper frequency range when the input capacitance affects the calibration too much. As in the case

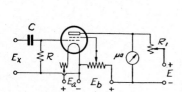

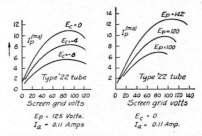

Fig. 120.—Shield-grid voltmeter.

Fig. 121.—Characteristics of screen-grid tubes.

of the three-element tube, the automatic negative grid bias produced by E_x decreases the plate current and, by choosing an operating point on the straight portion of the plate-current characteristic, the decrease in I_p due to the grid rectification can be made more pronounced than for plate rectification. The advantage of using a shield-grid tube is that the plate current depends on *both* the negative grid bias of the control (input) grid *and upon* the *screen-grid voltage*, as can be seen from the characteristics of the 222 shield-grid tube shown in Fig. 121. Hence, as the screen-grid

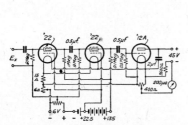

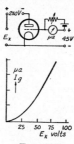

Fig. 122.—Space-charge-tube voltmeter.

Fig. 123.—Inverse - triode voltmeter.

potential is increased toward the value of the plate potential, for a fixed-control grid bias, the plate current passes through a maximum and decreases again as the screen grid and plate potential approach each other and a certain negative control bias produces a most effective decrease in plate current. This happens for a screen-grid potential which produces optimum plate current. In Fig. 134 a screen-grid *RMS* voltmeter with amplification is shown. Figure 122 shows a space-charge tube voltmeter

[1] King, R., *Proc. I.R.E.*, **18**, 1388, 1930.

with amplification.   The dimensions are suitable if 222 type double-grid tubes and 112-A output tubes or their equivalent are used.   This meter reads down to 0.0006 volt, but, as in the case of all sensitive tube volt-meters for accurate work, the calibration should be taken at the time of the measurement.

Tube voltmeters with decreased sensitivity without using potentiome-ter systems are known as the "inverse tube voltmeters."   This type has already been described in connection with the determination of peak voltages.   Figure 123 illustrates the performance of such an instrument. The test voltage E_x is then impressed on the plate in series with the B battery and the much smaller effect noted in the grid branch.

71. Notes on the Design of Tube Voltmeters.—The design of tube voltmeters depends upon whether the meter is to cover a wide range in frequency and voltage, respectively, and upon whether peak voltages and effective voltages are to be determined directly or by slide-back methods.   It also depends upon whether or not grid or plate rectification is to be used or whether both rectifications exist simultaneously.   The latter is undesirable for most laboratory work.   As far as the slide-back methods are concerned, the design is self-evident.   Voltages taken from a direct-current source are then used to compensate the effects of the test voltage and must therefore correspond to the order of the peak value of the test voltage.   The voltage range is then very flexible but requires high direct voltages to measure high-test voltages unless the inverse tube action (test voltage in series with B battery, Fig. 104) is employed.   The theory given in connection with Fig. 113 leads to formulas from which the change in the plate-current reading of a tube voltmeter using grid recti-fication (grid condenser and leak) and working along a linear portion of the plate-current characteristic (preferably right above the lower bend) can be computed.   The ordinary direct-reading tube voltmeters, espe-cially the one designed by M von Ardenne[1] and also used by E. T. Dickey[2] can be computed in a simple manner, especially when the *direct*-current load R in the external plate circuit is a high resistance (a fraction to several megohms).   A capacity load C as in Fig. 124 exists for the variable plate currents.   The value of the capacity load C is from about 0.02 to 1 μf depending upon the frequency range.   When a test voltage E_x acts, the direct-current reading I_p in the plate meter increases to some value $I_p + \delta I_p$, if δI_p denotes the average value of the corresponding voltage fluctuation i_p taking place about I_p.   Therefore, it can give only an upward rectification effect δI_p when the positive fluctuations above I_p include more area than the negative fluctuations below it, since for equally

---

[1] *Jahrb. d. drahtl.*, **29**, 82, 1927; *Z. tech. Physik*, **8**, 235, 1927; C. M. Jansky and C. B. Feldman, *J. Am. Inst. Elec. Eng.*, **47**, 126, 1928; H. R. Lubcke, *Proc. I.R.E.*, **17**, 864, 1930.

[2] *Loc. cit.*, Fig. 110.

shaded areas no change in the plate-meter reading can be noted. There are two ways of bringing about this condition. One is that the operating point P, by an appropriate choice of the negative grid bias (E_c), is placed in the curvature of the I_p characteristic so that the current swings i_p (due to distortion) above the normal plate current $I_p = I_0$ are comparatively high and enclose sufficient area to outbalance the areas of reduced negative i_p swings below the I_0 line. However, this would only be a means of covering a comparatively small voltage range if only the curved portion is employed. But when the grid bias is chosen very low, corresponding to about the case indicated in Fig. 124 ($I_0 = 10$ μa when a 200 microammeter is used), a much larger portion of the characteristic can be used because, for large values of E_x, the variable current i_p due to E_x may utilize that portion of the working characteristic (only limited by the magnitude of the peak value of E_x from which an appreciable grid current begins) which is essentially linear except for the lower curvature. Taking into consideration only the terms up to the second order, one finds for the current fluctuations

$$i_p = \rho \frac{\partial F(E_1)}{\partial E_1} + \frac{\rho^2}{2} \frac{\partial^2 F(E_1)}{\partial E_1^2} = \rho\, g + \frac{\rho^2}{2} \frac{\partial g}{\partial E_1}$$

for $\rho = \mu e_g - i_p R$ for the test voltage $e_g = e$ sin θ of effective value E_x. The quantity g denotes the steepness of the working characteristic, and $\partial g/\partial E_1$ the curvature of the static characteristic in the operating point. One may without any great error put $g = g_m$ which holds for the steepness of the working portion of the I_p, E_g characteristic. One obtains

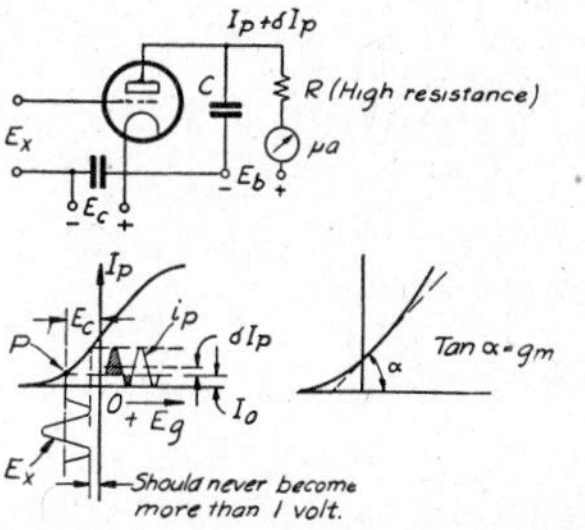

FIG. 124.—Actions in a tube voltmeter with a capacitance load C.

$$i_p = g_m[\mu e_g - i_p R] + \frac{\partial g_m}{\partial E_g}\left[\frac{e_g - i_p R}{2}\right]^2$$

and for the change δI_p noted in the current reading

$$\delta I_p = \mathrm{av}(i_p) = \mu g_m\, \mathrm{av}(e_g) - R\, g_m \delta I_p + \frac{\partial g_m}{\partial E_g} \frac{1}{2} \mathrm{av}[\mu e_g - i_p R]^2$$

But $\mathrm{av}(e_g) = 0$ for $e_g = e$ sin sin θ and, by neglecting insignificant terms, the above expression leads to

$$\delta I_p = \frac{1}{4} \frac{\partial g_m/\partial E_g}{g_m} \frac{\mu e^2}{R + r_p} \tag{30}$$

if g_m denotes the average slope of the static I_p, E_g characteristic, $\partial g_m/\partial E_g$ the curvature at the operating point, and r_p the internal tube resistance. For tube voltmeters of this kind, the indicated plate current $I_p + \delta I_p$ is small and the arbitrary zero setting $I_p = I_0$ even smaller. For a sensitive arrangement it is necessary to have the change $R\ \delta I_p$ in the direct voltage across R large compared with the input voltage, and

$$\frac{R\,\delta I_p}{e} = \underbrace{\frac{\partial g_m/\partial E_g}{g_m}}_{\substack{\text{rectification}\\\text{action}}} \underbrace{\frac{\mu R}{R + r_p} \frac{e}{4}}_{\substack{\text{voltage}\\\text{amplifica-}\\\text{tion}}} \qquad (31)$$

Hence, for a large direct-current load (large value of R), the voltage amplification becomes almost equal to the amplification factor μ effective for the operating region. But for great sensitivity it is necessary to have the value of the curvature to that of the steepness at the operating point large also. A high mu tube with large plate loads R will therefore give a very sensitive meter, although ordinary tubes with a comparatively small amplification factor ($\mu = 2.8$ to 8), but with the straight portion of the I_p, E_g characteristic mostly in the region of negative grid voltages, gives a wider voltage range without drawing grid current for the upper voltage limit. For this reason a 171 type tube or its equivalent is very suitable for a wide voltage range, but because of its low amplification factor ($\mu = 2.8$ to 3.2) it is suitable only from about 0.2 volt upward.

The design of such a tube voltmeter for a certain range is then an easy matter, since the effective voltage E_x to be measured produces a current change

$$\delta I_p = \frac{\mu E_x}{r_p + R} \qquad (32)$$

where E_x stands for the *largest* effective value of the desired range, and μ for the amplification factor of the tube for the particular voltage range. The plate current indicated by the microammeter is larger by the value I_0 which is the small direct current corresponding to the arbitrary zero setting. Although μ of a tube varies but little over the normal work range when used as an amplifier, as a rule it is somewhat smaller for the operating point (for current I_0). For a peak factor p, the maximum test voltage has a peak value pE_x. Since the grid draws currents for decelerating voltages of as much as -1 volt, the negative grid bias can be computed from

$$E_c = pE_x + 1 \qquad (33)$$

which for sinusoidal voltages would be ($1.41\,E_x + 1$) volts. Approximately

$$E_b = \mu E_c = \mu[pE_x + 1] \qquad (34)$$

If a microammeter with an arbitrary zero reading I_0 and a full range I is to be used, $(I - I_0) = \delta I_p$ is the full range of the voltmeter corresponding to the largest effective test voltage E_x to be measured. According to (32), the required load resistance R can then be computed from

$$R = \frac{\mu E_x - (I - I_0)r_p}{I - I_0} \qquad (35)$$

Example.—Suppose a 200 microammeter is used in the plate branch, and that 10 ma denotes the arbitrary zero setting ($I_0 = 10$) for which $E_x = 0$ volt. For a desired voltage range $E_x = 0$ to 100 volts, an amplification factor $\mu = 3$ measured for 200 μa with one of the methods described in Sec. 164 and a corresponding plate resistance $r_p = 10^5\,\Omega$, according to (35) the required load resistance becomes $R = \dfrac{3 \times 100 - (200 - 10)10^{-6} \times 10^5}{(200 - 10)10^{-6}} = 1.48$ megohms (use $1.5 \times 10^6\,\Omega$). The negative grid bias required for sinusoidal voltages and no grid current at any time, according to (33), becomes $E_c = 1.41 \times 100 + 1 = -142$ volts, and the voltage supplied by the B battery, according to (34), is $E_b = 3 \times 142 = 426$ volts. In order to see to what extent it is correct to use the approximate formula (34), one calculates the internal tube drop $r_pI = 10^5 \times 200 \times 10^{-6} = 20$ volts, which is small compared to $E_b = 426$ volts, even for the extreme limit of the entire voltage range.

72. Notes on the Calibration of Tube Voltmeters.—Slide-back tube voltmeters require no calibration, since the measurement is carried out by a voltmeter measuring the extra voltage required along a direct-current

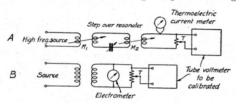

Fig. 125.—Calibration of a tube voltmeter.

potentiometer in order to balance out the effect of the peak value of the test voltage. This voltmeter reading gives the means of detecting the peak voltage. All other types of tube voltmeters are conveniently calibrated with a resistance potentiometer and the voltage applied to the tube voltmeter is computed by the *IR* drop. This can be done with a suitable electrometer or, as in most cases, with a thermoelectric-current meter as indicated by *A* and *B* of Fig. 125. For rough calibrations a 60-cycle current can be used, especially if the tube voltmeter is to be employed in the audio-frequency range or if the construction of the voltmeter is such that its frequency factor at 60 cycles/sec is about the same as in the high-frequency range for which it is to be used. However, there seems to be no great inconvenience in calibrating the instrument in the frequency range for which it is used, and using a sinusoidal current which has been purified by a step-over resonator. The voltage applied can then be varied by the potentiometer tap *T* as well as by the variable mutual inductance M_1 to the generator.

73. Generators for the Production of Standard Voltages.—If only standard voltages which are not extremely small are to be generated in the high-frequency range, the generator shown in Fig. 126 will do for many purposes. R_s denotes a pure fixed resistance which consists of a short straight piece of constantan wire sealed in a glass tube, or some other form of high-grade resistance. For certain work a 1-ohm resistance will do (field-intensity work). The heater resistance of the thermoelectric current indicator is about 30Ω. The voltage is $E = IR_s$. For the circuit in Fig. 127 the step-over resonator and a variable mutual M is used and the normal voltage computed from $E = \omega IM$ volts, if $\omega/2\pi$ is in cycles per second, I in amperes, and M in henries.

Damping apparatus (attenuation boxes) can be used in the normal high-frequency range for which the frequency is not too high to produce

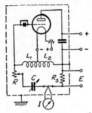

Fig. 126.—Production of a standard high-frequency voltage E by means of R_s and I.

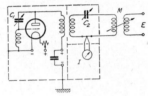

Fig. 127.—Production of a standard high-frequency voltage E by means of M and I.

standard voltages over a great range and down to very small voltages. The input current I_1 flowing to the attenuation box is then measured with a thermoelectric meter and the output current I_2, passing through a load resistance equal to that for which the box is designed (normally 600Ω), is computed from the attenuation ratio. A portion R_s of this load resistance then produces the standard voltage I_2R_s. The procedure is described in Sec. 36 together with Fig. 53.

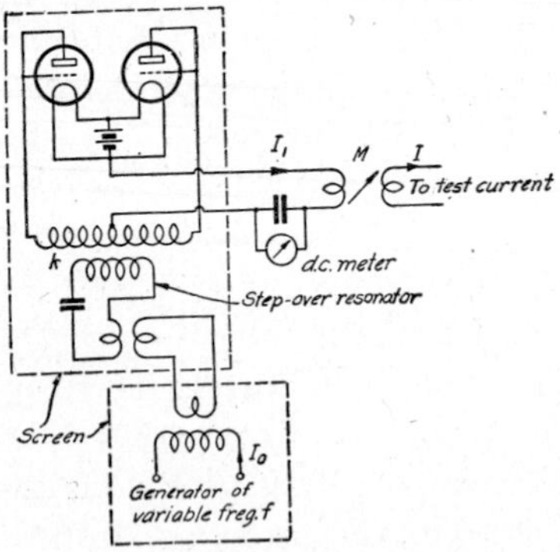

Although this device produces very small voltages, it has the disadvantage of not working with great accuracy in the upper high-frequency range unless a special design is provided. In testing receivers which may have a high-frequency voltage amplification from 1000 to 5000, great difficulties occur where the small voltages are impressed on the first stage of such amplifiers by apparatus just described, since even with very good shielding the high-frequency fields of the source and other portions may affect the receiver under test and produce voltages which are not entirely due to the voltage thought to be applied. This happens because the generator produces a current of the same frequency as the small standard voltage which is applied. Hence, very strong high-frequency fields are back of such a generating system. A remedy for this is to generate only the small current which produces the small input voltage.

Fig. 128.—Determination of small standard high-frequency currents I in terms of a direct current measured with a microammeter.

Figures 128 and 129 show this method.[1] In the tube generator of Fig. 128, the high-frequency current I_0 of frequency f works through the step-over resonator toward a full wave rectifier. The step-over resonator suppresses any double or other harmonic frequency and impresses only a voltage of frequency f on the rectifier. The output branch of the rectifier then contains a direct-current component and a strong component I_1 of frequency $2f$ both produced in this branch. If the coupling κ is loose so that I_1 is only a small current, the direct-current meter will indicate directly the magnitude of I_1. The small output current I flowing to the measuring circuit can be found by means of I_1 and M. If the original current I_0 of frequency f is modulated by a sinusoidal voltage which is in series with the plate battery of the generator, the modulation of I_1 will be twice as large. Figure 129 gives a circuit where the same tube generates the alternating-current component I_0 of frequency f in the plate branch and rectifies by means of the grid-filament branch, the current induced in it by the back feed κ. A

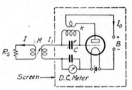

F I G . 129.—Generation of small standard voltages by means of the grid current of a high-frequency generator.

direct-current meter in the grid branch then indicates for small currents I_1 of frequency $2f$ the effective value of I_1. The test voltage of frequency $2f$ is $I R_s$. If the test voltage requires modulation, the modulation voltage is applied again in series with the B battery and twofold modulation will be experienced in the output current I.

74. Determination of the Terminal Voltage of a Thermocouple.—In Fig. 60 the direct voltage E is at first connected through terminals 1 and 2. The galvanometer G is connected to terminals 5 and 6 for a certain voltage E, which by means of its current I_0 heats the couple and causes the deflection d_1. The input switch is then thrown toward 3 and 4 and the deflection d_2 noted. The average deflection $(d_1 + d_2)/2 = d$ corresponds to the average voltage $E = (E_1 + E_2)/2$ of the thermocouple.

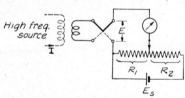

FIG. 130.—The compensation method.

If the galvanometer is connected to terminals 7 and 8 and the same average deflection d is obtained by the slider along R, the voltage drop between the fixed and sliding contact can be read. Hence, by subtracting the voltage drop in the series resistance r, the terminal voltage E for the heating current I_0 is obtained.

Figure 130 shows a compensation method with a standard voltage E_s used in connection with a potentiometer $(R_1 + R_2)$. The voltage of the thermocouple is connected against a portion of the standard voltage

[1] ROBERTS, W. VAN B., *J. Franklin Inst.*, **201**, 301, 1926.

E_s and the traveling contact along the potentiometer is moved until the galvanometer current disappears. Then

$$E = \frac{R_1}{R_1 + R_2} E_s$$

75. Determination of the Voltage Sensitivity of a Telephone Receiver. The telephone-comparator method (Fig. 131) is used with T_s as a standard receiver (reference receiver) and T_x as the receiver to be tested. The shunt resistances R_s and R_x must be small compared to the respective impedances of the receivers. By means of R_1 the small current I can be varied. The resistance R_s and R_x shunting T_s and

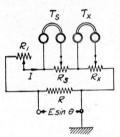

T_x, respectively, are varied until each receiver gives the same loudness. It is then necessary to bring alternately first one and then the other receiver to the ear. The voltage sensitivity is then R_s/R_x, which is the ratio of the voltage E_s across the standard phone to terminal voltage E_x across the test phone.

Fig. 131.—Telephone comparator.

76. Notes on Harmonic-voltage Analyzers.— The methods described in Sec. 56 for the measurement of harmonic-current content can be used to analyze distorted voltage waves also, since in all schemes a voltage is impressed on the measuring circuit. A distorted voltage wave is of the form

$$E = E_1 \sin \theta + E_2 \sin 2\theta + E_3 \sin 3\theta + \cdots E_m \sin m\theta$$

and the percentage of any one harmonic can be expressed as the ratio of the amplitude E_m of the harmonic to the fundamental, that is, by $100E_m/E_1$. The same value would be obtained if the effective values $E_m/\sqrt{2}$ and $E_1/\sqrt{2}$ were used. However, when the distortion is due to many prominent higher harmonic voltages, it is in many cases sufficient to express the harmonic-voltage content by the ratio of the effective values of all higher harmonic voltages to the effective value of the fundamental voltage which leads to

$$\frac{\sqrt{E_2{}^2 + E_3{}^2 + \cdots E_m{}^2}}{E_1}$$

Fig. 132.— Resonance bridge as harmonic analyzer.

Again, it does not matter whether the maximum values or the effective values are used. Figure 132 indicates the well-known resonance bridge which can be used.[1] It can be perfectly balanced only if a pure sinusoidal voltage is impressed on the network. Hence, if the bridge is adjusted by varying C, or L and R_3 for the

[1] Wolff, I., *J. Optical Soc. Am.*, **15**, 163, 1927; G. Belfils, *Rev. gén. élec.*, Apr. 3, 1926; C. Chiodi, *L'electrotecnica*, **15**, 166, 1928; and applied to measurements on tube circuits, D. F. Schmit and J. M. Stinchfield, *Electronics*, **1**, 79, 1930.

fundamental frequency $\omega/2\pi$, $(\omega L = 1/\omega C$ and $R_1/R_2 = R_3/R_4)$ the balance adjustment *at best* can lead only to a *minimum* deflection d, since a small voltage e due to all other harmonics remains across the terminals P_1P_2 of the balance indicator. Thus, if the bridge is adjusted for the fundamental $(1/\omega C = \omega L)$ and besides a higher harmonic voltage of frequency $m\omega/2\pi$ is also present in the impressed voltage E, the remaining maximum value e_0 of the voltage due to the effect of $E_m \sin m\omega t$ and acting across the indicator becomes

$$e_0 = \underbrace{\frac{E_m R_1}{R_1 + R_2}}_{\substack{\text{voltage drop} \\ \text{across } R_1}} - \underbrace{\frac{E_m R_3}{R_3 + R_4 + jm\omega L - \dfrac{1}{jm\omega C}}}_{\text{voltage drop across } R_3}$$

$$= E_m\left[\frac{k}{1 + k} - \frac{kR_4}{(1 + k)R_4 + j\omega L\left[m - \dfrac{1}{m}\right]}\right] \tag{36}$$

The largest value which the peak voltage affecting the indicator can ever obtain is then

$$e_{\text{opt}} = \frac{k}{1 + k}E_m \tag{37}$$

But $k = R_1/R_2$ and the optimum value is then equal to the voltage drop produced across R_1 by the particular harmonic component. Hence, the bridge behaves as though the LC branch did not exist. However, a condition of this kind can be approximated in effect if the ratio k is chosen small, but not so small that the available voltage across the indicator is cut down too much, thereby impairing the sensitivity of the voltage analyzer. A value of $k = 0.5$ is suitable and a ratio $\omega L/R_4$ of about 5 or larger makes the factor

$$F = \frac{1}{\sqrt{1 + \left\{\dfrac{(1 + k)R_4}{\omega L\left(m - \dfrac{1}{m}\right)}\right\}^2}} \tag{38}$$

in

$$e_0 = e_{\text{opt}} F \tag{39}$$

almost unity. Thus choosing $\omega L/R_4 = 5$, a second harmonic present only in addition to the fundamental which is balanced out, the factor F is 0.98, while with only a third harmonic present $F = 0.995$. Since R_4 is essentially the effective resistance of the variometer L and for any still higher harmonic current which flows through it, its value is larger than that given by the above ratio, and F must be still closer to unity.

If an indicator is used which does practically *not* absorb any current from the bridge and whose meter responds with the square law of the applied voltage, it can be made to read the effective voltage across the points P_1P_2 directly.　Sensitive indicators of this type consist of a stage of voltage amplification with an additional output tube powerful enough to operate a thermoelectric indicator (Fig. 133).　The dimensions given in Fig. 133 are about suitable for a 240 type tube or its equivalent in the first stage, and a 171 type tube or its equivalent for the output stage. In order to make the bridge indicator even more sensitive and to do away with the slow response of a thermoelectric indicator, the two-stage

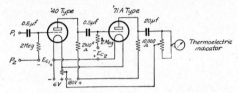

Fig. 133.—Sensitive bridge indicator.

amplifier with a shield-grid output meter responding to the square law as in Fig. 134 can be used.　High μ tubes ($\mu = 30$) of the 240 type or its equivalent are used for the first two stages, while a 222 type double-grid tube or its equivalent is used for the root-mean-square tube voltmeter by adjusting the filament voltage E_a to about 2.8 volts.　Because of the coupling characteristic of each indicator (Figs. 133 and 134), the calibration will hold only from the commercial power frequency up to about 3 kc/sec and can be used to measure the total higher-harmonic content in output tubes of broadcast receivers.　For higher frequencies, direct-

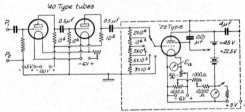

Fig. 134.—Sensitive tube voltmeter with a flat frequency characteristic from 30 to 3000 cycles/sec.

current amplifiers should be used.　Since a bridge is used in this work, it seems best not to employ this method above the audio-frequency range, but, instead, the harmonic analyzers described in Sec. 56 which are also more accurate, especially if methods with a search frequency are employed.

　　The indicators shown in Figs. 133 and 134 will measure the effective voltage across terminals P_1P_2 of the resonance bridge shown in Fig. 132. The bridge is balanced for the fundamental voltage component and the effective output voltage $e = \sqrt{e_2^2 + e_3^2 + e_4^2 + \cdots e_m^2}$ due to the effective values (e_2 of frequency $2f$, e_3 of frequency $3f$, etc.) of all the higher harmonics is measured by a single reading of the indicator connected across terminals P_1P_2. If the resultant effective input voltage E_x containing the effective values of all harmonic components (E_1 of frequency f; E_2 of frequency $2f$, etc.) is also measured by a single reading, the total *higher*-harmonic content

$$\rho = \frac{\sqrt{E_2{}^2 + E_3{}^2 + E_4{}^2 + \cdots}}{E_1} \tag{40}$$

with respect to the effective value of the fundamental can be computed from these two readings if the resistance across which the measured effective voltages e and E_x act are known. Because of the circuit relations given above, the harmonic content e is essentially due to the drop along resistance R_1, while the test voltage is applied across $R_1 + R_2$ which for $k = R_1/R_2$ gives

$$\frac{\sqrt{e_2{}^2 + e_3{}^2 + e_4{}^2}}{\sqrt{E_2{}^2 + E_3{}^2 + E_4{}^2}} = \frac{R_1}{R_1 + R_2} = \frac{k}{1 + k}$$

or the corresponding higher-harmonic input content in terms of the measured P_1P_2 voltage as

$$\sqrt{E_2{}^2 + E_3{}^2 + E_4{}^2} = \frac{1 + k}{k}e \tag{41}$$

Hence, the percentage of higher-harmonic content can be computed from

$$\rho = \frac{100e}{E_1}\frac{1 + k}{k} \tag{42}$$

where ρ is in percentage, which gives $300e/E_1$ for $k = R_1/R_2 = 0.5$ where

$$E_1 = \sqrt{E_x{}^2 - \{E_2{}^2 + E_3{}^2 + E_4{}^2\}} = \sqrt{E_x{}^2 - \frac{e^2(1 + k)^2}{k^2}} \tag{43}$$

$$= \sqrt{E_x{}^2 - 9e^2}$$

for $k = 0.5$. Therefore it is necessary to have a calibration of the bridge indicator in order to measure the effective voltage e across P_1P_2 when the bridge is adjusted to the fundamental frequency and the voltage E_x across the input. Unless a multirange tube voltmeter is used, the much larger resultant effective voltage E_x at the input side must be measured with another tube voltmeter or some other suitable r.m.s. voltmeter. No calibration of the bridge voltmeter is, however, necessary if the equal-deflection method indicated in Fig. 135 is employed, for which the bridge voltmeter is also used to measure the equivalent voltage of the input. The method consists then of connecting the effective-voltage indicator against the terminals P_1P_2 and varying C, or L, or both, until a minimum deflection is noted (satisfies $\omega L = 1/\omega C$). Hereafter R_3 is varied until the final minimum deflection d is noted on the bridge indicator ($R_1/R_2 = R_3/R_4$ is satisfied). Now, the double-pole double-throw switch is connected towards the

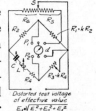

Fig. 135.—Equal-deflection method of the resonance bridge as analyzer.

potentiometer $(R_5 + R_6)$ and the sliding contact S is moved until the same deflection d is obtained, which means that the effective voltage drop across resistance R_5 must be equal to the higher-harmonic content $e = \sqrt{e_2{}^2 + e_3{}^2 + e_4{}^2 + \cdots}$ measured when the indicator was connected toward P_1P_2. But since the resultant effective distorted input voltage E_x acts across the potentiometer resistance $R_5 + R_6$, one has for

$$p = \frac{k}{1+k}$$

$$\frac{E_x}{e} = \frac{R_5 + R_6}{R_5} \tag{44}$$

But, according to (40) and (41),

$$\frac{E_x}{e} = \frac{\sqrt{E_1{}^2 + E_2{}^2 + E_3{}^2 + \cdots}}{p\sqrt{E_2{}^2 + E_3{}^2 + \cdots}} = \frac{\sqrt{1+\rho^2}}{p\rho} \tag{45}$$

and, equating the right sides of (44) and (45), the total higher harmonic content in percentage becomes

$$\rho = \frac{100\,R_5}{\sqrt{p^2[R_5 + R_6]^2 - R_5{}^2}} \tag{46}$$

where ρ is in percentage. Hence, for $k = 0.5$, one has $p^2 = \frac{1}{9}$ and, if a total potentiometer resistance $R_5 + R_6 = 3000\,\Omega$ is chosen, then

$$\rho = \frac{0.1\,R_5}{\sqrt{1 - [R_5/1000]^2}} \tag{47}$$

where ρ is in percentage and for low percentage distortion the square-root value is close to unity. The entire computation requires only the knowledge of R_5 and, if the total higher-harmonic distortion ρ is less than 10 per cent, the percentage distortion is $\rho = 0.1R_5$. This means the potentiometer can be calibrated directly in percentage distortion.

CHAPTER V

DETERMINATION OF FREQUENCY

In the early days of radio it was customary to deal with wave length exclusively. For most of today's work, frequencies are dealt with and instruments which measure this quantity are called frequency meters (wave meters). If v is the velocity of propagation in centimeters per second, λ the wave length in centimeters, and T the time in seconds for the electromagnetic wave to pass through a distance of one wave length,

$$v = \frac{\lambda}{T} = f\lambda \tag{1}$$

if f is the frequency of the current producing the wave in cycles per second. In free space the wave is propagated with the velocity of light ($v = c = 2.9982 \times 10^{10}$ cm/sec), and using the approximation $c = 3 \times 10^{10}$ cm/sec, the frequency is

$$f = \frac{3 \times 10^5}{\lambda} \tag{2}$$

where f is in kilocycles per second and λ is in meters. When high-frequency currents pass along conductors, somewhat smaller velocities exist. Nothing will be changed so far as the impressed frequency is concerned, but the wave length must also decrease according to the above equation. The wave length is therefore not a constant as is the frequency. In a laboratory currents are worked with and are measured by means of their effects, at least in most of the work. Hence, for a physical reason also, it is more natural to deal with frequency. There are exceptions, however, as when frequency is standardized with a parallel-wire system by noting either the nodal points or the antinodes, respectively, to locate half wave-length distances. It then becomes necessary to deal with the wave length first and find the equivalent frequency by means of the velocity of propagation along the wire. As far as distance and height are concerned—when dealing with wave reflections between ground and the ionized layer above it—the concept of wave length is important. For measurements at the sender and receiver, the frequency is again the physical quantity. The wave length may differ somewhat along the sender and receiver antennas, along the path between ground and the ionized layer, and very greatly within the ionized layer.

If the path of wave propagation varies rapidly as in the case of indirect sky rays passing by way of the ionized layer of the atmosphere, an action similar to the Doppler effect can have an effect upon the frequency of the received high-frequency current. If the length of the path between the sender and the receiver aerials is changed, the action is as though the sender and receiver stations moved relatively with respect to each other. The frequency of the received current is then somewhat different, and, besides, undesirable frequency modulation may give rise to distortion. The discrepancy of the received frequency from the actual sender-carrier frequency becomes more as the change in the length of the indirect path per unit time increases. Suppose the change in the transmission path is 3×10^6 cm/sec (which is a possible value), a frequency discrepancy as high as 2 kc/sec would occur for a 20-Mc carrier, corresponding to a wave length of 15 m in vacuum. This is why printed letters sent out at a transmitting station appear somewhat tilted at the receiving station when received on a drum. Considerable distortion may take place in television transmission by means of the "electromagnetic Doppler effect."

The calibration of frequency as a significant quantity is based on that of time, since $f = 1/T$ and T the period denotes the time during which 1 cycle is completed. Therefore precision measurement of frequency is reduced to a comparison of the reciprocal of the frequency to be found with the best standard of time such as given to laboratories by the time signals. If in this way a primary standard is obtained, the calibration can be transferred to secondary standards which in turn are used to measure frequencies in the laboratory. Very high standards are required for both delicate laboratory and commercial work and precision determination of frequency is most important. For many laboratory measurements, secondary standards are sufficient and frequency meters also known as "wave meters" are used. They are generally based on the resonance principle but as a rule do not indicate directly. Direct indicating instruments are simpler to use but are not very accurate when working over a wide range. However, they serve well as switchboard instruments where high-frequency accuracy is not required. For a limited frequency range, several piezo-electric resonators producing glow-discharge patterns can be used with rather high accuracy.

77. Remarks on the Frequency Range.—It is difficult to draw exact lines between low, middle, and high frequencies in modern applications. For instance, high-frequency carrier work is carried on down to 25 kc/sec, and even lower, while for some work in acoustics supersonic sound waves and corresponding currents with frequencies as high as 100 kc/sec, and even higher, are used. In a radio receiver audio frequencies as low as 20 cycles/sec are dealt with and high frequencies as high as 1.5 Mc/sec, if only the upper broadcast range—and not the effects of harmonics—is taken into consideration. An acquaintance with frequency determination from very low frequencies on up into the megacycle range is therefore necessary in laboratory work. Inasmuch as apparatus which work well in the high-frequency range are not always very suitable in the audio-frequency band, different methods must be employed.

It is possible to make alternating currents audible from 15 cycles/sec to about 20 kc/sec, the extreme limits depending upon the observer's ear. There are frequencies above and below this range which may cause pain to the ear but which can not be recognized as sound. The transmission of speech includes a frequency range from about 300 cycles/sec to 6 kc/sec. A base note can go down as far as 100 cycles/sec. Vowels include a range up to about 5.7 kc/sec, while the consonants reach into the 9 kc/sec range. For good voice transmission, currents between 0.1 to 5 kc/sec should not be suppressed. For good music transmission a frequency band from 0.025 to 10 kc/sec is desirable. In this discussion anything above 20 kc/sec is taken as the useful high-frequency range.

78. Laboratory High-frequency Meters.—One can distinguish between frequency meters which act as resonators and those which are

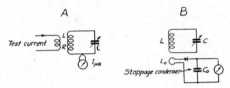

Fig 136.—Frequency meters based on the resonance principle.

in principle calibrated high-frequency generators. The resonator type of frequency meter is more reliable and the simplest representative meter is shown in Fig. 136A, where a thermoelectric indicator μa of low heater resistance gives a decided resonance deflection when, by an adjustment of a good air condenser C, the circuit is tuned to the fundamental frequency of a loosely coupled test circuit. This type of meter is based upon the fact that for L in henries, C in farads ($= 10^6 \mu$f), and effective circuit resistance R in ohms, the frequency f_0' in cycles per second, for the damping factor $\alpha = R/2L$ and logarithmic decrement $\delta = R/2f_0L$ per cycle, is

$$f_0' = \frac{1}{2\pi}\sqrt{\frac{1}{CL} - \alpha^2} = f_0\sqrt{1 - \left(\frac{\delta}{2\pi}\right)^2} = f_0\sqrt{1 - \frac{R^2C}{4L}} \qquad (3)$$

where

$$f_0 = \frac{1}{2\pi\sqrt{CL}} \qquad (4)$$

is the natural frequency of the frequency meter with no circuit losses, that is, for $R = 0$. Therefore if the damping factor α is very small, a frequency meter of this type could be calibrated from a knowledge of C and L. A procedure of this kind can be used when high precision is not required, although it is better simply to calibrate this frequency meter by the resonance current $I = I_r$ by means of a comparison against a standard frequency meter. Then a knowledge of the magnitude of α is not required and is important only as far as the sharpness of the resonance setting is concerned. For the sharpness of resonance $S = \pi/\delta$ and the current I in the circuit for any frequency f is

$$I = \frac{I_r}{\sqrt{1 + S^2 \left[\dfrac{f}{f_0} - \dfrac{f_0}{f}\right]^2}} \tag{5}$$

since $S = \pi/\delta = \omega_0 L/R$ and $I_r = E/R$. But L/R is the time constant and it must be as large as possible in order to make the sharpness S of resonance large. This can hardly be done in the very low frequency range and frequency meters as indicated in Fig. 136 are used only in the actual high-frequency range. Having the resonance reading I_r for f_0, and a reading I corresponding to f, the sharpness of resonance according to (5) is given by

$$S = \frac{\sqrt{(I_r/I)^2 - 1}}{\dfrac{f}{f_0} - \dfrac{f_0}{f}} \tag{5a}$$

By choosing a low-loss coil for L together with a high-grade air condenser C and coupling only about one turn L_0 of a loosely coupled aperiodic detector with a portable galvanometer as in Fig. 136B, the sharpness of resonance can be made even better. An ordinary crystal rectifier (galena) and by-pass condenser C_0 are used in the indicator branch. A good frequency meter works with logarithmic decrements as low as $\delta = 0.01$.

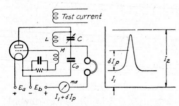

FIG. 137.—Tube-frequency meter (I_1 steady plate current when tube generates oscillations; I_2 steady plate current when no oscillations are generated; C_o by-pass condenser).

Figure 137 shows a circuit which is a generator of oscillations and a rectifier. Therefore the circuit acts as a tube voltmeter when voltages due to an external source are induced in the very selective CL branch. The change δI_p in the steady plate current is then a measure for the magnitude of the induced external voltage. In order to obtain a very selective frequency meter, the back coupling M of the oscillator is chosen loose. The resonance curve is then very sharp. Care must be taken that there is no "drawing" effect. By drawing effect is meant forced synchronization with consequent frequency jumps. The action of this frequency meter is the following. If a loosely coupled resonator acts on coil L and is in resonance with the CL circuit, it will draw energy from the tube generator and reflect an ohmic resistance into the CL branch. The amplitude of oscillation of the frequency meter will therefore decrease and the milliammeter will show the resonance deflection by a decided increase in the steady plate current. If the coupled circuit, the natural frequency of which is to be found, is not tuned exactly, a small resistance and an additional self-induction or an additional capacitance is reflected back into the CL branch, depending on which side of the resonance curve the detuning exists. Therefore a detuning of the CL circuit also takes place. But if the natural frequency of the test circuit is too far off the frequency of the tube generator, practically no action is reflected into the CL branch and the normal plate current $I_p = I_1$ is maintained. The detuning is the difference between the natural frequency of the test circuit and the effective frequency of the tube generator for the range of the resonance curve except for the resonance point. Therefore when the tube-frequency meter is calibrated, the resonance deflection noted by the milliammeter corresponds to the actual frequency of the test circuit. Such a frequency meter is very sensitive and especially so when the test circuit carries a high-frequency current whose frequency is to be found. A very loose coupling between the test circuit and the frequency meter (up to 2 m) is then possible. Knowing the frequency calibration for different settings of the variable-air condenser C, the setting of C is varied until the telephone receiver T gives a low beat note, for instance, 60 cycles/sec, checked against a 60-cycle sound of a power circuit. This corresponds to a frequency f_1. The condenser C is then varied through zero beat until a 60-cycle beat is again produced which corresponds to a frequency f_2. The average value $0.5(f_1 + f_2)$ is then the desired frequency. Figure 20 shows a calibrated tube generator which can be used for a rough calibration of frequencies. It is known as heterodyne, auxiliary generator, or local oscillator. The grid and plate coils $(L_1 + L_2)$ are formed by a single coil with a suitable tap toward the filament return. It can be readily built to cover the entire useful high-frequency range by using about six interchangeable coils $(L_1 + L_2)$ with a frequency-calibration curve on it with respect to the dial settings of the variable condenser. A 201 type tube, or its equivalent, with about 90 volts in the plate gives sufficient power for almost any laboratory work and a slow-motion device on the condenser provides a way of adjusting to zero beat if the frequency of a near-by current is to be determined. Switches S_1 and S_2, respectively, are provided to shunt a grid meter (a direct-current meter of 1-ma full deflection) or a telephone receiver. Either instrument can be used as a most sensitive resonance indicator if a loosely coupled CL circuit is to be calibrated. It is then unnecessary to have a meter in the CL circuit. But as the CL circuit goes through resonance corresponding to the frequency setting of the generator, a decided "grid dip" will be noted. At the same time a click is noticed in the telephone receiver. In order to do this, a loose coupling is required and very little energy is drawn by the *CL* circuit.   If the coupling is chosen too small, the dip will not be pronounced and a faint breathing noise will be noted in the receiver.   For a too close coupling, one resonance circuit takes the other one along (drawing effect) and double dips as well as two clicks at two different settings of the 0.001-μf condenser will be noted.   The actual resonance setting is somewhere between the two settings, and the two settings are not the same when the dial of the 0.001-μf condenser increases or decreases the capacity.   Therefore it is necessary to reduce the coupling until the two clicks coincide.   Figure 138 shows the dynatron frequency meter.[1]   In reality, the circuit acts as a pliodynatron.

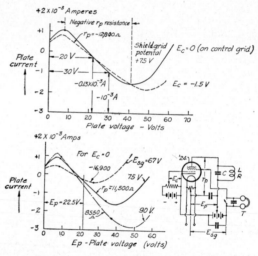

Fig. 138.—Dynatron frequency meter (dynamic resistance $r_p = -(30 - 20)/(10^{-3} - 0.13 \times 10^{-3}) = -11500\,\Omega$).

The ordinary double-grid tube (222 or its equivalent, or the 224 type tube or its equivalent as shown in the figure with an indirectly heated cathode) can be used for this work.   When the shield-grid connection is used, as in the figure, the plate resistance has a negative resistance action r_p over quite a range and, for instance, for the 224 type tube is about $-12,800\,\Omega$ if the control-grid bias E_c is zero (control grid and indirectly heated cathode connected), as can be computed from the plate-voltage change to corresponding plate-current change along the almost straight-line drooping characteristic.   Therefore when $E_c = 0$ is chosen and a screen-grid voltage anywhere between 67 and 90 volts is used for a plate voltage $E_p = 22.5$ volts, the plate resistance r_p is negative and practically constant along the linear portion of the characteristic with the operating point about at the middle of this portion.

[1] WORTHEN, C. E., *Gen. Rad. Experimenter*, **4**, 1, May, 1930; P. D. ZOTTER, *Q. S.T.*, **14**, 39, 1930, and H. IINUMA, *Proc. I.R.E.*, **18**, 537, 1930.

The tank circuit of effective constants C, L, and R in the actual plate branch is the characteristic element of the dynatron frequency meter. From the theory given in Sec. 9 in connection with Fig. 18, oscillations are excited in the circuit when the impedance of the tank circuit which is about equal to $L/(CR)$ is equal to or smaller than the negative plate resistance r_p over the work range. For the equality, the effective tank resistance L/CR is just neutralized, while in the other case growing oscillations take place until a steady amplitude is finally maintained because of the energy balance between circuit losses and power supply as well as the limitation of the negative tube characteristic. The frequency of oscillations is

$$f = \frac{1}{2\pi}\sqrt{\frac{1}{CL} - \left[\frac{R}{2L} + \frac{1}{2C(-r_p)}\right]^2} \qquad (6)$$

if the *negative* absolute value of r_p as indicated is to be inserted. The frequency is, therefore, of the form

$$f = [1 + p]f_0 \qquad (6a)$$

for

$$f_0 = \frac{1}{2\pi\sqrt{CL}} \text{ and } p \leqq \frac{0.5R}{L/CR} \qquad (7)$$

The value of p with customary parallel-resonance circuits is very small compared with unity. Even in the megacycle range such as 25 Mc/sec, it is only about a few ten-thousandths, while at lower frequencies it is usually below 0.0002. Hence, if $(-r_p) = L/CR$, sustained oscillations are just possible, and f very nearly equals f_0 where C also includes the plate to cathode interelectrode capacitance. Experience has shown that a dynatron will produce oscillations from a few cycles up to about 25 Mc/sec., if the oscillation constant CL is varied and the effective resistance $L/(CR)$ chosen such that it is neutralized by the negative alternating-current resistance r_p. A commercial design uses the General Radio precision-frequency (wave) meter as the CLR branch and the circuit shown in Fig. 138 with the control grid connected to the indirectly heated cathode with about 90 volts on the screen grid and 22.5 volts on the plate. The dynatron frequency meter keeps the frequency calibration much better than the ordinary tube frequency meter (Fig. 20) and changes in operating voltages have a very small frequency effect so that accuracies in the neighborhood of one tenth of 1 per cent are possible and in some cases even better. When an ordinary frequency meter (Fig. 136A) is used as the CLR branch in Fig. 138, the frequency meter can also be operated such that only the sharpness of resonance is increased by having just enough negative plate resistance r_p acting so that $L/(CR)$ is decreased to about zero. This is then done by adjusting the negative grid bias E_c on the control grid until self-oscillations are just about to start. This also gives the circuit described on page 87 for obtaining a very sensitive zero-current indicator of the differential transformer. If the dynatron frequency meter acts as a generator, a telephone receiver T in the shield-grid branch is used to note beat notes produced by the interaction of the dynatron oscillations and an induced small current whose frequency is to be determined. Harmonics up to fifteen times the fundamental can then be used to calibrate points.

In all the circuits described, a CL circuit with a small decrement is employed and the frequency is given by $f = 1/(2\pi\sqrt{CL})$ to a good degree of approximation. Hence, if ΔL denotes a small increase in the inductance L, it will decrease the frequency by a value Δf, since

$$f - \Delta f = \frac{1}{[2\pi\sqrt{C(L + \Delta L)}]}$$

If the effective capacitance C is decreased by an amount ΔC so as again to produce the original frequency,

$$f = \frac{1}{(2\pi\sqrt{(C - \Delta C)(L + \Delta L)})} = \frac{1}{(2\pi\sqrt{CL})}$$

and $\Delta L(C - \Delta C) = L\Delta C$. Hence,

$$\Delta L = \frac{L}{C - \Delta C}\Delta C \cong \frac{L}{C}\Delta C \tag{8}$$

when only small changes ΔL in L occur so that $\Delta L\,\Delta C$ becomes negligible. This gives a method for measuring small L changes by means of a small but measurable variation in the setting of a vernier condenser connected in parallel with C. The change Δf is noted as a beat tone in a constant-frequency generator of frequency f. The beat frequency Δf is reduced to zero by varying the setting of the vernier condenser. This method is followed up on page 247.

Instead of indicating the condition of resonance by a thermoelectric indicator as in Fig. 136A, a tube voltmeter with very high input imped-ance can be used to note the resonance voltage across C. In each case where either the current or the corresponding voltage for indicating resonance is used, special precautions must be taken when the resonance setting of the second and third harmonic is taken. This is discussed in Sec. 6 in connection with Fig. 13.

79. The Effect of Harmonic Content on Frequency Meters.—If E_1, E_2, E_3, E_4, . . . E_m denote the effective values of the fundamental, second-harmonic component, etc., when the frequency meter of Fig. 136A is tuned to the fundamental and a distorted e.m.f. is induced, the response current I_r registered by the microammeter and expressed in amperes for the sharpness $S = \pi/\delta$ of resonance becomes

$$I_r = \frac{E_1}{R}\sqrt{1 + \sum_{m=2}^{m=\infty}\left[\frac{m}{m^2-1}\frac{E_m}{S}\right]^2}$$

$$= \frac{E_1}{R}\sqrt{1 + \left\{\frac{4}{9}E_2{}^2 + \frac{9}{64}E_3{}^2 + \frac{16}{225}E_4{}^2 + \cdots\right\}\frac{1}{E_1{}^2 S^2}} \qquad (9)$$

since, because of $\omega L = 1/(\omega C)$ and $\delta = R/(2fL)$, the current contribution due to the mth harmonic is practically

$$I_m \cong \frac{E_m}{m\omega L - \dfrac{1}{m\omega C}} = \frac{E_m}{m\omega L - \dfrac{\omega L}{m}} = \frac{m}{m^2-1}\frac{E_m}{\omega L} =$$

$$\frac{m}{m^2-1}\frac{\delta}{\pi R}E_m = \frac{m}{m^2-1}\frac{E_m}{RS}$$

for $m = 2, 3, 4$, and for the fundamental $I_1 = E_1/R$ and

$$I_r = \sqrt{I_1{}^2 + I_2{}^2 + I_3{}^2 + I_4{}^2 + \cdots I_m{}^2} \qquad (9a)$$

Hence, if a frequency meter is used with an effective logarithmic decrement $\delta = 0.01$, a second-harmonic induced voltage as high as 25 per cent and a third harmonic as high as 10 per cent, both with respect to the fundamental, gives $E_2/E_1 = \frac{1}{4}$ and $E_3/E_1 = \frac{1}{10}$. The sharpness of resonance then is $S = \pi/0.01 = 314$ and the current response in the resonance indicator becomes

$$I_r = \frac{E_1}{R}\sqrt{1 + \frac{\dfrac{4}{9\times 16} + \dfrac{9}{64\times 100}}{314^2}} \cong \frac{E_1}{R}\sqrt{1 + \frac{1}{(6\times 314)^2}} \cong$$

$$\frac{E_1}{R}\left[1 + \frac{1}{2(6\times 314)^2}\right]$$

The microammeter μa then registers a resonance current which is practically the correct value E_1/R due to the fundamental alone. But suppose the resonance indicator adds enough resistance so that δ is as high as 0.314, then $S = 10$. Therefore, when only a pronounced second harmonic is present and as strong as 50 per cent of the fundamental, which may happen, $E_2/E_1 = 0.5$ and the indicated current

$$I_r = I_1\sqrt{1 + \frac{4}{9}\left(\frac{E_2}{E_1 S}\right)^2} = I_1\sqrt{1 + \frac{1}{900}} \cong I_1\left[1 + \frac{1}{1800}\right]$$

if I_1 denotes the true resonance current E_1/R. The registered current is then only 0.056 per cent too high. However, the error may become appreciable if an auxiliary resistance is inserted in the resonator tuned to the fundamental and may play a part in the resistance variation method described in Sec. 126.

If a tube voltmeter or some other voltmeter of very high input impedance is used to note the fundamental resonance in the $C\,L\,R$ circuit of Fig. 136, the microammeter μa is dispensed with, and the voltage across C is measured. It is practically equal to the voltage across the coil L and, if I_1 denotes the fundamental component of the coil current, one has, for the effective voltage due to the fundamental only,

$$I_1 \omega L = \frac{E_1}{R} \omega L = \frac{\pi}{\delta} E_1 = SE_1$$

and for any higher harmonic of frequency $m\omega/2\pi$, the effective voltage contribution

$$I_m m \omega L = \frac{m^2}{m^2 - 1} E_m$$

measured also by the tube voltmeter, but in quadrature, since the square root relation of $(9a)$ also applies to the effective voltages. Hence, the resultant effective voltage E_r measured across L becomes

$$E_r = \sqrt{[SE_1]^2 + \sum_{m=2}^{m=\infty} \left[\frac{m^2}{m^2-1} E_m \right]^2} = SE_1 \sqrt{1 + \sum_{2}^{\infty} \left[\frac{m^2}{m^2-1} \frac{E_m}{SE_1} \right]^2}$$

$$= E_0 \sqrt{1 + \frac{\frac{16}{9} E_2{}^2 + \frac{81}{64} E_3{}^2 + \frac{256}{225} E_4{}^2 + \cdots}{S^2 E_1{}^2}} \qquad (10)$$

if E_0 stands for the true resonance voltage across the tuning condenser C. Hence, applying this formula to the above example for the sharpness $S = 10$ of resonance and only a powerful second harmonic of 50 per cent strength with respect to the fundamental, since $E_2/E_1 = 0.5$, the apparent measured resonance voltage is

$$E_r = E_0 \sqrt{1 + \frac{16}{9} \left[\frac{E_2}{E_1 S} \right]^2} = E_0 \sqrt{1 + \frac{4}{900}} \cong E_0 \left[1 + \frac{2}{900} \right]$$

The measured apparent resonance voltage is then 0.222 per cent too high. The error for the resonance setting with a voltmeter is therefore greater than when resonance is indicated with a current meter. This can also be understood from the respective correction terms in formulas (9) and (10), since for the current measurement the series $\frac{4}{9}\alpha + \frac{9}{64}\beta + \frac{16}{225}\gamma$ and for the voltage readings the series $\frac{16}{9}\alpha + \frac{81}{64}\beta + \frac{256}{225}\gamma$ play a part.

80. Direct-indicating Frequency Meters.—The voltage across a good condenser is a function of the frequency, if the current is kept constant. The same holds true for a pure inductive reactance where, for a constant current I through L, the voltage $2\pi f L I$ is directly proportional to the frequency f. When the current I is not constant, in each case the terminal voltage also becomes a function of the current which would be a great drawback if such reactances were used in direct-indicating frequency meters (by means of the terminal voltage), since the current would have to be adjusted to the value used for the calibration. However, if a pure inductive reactance $2\pi fL$ is connected in parallel with a condenser of reactance $1/(2\pi fC)$, the ratio of the coil current to the condenser current is proportional only to the *square* of the frequency f, with a proportionality constant $4\pi^2 CL$, and no longer dependent on the total current passing to the parallel combination. For a pure resistance R in multiple with an inductive reactance $2\pi fL$, the ratio of resistance to coil current is directly proportional to f with a factor of proportionality of $2\pi L/R$, while for a capacity reactance $1/(2\pi fC)$, used instead of the coil, gives an inverse-frequency law for resistance to condenser current with a constant of proportionality of $1/(2\pi CR)$. The effective-resistance components of the coil and the condenser are neglected in these formulas. Therefore, it is only necessary to find a means of measuring the ratio of the branch currents. This can be done by the heat effect of the branch currents and by means of the dynamometer principle. The hot-wire direct-reading frequency meter of G. Ferrié[1] and T. Carpentier is an example. The meter is indicated in Fig. 139 where a pure resistance R carries the current I_1 also passing through one hot-wire ammeter, and a high inductive reactance ωL carries the current I_2 flowing through the other ammeter. Then $I_1/I_2 = \omega L/R$ with a good degree of approximation. The respective pointers of the two independent hot-wire meters give deflections A and B, according to the squares of I_1 and I_2. For a certain current I of a certain frequency f, the deflections of α and β occur.

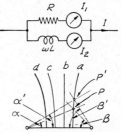

Fig. 139.—Direct-indicating frequency meter due to G. Ferrié and J. Carpentier.

The pointers will intersect at P. For a larger current $I + \delta I$ flowing to the parallel combination but of the same frequency f, other deflections under angles α' and β' will produce the intersection P'. For all currents of constant frequency f, the curve a is the locus for the intersections. For other frequencies f_1, f_2, f_3, the curves b, c, and d are obtained. Of course, an instrument of this type does not come up to present-day accuracy and is also affected by harmonics. Nevertheless, the operating principle underlying this and the other few direct-reading frequency meters is of general interest, even though most of them, except the piezo-electric glow resonator, may be grouped among frequency indicators rather than standards. In a manner similar to the Ferrié-Carpentier frequency meter, a resistance wire, whose dimensions and material are such that the effective resistance over the desired frequency range is kept constant, may be used in parallel with a resistance wire of iron which varies with f. The dynamometric direct-reading

[1] *Lumière élec.*, **32**, 427, 1910.

frequency meters due to G. Seibt[1] and O. Scheller[2] are based on the short-circuit ring dynamometer due to L. Mandelstam and S. Papalexi.[3] This principle is also made use of in the direct-reading frequency meter of the Weston Company employed for the lower-frequency range. As far as the operation is concerned, the frequency meter consists, as in Fig. 140, of two fixed coils S_1 and S_2 which are mounted perpendicular to each other with a pivoted short-circuit ring (conveniently of aluminum) S_3. When the branch currents I_1 and I_2 pass through S_1 and S_2, respectively, the deflection of S_3 is proportional to the product $I_1 I_2$, since the two magnetic fields of coils S_1 and S_2 generally produce a resultant field which is elliptically polarized, that is, an elliptical revolving field. This field takes the short-circuit ring along, since it has a tendency to place the plane of the ring into the major axis of the ellipse. Hence, if one branch current I_1 passes over R and the other I_2 over $2\pi fL$, the ratio I_1/I_2 varies with f and the deflection of S_3 can be directly calibrated in frequency.

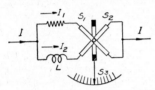

FIG. 140.—Dynamometric direct-indicating frequency meter.

A frequency meter of similar construction is also due to W. Hahnemann. Special constructions are needed for the high-frequency range. The thermocross bridge (Fig. 59) and the three thermocross arrangement of Fig. 143 can also be used to make a direct-reading frequency meter, since these indicators deflect proportional to $\int i_1 i_2 dt$. Direct-reading high-frequency meters working only over a small range (say 100 cycles/sec) about the actual resonance setting (say 500 kc/sec) can also be obtained by using the deflections of an ordinary frequency meter. The circuit of Fig. 136B, for which the capacitance C, inductance L, and the coupling to the aperiodic indicator circuit are all fixed, can be used for this purpose. The frequency meter is then so coupled to a source that at the desired high frequency f the resonance deflection is just equal to the maximum reading of the indicator. If then the frequency of the source is changed by a small amount $\pm\Delta f$, the reduced indicator deflection is a measure for the frequencies $f + \Delta f$ and $f - \Delta f$, if Δf is relatively small and the resonance curve essentially symmetrical over the work range with respect to the maximum response. However, this scheme does not tell directly whether the frequency has been lowered or raised by Δf, unless a small variable vernier condenser is used in parallel with C. (If an increase in the vernier capacitance is required to restore maximum deflection, the frequency is raised.) A frequency indicator which avoids this complication and is very accurate is the piezo-electric glow-discharge resonator due to E. Giebe and A. Scheibe.[4] It uses a

[1] *Jahrb. d. drahtl.*, **22**, 504, 1916.
[2] *Jahrb. d. drahtl.*, **22**, 507, 1916.
[3] *Ann. Physik.*, **33**, 490, 1910.
[4] *Z. Physik.*, **33**, 335, 1925.

quartz resonator which with the "crevasse" method of indication was originally used by W. Cady.[1] The direct-indicating Giebe-Scheibe luminous piezo meter of the Loewe Radio Co., Berlin, consists of about five piezo-electric resonators, 1, 2, 3, 4, 5, in a mixture of helium and neon gas of 10- to 15-mm pressure of mercury. The crystal 3 corresponds to the desired high frequency and crystals 2 and 1 are successively at a somewhat smaller frequency, just as for crystal 4 a somewhat higher frequency $(f + \Delta f)$ and for 5 the resonance frequency $(f + 2\Delta f)$ exists. The resonator which is affected will glow up with a characteristic pattern and the indicator works similarly to the commercial frequency indicator where several vibrating reeds are used for a frequency range from about 58 to 62 cycles/sec. The reed for which the natural frequency is the same as the frequency to be indicated will vibrate. In the Giebe and Scheibe glow-discharge indicator it is easy to indicate the resonance condition, since only a suitable pick-up coil is connected across the several resonators and a large glow discharge takes place just before accurate resonance response takes place. When the frequency to be adjusted is then further varied by a small amount toward the desired frequency, the large glow discharge of the tube gradually concentrates toward the crystal and at resonance (which is very sharp) it gives a distinctive glow-discharge pattern on the crystal which is characteristic to the mode of crystal vibration and the order of it. Since in this indicator only a small window in front of the crystals is used, only the distinctive glow patterns will be seen and the bright spot moves from the left to the right as the test frequency is varied from a lower value to a somewhat higher value. The accuracy, however, is not good enough for primary-frequency standardization. Here it is more convenient to use a piezo oscillator with a proper temperature control and *no* glow discharge. The vibrations of the quartz resonator can be expressed by

$$\alpha\frac{d^2y}{dt^2} + \beta\frac{dy}{dt} + \gamma y = kE \tag{11}$$

where y denotes the displacement at any time t due to a sinusoidal voltage E acting across the resonator coatings. The equivalent electrical constants of the series combination are $C = k^2/\gamma$; $L = \alpha/k^2$ and $R = \beta/k^2$ for a quartz rod vibrating longitudinally along the y dimension but excited by the voltage E along the piezo-electric x dimension which is perpendicular to the optic axis and the y dimension. If the air-gap effect and the capacity effect of the electrode mounting in shunt to the equivalent series combination are neglected, Eq. (5) of this chapter can be taken for the equivalent current I at any frequency f and the equivalent resonance current I_r for the frequency f_0. The sharpness of resonance is then

$$S = \frac{2\pi f_0 L}{R} = \omega_0\frac{\alpha}{\beta} \tag{12}$$

[1] *Phys. Rev.*, **17**, 531, 1921; **18**, 142, 1921; *Proc. I.R.E.*, **10**, 83, 1922.

that is considerably larger than for any electric resonator. If the decrement is found to be $\delta = 0.00005$, the sharpness of resonance becomes $S = \pi/\delta$, that is, very favorable.

81. Calibration of Frequency Meters.—The calibration of a frequency meter is usually carried out by means of a standard frequency meter. In the method indicated in Fig. 141, distorted currents from a tube generator are rectified by a thermionic tube which can also be an ordinary three-element thermionic tube with the grid and plate connected together. The rectifier makes the harmonic content still richer. A step-over resonator is used to transfer a small amount of the energy to the frequency meter to be calibrated or to a standard frequency meter which is used for comparison. For a certain setting of condenser C_1, the step-over resonator is tuned by means of C_3 to the fundamental frequency f of the oscillator. This condition exists when a maximum deflection occurs

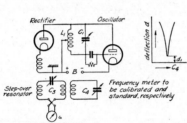

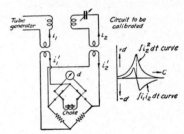

Fig. 141.—Calibration with a step-over resonator.   Fig. 142.—Calibration with a thermo-cross bridge.

on the thermoelectric indicator d. Then the frequency meter to be calibrated is tuned to f and resonance occurs when the indicator of the step-over resonator passes through a decided and sharp minimum d_1. The test-frequency meter is then removed and a standard frequency meter loosely coupled to the resonator and resonance obtained in the same way. The reading on the standard is then the desired frequency. Next, the same process is repeated for the second and, if possible, for the third harmonic, giving the calibrations for frequencies $2f$ and $3f$, respectively. Hereafter another suitable setting of C_1L_1 is chosen corresponding to a fundamental frequency f_1 of the oscillations and the calibration points for f_1, $2f_1$, and, if possible, for $3f_1$ are obtained, and so on. A very wide frequency range can be covered with this scheme. The purpose of the step-over resonator is to induce only pure sinusoids in the frequency meter and to give sharper resonance indications, since the absorption type of resonance curve utilized when taking the frequency-meter settings is very sharp. Figure 142 uses the thermocross bridge, to which a circuit to be calibrated in frequency is loosely coupled, as an indicator. A few turns of the thermocross bridge are loosely coupled to the oscillator and about the same number of turns of the bridge are loosely coupled to the test circuit.   The galvanometer deflection d of the bridge will then pass through zero when the test circuit is exactly in tune with the oscillator which should produce a pure sine wave, since for this case $\int i_1 i_2 dt = 0$, and the currents i_1 and i_2 are one-quarter period out of phase.   The method indicated in Fig. 143 likewise produces zero deflection for resonance, since again by means of the connection of the three thermocrosses the $\int i_1 i_2 dt$ effect is produced.   In each case the frequency of the tube generator (which is conveniently shown in Fig. 20) is accurately found by the grid dip which occurs when a standard fre-quency meter is coupled to it.

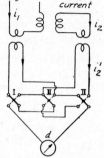

If a tube voltmeter of high input impedance is used to measure the terminal voltage E across the condenser C of a resonator, the natural frequency of the CL branch can also be computed from the current and voltage readings by means of

$$f = 159\frac{I}{E\,C} \qquad (13)$$

where f is in kilocycles per second, I in amperes, E in volts, and C in microfarads, which is the outcome of the well-known relation $\omega CE = I$.   This method is not to be used for the calibration of frequency meters but may be of value for certain circuits with natural frequencies of interest.

Fig. 143.—Calibration by means of three thermo elements.

82. Determination of the Frequency of Received Currents.—Sometimes it is desirable to check up on the frequency of a remote station and use this method to compare frequency standards in different countries.   It is as follows: Laboratories located in different countries tune in on the same station at exactly the same time and determine the fre-

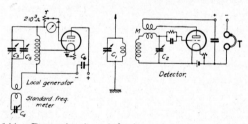

Fig. 144.—Determination of the frequency of a remote station.

quency of the received current.   If the standards of various laboratories are alike, there should be no difference in the f setting.   For such work it is best to choose suitable short-wave stations or low-frequency stations (20 to 100 kc/sec) which can be readily picked up anywhere.   All other points of the frequency meter can be obtained by the harmonic methods after several points have been secured in this way.   Figure 144 gives a

circuit for such work.   A local generator is coupled a certain distance[1]
from the receiver.   The frequency of the local oscillations is varied
until a beat current becomes audible in the telephone receiver T.   The
frequency of the local generator is then varied further until zero-beat
condition is obtained, and the frequency of the local generator is determined by a loosely coupled frequency meter.   The correct frequency is
obtained when the grid meter just registers a dip for a certain setting of
C_4.   For long-distance stations, a few stages of high-frequency amplification are used between the antenna and the detector, and the local
generator is then conveniently loosely coupled toward the detector
stage so that very high frequency amplification can be used without
blanketing out the signals to be received.   For receiving long-wave
transoceanic power stations (corresponding to about the range 20 to
150 kc/sec), about three stages of resistance-capacity coupled amplification with a regenerative output detector and one or two stages of audio-
frequency amplification are sufficient.   It should be noted that for this

kind of work it is unnecessary to have the received
current modulated, since audibility is produced by the
local beat interference.   If several stations affect the
receiver (which is especially the case when the frequency of a long-distance station is to be measured and
some near-by stations of a neighboring frequency or
some harmonic frequency also produce beat tones), the
zero-beat method is unsuitable because, as the current
whose frequency is to be determined passes about
through zero-beat tone, another signal may produce a

FIG. 145.—F r e -
quency determination
of a remote station by
means of the equal-
pitch method.

tone and drown out the desirable zero-beat condition.   It is better to
adjust to a suitable beat tone as in Fig. 145.   In this method the measurement is carried on by adjusting to the same pitch of the beat note on each
side of the resonance curve.   For simplicity, only the generator is shown.
Antenna, amplifier, and detector are as just described.   The process of
measurement is:

   1. Adjust the frequency of the local generator to about the value to be determined.
   2. The condenser C_1 of the antenna (Fig. 144) is varied until the telephone receiver
produces a beat tone.
   3. The setting of C_2 (Fig. 144) and the back feed M of the regenerative detector
are varied until optimum loudness is obtained without producing self-oscillations in
the detector.
   4. The condenser C_3 of Fig. 145 for the switch S open is varied until a suitable
pitch of the beat tone is heard.   In many cases a 1000-cycle note will do and may be
readily secured by listening at the same time to a 1000-cycle tuning-fork oscillator
(buzzer type of the General Radio Company will do) and adjusting to zero beat
between both tones.
   5. Switch S is closed and C_0 varied until the same beat tone is heard again.   This
can be readily done by quickly opening and closing the switch while varying C_0 until
the same pitch is heard.

   [1] Otherwise the energy of the local generator paralyzes the sensitive detector.

The condition with S open and S closed then corresponds to the frequencies $f - f_a$ and $f + f_a$, where f is the frequency of the received current, and f_a the pitch of the beat tone for each position of S. The frequency f_1 of the local generator is measured with the loosely coupled standard frequency meter when S is open and the frequency f_2 when S is closed. The frequency of the received current is found from $\frac{1}{2}(f_1 + f_2)$.

83. Notes on Methods Using Harmonic Multiplication and Division.— For calibration work of the entire useful high frequency, higher harmonics and so-called "subharmonics" greatly facilitate the work, since it is then possible to cover the entire range with only one accurate reference frequency which is conveniently

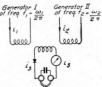

Fig. 146.—Arrangement for the production of audible beat currents.

produced by a thermostatically controlled piezo-electric quartz oscillator. In Fig. 146, two generators of fundamental frequencies f_1 and f_2 act on the same detector which can be used for listening to any beat notes or indicating the condition of zero beat. The rectifier can be an ordinary galena detector, a two-element thermionic rectifier, or a three-element tube in the detector connection.

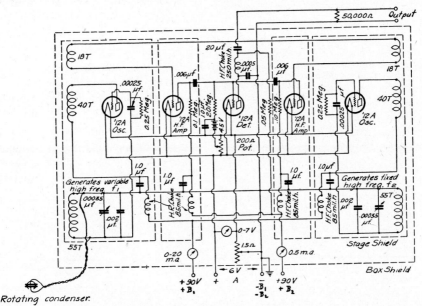

Fig. 147.—Compact laboratory beat-frequency generator. (Rotating condenser for warbling beat note in certain acoustic measurements.)

Figure 147 gives a beat-frequency generator of fixed high frequency f_2 and variable high frequency f_1. The pulling effect near the zero-beat frequency is minimized here by using a very loose coupling between the two high-frequency generators of frequencies f_1 and f_2, respectively, and a stage of high-frequency amplification for each high-frequency oscillation before mixing them in the rectifier. According to the experience of the Sound Laboratory of the Bureau of Standards, a circuit of this type works satisfactorily down to about 10 cycles/sec, and with a fairly good wave shape (harmonic content less than 5 per cent). UX 112-A tubes or their equivalent perform well when the fixed condenser 0.002 μf in the respective high-frequency oscillators is of good make and all tubes are surrounded by heavy brass tubes to keep the oscillator coils (55 turns) free from appreciable temperature effects. For other details: the oscillator coils which produce the high frequencies f_1 and f_2, respectively, are wound on $3\frac{1}{2}$-in. diameter bakelite tubing about 6 in. in length. The three coils are wound approximately 2 in. on centers, although this distance is not critical. The tuning coil contains 55 turns, the plate coil 40 turns, and the coupling coil 18 turns, all of No. 26 A.w.g., double-cotton-covered wire. The tuning or grid coil is placed in the center. Each oscillator is placed inside a separate metal box of about $\frac{1}{4}$-in. thickness. The same is true for each high-frequency amplifier stage, while the detector stage (frequency mixer and rectifier to produce frequency $f_1 - f_2$) is not shielded separately and a proper negative grid bias is used for the detector tube. The entire assembly is surrounded by a large metal box which is grounded. The audio frequency at the output terminals is about 4 volts and varies only a small percentage over most of the audio range. A sharp cut-off at the upper limit of the audio range is due to the by-pass circuit in the output of the detector stage. This circuit prevents any high-frequency currents from being passed from the oscillators and supersonic harmonics of the audio frequency on through the output. When an absolute elimination of harmonics is required, a two-stage filter should be used. As to the design of the variable condenser (0.00035 uf) with the audio-frequency calibration ($f_1 - f_2$) on its dial, it is desirable to set the oscillator frequency with the same precision at any frequency. This requires a variable-air condenser which gives a frequency variation with the logarithm proportional to the rotor angle. The curve between the audio frequency ($f_1 - f_2$) against the dial setting is then a sloping straight line when plotted on semilogarithmic paper (ordinary scale for rotor angle and logarithmic scale for audio frequency). Choose the fixed high frequency f_2 so that maximum and minimum audio frequency occur for minimum and maximum high frequency f_1 of the variable oscillator. The audio frequency will then increase as the capacitance of the air condenser is increased.

With reference to Fig. 146, the instantaneous value of the current i_3 is

$$i_3 = \{I_1 \sin (\omega_1 t + \varphi_1) + I_2 \sin (\omega_2 t + \varphi_2)\}^q$$

Since the value $q = 2$ is of importance only for customary detectors,

$$i_3 = I_1{}^2 \sin^2 (\omega t + \varphi_1) + I_2{}^2 \sin^2 (\omega_2 t + \varphi_2) \text{ currents of frequencies}[1]$$

$$2f_1, 2f_2, \text{ and zero}$$

$$+ I_1 I_2 \cos [(\omega_1 - \omega_2)t + \varphi_1 - \varphi_2] \text{ *audible beat component* of}$$

$$\text{frequency } f_1 - f_2$$

$$- I_1 I_2 \cos [(\omega_1 + \omega_2)t + \varphi_1 + \varphi_2] \text{ current of high frequency}$$

$$f_1 + f_2 \quad (14)$$

Hence, if m and n denote whole numbers, such as 1, 2, 3, 4, etc., mf_1 is any possible harmonic of generator I, and nf_2 any possible harmonic of generator II. The telephone receiver in the detector circuit will there-

---

[1] Since $I^2 \sin^2 x = 0.5I^2 - 0.5I^2 \cos 2x$.

fore give a tone whenever the frequency $(mf_1 - nf_2)$ falls in the audible-frequency spectrum. Hence, if frequency f_1 is gradually varied, at first a high-pitched tone is heard, which gradually becomes lower in frequency until it passes through the silent[1] region ($+16$ over zero to -16 cycles/sec) in order to raise again in pitch until the frequency $(mf_1 - nf_2)$ falls again in the supersonic range. For measurements the case

$$mf_1 = nf_2 \qquad (15)$$

plays a part because zero-beat frequency exists for such a condition. For the same reason as in the last section, it is often better to adjust the circuits for a suitable beat note, that is, make

$$mf_1 - nf_2 = f_b \qquad (16)$$

where the beat frequency f_b can be found by a tuned vibration galvanometer[2] or a sonometer (see Fig. 157). If the beat notes are too weak, as is often the case, a tuning-fork drive of known pitch is used and the circuits are adjusted until zero beat occurs between the sound due to f_b noted in a telephone receiver and the sound coming from the tuning fork. To find the order of the harmonic, for instance, for fundamental frequency f_1, an auxiliary generator, such as shown in Fig. 20, with a rough calibration can be used. It is also possible to find the order of a high harmonic by adjusting for absolute zero beat for the harmonic mf_1 and the next harmonic $(m + 1)f_1$ and measuring the approximate frequencies mf_1 and $(m + 1)f_1$ with an ordinary frequency meter. The difference between the two readings then gives the approximate value of the fundamental frequency, since

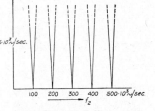

$$f_1 = (m + 1)f_1 - mf_1 \qquad (17)$$

and by dividing the consecutive frequency readings by this value f_1 gives the order m and $(m + 1)$ of the harmonics. Hence, if in (15) either f_1 or f_2 is known, the corresponding frequency of any higher harmonic can be found.

Fig. 148.—Full lines represent pitch of sound and dotted portions the supersonic conditions.

An application is as follows: Let the fundamental frequency f_1 of the first generator be fixed and 100 kc/sec. If the frequency f_2 is gradually increased from a small value, the telephone receiver in the detector from about $f_2 = 85$ kc/sec on will start to sound with a high-pitched tone. With a further increase, the beat note becomes lower (Fig. 148) until, for $f_2 = 100$ kc/sec, zero-beat frequency is reached. A further increase in f_2 again produces a beat current of increasing frequency. If the coupling to the detector is properly chosen, the condition for the critical zero fre-

[1] Automatic synchronization is not taken into consideration here.
[2] The General Radio oscillograph galvanometer can be used for this purpose.

quency can be readily adjusted with the visual indicator. Thus are obtained successively the critical zeros in the beat frequency for

$$af_1 = f_2 = 100 \atop \begin{aligned} = f_2 &= 200 \\ = f_2 &= 300 \\ = f_2 &= 400 \end{aligned}\Bigg\} \text{kc/sec for } a = \begin{cases} 1 \\ 2 \\ 3 \\ 4 \end{cases}$$

and the calibration points $f_2 = f_1$, $2f_1$, $3f_1$, $4f_1$, etc., for the second generator. But if the frequency f_1 is changed and the fixed f_2 frequency is known, the calibrations $f_1 = f_2$, $f_2/2$, $f_3/3$, $f_2/4$, etc., for the first generator are obtained. Hence, if a frequency meter is loosely coupled to either one of the generators, points pf and f/p can be calibrated. If the beat tone is produced by a so-called "fractional-reference" frequency such as for all values of f/p and p of a higher order such as $p = 10$, it is best to couple the frequency meter to the generator which produces the higher harmonic. The beat tone will then be much louder. For small values of p it does not matter to which generator the frequency meter is coupled, especially if a detector with successive audio-frequency amplification is used. In taking such a series of harmonic readings, it will be noted that the values of p are *not always* whole numbers, such as 1, 2, 3, 4, etc., but may have values such as 1.25, 1.5, 1.66, etc., and it may seem that Fourier's theorem no longer holds. However, this is not the case, since in Eq. (15) all integer values of m and n occur and zero-beat conditions hold for any such values as make $mf_1 - nf_2 = 0$. In this equation the ratio of the whole numbers for m and n must be chosen so that it is equal to the corresponding fundamental-frequency ratio of the two generators, that is,

$$\frac{f_1}{f_2} = \frac{m}{n} \tag{18}$$

Hence, if, for the reference frequency f, $pf = 1.66f$ the case is simply $1.66f = \frac{5}{3}f$. Now if f is found from the measurement to be the fundamental frequency f_1, one obtains from $1.66f_1 = \frac{5}{3}f_1$ the relation $5f_1 = 3f_2$. The fifth harmonic of the first generator then beats with the third harmonic of the second generator. But if the measurement shows that the calibration frequency is $f_1/1.66$, it is found that $3f_1 = 5f_2$ and the third harmonic of the *first* generator beats with the fifth harmonic of the *second* generator. Therefore one has the case of beats between higher harmonics. The beat tone is then much weaker but is a means of getting more calibration points.

Example.—Suppose $f_1 = 106$ kc/sec and the second generator has a fundamental frequency $f_2 = 160$ kc/sec. A combination current is then obtained whose interference frequency is $160 - 106 = 54$ kc/sec. The beat current *cannot* then be audible. But the first generator also has a harmonic $2f_1 = 212$ kc/sec, whose current together with the fundamental current due to the second generator produces the combination current of beat current $212 - 160 = 52$ kc/sec, which is again supersonic, that is, beyond audibility. But the two combination currents just mentioned interfere with each other in the detector and produce a beat note of frequency $54 - 52 = 2$ kc/sec, and an adjustment of f_2 to a value of $f_2 = 159$ kc/sec must give the zerobeat frequency condition of this beat note. The ratio $f_2/f_1 = {}^{159}\!/_{106} = 1.5$ shows that the second harmonic of the second generator beats with the third harmonic of the first generator. This zero-beat condition can also be proved with the harmonic frequency $3f_1 = 318$ kc/sec, since

$$3f_1 - f_2 = 318 - 160 = 158 \text{ kc/sec} = f_3$$
$$f_2 - f_1 = 160 - 106 = 54 \text{ kc/sec} = f_4$$
$$f_3 - f_4 = 104 \text{ kc/sec} = f_5$$
$$f_1 - f_5 = 2 \text{ kc/sec} = f_{\text{audio beat}}$$

and it can again be seen that f_2 must be changed to 159 kc, in order to bring the tone of 2 kc/sec to zero frequency. Hence, the combination currents which are supersonic combine again with other inaudible combination currents to produce finally lowfrequency effects and, if proper adjustments are made, the condition of zero-beat frequency.

Harmonic methods seem involved at first, but practice will show that it is not very difficult to determine the order of harmonics, since one reference frequency (either f_1 or f_2) is known and, as shown in connection with Eq. (17), the order of harmonic can be found with an approximate frequency calibration and two consecutive harmonics.

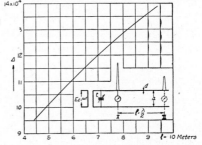

FIG. 149.—Frequency calibration by means of a parallel-wire system and correction curve (a = distance between centers = 4.2 cm. and diameter d = 0.14 cm).

84. Modified Lecher Wire System for the Determination of Frequency.—

A parallel-wire system bridged over with a current meter of negligible resistance can be used for the determination of frequency. The arrangement in Fig. 149 can be used for this purpose. The sliding bridge across the parallel-wire system may consist of a thermoelectric meter with a maximum reading of about 0.1 amp and about 5-Ω heater resistance. In shunt to the meter is a stout copper wire (about 2 mm in diameter) to make the effective resistance of the parallel combination negligibly small as far as wave reflections are concerned at the meter bridge. A still better arrangement consists of a small student galvanometer in series with a fixed crystal detector and this series combination in shunt with the stout copper wire. The indicator is then sensitive and when mounted upside down can be readily read off from below the parallel-wire system. Inasmuch as this method is based on voltage and current distributions along the double line, it is best to deal in terms of wave length first, since this is the physical quantity which is measured. For practical reasons it is then well to work with short wave lengths which are somewhere between 4 and 20 m and find the calibration for longer wave lengths by means of the harmonic method just described with a loosely coupled tube generator (Fig. 150) whose frequency range is lower than that of the exciting voltage $E\epsilon^{j\omega t}$. The circuit is then essentially the network investigated at one time by the Bureau of Standards[1] and settings on the frequency meter to be calibrated consist in the comparison of the harmonics of the auxiliary generator with the short half wavelength distributions along the double line. The meter bridge is moved along the double line and the distance l between two maximum current settings noted. This distance is equal to half the wave length developed along the line. In order to keep the double line short, a variable-air condenser C is connected across the line near the input side where the voltage is impressed and the setting of the condenser C is changed so that the two maximum current settings of the meter bridge (a distance $l = \lambda/2$ apart) occur closer to the input side. The distance l is carefully scaled off and expressed in meters. Since the true wave length λ_0 in free space differs somewhat from λ, a correction term Δ must be used, and

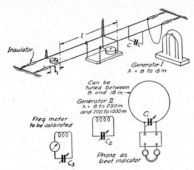

Fig. 150.—Modified Lecher wire system.

$$\lambda_0 = 2l[1 + \Delta]$$

where λ_0 and l are in meters, giving the corresponding frequency

$$f = \frac{1.4991 \times 10^5}{l}(1 - \Delta) \qquad (19)$$

where f is in kilocycles per second, which is used in the computation. If an accuracy of from $\frac{1}{10}$ to $\frac{1}{2}$ per cent is sufficient, the term Δ can be ignored. The correction term Δ depends on the frequency, resistance, and inductance of the double line and can be read off from the graph of Fig. 149 if the dimensions given are used. Otherwise, it can be computed from

$$\Delta = \frac{\sqrt{r_0}}{8 \log_\epsilon B \sqrt{\omega[1 - (d/a)^2]}} \qquad (20)$$

where

$$B = \frac{1 + \sqrt{1 - (d/a)^2}}{d/a} \qquad (21)$$

For ordinary parallel lines, the distance a between the two conductors is relatively large compared with the diameter d of the conductor and $B \cong 2a/d$. The distance a is to be measured between the axis of the

[1] DUNMORE, F. W., and F. H. ENGEL, *Bur. Standards, Sci. Paper* 469, 1923; also see *Sci. Paper* 491, 1924.

parallel conductors. The quantity r_0 denotes the direct-current resistance per centimeter length of the double line and in the e.m. c.g.s. system is (10^9e.m.u. $= 1\Omega$). The frequency $\omega/2\pi$ in (20) is expressed in cycles per second. A numerical example is given in *Bureau of Standards Scientific Paper* 491. Computations show that small nonuniformities in wire diameter d leave no appreciable effect on Δ. The same holds true if there are slight variations in the spacing a. Even for a spacing $a = 4.7$ cm between conductors instead of $a = 4$ cm for the given range (16 to 34 Mc/sec), the average deviation is only 0.003 per cent. The above frequency range requires a parallel-wire system of about 14 m in length and the room must be somewhat longer in order to have space for the insulators (about 14 cm long) and the coil springs to keep the conductors stretched (Fig. 150). The high-frequency generator I delivers about 50 watts and is loosely coupled to the input semiloop, and the condenser is varied so that the first current loop comes close to the input end. The meter bridge is moved toward the open end until another maximum current reading is noted. The frequency meter to be tested is coupled loosely toward generator I and tuned to its fundamental frequency and f computed from l and Δ by (19). Hereafter the frequency of generator I is changed and another calibration point obtained. By this procedure calibrations up to $\lambda = 18$ m can be carried out. For frequencies corresponding to still longer wave lengths, the method is as follows:

1. The generator I is so adjusted that $l = 5$ m; that is, the wave length λ developed along the parallel line is 10 m. This corresponds to about 30 Mc/sec.

2. The beat-frequency indicator (which contains two stages of audio-frequency amplification) is tuned to this frequency so that any higher harmonics of the generator I cannot affect this indicator.

3. The frequency of generator II is varied until it produces about the same fundamental frequency as generator I. A strong beat tone will be heard which will disappear when the frequency of II is exactly that of generator I.

4. The frequency meter is now coupled toward generator II and the calibration for f obtained by means of the resonance setting. This corresponds to a frequency of 30 Mc/sec. The condenser setting C_2 of generator II is increased until the next beat tone appears. The setting of C_2 is further increased until for zero-beat note the frequency of generator II is $f/2 = 15$ Mc/sec. This frequency is transferred again to the frequency meter to be calibrated. This would correspond to a wave length of about 20 m. In this way calibrations can be carried on up to $40\lambda = 400$ m, corresponding to a frequency range down to about 750 kc/sec.

5. In order to extend the range still farther, the fundamental frequency of generator I is changed to a value which gives, for instance, a length $l = 9$ m, that is, $\lambda = 18$ m and $\lambda_0 = (1 + \Delta) = 18 \times 1.00136 = 18.0248$ m, which is 2.48 cm larger than the wave length developed along the line.

If the beat-note procedure is carried on in this way up to about $25\lambda_0$ by means of the higher harmonic settings of generator II, the calibration will be extended to about 900-m wave length, that is, down to frequencies of about 333 kc/sec. This is about the limit which can be obtained with a line of about 14 m in length. If still lower frequencies are required, a longer line must be used, or one of the harmonic methods described later, in order to extend the range farther down.

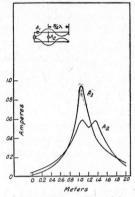

FIG. 151.—Double-hump phenomenon for improper length of Lecher wire system (abscissa gives position of meter bridge with regard to an arbitrary origin).

In the theory given in the *Bureau of Standards Scientific Paper* 491, it is shown that special precautions are to be taken with respect to the free-end effects of the double line. It is the distance l_1 indicated in Fig. 150. For all measurements carried on in the Bureau of Standards, this distance was always small compared to the quarter wave-length distribution or any other odd multiple of it, because, for such free ends, radiation would take place and the well-known double-hump phenomenon would occur. This double-hump phenomenon is due to the well-known interaction between the tuned open-end branch and the tuned branch from the meter bridge to the input side, the bridge forming the coupling. This was also substantiated by E. Takagishi[1] as brought out in Fig. 151.

85. Calibration of a Frequency Meter by Means of Lissajous Figures on a Cathode-ray Tube.—The method shown in Fig. 152 is perhaps the earliest precision procedure employed in several laboratories to calibrate frequency meters with the harmonic method. It was also used at one time in the Bureau of Standards (*Scientific Paper* 487) in connection with a cold-cathode-ray tube. The method makes use of the procedure described in Sec. 25, where it is shown that the fluorescent cathode spot describes a stationary figure whenever the frequencies of the voltages across the two deflection condensers are either alike or such that they have a ratio of two whole numbers. This is brought out in Fig. 37, and especially in Figs. 39 and 40, the first two rows of Fig. 40 being particularly useful for

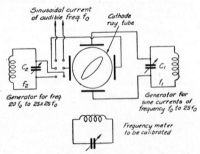

FIG. 152.—Cathode-ray tube for the calibration of a frequency meter.

frequency-calibration work. A standard audio frequency f_0, taken from a source which is stabilized by a relaxation oscillator whose fundamental frequency f_0 is an exact integer fraction of the frequency pf_0 of a piezo generator, is the reference frequency. How this is done is described in connection with Fig. 160. The measurement for the circuit of Fig. 152 is then as follows:

[1] *Proc. I.R.E.*, **18**, 513, 1930.

1. The double-pole double-throw switch is connected toward the source of the standard audio frequency f_0. For simplicity, take $f_0 = 1$ kc/sec. The generator of frequency f_2 is therefore not in the circuit. The condenser C_1 corresponding to a frequency $f_1 < f_0$ is decreased until a rectangular figure appears on the fluorescent screen of the tube. This indicates that the amplitudes of the component deflections are in the ratio of the two sides of the rectangle. The coupling (not shown in the figure) to the generator producing the smaller amplitude is increased until an approximately square-shaped area appears. Next, the condenser C_1 is *slowly* varied until a stationary pattern appears. In this case it is almost a circle (generally an ellipse) and gives the condition $f_1 = f_0$. The frequency meter is then loosely coupled to a generator of frequency f_1 and the calibration point $f_1 = 1$ kc/sec is obtained. The generator f_1 must have sufficient energy (about 50 watts) so that the reaction from the frequency meter does not change the frequency; otherwise the stationary pattern begins to spin around as the frequency meter approaches resonance.

2. The value of C_1 is still further decreased until the next stationary pattern $f_1 = 2f_0 = 2$ kc/sec is obtained in the same way. It is possible to carry on the work up to $f_1 = 25f_0$.

3. For still higher frequencies the double-pole double-throw switch is thrown on a generator of frequency range f_2. The generator of frequency f_0 is then dispensed with and the generator f_1 together with the calibration points of the frequency meter used. This means the setting $f_1 = 14 f_0$, for instance, is used and C_2 is changed until the stationary parabola figure for the frequency ratio $1:2$ appears. The frequency meter is then loosely coupled to a generator of frequency f_2 and the calibration $f_2 = 2f_1 = 28f_0 = 28$ kc/sec is obtained. The setting for the Lissajous figure $1:3$ gives the calibration $3f_1 = 48$ kc/sec, etc. Intermediate points are obtained by using another f_1 setting.

It is also practical to carry this calibration as high as to the twenty-fifth harmonic of f_1, that is, extend the range up to $f_2 = 25f_1 = 25^2 f_0 = 625$ kc/sec. The range can be extended in a similar way by using frequency generators f_1 and f_2 of a still higher range and the calibration points so far obtained on the frequency meter. It is also possible to do this by choosing the original reference frequency f_0 higher, which can be readily done with relaxation oscillations. Since this is a precision measurement, the settings of the f_1 generator, when secured from the calibration points already obtained for the frequency meter, should be carefully checked. This is readily done by throwing the switch toward the source of frequency f_0 when the corresponding figure must appear. If this is not the case, C_1 is slightly changed until the rotation of the figure slows down and and finally stops. Generally $f_1 = mf_0$ where $m = 1, 2, 3 \cdots$ If the switch is thrown toward generator f_2, any stationary figure is secured by varying C_2. The frequency meter then gives the calibration $f_2 = nf_1 = m \, nf_0$ where n are again integers as 1, 2, 3, 4, etc. The accuracy of this method depends therefore upon the reference frequency f_0 and any percentage error in f_0 exists in the calibration mnf_0 also, provided the frequency meter is very selective and the resonance setting carefully made. It is also possible to use such ratios as $2:5$ in the Lissajous figures in order to obtain more points, but experience has shown that it is easier to work with straight ratios such as $\frac{1}{1}$, $\frac{1}{2}$, $\frac{1}{3}$, $\frac{1}{4}$, etc.

This method can also be used to calibrate a beat oscillator with a 60-cycle source. It is then easy to find points up to about 3000 cycles/sec with the first run calibration. The intermediate patterns can be easily eliminated and rough checks of the order of harmonic made by means of tuning forks. The calibration above 3000 cycles/sec is obtained in the same way as above.

86. Calibration by Means of Gear-shaped Figures on the Fluorescent Screen of a Cathode-ray Tube.—The method shown in Fig. 153 is based on the application of a circular revolving field[1] produced by a sinusoidal voltage $E_1\epsilon^{j\omega_1 t}$ of known frequency $\omega_1/2\pi$. Use is made of the fact that the size of the circular trace of the fluorescent spot is a function of the accelerating voltage acting on the anode of a hot-cathode-ray tube, the circle being larger for smaller anode potentials. Hence, if a sinusoidal voltage $E_2\epsilon^{j\omega_2 t}$ is connected in series with the direct voltage E, the radius of the circular trace (dotted circle) will increase rythmically to a value R_{max} and decrease to a value R_{min}, since the anode potential fluctuates between $(E + E_2)$ and $(E - E_2)$. If the frequency $f_2 = \omega_2/2\pi = 4f_1$, the plate potential is four times $(E + E_2)$ and $(E - E_2)$ during one complete circulation of the cathode spot. This means the radius of the trace becomes R_{max} four times and R_{min} four times.

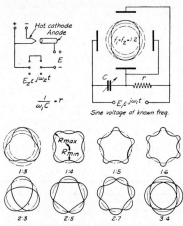

FIG. 153.—These diagrams are due to a superimposed variable voltage $E_2\epsilon^{j\omega_2 t}$ on the accelerating voltage E.

But if f_2 is not exactly $4f_1$, the gear-shaped pattern turns around, which shows to what extent untrue multi-harmonic synchronism exists. For the ratios $f_1:f_2$ as $\frac{2}{3}$, $\frac{2}{5}$, etc., the other indicated patterns are obtained which readily show again the frequency ratio if the voltages E_1 and E_2 are practically sinusoidal.

87. Ordinary Harmonic Method.—This method makes use of the distortion of a current wave. A higher harmonic of frequency mf is emphasized in order to produce directly a deflection on the frequency meter to be calibrated. It has the advantage over the beat method that any other measurements carried on in a laboratory will not produce undesirable beat notes and that careful shielding is unnecessary. Figure 154 shows the circuit. A voltage of fundamental frequency f_0 is impressed. This frequency is again somewhere in the audible range so that many calibration points can be obtained in the desired high-frequency range. The source of f_0 is conveniently the output branch of a multivibrator or some other relaxation oscillator whose fundamental frequency f_0 is an integral

[1] KIPPING, N. V., *Elec. Communication*, **3**, 78, 1924.

fraction of a constant-frequency source such as a piezo oscillator. A magnetostriction oscillator can also be used, but the accuracy is not so high as when a properly designed piezo oscillator with a thermostatic control is used. The same holds also when a tuning-fork drive is used for the production of f_0, in which case it is necessary to use a synchronous clock to check the accuracy of f_0. The audio frequency affects at first a contact-rectifier circuit so as to produce decided distortion. The output of this circuit is amplified (a shield-grid tube can also be used to avoid back action) and then impressed upon another stage of amplification with a large negative grid bias E_c to make the current variations in the plate current I_p rich in harmonics. The condenser C is then varied until CL is the oscillation constant corresponding to the fundamental frequency f_0 and the loosely coupled frequency meter tuned until a maximum reading is obtained. This gives the calibration point for $f = f_0$.

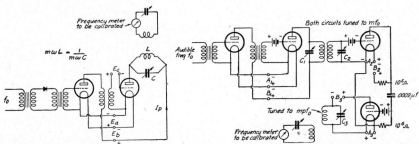

Fig. 154.—Calibration of a frequency meter by means of the harmonic method.

Fig. 155.—Double-frequency multiplication method.

The oscillation constant CL is then chosen of such a magnitude that it corresponds to any higher harmonic, that is, $m\omega L = 1/(m\omega C)$. It is then possible to go up to the two hundredth harmonic for which $m = 200$ and $f = 200f_0$. The drawback of such a high order of harmonic is that successive calibration points come very close together. To avoid this, the double-frequency multiplication in Fig. 155 is employed. The circuits with condensers C_1 and C_2 are then tuned to a suitable harmonic of the $m$fold frequency (mf_0). By means of two other stages of distorted amplification, suitable harmonics of mf_0 are tuned out, giving the frequencies mpf_0 where p again is 1, 2, 3, etc., and the frequency mpf_0 is used for the calibration of the frequency meter.

Example: $f_0 = 1$ kc/sec. C_1 and C_2 are changed until the corresponding circuits are tuned to $20f$. Choosing $p = 1$, that is, also tuning the final output branch to $20f_0$, gives the calibration point $f = 20$ kc/sec. The final output branch is tuned by means of C_3 to the second harmonic, that is, for $p = 2$ to $40 f_0$, giving the calibration of 40 kc/sec. For $p = 100$, the calibration is already in the megacycle range which gives the setting $f = 2$ Mc/sec.

88. Calibration with a Piezo Oscillator.—The method indicated in Fig. 156 can be used with one fundamental crystal frequency or with several fundamental crystal frequencies which give more intermediate points. When no thermostatic control and no special crystal holder is used, the method gives calibrations better than one-tenth of 1 per cent if the piezo-electric reference frequencies have been obtained with one of the precision methods. The switch S is used to connect the piezo-electric element across either the grid and the filament or the grid and the plate, depending upon which connection starts the crystal oscillation more easily. If a disk piezo-electric quartz

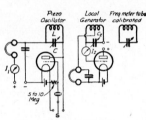

plate with a Curie cut is used and the thickness along the piezo-electric axis is a in millimeters, and the diameter d in millimeters, the fundamental frequencies in kilocycles per second can be approximately computed from $f_1 = 2870/a$; $f_2 = 2715/d$; and $f_3 = 3830/d$. Any one of the three frequencies f_1, f_2, or f_3 with

Fig. 156.—Calibration of a frequency meter with a Piezo oscillator.

harmonics up to the twentieth can be used to obtain calibration points if the local oscillator is used to obtain zero-beat notes. Since harmonics of the local generator are being dealt with here also, the case of Eq. (15) exists and it is also possible to obtain calibration points such as $f/2, f/3, f/4$, etc. From a practical standpoint this can be carried down to about $f/10$ without amplification. Very many calibration points are, therefore, obtainable as indicated in Table IV where a rectangular quartz plate $31.855 \times 25.155 \times 3.12$ mm, with a thickness 3.12 mm, along the piezo-electric axis was used instead of a disk. The process of measurement is as follows:

    1. The frequency meter is calibrated approximately by means of the local generator (use circuit of Fig. 20) by the grid-dip method.

    2. All three circuits are loosely coupled to each other as in Fig. 156.

    3. One of three fundamental piezo-electric oscillations (f_1, f_2, and f_3, respectively,) is started. When the oscillations fall in, the current I_1 sinks to a smaller value. To start the oscillation with the crystal between the grid and the filament, the condenser is turned from a smaller setting toward increasing capacitance values. After the oscillations set in, a further increase of the C setting will decrease the reading of I_1 still more until at current resonance of the CL branch the oscillations break off and can no longer be obtained for larger C settings. For the crystal connected across the plate and the grid, the crystal oscillation is pulled in by decreasing the C settings from its maximum value toward current resonance. In each case it must be noted that it is not of advantage to increase the output power of the crystal oscillator by changing C for a setting too close to current resonance. This is for two reasons. If current resonance is almost secured, the wave form of the output current is less distorted, which is undesirable in a harmonic method. It is then also easier to interrupt the piezo oscillation while absorbing energy from the circuit. The main disadvantage, however, is that, for the tank circuit almost in resonance, the plate branch reacts

strongly on the input branch and somewhat affects the frequency of the circuit, while, for settings suggested above, the plate circuit has not much effect, especially when the setting is at a point of the dial for which the crystal was calibrated.

TABLE IV

kc/sec		kc/sec		kc/sec	
7.992	$= f_1/10$	239.775	$= 3f_1$	1,438.65	$= 18f_1$
8.880	$= f_1/9$	308.18	$= f_3/3$	1,475.74	$= 14f_2$
9.991	$= f_1/8$	316.23	$= 3f_2$	1,518.575	$= 19f_1$
10.541	$= f_2/10$	319.7	$= 4f_1$	1,581.15	$= 15f_2$
11.418	$= f_1/7$	399.625	$= 5f_1$	1,598.5	$= 20f_1$
11.712	$= f_2/9$	421.64	$= 4f_2$	1,686.56	$= 16f_2$
13.176	$= f_2/8$	462.27	$= f_3/2$	1,791.97	$= 17f_2$
13.321	$= f_1/6$	479.55	$= 6f_1$	1,849.08	$= 2f_3$
15.058	$= f_2/7$	527.05	$= 5f_2$	1,897.38	$= 18f_2$
15.985	$= f_1/5$	559.475	$= 7f_1$	2,002.79	$= 19f_2$
17.568	$= f_2/6$	632.46	$= 6f_2$	2,108.2	$= 20f_2$
19.981	$= f_1/4$	639.4	$= 8f_1$	2,773.62	$= 3f_3$
21.082	$= f_2/5$	719.325	$= 9f_1$	3,698.16	$= 4f_3$
26.352	$= f_2/4$	737.87	$= 7f_2$	4,622.7	$= 5f_3$
26.642	$= f_1/3$	799.25	$= 10f_1$	5,547.24	$= 6f_3$
35.137	$= f_2/3$	843.28	$= 8f_2$	6,471.78	$= 7f_3$
39.962	$= f_2/2$	879.175	$= 11f_1$	7,396.32	$= 8f_3$
52.705	$= f_2/2$	924.54	$= f_3$	8,320.86	$= 9f_3$
79.925	$= f_1$	948.69	$= 9f_2$	9,245.4	$= 10f_3$
92.454	$= f_3/10$	959.1	$= 12f_1$	10,169.94	$= 11f_3$
102.727	$= f_3/9$	1,039.025	$= 13f_1$	11,094.48	$= 12f_3$
105.41	$= f_2$	1,054.1	$= 10f_2$	12,019.02	$= 13f_3$
115.567	$= f_3/8$	1,118.95	$= 14f_1$	12,943.56	$= 14f_3$
132.077	$= f_3/7$	1,159.51	$= 11f_2$	13,868.1	$= 15f_3$
154.09	$= f_3/6$	1,198.875	$= 15f_1$	14,792.64	$= 16f_3$
159.85	$= 2f_1$	1,264.92	$= 12f_2$	15,717.18	$= 17f_3$
184.908	$= f_3/5$	1,278.8	$= 16f_1$	16,641.72	$= 18f_3$
210.82	$= 2f_2$	1,358.725	$= 17f_1$	17,566.26	$= 19f_3$
231.135	$= f_3/4$	1,370.33	$= 13f_2$	18,490.8	$= 20f_3$

4. The frequency of the local generator is at first adjusted to the fundamental frequency of the quartz oscillator which is noted by the zero-beat note in the telephone receiver in the piezo oscillator. The frequency meter is then tuned and the dip noted in the I_2 reading gives the condition for the calibration point of frequency f which is one of the frequencies f_1, f_2, and f_3 of the piezo-electric element.

5. The C_2 setting of the local oscillator is decreased until zero-beat condition for the second harmonic is obtained, which gives the calibration point $2f$. This is carried on until the calibration point $20f$ is obtained.

6. In a similar way the calibration points $f/2$, $f/3$ down to $f/10$ are obtained by choosing the frequency settings of the local oscillator correspondingly lower than f of the piezo oscillator. For these readings the telephone receiver of the local generator is used, since the weaker harmonics are produced in this circuit and the method then becomes more sensitive.

89. Calibration of a Piezo Oscillator.—If the accuracy of a good frequency meter is sufficient, the method just described can be used with the exception that now the readings of the frequency meter are known and the fundamental frequency or several of the fundamental frequencies of the piezo-electric element are to be found. Several harmonics are used in the calibration to increase the accuracy.

Example.—For the fundamental and several other harmonics, the readings 79.875, 159.9, 479.3, 560.03, and 639.4 kc/sec are obtained. For frequency calibrations of harmonic submultiples, $159.9/2 = 79.95$; $479.3/6 = 79.88$; $560.03/7 = 80.0$; $639.4/8 = 79.92$ kc/sec; and for the average values of all equivalent and real fundamental frequencies $f_1 = 79.925$ kc/sec. For the other fundamental frequencies (along the Y-axis and coupling frequency),

Measured Frequency		Measured Frequency	
$f_2 = 105.43$		$f_3 = 924.2$	
$2f_2 = 210.8$		$2f_3 = 1850.8$	
$3f_2 = 316.2$	$f_2 = 105.41$ kc/sec, average	$3f_3 = 2777.0$	
$4f_2 = 421.3$		$4f_3 = 3698.0$	$f_3 = 924.54$ kc/sec, average
		$\dfrac{f_3}{2} = 461.5$	

It is necessary to use one of the harmonic methods controlled by a precision piezo crystal for the precision calibration of another crystal. The methods described in the next section are very convenient for this, since relaxation oscillations are used for stepping down the fundamental frequency of the standard crystal to a suitable audio-frequency value f/p in order to obtain many more points in the high-frequency range by this new reference frequency. In addition, this reference frequency can be readily checked by an oscillogram with the marks of a half-second pendulum used in the Sound Laboratory of the Bureau of Standards. This pendulum (Geodetic Survey pendulum) swings in a vacuum and the swings are marked by means of a photoelectric cell acting on an amplifier, the output of which produces the timing marks. A synchronous clock, such as, for instance, the "syncro clock" of the General Radio Company, can be used for the same purpose. When run over very long periods, this can be checked against the time signals when a chronograph is available. However, if a well-designed piezo standard with a thermostatic control is available, it is necessary only to step down this frequency f, as mentioned above, to some value f/p where $p = 2, 3, 4, 5$, etc., and use a suitable high-frequency harmonic $\dfrac{m}{p}f$ to produce an audible beat note of frequency f_b with the frequency f_x of the test crystal which is to be calibrated. The unknown frequency is then computed from

$$f_x = \frac{m}{p}f \pm f_b \tag{22}$$

The beat tone can be measured with a sonometer if amplified or with a syncro clock.   A sonometer is indicated in Fig. 157.   The audio current whose frequency is to be measured passes through the armature of an ordinary telephone receiver which sets a section of suitable length l of piano wire into resonance vibration.   This apparatus is usually calibrated by means of tuning forks or a beat oscillator, giving an accuracy of about 2 per cent which is sufficient for the above work, inasmuch as such an error in the beat frequency f_b for many purposes is a negligibly small part of the high frequency f_x.   If a calibrated beat-frequency oscillator (Fig. 147) is available, the method is even quicker.   The beat frequency is varied until it produces zero beat with the beat frequency f_b obtained in the piezo oscillator.

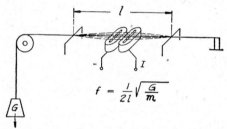

$$f = \frac{1}{2l} \sqrt{\frac{G}{m}}$$

FIG. 157.—Sonometer, a vibrating-string frequency meter for audible currents (m is mass of wire per centimeter length and G is weight in grams).

Example.—Suppose a standard crystal frequency $f = 100$ kc/sec is stepped down by means of relaxation oscillations to a fundamental frequency $f/p = 10$ kc/sec, and this frequency again to 1 kc/sec, in order to check it against time signals by means of a syncro clock working with a chronograph.   If for the ninety-fifth harmonic of frequency f/p, a beat note of $f_b = 85$ cycles/sec is observed, the frequency of the test crystal is (950 ± 0.085) kc/sec.   The plus sign holds when the frequency of the test crystal is higher than that of the ninety-fifth harmonic and f/p and the negative sign when it is lower, which can be found by means of the generator frequency meter of Fig. 20 which is first set against the piezo oscillator to be calibrated and then against the branch with the ninety-fifth harmonic.   If a smaller capacitance setting (higher frequency value) is required for the latter zero-beat adjustment, the 0.085 must be subtracted.   If the frequency as read off on the beat oscillator is not accurate enough, as, for instance, in the case of calibrations in the lower-frequency range, the beat note of frequency f_b is amplified and the frequency measured by a timing wave on an oscillogram.

This method, although slower, has the advantage over the synchronous motor that it gives the f_b calibration in practically a moment and does not depend on any frequency variations which may take place during the long run of a synchronous motor.   But if care is taken, these variations are not likely to happen for proper relaxation oscillations and a good standard crystal of frequency f.

90. Precision Calibration of Frequency by Means of Piezo Crystals.— If well-designed piezo oscillators are used, it is possible to obtain a frequency standard with a precision of about one part in a hundred million. For instance, such an accuracy is obtained by means of 100 kc/sec oscillations obtained from three piezo-electric quartz elements[1] which are automatically interchecked.   A clock-controlled current maintained at a fraction of the crystal frequency is used to make daily checks against time signals, and specially shaped piezo-electric elements are employed with a temperature coefficient as low as 0.0001 per cent per degree centigrade. Other methods[2] (which use only one piezo-electric crystal and only one of the fundamental oscillations) are also based on a standard frequency f taken from a high-precision piezo oscillator.   Either multivibrators are used for stepping down the frequency f to a new reference frequency f/p, the harmonics of which are used in the calibration, or in the other method an auxiliary source is adjusted within a measurable beat note to the frequency of the piezo oscillator whose frequency is to be determined. This auxiliary source is obtained by using the harmonics of a generator of fundamental frequency f/p which is kept accurately set in terms of the much higher frequency f of the standard piezo oscillator.   No relaxation oscillations are used if a visual beat indicator is employed to note the subharmonic synchronization.   However, this method is more involved and care must be taken that the generator of frequency f/p does not slip out of step.

When station frequencies in the broadcast range are to be checked, the circuit of Fig. 158 can be used.   A Curie cut quartz disk with its thickness frequency is used.   The two metal electrodes of the crystal holder are separated by means of a pyrex ring.   Its diameter is so chosen as to fit the quartz disk to within 0.01 in.[3]   The pyrex ring is made thicker than the quartz disk so as to leave a small air gap of about one-quarter

[1] MARRISON, W. A., *Proc. I.R.E.*, **17**, 1103, 1929, or *Bell System Tech. J.*, **8**, 493, 1929.   Precision crystals of the Marrison type make use of the fact that quartz plates cut in the plane of the optic and electric axes (Y cuts) have normally positive temperature coefficients, while plates cut in the plane of the optical but perpendicular to one of the piezo-electric axes (Curie or X cuts) show negative temperature coefficients.   The ideal cut would be that for which, for normal room-temperature changes, the temperature coefficient is so small as to have no appreciable effect on the frequency.   Since the temperature coefficient does *also* vary in the same plane with the shape and size of the cut, the relative dimensions of the crystal also play a part.   Thus a certain doughnut-shaped crystal cut from Y-cut plate may have a temperature coefficient as low as +0.0004, while another ring-shaped crystal element has a value of +0.0037.   For this reason and on account of the easier way of mounting the piezo-electric element, ring-shaped crystals of certain relative dimensions may be used to great advantage.

[2] CLAPP, J. K., *J. Optical Soc. Am.*, **15**, 25, 1927; L. M. HULL and J. K. CLAPP, *Proc. I.R.E.*, **17**, 252, 1929; H. L. BOGARDUS and C. T. MANNING, *Proc.*, *I.R.E.*, 1225, 1929; E. L. HALL, *Proc. I.R.E.*, **18**, 490, 1930.

[3] Similar to the design of a portable piezo oscillator described by W. H. Brattain, and V. E. Heaton, *Bur. Standards J. Research*, **4**, 345, 1930.

of the wave length of the supersonic waves produced by the plate. Since the temperature coefficient of a Curie cut disk is of the order of $(1 \text{ to } 3)10^{-3}$ per cent per degree centigrade, a thermostatic control is required. An improved thermostatic control, such as developed by W. A. Marrison[1] and also used in a portable piezo oscillator designed by the Bureau of

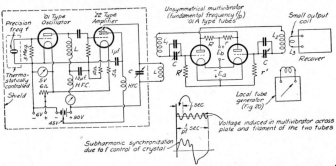

Fig. 158.—Precision calibration system for checking up station frequencies.

Standards, should be used for such precision work. Thermostatic-controlled chambers are commercially available today. A temperature regulation of this type has two operating functions. For one, a thermostat holds the operating temperature to within very narrow limits. The other operation consists in a heating system of such a nature that the thermostat will trip of the order of once a minute, while a thermal attenuation will reduce the effect of the amplitude of the thermostat operation. The Bureau of Standards design consists essentially of a heat-insulated box with walls of ½-in. pine and ½-in. balsam wood. A hollow copper cylinder ⅜ in. thick is located inside the box and mounted on heavy bronze coil springs to take care of any mechanical vibrations. The outside of the cylinder is covered with a thin layer of asbestos for insulation. A heating wire of nichrome is wound on it, the turns toward the ends being closer than for the

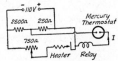

Fig. 159.—Temperature-control unit.

inside section of the cylinder in order to deliver the heat losses at the ends of the cylinder. A mercury thermostat is used and placed in a groove in the copper cylinder directly under the heating wire so as to be in close thermal contact with it. A deep hole is drilled into the wall of the copper cylinder (parallel to the axis) in order to have a place for thermometer observations. The inside of the cylinder is lined with ⅜-in. asbestos. The inside space along the cylinder axis consists of three compartments separated by asbestos disks. The middle compartment contains the piezo crystal and the other compartments decrease the end effects. Figure 159 shows the design of the temperature control. When the mercury thermostat closes, a current $I = 8 \times 10^{-3}$ amp flows and

[1] *Proc. I.R.E.*, **16**, 976. 1928.

opens the heater circuit. Hence, the voltage across the thermostat is small when its contacts are open and the thermostat can readily make and break the entire heating current. The frequency of the thermostatic operation is therefore increased and makes the temperature within the cylinder independent of any large variations in the outside temperature. By means of the variable 750Ω resistor, the length of the epoch during which the heating current is on can be set approximately equal to the length of the period during which the heater is not in use.

As far as other details of the arrangement of Fig. 158 are concerned, it will be noted that the crystal oscillator is a separate unit. The output circuit can be tuned if necessary, since a shield-grid tube of the 222 type or its equivalent is used and no appreciable reaction can take place on the actual piezo oscillator using a 201 type tube or its equivalent. The loading coil L is either a universal wound or a honeycomb coil with a distributed capacitance with its gravest natural frequency above that of the piezo-electric disk. The piezo-electric oscillations will then have a small and fixed amplitude. The $(10 + 5)\Omega$ resistances in the respective filament leads of the second tube give the proper filament drop if the 5-volt terminals of the 201 tube are used as supply and the 10Ω portion provides the C bias. H.F.C. are high-frequency chokes with their size depending on the frequency of the crystal.

The frequency f of the crystal is conveniently chosen as an integer multiple of 10 kc/sec. It is then easy, by either single or twofold harmonic division, to obtain an audio frequency of 10 kc/sec and 1 kc/sec and operate a synchronous motor whose integral revolutions during a day's run can be checked against time signals. It is also possible, by means of contact points or the like, to obtain 1-sec marks. Another feature of the 10-kc factor in the standard crystal frequency f is that the assigned broad decimal frequencies of 96 channels in the 550- to 1500-kc/sec band can be directly checked. Harmonic division with relaxation oscillators or, by checking subharmonic synchronism of a piezo oscillator with respect to the fundamental frequency of a low-frequency generator, can be carried out to about one-fortieth of the piezo frequency f. For practical reasons it does not seem wise to work with subharmonics which are much more than about one-tenth of the frequency f. It is best to use another stage of harmonic division if larger fractions are required. A value of $f = 50$ kc/sec is then very suitable, since a harmonic division of 5 which is readily accomplished gives the desired audio frequency of 10 kc/sec, and another tenfold division the 1-kc/sec current which may operate a synchronous clock. It is not difficult to obtain and grind a crystal for a frequency of 50 kc/sec, as can be seen in the design formulas of Sec. 210. Therefore, by using $f = 50$ kc/sec, the multivibrator condensers are varied together until a fundamental frequency $f/p = 10$ kc/sec is obtained. (For details of the multivibrator, see Sec. 15.) The fifth harmonic of the multivibrator is then controlled by the frequency f of the piezo crystal (Fig. 158), thus maintaining the fundamental of the multivibrator at exactly 10 kc/sec. As brought out in Sec. 15, this can easily be done, since the inherently unstable multivibrator is readily controlled by a voltage whose frequency is either equal to or an integer multiple of the fundamental frequency of the multivibrator which is rich in powerful harmonics. It is an easy matter to indicate the effect up to the two hundredth harmonic of the fundamental multivibrator frequency. An unsymmetrical multivibrator with plate resistors $R > r$ and grid leaks R' and r' should be used, since, according to experimental investigations by L. M. Hull and J. K. Clapp,[1] the odd ratio of control occurs just as readily as the even ratio of control, while with the symmetrical multivibrator there is a strong tendency to control the even ratios better. The resistances in one tube are then chosen twenty to fifty times as great as in the other tube, in order to provide unsymmetry. Thus, in some cases $R = 500,000\Omega$ and $r = 20,000\Omega$, while the corresponding grid leaks R' and r' can be chosen equal, 0.5 megohm, for instance. By doing this, the tube with the lower plate resistance r shows a comparatively large variable plate current I, as indicated in Fig. 158, which has about the same form as the relatively small plate current i through the other tube. For one tube, the operating point will then sweep over the entire characteristic from saturation to cut-off, while the other tube works essentially as a customary resistance-capacitance coupled amplifier. The indirect subharmonic synchronization then becomes unusually stable. The synchronizing voltage of the crystal frequency f induced across L_1 must have a certain value to bring about controlled relaxation oscillations. The proper condition is recognized when the two condensers C whose shafts work on a common drive can be varied over a considerable range of the C setting without changing the same fundamental frequency f/p in the small output coil of the multivibrator, if from a certain C setting on the next integer harmonic submultiple begins and holds for quite a range of C settings. If the multivibrator is varied in the audio-frequency range, a continuous variation in the C setting would produce successive octaves in the telephone receiver inserted in the output branch. However, if the induced voltage due to the crystal oscillation is not sufficient, a continuous variation of C gradually changes the pitch of the sound heard.

The measurement of the frequency of a remote broadcast station is then as follows: The remote station is tuned in and the output coil L_3 of the high-frequency amplifier is coupled loosely to the output coil L_2 of the multivibrator and to the output coil of the heterodyne generator (shown in Fig. 20). The harmonic currents of the multivibrator can have only frequencies which are integer multiples of 10 kc. Hence, when

[1] *Loc. cit.*

the heterodyne frequency is set to the assigned frequency of the station (say 300 kc/sec), no beat note should be heard in the telephone receiver of the heterodyne (local generator), if the station is sending with the correct frequency. If this is not the case, the frequency is off by the same number of cycles per second as that of the beat actually heard.

When a piezo oscillator to be used for the particular broadcast station is to be adjusted to the exact frequency instead of the frequency of the received current, this oscillator is coupled in place of coil L_3 and the air gap of the piezo holder is adjusted until zero-beat note is heard.

As far as the coupling to the multivibrator is concerned, the standard piezo oscillator can be coupled either through a shield-grid amplifier as in Fig. 158 or through a shield-grid input stage as in Fig. 160. The coupling resistances R_1 and R_2, respectively, act then on the first and second multivibrators which produce fundamentals of 10 and 1 kc/sec, respectively.

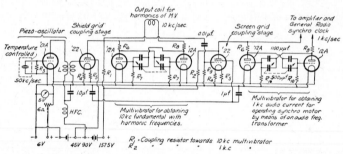

Fig. 160.—Standard frequency system ($R_1 = 10{,}000\Omega$; $R_2 = 10{,}000\Omega$; $R_3 = 5$ to 10 megohms; $R_4 = 10\Omega$; $R_5 = 5\Omega$; $R_6 = 0.2$ meg.; $R_7 = 25{,}000\Omega$; $R_8 = 10{,}000\Omega$, and $R_9 = 0.5$ megohm; $R_{10} = 0.4$ meg.).

Instead of the shield-grid tubes, ordinary three-element tubes with neutralization can be used. The synchronous clock is used to note the accuracy of the standard crystal frequency of 50 kc/sec by means of a chronograph and the daily time signals. Also in this circuit, the plate load of the standard piezo oscillator of a loading inductance L (honeycomb or universal-wound coil) must have such a distributed capacitance that the coil acts as an inductive reactance for a 50-kc current passing through it and such that its amplitude is not so large as to react back on the crystal frequency. A synchronous clock is commercially available (General Radio Company). It can be used for checking the frequency by taking a long run and computing from the dial reading the number of revolutions made during the long run. It keeps correct time when driven by a 1-kc current. A microdial on the clock, used to record time intervals recorded by the clock, may be compared with time intervals of some other system. It is then possible to use the daily time signals to check the correctness of the 50-kc piezo standard. This clock has a 100-tooth rotor and is excited by two U-shaped electromagnets which carry the amplified 1-kc current. On a properly biased current the rotor will make 10 r.p.s. for a 1-kc feed. The biasing direct current is about 40 to 50 ma. By means of gearing, the clock indicates true solar time for an impulse feed with a fundamental frequency of exactly 1 kc/sec. This clock can also be used at some other frequencies of the lower frequency range. With this particular number of teeth it can be readily used for frequency determinations from about 250 to 1800 cycles/sec. The entire audio-frequency range can be calibrated with it when a stroboscopic method (see next section) is used.

91. Notes on Low-frequency Measurements.—The method just described, using a synchronous motor with an appropriate number of rotor teeth, can be used for the audio-frequency range from 100 to 5000 cycles/sec. For testing still higher frequencies the harmonic division can be used to express a higher audio frequency by means of one-half or one-third of its number of cycles per second. The dial indicates for a certain number of rotor teeth the number of revolutions made during a certain run and, by noting the time of the test run, the frequency can be computed. The longer the test run, the more accurate is the determination of frequency and a synchro clock for a 24-hr run will give an accuracy better than one part in one hundred thousand if the second hand reading is used. This precision is further increased when use is made of a microdial attachment to check the clock against the daily time within 0.01 sec. This leads to a precision of one part in 10^7. However, this precision has only a meaning when no variations take place in the test frequency with an average value which is either positive or negative. Of course, this is the drawback of any long-run method of this type. To check partially such a condition, a clock can be used which also gives second marks which are checked on a revolving drum against second marks of a precision chronometer. In order to prevent a cumbersome count, 10-sec or even 100-sec marks can be used for the check.

Stroboscopic methods can also be employed for the determination of frequency. The principle is based on the fact that a revolving wheel with spokes appears to stand still if it is successively illuminated at instants when all spokes are in the same position in space, that is, if one spoke has just moved into a position of the next spoke or some other spoke during the intervals of no illumination. The same also happens when glow-discharge spokes are used and successive glow discharges take place. When the angular speed of the spokes is increased, a certain number of revolutions will be found for which the discharge tubes acting as spokes stand still. The simplest stroboscopic apparatus consists of a black disk with a single white radius drawn on it. If the wave-group frequency of an oscillating spark discharge is to be found, the black disk is exposed to the flashes of the spark gap and the speed of the disk is increased until the white radius appears stationary. The revolutions per second of the disk are then equal to the wave-group frequency per second. If 10 equally spaced white radii are used, only one-tenth of the revolutions per second are required to produce a stationary pattern of the radii. Hence, if as in Fig. 161 a single neon tube is used on the disk with the two slip rings, and the disk is gradually speeded up, stationary patterns of the tube as indicated may appear. The discharge-group frequency is then equal to the apparent number of glow-discharge tubes as seen on the disk times the revolutions per second of the disk. It is also possible to see whether single or multiple spark discharges take place. The stroboscopic

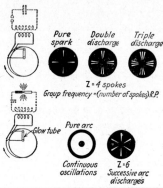

method is therefore useful in many ways. The lower representation of the figure shows whether a Poulsen arc oscillator actually produces sustained oscillations or arc oscillations of the third type, consisting of discrete damped wave trains which usually occur with a group frequency in the audible range. It is difficult in this way to measure the speed accurately; but if a synchronous motor is used as above, this objection of the stroboscopic method is overcome. Thus, the commercial synchro clock described above[1] uses a small glow-discharge tube mounted below the edge

FIG. 161.—Stroboscopic methods using glow-discharge tubes.

of the rotor teeth. It is ignited from the alternating voltage across the input circuit. At synchronism, the stroboscopic effect causes the rotor teeth to appear stationary. The method then consists of flashing a small neon lamp in front of the revolving rotor in such a way that the audio frequency to be measured acts through an amplifier (if necessary) to supply the proper ignition voltage only during a very small portion of a half cycle. The neon lamp for this purpose again uses a proper bias. If, therefore, a synchronous motor rotating at 10 r.p.s. is available and it is necessary to adjust a beat oscillator to be calibrated to 600 cycles/sec, a disk with 60 radii (spokes, teeth, etc.) is required and the frequency of the beat oscillator is adjusted until the 60 radii appear stationary. But if the frequency of the oscillator differs from $N\left(p\dfrac{m}{n}\right)$ by $\dfrac{1}{n}$ cycles/sec, the pm radii will appear to revolve at a rate of 1 radius/sec where N denotes the number of revolutions per second. This is true because a disk of p radii illuminated with a glow lamp igniting mp times during each revolution looks like a disk having mp radii (where

[1] See also paper by L. B. Arguimbau, *Gen. Radio Experimenter*, No. 6, **5**, p. 5, November, 1930; Harold S. Wilkins, *Gen. Radio Experimenter*, No. 5, **5**, p. 3, October, 1930.

$m = 1, 2, 3,$ etc.) and if the lamp ignites p/n times for each revolution ($n = 1, 2, 3,$ etc.), the disk appears to have p spokes. Since for modern frequency standardization a decimal-frequency standard, giving by harmonic division 1 kc/sec, is conveniently used, it can also be employed for low-frequency standardization by using as in the General Radio stroboscopic frequency meter disks as shown in Fig. 162. They are 8-in. disks working on a 1-kc synchronous motor. The pattern of the

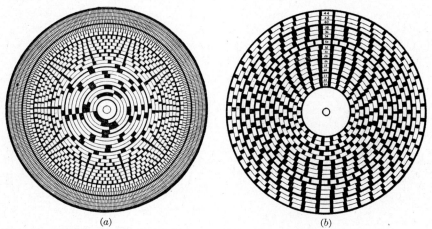

(a) (b)

FIG. 162.—Disks of a General Radio stroboscopic frequency meter. (a) For audio frequencies; (b) for commercial frequencies.

left disk covers the entire audio-frequency range up to 10 kc/sec. Since this particular synchronous motor makes 10 r.p.s., 10-, 20-, 30-, . . . 80-, 90-, and 100-cycle calibrations can be obtained by direct comparison. Such direct comparisons are also possible for every 100 cycles/sec up to 1 kc/sec and then every ½ kc/sec up to 5 kc/sec with the exception of the 1.5-kc/sec setting. It is also possible to see stationary patterns for every 5 cycles/sec up to 50 cycles/sec, and every 20 cycles/sec from 100 to 200 cycles/sec, as well as the 2-, 4-, 6-, 8-, and 10-kc patterns. The disk pattern to the right covers most of the power-frequency range.

The automatic beat-counter method of W. A. Marrison[1] can be employed for the accurate determination of small beat fre-

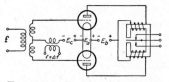

FIG. 163.—Slow-beat indicator.

quencies (a few cycles). It consists of a balanced modulator and, as in Fig. 163, a balanced relay is used in the plate circuits. If Δf denotes the small difference frequency between the fundamentals of two piezo crystals which are adjusted to almost the same frequency, the balanced relay will make one contact for each cycle difference. The contact operates a

[1] *Loc. cit.*

counter as used in adding machines and, by noting the time intervals
during which the counts are taken, the degree of synchronism between
two high frequencies f and $(f + \Delta f)$ can be measured with great precision.

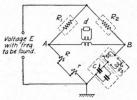

Fig. 164.—Resonance
bridge as frequency indicator (d denotes the deflection
of the indicator).

Bridge methods can be used for measuring
audio frequencies in work for which a high precision is not required. The resonance bridge
of Fig. 164 can be used as has been done by
several investigators.[1] The frequency measurement depends on adjusting C, L, or both, until
the indicator passes through a minimum ($\omega L = 1/(\omega C)$), and then adjusting $R_1 : R_2 = (R + r) :$
R_3 for absolute zero when the impressed voltage of the unknown frequency is sinusoidal, otherwise the frequency (cycles per second) will
occur for a minimum and is measured just the same by

$$f_r = \frac{1}{2\pi\sqrt{CL}} \tag{23}$$

with C in farads and L in henries. The sharpness of resonance of the
resonance bridge is

$$S_B = S\frac{R_3}{R_3 + R + r} \tag{24}$$

if S denotes the sharpness of resonance of the C, L, R_3 branch, R_3 being
practically the effective resistance of the variometer L. It is also assumed
that the voltage of the frequency f_r to be measured and impressed across
the bridge is constant. If $R_1 = R_2$, one has $S_B = S/2$. If E denotes
the constant effective value of an impressed sinusoidal voltage of frequency f and e the effective value across bridge points AB when the
output transformer is removed, for the resonance frequency f_r of the CL
arm one has the relation

$$P = \frac{e}{E}\left[1 + \frac{R + r}{R_1}\right] = \frac{jS_B\left[\dfrac{f}{f_r} - \dfrac{f_r}{f}\right]}{1 + jS_B\left[\dfrac{f}{f_r} - \dfrac{f_r}{f}\right]} \tag{25}$$

Equations (24) and (25) can be used to find the sharpness S_B of resonance
by means of tube voltmeters. The operation of the bridge as a frequency
meter depends greatly upon the magnitude of the frequency. For the
range from about 350 to 5000 cycles/sec, a variometer L with a maximum
reading of about 200 mh is used, and the capacitance C consists of fixed

[1] Grueneisen, E. and E. Giebe, Z. Instrumentenk., **30**, 147, 1910; and **31**, 152,
1911; A. Heydweiller and H. Hagemeister, Verh. d. D. Phys. Ges., **18**, 52, 1916;
E. Giebe and E. Alberti, Z. tech. Physik, **6**, 192, 1925; H. A. Apfel and
J. T. O'Leary, Trans. A.I.E.E., **46**, 504, 1927; G. W. Pierce, Proc. Am. Acad. Arts
Sci., **63**, 23, 1928; S. Jimbo, Proc. I.R.E., **17**, 2011, 1929.

condensers of 0.04, 0.2, and 1 μf which are used either singly or in parallel. The Campbell bridge shown in Fig. 165 can also be used as a frequency meter. If E denotes the voltage measured by the tube voltmeter when the frequency of current I is f, and E_r the voltage measured for the resonance frequency f_r, for a constant current flow I,

$$E_r = rI \text{ and } S = \frac{2\pi f_r M}{r} \tag{26}$$

since for the sharpness S of resonance

$$E = E_r \sqrt{1 + S^2 \left[\frac{f}{f_r} - \frac{f_r}{f} \right]^2}$$

$$S = \frac{\sqrt{(E/E_r)^2 - 1}}{\dfrac{f}{f_r} - \dfrac{f_r}{f}} \tag{27}$$

For low-loss coils and a low-loss condenser this circuit gives very sharp resonance settings and the Campbell bridge is then most suitable as an audio-frequency meter.

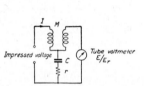

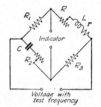

FIG. 165.—Campbell bridge as frequency indicator.

FIG. 166.—Direct-reading audio-frequency bridge.

Figure 166 shows a direct-reading audio-frequency bridge[1] which utilizes Hay's bridge.[2] The bridge is balanced when

$$R_1 R_3 = [R + r + j\omega L] \left[R_2 + \frac{1}{j\omega C} \right]$$

which for a negligible value of r in comparison with R for the imaginary part of the solution gives $\omega^2 = R/(CLR_2)$. Inserting this in the real part when solving for the frequency,

$$f = kR \tag{28}$$

for the constant

$$k = \frac{1}{2\pi \sqrt{L[R_1 R_3 C - L]}} \tag{28a}$$

giving therefore a method where the frequency f is directly proportional to the R setting. If maximum sensitivity is to occur at 1 kc/sec, one must make $k = 1$ and $L = 1/(2\pi)$ henries and $C = (1/2\pi)$ μf because this choice

[1] SOUCY, C. I., and B. D. F. BAYLY, *Proc. I.R.E.*, **17**, 834, 1929; K. KUROWKAWA and T. HOASHI, *J. Inst. Elec. Eng.* (Japan), No. 437, p. 1132.

[2] HAY, C. E., *Inst. P. O. Engs.*, November, 1912.

will make the phase angle of the reactive arms 45 deg at 1 kc/sec.   There
is then in Eq. (28a) the product $R_1R_3 = 2 \times 10^6$ and, in order to make all
bridge arms equal at 1 kc/sec, one must make $R_1 = R_3 = 1410\,\Omega$.   The
bridge covers a range from 50 to 5000 cycles/sec.   For frequencies below
1 kc/sec, R consists of a four-dial decade box calibrated in hundreds, tens,
and units and the variable resistance R_2 uses a four-dial box variable in
thousands, hundreds, tens, and units, while below 100 cycles/sec a fixed
10,000$\,\Omega$ resistance is conveniently connected in series with the R_2 box.

Figure 167 shows a circuit for determining an unknown frequency
f_x by means of a standard frequency f_s.   A variable standard resistance R

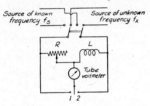

(decade box) is connected in series with a coil
of effective inductance L and resistance r.
When the double-pole double-throw switch
is connected toward the source of the unknown
frequency, the resistance R is varied until
the tube voltmeter gives the same reading
for connection 1 and connection 2.   This

FIG.   167.—Determination
of f_x in terms of f_s and circuit
settings.

connection is fulfilled for $R = R_1 =$
$\sqrt{[2\pi f_x L]^2 + r^2}$.   The same is done for a volt-
age of standard frequency f_s impressed for which condition $R = R_2 =$
$\sqrt{[2\pi f_s L]^2 + r^2}$.   The unknown frequency is then computed from

$$f_x = f_s\sqrt{\frac{R_2{}^2 - r^2}{R_1{}^2 - r^2}} \qquad (29)$$

Hence, if the effective coil resistance is small compared to the R values,
$f_x = \dfrac{R_2}{R_1}f_s$.   This method can also be used for high frequencies and for

R values in the neighborhood of from 3000 to 5000$\,\Omega$.   A calibration of
the tube voltmeter is not required, since the equal-deflection method
is used.   The applied voltages should not contain an appreciable harmonic content and the self-capacitance of the L coil should be small.

CHAPTER VI

DETERMINATION OF CAPACITANCE

One must distinguish between absolute and relative *methods*. For the latter the unknown capacitance is determined by means of a known capacitance, while for the absolute methods the determination is carried out by means of other electrical quantities. Thus C can be determined by using the resonance relation $2\pi f = 1/\sqrt{CL}$ if f and L are known. If substitution methods are used, many of the absolute methods can be converted into relative methods. Since in many cases the high-frequency value of capacitance differs somewhat from the static (practically the same as measured with low audio frequencies) value, for accurate work a capacitance calibration should be carried on for the frequency range for which a condenser is used. This is especially true when effective distributed capacitance along lines and for coils is to be determined as well as with condensers whose dielectric is not air.

Capacitance is defined as the ratio of quantity of electricity to voltage; that is, it expresses the ability to hold or store a quantity of electricity and, if the charge is expressed in terms of the terminal voltage of the condenser, capacitance denotes the factor of proportionality. Moreover, one must distinguish between practical and absolute *units*. The practical unit is the farad which happens to be a very large quantity, and all the more so when dealing with high-frequency phenomena. It is therefore customary to use the microfarad (μf) and in the case of very small capacitance values, as met with in interelectrode capacitances in vacuum tubes, the micromicrofarad ($\mu\mu$f) which bears the interrelation

$$1 \ \mu\mu\text{f} = 10^{-6} \ \mu\text{f} = 10^{-12} \text{ farad} \tag{1}$$

In the absolute *electrostatic* system the unit of capacitance is the centimeter (cm) which is related to the practical system by

$$1 \ \mu\text{f} = 9 \times 10^5 \text{ cm} \tag{2}$$

which shows that the micromicrofarad is approximately equal to the absolute centimeter unit of the e.s. system. This relation will assist the reader of continental European literature, since the tube capacitance, etc., is usually given in centimeters. An input capacitance of 25 cm is then approximately 25 $\mu\mu$f. There also exists an absolute *electromagnetic* unit for capacitance. Its unit is the reciprocal of an acceleration (sec²/cm), since for the velocity $c = 3 \times 10^{10}$ cm/sec, e.m. cap = e.s. cap/c^2. There is then the relation

$$1 \ \mu\text{f} = 10^{-15} \text{ sec}^2/\text{cm} \tag{3}$$

which occurs very seldom in high-frequency work. It may be of use, however, when the CL product along an aerial wire or any other high-frequency line is utilized for computing the effective phase velocity along the line.

92. Formulas for Ordinary Condensers.—Usually condensers are built by means of plates, although in some cases the metallic poles may be cylindrical or of some other shape. For a condenser for which two parallel metallic areas of S cm^2 each are separated a distance d cm, one has approximately

$$C = \frac{\kappa S}{36\pi d} 10^{-5} \text{ microfarads} \tag{4}$$

if κ denotes the dielectric constant. If a condenser consists of N parallel plates and such that all odd plates are interconnected and form one pole and the remaining even plates lead to the other pole of the condenser, the above formula still holds if S is substituted by $S(N - 1)$. If the edge effects of a variable condenser with N semicircular plates of external radius $R^{(cm)}$ and internal radius $r^{(cm)}$ are neglected, the capacitance for the maximum setting is

$$C = 0.139\kappa \frac{[N - 1][R^2 - r^2]}{d} 10^{-6} \tag{5}$$

where for air $\kappa = 1$. The calibration curve of a variable condenser of this type (that is, with semicircular areas with radius vector $\rho = R = $ constant is essentially linear and given by

$$C = a + b\theta \tag{6}$$

where a and b are constants and θ the angle of the set of movable plate against the setting of the smallest or residual capacitance $(C = a)$. These constants are conveniently found by measuring C for two angles θ and determining the slope b and intercept a of the line connecting the two points C_1, θ_1 and C_2, θ_2 with the $\theta = 0$ axis. The value of C_0 obtained is then not exactly equal to the residual capacitance but close enough for rough-calibration work. For practical purposes, condenser settings close to zero angle are of no advantage, since any losses of the condenser make the phase angle of the condenser most unfavorable for small C settings and it is customary to use a condenser only from about 10 deg upward. If the movable plates use a logarithmic spiral as a boundary curve (that means, the radius vector $\rho = $ constant ϵ^θ, the *percentage* capacitance change is constant. For parabolic spirals $(\rho = $ constant $\sqrt{\theta})$ the condenser across a fixed inductance L can be used to obtain a linear relation of the natural wave length of the parallel combination with respect to the θ settings of the condenser. The characteristic calibration curve of such a condenser is then practically a parabola, that is, expressed by

$$C = a + b\theta^2 \tag{7}$$

Variable condensers can be designed for linear wave length, linear frequency, and the same percentage detuning. The variable capacitance of a beat-frequency generator, for which a low-frequency setting can be made just as accurate as an audio-frequency setting on the upper end of the scale, utilizes a logarithmic scale. The radius vector ρ which determines the boundary curve of the variable plates indicated in Fig. 168 for a *linear-frequency* scale is given by

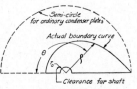

FIG. 168.—Shape of special condenser plates (ρ and r_0 in centimeters).

$$\rho = \sqrt{G + r_0^2} \qquad (8)$$

where

$$G = \frac{4A^2}{B^2 D \left[\dfrac{A}{B\sqrt{C_{\min}}} - \theta \right]^3}$$

θ = angle in radians (1 deg = 57.3 radians)

$$A = \frac{159.2}{\sqrt{L}}$$

L = fixed inductance across the variable condenser in microhenries

$$B = \frac{f_{\max} - f_{\min}}{\pi}$$

$f_{\max}$ = maximum frequency reading in kilocycles per second, when all plates are out, that is, for $C_{\min}$

$f_{\min}$ = minimum frequency reading in kilocycles per second, when all plates are in, that is, for $C_{\max}$

$C_{\min}$ and $C_{\max}$ are expressed in microfarads

$$D = \frac{10^{-5}N}{36\pi t}$$

t = distance between two plates in centimeters

N = number of air spaces in condenser

For the boundary curve of a variable-air condenser which produces a *constant percentage detuning* when connected in multiple with a fixed inductance L, for the radius vector,

$$\rho = 10.7\sqrt{HKC_{\min}\epsilon^{K\theta} + P} \qquad (9)$$

where

θ in degrees for

$$K = 1.278 \times 10^{-2} \log_{10} \frac{C_{\max}}{C_{\min}}$$

$$P = 8.73 \times 10^{-3} r_0^2$$

$$H = \frac{S_{\max} - 180P}{C_{\max} - C_{\min}^*}$$

$S_{\max}$ entire plate area in square centimeters

$C_{\max}$ and $C_{\min}$ the maximum and minimum condenser settings which cover the desired frequency range

For the boundary curve of a condenser plate of a beat-frequency generator,

$$\rho = \sqrt{\frac{4AB^2\epsilon^{A\theta+D}}{G[F_1 - \epsilon^{A\theta+D}]^3} + r_0^2} \qquad (10)$$

where

$$A = \frac{\log_{10} \dfrac{f_2}{f_1}}{\theta_2 - \theta_1}$$

f_2 the audio-frequency reading for a setting θ_2 in kilocycles per second and θ in
f_1 the audio-frequency reading for a setting θ_1 degrees

It is convenient to take the settings

$\theta_1 = 10$ deg. and $\theta_2 = 175$ deg. and cover most of the desired audio-frequency range with it

$$B = \frac{159.2}{\sqrt{L}}$$

L = the fixed inductance in microhenries which is connected across the variable-air condenser

$$D = \log_{10} f_{min} = \log_{10} \left[F_1 - \frac{B}{\sqrt{C_{min}}} \right]$$

C_{min} = minimum capacitance in microfarads for $\theta = 0$ deg.

f_{min} = audio frequency in kilocycles per second, when all condenser plates are turned out

F_1 high frequency in kilocycles per second, of fixed oscillator

$$C = \frac{C_v}{S}$$

C_v maximum capacitance in microfarads of variable-air condenser

S active surface in square centimeters of variable-air condenser when all plates are turned in

93. Determination of the Static and Low-frequency Capacitance of a Condenser.

—The static capacitance of a condenser is measured with a ballistic galvanometer of Fig. 169. The condenser C_x is at first charged to a voltage E by closing the switch toward 1. It is then discharged by connecting the switch to terminal 2. If d denotes the first maximum throw on the galvanometer of ballistic constant k,

Ballistic galvanometer

Fig. 169.—The ballistic-galvanometer method.

$$C_x^{(\mu f)} = k \frac{d}{E} \qquad (11)$$

If d is in millimeters and E in volts, the ballistic constant is in microcoulombs per millimeter deflection. It is readily found by experiment if a known capacitance $C_1^{(\mu f)}$ is used in the same way to produce for a voltage E_1 the deflection d_1, from which measurement

$$k = \frac{C_1 E_1}{d_1} \qquad (12)$$

A direct voltage of 110 volts is sufficient to calibrate ordinary variable condensers. If the same voltage $E_1 = E$ is used as for the test condenser, $C_x = C_1 d/d_1$. If great precision is not required, such a measurement will hold over the entire high-frequency range for good air condensers, since the frequency factor is practically unity. For the quick determi-

nation of certain condensers where great precision is not required, audio-
frequency bridges as in Fig. 170 can be used. A 1000-cycle source
(tuning-fork buzzer or the like) is then conveniently employed. For the
upper arrangement a balance is obtained by
means of a variable standard C_s and the values of R_1 and R_2, and the unknown capacitance computed from

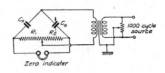

$$C_x = \frac{R_2}{R_1} C_s \qquad (13)$$

which holds for the balance condition of the
bridge for which the sound in the telephone
receiver practically disappears. The resistances $(R_1 + R_2)$ can also be a thin slide
wire with a traveling contact. By choosing,
for instance, $R_2/R_1 = 100$, an unknown
capacitance can be determined with a standard air condenser C_s whose capacity values are

Fig. 170.—Condenser bridge
for the quick determination of
capacitance.

a hundred times smaller. It is possible to cover a range from 0.05 to 10
μf if the ratio R_2/R_1 is properly chosen. The lower bridge of Fig. 170
employs only condensers in the four bridge arms. The ratio C_3/C_4 is
chosen so that the unknown capacitance C_x is brought within the range of
the variable-air condenser C_s. This bridge can be made direct reading, if

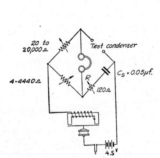

Fig. 171.—Capacity bridge.
(*General Radio Company.*)

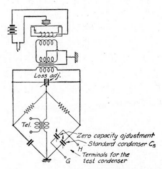

Fig. 172.—Bridge for the measurements of very small capacitances.
(*General Radio Company.*)

the dial of the variable standard condenser C_s is calibrated for certain
ratios of C_3/C_4. As in the case of all bridges of this type, an accuracy of
only a few per cent is normally obtained. Figure 171 shows a useful
bridge of the General Radio Company for determining capacitances from
0.001 to about 10 μf quickly. The unknown capacitance C_x can be read
off by means of the dial settings and the ratio of the arms. The standard
reference capacitance is a fixed mica condenser ($C_s = 0.05\ \mu f$). The
variable series resistance R gives a rough calibration of the power factor

of C_x and can be used to distinguish between low- and high-loss condensers. This self-contained capacitance bridge is especially useful when matching coupling condensers in amplifiers and for similar work. The portable capacitance bridge indicated in Fig. 172 covers the lower capacity range either up to 30 $\mu\mu f$ or up to 600 $\mu\mu f$, respectively. The first range gives a means of measuring quickly the interelectrode capacitances. A telephone receiver is again used as a zero-current detector. For the determination of such small capacitances, a substitution method is used. The bridge is initially balanced with the standard condenser set at maximum value by adjusting a parallel vernier condenser. The unknown condenser C_x is then connected to the terminals GH and the standard condenser readjusted to obtain again a bridge balance. The resistance balance is made by means of a double stator condenser connected in parallel with the ratio arms as indicated in the figure. The three interelectrode capacitances of vacuum tubes are delta-connected as in Fig. 173. As brought out on page 42, the customary measurement of any one capacitance includes the capacitance of the two others in

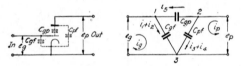

Fig. 173.—Showing that the three interelectrode tube capacitances are delta connected.

series. But a direct measurement of any one is possible if the third terminal of the delta is connected to the common point of the ratio arms, since then one of the two undesirable capacitances is connected across one of the ratio arms. The desired interelectrode capacitance acts only across terminals GH of Fig. 172. This is done in the commercial bridge of Fig. 172 by a special socket adapter, which makes this connection automatic. The self-capacitance of the adapter is eliminated by connecting the adapter in the circuit when the initial balance is made.

It should be understood that, even in the audio-frequency range, a high-precision capacitance calibration is possible only when careful shielding is provided and the bridge is symmetrical. For this reason the ratio arm must be 1:1 and the unknown capacitance C_x expressed either by the setting of a variable standard of the same magnitude or by a substitution method for which two capacitances are used successively in the same arm of the bridge.[1]

94. Determination of High-frequency Capacitance.—Generally it may be said that the measurement of high-frequency capacitance is simpler. If precision calibrations of condensers are to be made which are to hold in the high-frequency range also, the methods just described

[1] This is discussed in detail by J. Field, *Gen. Radio Experimenter*, January, 1930.

are unsatisfactory. It is then customary to use good high-frequency standards (good variable-air condensers, for instance). The customary Wheatstone bridge methods require careful shielding and grounding (Wagner ground, see page 241) in the audio-frequency range and are hardly useful for frequencies much higher than about 50 kc/sec, unless the Giebe[1] bifilary bridge is employed. But even with this bridge great difficulties arise in the very high frequency range. The differential method with a balanced-air transformer indicated in Fig. 174 avoids many difficulties. The high-frequency voltage is impressed between points 3 and 4 and the traveling contact 4 is moved until, for short-circuited C_s and C_x terminals, the zero-current detector across the secondary of the balanced transformer does not indicate. With C_x and a variable standard condenser C_s in the circuit, the setting of C_s is varied until the zero-current indicator passes through a decided minimum. By resetting contact 4 along a slide wire (constantan wire of a few ohms resistance),

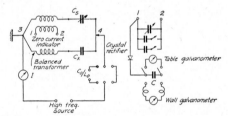

Fig. 174.—Differential system for measuring high-frequency capacitance.

an absolute balance is obtained. The setting of C_s then gives directly the effective high-frequency value of C_x. This method has also the inherent advantage that the test sample and the standard are compared at the same time and any variations in the supply current I cannot affect the measurement. The differential transformer has no effect on the circuit, since it is balanced. Although the value of the supply current does not affect the measurement, too small a supply current decreases the sensitivity of the method. The variation of C_s during the setting of the balance may tune the input circuit, which is not a desirable feature, or may decrease the value of I near the actual balance setting owing to the effective reactance of the differential system, which is still more undesirable, since then the sensitivity is decreased in a region where it should be great. To avoid this, either a fixed suitable inductance L_0 or capacitance C_0 is inserted in the input side so that the C_s settings avoid either conditions near resonance or antiresonance. For ordinary work a high-frequency current I of about 50 to 100 ma is more than sufficient for high sensitivity. An ordinary thermoelectric milliammeter (about 100 ma max) can be used as a zero-current detector. For cases where

[1] *Ann. Physik*, **24**, 941, 1907.

great precision is required, a crystal rectifier with a block condenser C is used in such a way that the rectified secondary current flows through an ordinary student galvanometer (1- to 2-ma full-scale deflection) which has its zero conveniently at the center of the scale, since the zero-current reading is a return point giving a very sharp zero dip. This connection is used to establish the approximate adjustment of C_s. By tuning the secondary of the balanced transformer by means of the condensers across 1–2, greater sensitivity is secured. The double-pole double-throw switch is then connected to a wall galvanometer and a very accurate zero balance obtained.

95. The Substitution Method.—The inductances $(L + L_0)$ of Fig. 175 are so chosen that the natural frequency of the circuit with C_x in it falls in the desired frequency range. The frequency of the loosely coupled generator is varied until the resonance indicator gives a maximum response. The test condenser C_x is then substituted by a variable standard C_s, and C_s is varied until maximum response again occurs. The setting of C_s then gives the high-frequency capacitance of C_x.

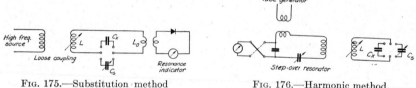

FIG. 175.—Substitution method   FIG. 176.—Harmonic method.

96. The Harmonic Method.—The circuit is shown in Fig. 176. This procedure utilizes the fundamental and any of the higher harmonic frequencies of a tube generator. The step-over resonator gives a sharp dip on the thermoelectric indicator when the actual measuring circuit passes through resonance. The method consists in connecting at first the test condenser C_x across a variable inductance L whose calibration need not be known. The step-over resonator is tuned to the fundamental frequency f of the tube generator, noted by a maximum response on the thermoelectric meter. The measuring circuit is then tuned by means of L, noted by a decided dip in the reading of the thermoindicator of the step-over resonator. This adjustment satisfies the relation $f = k/\sqrt{C_xL}$. The step-over resonator is tuned to the second harmonic. The measuring circuit with C_s in place of C_x is tuned by means of the variable standard C_s which satisfies the relation $2f = k/\sqrt{C_sL}$. The unknown capacitance is then $C_x = 4C_s$. If the third harmonic were used (which is usually not so powerful in tube circuits), by comparing the oscillation constants, $C_xL = 9\ C_sL$ or $C_x = 9C_s$.

97. The Resonance Methods.—The procedures described in connection with Figs. 175 and 176 belong also to the resonance methods. The simple resonance method determines the unknown capacitance C_x by means of the natural circuit frequency f for a known inductance L across C_x. If the capacitance is in microfarads, the inductance in microhenries and f in kilocycles per second, from $f = 159.2/\sqrt{C_x L}$,

$$C_x = \frac{25{,}345}{f^2 L} \qquad (14)$$

The measurement is conveniently carried out by using the tube generator of Fig. 20, which in a loose coupling indicates by the grid dip the resonance condition of the $C_x L$ circuit and by its dial setting gives directly the frequency within a small percentage. A standard frequency meter is then loosely coupled to the tube generator and the setting of the condenser of the standard frequency meter varied until a grid dip occurs again. This gives the accurate value of f. The value of L is found with one of the methods described in Chap. VII, or by the same method with a known condenser instead of C_x.

98. Fleming's Method for the Determination of High-frequency Capacitance.—An ordinary three-element electron tube is used to indicate the zero balance of the capacity bridge of Fig. 177. A table galvanometer (about 1-ma full-scale deflection) is inserted in the grid branch and indicates a current for any positive grid potential. The positive grid potential is partially due to the voltage drop across the filament and partially due to a 1.5-volt dry battery which puts a positive bias on the grid. For $C_1 = C_2$, the standard capacitance C_3 is gradually varied until the galvanometer indicates no further current decrease. The bridge points are then at the same potential and $C_x = C_3$. For more accurate work,

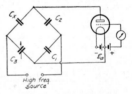

Fig. 177.—Grid-current method for adjusting to equipotential points.

the bifilary-bridge connection with careful shielding and proper grounding should be used.

99. Determination of the Effective Capacitance of a Space Condenser. In high-voltage engineering and for high-power work, the plates of customary types of high-frequency condensers have the form of cylinders with rounded caps on each side or some other form which avoids corona discharges. Two or more of such cylinders or other spacious poles are used and the capacitance is varied by the relative position. Capacity effects then occur in all directions and especially toward ground.

If one space pole is A and the other B, the effects toward ground and the correct capacitance can be found by means of the circuit in Fig. 174. It is then necessary that the ground at the mid-point of the differential transformer be disconnected and the determination is as follows:

1. The space condenser C_x is connected into the differential system and the space pole B is grounded. The balance of the system for the balance setting $C_s = C_1$ gives the relation $C_1 = C_{A-B} + C_{A-0}$.

2. The balance is carried out for space pole A grounded, leading to the balance setting $C_s = C_2$ for which $C_2 = C_{A-B} + C_{B-0}$.

3. The two space poles A and B are connected, forming one pole of the unknown condenser and the ground the other pole. A balance $C_s = C_3$ is made for which $C_3 = C_{A-0} + C_{B-0}$.

The effective capacitance C_3 of the space condenser is then

$$C_x = C_{A-B} + \frac{C_{A-0} C_{B-0}}{C_{A-0} + C_{B-0}}$$
$$= 0.5\left\{ C_1 + C_2 - C_3 + \frac{[C_1 + C_3 - C_2][C_2 + C_3 - C_1]}{C_3} \right\} \qquad (15)$$

100. Determination of the Frequency Factor of a Condenser.—The ratio of high-frequency capacitance to static capacitance of a condenser is called the "frequency factor." The frequency factor is practically unity for a properly designed air condenser. For this reason such a condenser can be used to measure the effective high-frequency capacitance of a test condenser C_x with the method of Fig. 174 and the static capacitance with the ballistic method shown in Fig. 169. In the latter method the standard air condenser is used to obtain the correct value of the ballistic constant. The high-frequency capacitance C_x is measured for several points of the high-frequency range in order to see to what extent the frequency factor varies.

101. Absolute Methods for the Determination of High-frequency Capacitance.—One procedure consists of measuring the current I passing through a test condenser C_x and the terminal voltage E across C_x. If a properly designed tube voltmeter with negligible current consumption (both direct current and displacement current) is used and a pure sinusoidal voltage is impressed on the measuring system, the unknown capacitance is computed from the relation $C_x = 10^3 I/(\omega E)$ microfarads if E and I are in volts and amperes, and the frequency $\omega/2\pi$ in kilocycles per second. With present frequency standards there is no difficulty in determining the frequency with great accuracy, but the measurement of both voltage and current is a drawback if high accuracy is necessary. The absolute method of Fig. 178 depends on the knowledge of a standard resistance R and the frequency only, since it is only necessary to adjust the value of R so that the high-frequency current I_1 passing through R and C_x produces the same terminal voltage for which $R = 1/(2\pi f C_x)$. The unknown capacitance is then computed from

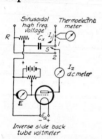

Fig. 178.—Absolute determination of capacitance.

$$C_x = \frac{159.2}{f R} \qquad (16)$$

where C_x is in microfarads, f in kilocycles per second, and R in ohms. The general procedure of the measurement consists in connecting the single-pole switch toward 1 and adjusting the negative grid bias until for a certain value $E = E_1$, the plate current *just* disappears. The inverse tube voltmeter then offers an *infinite* impedance toward the terminals of the test condenser C_x and as such cannot affect the conditions of C_x. There is then the relation

$$\mu E_1 + \frac{I_1\sqrt{2}}{\omega C_x} = 0$$

since $I_1\sqrt{2}/(\omega C_x)$ denotes the maximum value E_p' of the plate voltage. The single-pole double-throw switch is now connected toward 2 and the negative grid bias changed until, for a value $E = E_2$, the plate current I_2 *just* disappears which satisfies the relation $\mu E_2 + I_1 R\sqrt{2} = 0$; where $I_1 R\sqrt{2}$ now denotes the maximum plate voltage E_p'' existing across the standard resistance R. The unknown capacitance is computed from

$$C_x = \frac{159.2}{f R} \frac{E_2}{E_1} \tag{17}$$

where C_x is in microfarads, f in kilocycles per second, and R in ohms, since $I_1\sqrt{2} = -\mu\omega C E_1 = -\mu E_2/R$. Hence, if for the second circuit adjustment R is varied (for a constant current flow I_1) until the plate current just disappears again for the same grid bias $E_2 = E_1$, the expression of (16) can be used in the computation and the actual value of the grid bias need not be known. The same is true for high-frequency current I_1 which flows through the C_x, R series combination.

102. Determination of a Comparatively Large Capacitance.—The measuring circuit of Fig. 179 is excited by a loosely coupled tube generator. The terminals 1, 2 are short-circuited and the setting of C_s is varied until the thermoelectric indicator gives for $C_s = C_1$ a maximum deflection d. The oscillation constant of the measuring circuit is then $C_1 L$. The test condenser C_x is connected across terminals 1, 2 and resonance deflection d again is obtained for a setting $C_s = C_2$. The oscillation constant is then $C_2 C_x/(C_2 + C_x)$, and the unknown high-frequency capacitance is computed from

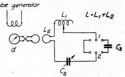

Fig. 179.—Determination of of a large capacitance.

$$C_x = \frac{C_1 C_2}{C_2 - C_1} \tag{18}$$

103. Determination of a Comparatively Small Capacitance.—The measuring circuit of Fig. 180 is excited by a loosely coupled tube generator. When C_x is *not* in the circuit, the measuring system is tuned for the resonance deflection d which is obtained for the setting $C_s = C_1$ and the oscillation constant $C_1 L$. The test condenser C_x is connected to terminals 1, 2 and resonance is obtained again for the setting $C_s = C_2$ and oscillation constant $(C_2 + C_x)L$, and the unknown capacitance computed from $C_x = C_1 - C_2$. Very small capacitances can also be determined by the parallel-wire system.[1] It can be shown that the input impedance of a parallel-wire system l cm in length is

$$Z = \begin{cases} Z_0 \text{ cotanh } \Omega \text{ for far end } AB \text{ open} \\ Z_0 \text{ tanh } \Omega \text{ for far end } AB \text{ short-circuited} \end{cases}$$

if Ω stands for the simplified electrical length $j\omega l\sqrt{CL} = j\frac{2\pi}{\lambda}l$ of the actual length l as indicated in Fig. 181, and the surge impedance Z_0 for high-frequency currents is $\sqrt{L/C}$. The quantities C and L denote the capacitance and inductance of the parallel-wire system per centimeter

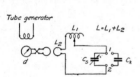

FIG. 180.—Determination of a small capacitance.

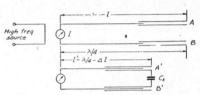

FIG. 181.—The parallel-wire method.

length and $\lambda^{(cm)} = 3 \times 10^7/f^{(kc/sec)}$. If $l = \lambda/4$, the open line is excited in the fundamental mode as for customary antennas and the indicator I shows the resonance deflection. If for the same exciting frequency the parallel-wire system is made shorter than the quarter wave-length distribution by sliding the metal tubes A and B more toward the input end, the condition for resonance for which the reactance of the line vanishes

$$\left(Z_0 \text{ cotanh } \Omega = \frac{Z_0}{j \tan \frac{2\pi l}{\lambda}} = 0 \text{ for } l = \frac{\lambda}{4} \right) \text{ is no longer fulfilled, since}$$

$$\frac{\sqrt{L/C}}{j \tan \frac{2\pi}{\lambda}l'} \neq 0$$

But if a condenser of suitable capacitance C_x is connected across the free end, a resonance effect will be noted again if the lumped reactance $1/(j\omega C_x)$ just makes up for the reactance of the removed portion Δl and

$$\frac{1}{j\omega C_x} - \frac{\sqrt{L/C}}{j \tan \frac{2\pi}{\lambda}\Delta l} = 0$$

[1] This method was used in the earliest days of radio. For sustained waves it is discussed in detail by G. C. Southworth, *Radio Rev.*, **1**, 577, 1920; **2**, 25, 1921; C. R. Englund, *Proc. I.R.E.*, **15**, November, 1927. The subject matter has also been dealt with in *Bur. Standards, Sci. Paper* 491, p. 514, 1924.

Since $\omega = 2\pi/(\lambda\sqrt{CL})$, the unknown capacitance C_x can be computed from

$$C_x = \frac{C\lambda}{2\pi} \tan \frac{2\pi\Delta l}{\lambda} \tag{19}$$

which for small values of l' leads to the approximation

$$C_x \cong \Delta l C \tag{20}$$

where Δl is in centimeters, and the capacitance per centimeter length of the parallel-wire system is

$$C = \frac{10^{-5}}{36 \log_\epsilon \left[\dfrac{a + \sqrt{a^2 - d^2}}{d} \right]} \tag{21}$$

where C is in microfarads and if the diameter d of copper wire and the spacing a between centers of the parallel wires are in centimeters. The method consists of connecting the unknown condenser C_x across the open terminals A and B and shortening the parallel-wire system, until resonance occurs for a length l' cm, and computing C_x from (19) where approximately $\lambda = 3 \times 10^7/f$ and f in kilocycles per second. The procedure is simplified and more accurate if the open parallel-wire system is first adjusted for the quarter wave-length distribution recognized by the resonance deflection I and the length $l = \lambda/4$ noted in centimeters. The unknown condenser C_x is then connected across A and B and the line shortened to a length l' for which resonance again occurs and the unknown capacitance is computed from

$$C_x = 0.636 l C \tan 90 \frac{\Delta l}{l} \tag{22}$$

The resonance indicator has some effect on the settings, and for more accurate work this indicator is dispensed with and resonance indicated either by a loosely coupled aperiodic detector or by the reaction on the tube circuit. A loosely coupled frequency meter can also be used. The adjustable Lecher wire also causes an error, since the capacitance C and inductance L per unit length are somewhat different for slip-over portions. To avoid this error, it is better to figure out approximately what the quarter wave-length distribution l is and use a length of an ordinary parallel-wire system about half as long, or shorter, and connect the unknown capacitance C_x across the open end. The frequency of the source is then changed until the fundamental mode with the C_x loading is excited, and the value of C_x computed by means of (19). It is also possible to measure a small capacitance C_x by means of the half wave-length distribution of the parallel-wire system. It is then necessary to short-circuit the free end with a current meter of negligible resistance.

This meter will act as a resonance indicator and the unknown capacitance which is connected at the input side is computed from

$$C_x = \frac{lC}{\pi} \cot an\ 180\frac{l}{\Delta l} \tag{23}$$

where l is the length of the line for the half wave-length distribution and the line short-circuited on either end, and Δl the change in length when C_x loading exists for the same exciter frequency. Methods of this type, of course, may claim only an accuracy in the neighborhood of 1 per cent.

The method indicated in Fig. 182 uses the heterodyne principle and is probably one of the most sensitive procedures for measuring very small high-frequency capacitances. (1) The condenser C_s of the tube generator I is set so that a current of about the frequency F is produced for which the small test condenser C_x is to be calibrated. This high frequency F is determined by means of a standard frequency meter. The frequency

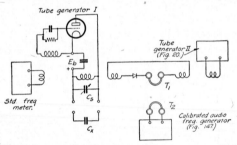

Fig. 182.—Heterodyne method for determining a very small capacitance.

of the generator I is then $F = k/\sqrt{C_s}$. (2) The tube generator II is set to a frequency to produce a suitable beat note f_1 between fundamentals which is heard in the telephone receiver T_1. This beat note is matched by the tone in the telephone receiver T_2 connected to a calibrated beat-frequency generator which should be completely shielded and put as far from all other apparatus as possible. (3) The small unknown capacitance C_x is connected across C_s and the new pitch f_2 of the beat note in T_1 is noted and matched by means of T_2 and the variable condenser of the calibrated audio-frequency generator. The somewhat lower high frequency of generator I is then found from the difference $f = f_1 - f_2$ and equal to $F - f = k/\sqrt{C_s + C_x}$. One finds

$$\left[\frac{F}{F-f}\right]^2 = \frac{C_s + C_x}{C_s} \quad\text{or}\quad \frac{1}{\left[1 - \frac{f}{F}\right]^2} = 1 + \frac{C_x}{C_s}$$

But $\rho = f/F$ is a very small quantity for small values of C_x and, since $1/(1 - \rho)^2 = 1 + 2\rho$, one finds $2f/F = C_x/C_s$ and the unknown small capacitance can be computed from

$$C_x = \frac{2fC_s}{F} \tag{24}$$

For still more accurate work the frequency $f = f_1 - f_2$ is found by noting the beat frequencies f_1 and f_2 by means of a synchronous clock. The ultramicroammeter of J. J. Dowling[1] can be made to act as a direct-indicating small-capacity meter. The circuit is then as in Fig. 183. The oscillator is so arranged that pronounced rectification effect takes place; that is, the work characteristic takes place along a curved portion and the operating point for the steady plate current for a particular frequency is somewhere on the lower bend of the work characteristic. The microammeter in the external plate branch is such that, for no test condenser C_x connected in parallel with C_s, it reads either zero or a small current only, so that a microammeter can be used. If C_x is connected across C_s, a change in plate current will cause a considerable deflection on the microammeter. The circuit can be calibrated in terms of shunted capacitance by using a small two-plate condenser with a

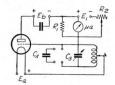

Fig. 183.—Tube generator capacitance meter.

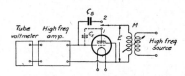

Fig. 184.—Method for the determination of extremely small capacitances C_x.

micrometer adjustment so that the shunted capacitance is known from the dimensions and settings. Another circuit[2] for measuring minute high-frequency capacitance is shown in Fig. 184. The unknown capacitance is in this particular case the very small interelectrode capacitance between the plate and the control grid of a shield-grid tube with a cold filament. The source must be such that the high-frequency voltage E remains essentially constant, irrespective of whether the single-pole double-throw switch is connected toward 1 or toward 2. With the switch on 1, a certain deflection is obtained on the tube voltmeter. With the switch on 2 the small condenser C_s is varied until the same deflection is obtained. The setting of C_s then measures the small interelectrode or any small capacitance C_x. The small standard condenser consists of a copper wire, with a diameter of 0.125 mm, along the axis of a cylinder with a diameter of 2.5 mm. The wire can be moved along the axis with a micrometer movement and an indicator. This condenser is about the same as the small variable cylinder condenser of T. Wulf.

[1] *Proc. Roy. Dubl. Soc.*, **16**, 17, 1921; *Engineering (London)*, **112**, 395, 1921; *Nature*, **107**, 523, 1921; *Phil. Mag.*, **61**, 81, 1923.
[2] Hull, A. W., and N. H. Williams, *Phys. Rev.*, **27**, 432, 1926.

104. Calibration of a Variable-air Condenser in Equal Parts.—A method which was used by the Bureau of Standards[1] at one time is especially adaptable if a comparatively large variable condenser C_x is to be calibrated by means of a much smaller standard variable condenser C_s. The condenser C_s is set to a suitable even value near the maximum value of C_s and connected across a coil with a loosely coupled aperiodic resonance indicator (about one turn working through a crystal rectifier into a direct-current microammeter). The resonance effect is produced in this circuit by a local oscillator (Fig. 20). Condenser C_s is now replaced by condenser C_x which is varied until resonance again occurs without changing the generator frequency. This gives the calibration point $C_x = C_1$. With this setting, C_s is connected in multiple with the test condenser and set to some small C_s setting, say $C_s = 100 \ \mu\mu\text{f}$. The generator frequency is then varied until the resonance indicator gives a maximum response. Next, the condenser C_s is set to such successive values as 200, 300, 400, 500, etc., $\mu\mu\text{f}$, and, for fixed frequency, resonance is produced by decreasing successively the C_x settings. The

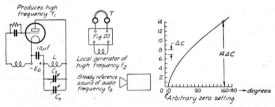

Fig. 185.—Method for dividing a variable air-condenser into equal parts.

calibration points $C_x = C_2'$, C_3', C_4', etc., are the capacity values for which each successive setting is smaller by the same amount (by 100 $\mu\mu\text{f}$) than the preceding setting. This is carried on until the useful minimum limit of the C_x calibration is obtained (about 5 deg). Next, the standard condenser C_s is again set to the suitable even value near 180 deg with $C_x = C_1$ in parallel. The frequency of the generator is changed until resonance occurs. The setting of C_s is then decreased again to its 100 $\mu\mu\text{f}$ value as above and C_x is varied until for some setting $C_x = C_2$ resonance occurs, which is another significant calibration point and the range C_2 down to C_1 is calibrated in equal parts as above. This method presupposes that the condenser to be calibrated does not change with the frequency within the frequency band over which the calibration is carried out. A much more sensitive method for dividing an air condenser in equal parts is shown in Fig. 185. The procedure is an equal beat-tone method which has a great resolving power. A standard variable-air condenser C_s is again connected in parallel with the variable test con-

[1] *Bur. Standards, Circ.* 74, p. 130, 1918.

denser C_x which is to be divided in such a way that the capacity difference between consecutive division points is equal to a known and fixed value ΔC. The circuit formed with L is in this case the external tuned plate circuit of a tube generator. The condenser C_x is set to its zero position, (minimum value), which for practical reasons may be the 10° setting as the arbitrary zero. The standard condenser is set to its maximum value (180 deg) and a plate coil of an effective inductance L is chosen so that the tube oscillator produces a fundamental frequency f_1 which falls into the range for which C_x is to be used. A tuning-fork oscillator, a calibrated beat-frequency oscillator, or for very precise work a fixed beat-frequency generator using two slightly different piezo crystals in parallel to produce an audible note of frequency f_0 is set on a table in the test room, so that the tone coming from a loud-speaker is faintly heard over the entire room. The fundamental frequency f_2 of a local generator (circuit of Fig. 20 will do) is varied with the measuring generator above resonance to such a value that $f_1 - f_2 = f_0$. Therefore it is necessary only to increase the frequency f_2 of the heterodyne generator until the beat tone observed in the telephone receiver T has the same pitch as the tone coming from the loud-speaker. This is easily done by using one earpiece of the telephone receiver T and listening with the other ear to the tone from the loud-speaker. Next, the setting of C_x is gradually increased. The tone heard in T will with both receivers on the ears become lower, pass through zero-beat region, and increase again in pitch. C_x is increased until a beat note of frequency f_0 is again obtained (use now only one earpiece), and the division on the dial of C_x is noted. The increase of capacitance between the arbitrary zero position of C_x and this new setting is ΔC. Next, the setting of the standard condenser C_s is decreased from its 180-deg setting to a somewhat lower value, for which the beat frequency f_0 is again secured in T. During this decrease the beat frequency passed through the silent region with succeeding increase in pitch. The setting of C_x is again gradually increased until f_0 is again secured which is the next division point with a capacitance setting which is larger by ΔC than the preceding one, and so on. In order to obtain the actual calibration of the equal ΔC calibration points, the equal increments ΔC are plotted against the corresponding condenser degrees of C_x as in Fig. 185 and a convenient equal division point (large value), say 14 ΔC, is calibrated with the method shown in Fig. 174. The same variable condenser C_s can be used as reference standard. If for this division the value 481 $\mu\mu f$ is obtained, the increase of capacitance per equal capacity division is $\Delta C = 481\frac{1}{14}$.

105. Determination of Distributed Coil Capacitance.—From the derivations in Sec. 3 [formulas (9) and (10) and (11)] it can be seen that the self-capacitance C_0 of a coil has the effect of increasing the effective values of inductance L and resistance R until a certain frequency $f \cong$

$1/(2\pi\sqrt{C_0 L})$ is reached.   This is also brought out by measurements.[1]   It should also be remembered that, because of the distributed nature of the coil capacitance, the coil goes into resonance for several modes which are not necessarily integer multiples of the fundamental, and that there are conditions for which selective absorption in the coil is due to voltage resonance and conditions for which current resonance is the cause.   Both happen with high inductance coils, such as, for instance, with poorly designed audio-frequency transformers.   If a coil is connected across a tuning condenser C as in Fig. 186, the distributed coil capacitance may

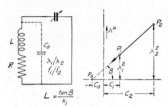

FIG. 186.—Graphic determination of coil capacitance C_0.

be considered as a condenser C_0 across the series combination of a pure inductance L and an ohmic resistance R.   The tuning condenser is also in parallel with C_0.   The determination of C_0 then consists of determining the resonance frequencies f_1 and f_2, respectively, for two different settings C_1 and C_2 of the variable-air condenser C by means of a loosely coupled tube generator (Fig. 20) and a standard frequency meter.   If the *analytic* solution is used,

$$f_1 = \frac{k}{\sqrt{C_1 + C_0}} \text{ and } f_2 = \frac{k}{\sqrt{C_2 + C_0}}$$

and the self-capacitance is computed from

$$C_0 = \frac{C_1 f_1^2 - C_2 f_2^2}{f_2^2 - f_1^2} \tag{25}$$

The self-capacitance C_0 can also be solved *graphically* and readily when the corresponding wave lengths λ_1 and λ_2 are used instead of the frequencies f_1 and f_2, since then the linear relations

$$\lambda_1^2 = k_1[C_1 + C_0]L \text{ and } \lambda_2^2 = k_1[C_2 + C_0]L$$

exist.   It is necessary only to find the points P_1 and P_2 for the coordinates C_1, λ_1^2 and C_2, λ_2^2, and the intercept P_0 of the straight line (passing through P_1 and P_2) with the horizontal axis determines the value of C_0.

Since, according to the above relations, $L = \dfrac{\lambda^2}{k_1[C + C_0]}$ and the graphical construction of Fig. 186, the slope of the straight line when taken to scale $\tan \beta/k_1$ denotes the inductance L, there is also a way of finding the true inductance of the coil.   The factor k_1 is equal to $36\pi^2 10^{16}$ if λ is in meters, C in farads, and L in henries.   A linear relation is also obtained if $1/f^2$ is plotted against C and leads to a similar graphical solution (see Fig. 194).

The *dielectric* method of determining the coil capacitance C_0 consists in placing a fixed condenser of a capacitance C across the coil so that the

[1] *Bur. Standards, Tech. Paper* 298, 1925.

fundamental resonance for the combination occurs for a frequency f_1. For this condition the relation $f_1 = k/\sqrt{C + C_0}$ is satisfied. The test coil is now submerged in oil or some other liquid of known dielectric constant κ and again the frequency of a loosely coupled heterodyne generator (Fig. 20) is varied until a pronounced grid dip occurs, but for the resonance frequency f_2 which is checked by a frequency meter for more accurate work. This condition satisfies the relation $f_2 = k/\sqrt{C + \kappa C_0}$. The coil capacitance is then computed from

$$C_0 = C\frac{f_2^2 - f_1^2}{f_1^2 - \kappa f_2^2} \tag{26}$$

where C_0 and C are in microfarads.

The *harmonic* method for the determination of coil capacitance is based again upon the connection of a variable standard air condenser C_s across a coil and tuning C_s for resonance of the desired frequency f_1 if a loosely coupled local generator (Fig. 20) excites the network. This happens for the setting $C_s = C_1$ and the condition $f = k/\sqrt{C_1 + C_0}$. The local generator is now set to twice the frequency, that is, $2f$ and C_s varied to some value C_2, until resonance again occurs

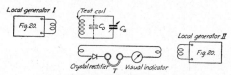

FIG. 187.—Beat method for finding coil self-capacitance C_0.

in the loosely coupled measuring circuit which satisfies the condition $2f = k/\sqrt{C_2 + C_0}$. The coil capacitance is computed from

$$C_0 = \frac{(C_1 - 4C_2)}{3} \tag{27}$$

With the system just described, the frequency of the local driver is doubled for the second adjustment. To make this adjustment more accurately, the beat method shown in Fig. 187 may be used. The oscillator I is set to the desired frequency f and C_s is varied until for some value $C_s = C_1$ the visual indicator of the aperiodic circuit, which is loosely coupled, indicates resonance condition. The generator II is then loosely coupled to the system and its frequency gradually increased until zero-beat condition is obtained, for which state the frequency of generator II also has the value f. The frequency of the generator I is then increased until zero beat again occurs, that is, for frequency $2f$ and the setting $C_s = C_2$ resonance occurs, which is noted by the reading of the visual indicator. The computation is as above by means of formula (27). In the process of the latter measurement it is of advantage, after the first adjustment for $f = k/\sqrt{C_1 + C_0}$, to set the condenser C_s to a value which gives about resonance with $2f$ by reducing the setting C_1 to a value which is about $C_1/4$. With this preliminary adjustment, the approach of the beat note and the final zero-beat condition for the double frequency can be observed distinctly. The accurate setting of C_s to the exact value of C_2 is made next. If the third harmonic is used for the measurement, the variable condenser C_s is set approximately to a value $C_1/9$ and the frequency of the driver I varied until for a frequency $3f$ another zero-beat condition is observed. This gives the exact setting of $C_s = C_3$ and from $3f = k/\sqrt{C_3 + C_0}$ and the fundamental relation $f = k/\sqrt{C_1 + C_0}$, the coil capacitance is computed from

$$C_0 = \frac{C_1 - 9C_3}{8} \tag{28}$$

Other methods utilize the condition of self-resonance of the coil (lowest frequency). Calling L the true inductance of the coil in microhenries and

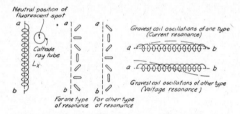

Fig. 188.—Indicates condition of voltage and condition of current resonance of coils. (Cathode-ray tube in the position as above is moved along the coil; the magnetic as well as the electric field of the test coil L_x affect the fluorescent spot.)

C_0 its effective self-capacitance in microfarads, for the resonance frequency f in kilocycles per second this quantity can be computed from

$$C_0 = \frac{25,345}{f^2 L} \tag{29}$$

A properly designed vacuum-tube voltmeter connected across the coil is used to indicate the resonance condition when a loosely coupled driver (Fig. 20) is varied upward in frequency until a decided sharp response takes place. Cathode-ray[1] and glow-discharge tubes can also be used for this work. One-point connections to small neon-glow tubes or other glow tubes brought in the neighborhood of the test coil will indicate the resonance condition. If a cathode-ray tube is used either no electrodes are employed or external deflection electrodes are used. Thus, if a cathode-ray tube with no deflection electrodes and with its axis perpendicular to the axis of a test coil is moved along the test coil as in Fig. 188, deflection ellipses as indicated may occur when the coil is in resonance. The cathode-ray tube can then be used to explore the charge distribution along a long coil. Hence, when a cathode-ray tube with external elec-

[1] RIDDER, C., *Arch. Elektrotech.*, **10**, 339, 1922.

trodes mounted at 90 deg, as in Fig. 189, is connected across the ends a and b of a test coil L_x, resonance condition can be observed by means of the resultant R. For the gravest coil oscillation for voltage resonance, the resulting deflection disappears when the coil ends a and b are short-circuited, while for the gravest oscillation for current resonance the deflection remains undisturbed if a and b are connected together. A linear deflection results for coil oscillations for voltage resonance if only one set of external deflection quadrants are used, but in such a way that the deflection plates form parallel plates as customary with internal electrodes of cathode-ray tubes and are connected across a and b.

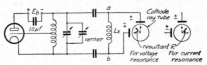

Fig. 189.—Indicates voltage or current resonance if two external deflection electrodes are used.

106. Notes on the Effect of Interelectrode Capacitances of Electron Tubes on the Input and Output Impedances of the Tube.—As far as the measurement of interelectrode capacitances is concerned, the discussion in Sec. 12 and the description of Sec. 93 in connection with Fig. 173 are of importance. This brings out that one must distinguish between true interelectrode capacitances (see Fig. 173) C_{gf}, C_{gp}, and C_{pf} and grid, plate, and filament capacitances C_g, C_p, and C_f' given by

$$C_g = C_{gp} + C_{gf}; \quad C_p = C_{gp} + C_{pf}; \quad C_f = C_{gf} + C_{pf} \tag{30}$$

It is the capacitances C_g and C_p and *not* alone the true interelectrode capacitances C_{gf} and C_{pf} which play a part for the *input* and the *output* branch of an electron tube *connected in a circuit* such as an amplifier, oscillator, or detector. But when the tube is *not* connected in a circuit and the grid-filament terminals are connected to a capacity bridge or the like, the delta connection of Fig. 173 shows that not the true inter-electrode capacitance C_{gf} is measured nor C_g, but C_{gf} shunted by a series combination of C_{gp} and C_{pf}. A similar capacitance combination would be experienced if any of the two other terminals (grid plate and plate filament, respectively) were used. The true interelectrode capacitances, however, can be measured directly if a special tube adapter is used in the tube-capacity bridge of the General Radio Company (page 216) or the method [the theory of which is described in Sec. 12 with the final formula (95)] is used which is mentioned under tube measurements on page 337.

As far as the input current i_g and the output current i_p in Fig. 173 are concerned, one must distinguish between *thermionic* and *displacement* currents between any two electrodes of the tube. Both currents together account for the resultant current effects observed. For instance, for the current across the direct path 1 to 2 at the input side, i_1 may be called the thermionic contribution and i_2 the displacement component which could *not* exist if C_{gf} capacitance were not effective. In the same way along the direct path between 2 and 3, the current i_3 may be called the thermionic and i_4 the displacement component, while the current i_5 between the plate and the grid is a displacement current and is the one which may give most of the trouble in amplifiers in the upper high-frequency range. When dealing with capacitances, it is more convenient to express the tube action by means of admittances and in the final result to use the reciprocal in order to have an expression for the more customary impedance at the input and the output side. Then there is $\partial i_g/\partial e_g$ as *input* admittance, $\partial i_p/\partial e_p$ as *output* admittance, and $\partial i_p/\partial e_g$ as the *mutual* admittance which is the effective steepness of the work region of the tube characteristic. In the delta circuit of Fig. 173 for these admittances,

$$\frac{\partial i_g}{\partial e_g} = \underbrace{\frac{\partial i_1}{\partial e_g}}_{\text{grid conductance } g_g} + j\omega\underbrace{[C_{gf} + C_{gp}]}_{\text{input capacitance } C_g}$$

$$\frac{\partial i_p}{\partial e_p} = \underbrace{\frac{\partial i_3}{\partial e_p}}_{\text{plate conductance } \frac{1}{r_p}} + j\omega\underbrace{[C_{pf} + C_{gp}]}_{\text{output capacitance } C_p} \qquad (31)$$

$$\frac{\partial i_p}{\partial e_g} = \underbrace{\frac{\partial i_3}{\partial e_g}}_{\text{mutual conductance } g_m} + \underbrace{j\omega C_{gp}}_{\substack{\text{mutual} \\ \text{capacitance}}}$$

from which

$$\left.\begin{array}{l} \text{Input admittance } Y_g = g_g + j\omega C_g; \\[2mm] \text{output admittance } Y_p = \dfrac{1}{r_p} + j\omega C_p; \\[2mm] \text{mutual admittance } Y_m = g_m + j\omega C_{gp} \end{array}\right\} \qquad (31a)$$

The input, output, and mutual tube impedances are then $Z_g = 1/Y_g$; $Z_p = 1/Y_p$ and $Z_m = 1/Y_m$. For accurate determinations it is therefore necessary to account for both the active and reactive components. This is followed up under tube measurements in Chap. XIII.

107. Determination of the Capacitance of Insulators.—The insulator is connected in place of condenser C_x in Fig. 174 and the dielectric resistance compensated by the traveling contact 4 along the slide wire. A small standard variable-air condenser C_s is then gradually increased until the zero-current indicator of the differential system *just* passes through the no-current condition for which setting $C_s = C_x$.

108. Notes on Antenna and Line Capacitance.—For the determination of effective antenna capacitance and line capacitance at high frequencies, no very accurate measurements are possible, since the conditions to ground change and the effective value of the measured capacitance depend on the potential distribution along the aerial system. It is then also necessary to distinguish between static or actual capacitance, apparent effective, and correct effective values. This is discussed in detail in the introduction of Chap. VII.

CHAPTER VII

DETERMINATION OF SELF-INDUCTANCE

As in the case of capacitance, one must distinguish between absolute and relative methods and between absolute and practical units. The coefficient of self-inductance is defined as $L = e/(di/dt)$. Therefore, it is the value of the induced voltage in a circuit branch when the current changes at unit rate. The practical unit is the *henry* and a branch of a circuit has the self-induction of 1 henry when 1 volt is induced across its terminals by a change of its current of 1 amp/sec. Since for high-frequency work the henry is altogether too large a unit, it is customary to use the millihenry (10^{-3} henry) and microhenry (10^{-6} henry). As far as the absolute system is concerned, one must again distinguish between the electrostatic unit and the electromagnetic unit of inductance. The latter plays a greater part and is expressed in centimeters, since it has the dimension of a length.

Then

$$1 \text{ cm [e.m.u.]} = 10^{-9} \text{ henry} \tag{1}$$

The e.s.u. has the dimension of $cm^{-1} \sec^2$, that is, the reciprocal of an acceleration. Because, for the inductance, the ratio of the electromagnetic to the electrostatic unit is equal to the square of the velocity of light, the electrostatic unit of inductance must be multiplied by 9×10^{11} in order to give the value in henries.

109. Notes on Formulas for Inductance.—Many formulas are available in literature for the calculation of inductance. However, the reliable formulas mostly presuppose such coil shapes and relative dimensions that they cannot always be used for efficient high-frequency work. The requirement for a good high-frequency coil is a large time constant (L/R), and small self-capacitance (universal-wound, honeycomb, and bank-wound coils for larger inductances). No doubt the best way to obtain a good value of inductance for a certain high frequency is by means of a measurement. Nevertheless, formulas which are not too involved and do not require too many computations are of use in predicting the approximate value of the effective high-frequency inductance.

The self-inductance of a straight round wire of length l cm, diameter d cm, and for a permeability μ is

$$L = 2 \times 10^{-3} l \left[\log_\epsilon \frac{4l}{d} - 1 + 0.25\,\mu \right] \text{ microhenries}$$

233

which for a copper wire in air reduces to

$$L = 2 \times 10^{-3}l\left[2.303 \log_{10} \frac{4l}{d} - 0.75\right] \tag{2}$$

This is the static (low-frequency) value and approaches the value $2 \times 10^{-3}l\left[2.303 \log_{10} \frac{4l}{d} - 1\right]$ with increasing frequency. According to *Circular* 74 of the Bureau of Standards, the inductance at any frequency and for any material can be computed from

$$L = 2 \times 10^{-3}l\left[2.303 \log_{10} \frac{4l}{d} - 1 + \mu\beta\right] \text{ microhenries} \tag{3}$$

where the frequency and material coefficient β is found from the Table V for the factor

$$\alpha = 0.1405d\sqrt{\frac{\mu f}{\rho}} \tag{3a}$$

if μ denotes the permeability which is unity for copper wire, ρ the volume resistivity in microhm-centimeters. For copper, $\alpha = 0.1071d\sqrt{f}$ if f denotes the frequency in cycles per second.

TABLE V

α	β	α	β	α	β	α	β
0.0	0.250	4.0	0.1715	12	0.059	50	0.014
0.5	0.250	4.5	0.154	14	0.050	60	0.012
1.0	0.249	5.0	0.139	16	0.044	70	0.010
1.5	0.247	6.0	0.116	18	0.039	80	0.009
2.0	0.240	7.0	0.100	20	0.035	90	0.008
2.5	0.228	8.0	0.088	25	0.028	100	0.007
3.0	0.211	9.0	0.078	30	0.024	...	0.000
3.5	0.191	10.0	0.070	40	0.0175		

For a grounded vertical-wire antenna, $L = 4.606 \times 10^{-3} \log_{10} \frac{4l}{d}$. This value is about three times as large as the value measured at low frequencies. For a horizontal wire h cm above ground, l cm long, and a diameter d cm, the formula is $L = 2 \times 10^{-3}l\left[2.303 \log_{10}\frac{4h}{d} + 0.25\right]\mu h$. For a parallel-wire system with a spacing a in centimeters between centers of the two wires, according to C. Snow[1] of the Bureau of Standards, the high-frequency inductance of a section l in centimeters of the parallel-wire system also depends upon the direct-current resistance r_0 in centi-

[1] *Bur. Standards, Sci. Paper* 491, p. 497.

meters per second per centimeter length, and the frequency $\omega/2\pi$ in cycles per second. The formula is

$$L = 10^{-3}l\left[4 \log_e \frac{1}{b} + \sqrt{\frac{r_0}{\omega[1 - (d/a)^2]}}\right] \text{ microhenries} \quad (4)$$

for

$$b = \frac{d/a}{1 + \sqrt{1 - (d/a)^2}} \quad (4a)$$

According to the above, the value of r_0 is in the e.m. c.g.s. system and, if measured for the entire length l in ohms and computed per unit length, the required absolute value of r_0 in Eq. (4) is obtained by the relation 1 ohm = 10^9 cm/sec in e.m.u. For a closely wound single-layer coil the H. Nagaoka and L. Lorenz formula is

$$L = \frac{\pi^2 K D^2 N^2}{l} 10^{-3} \text{ microhenries} \quad (5)$$

if N denotes the total number of turns, D the mean diameter of the coil in centimeters, l the length of coil in centimeters, and K a factor which varies with D/l. The values of K for different ratios D/l are given in Table VI.

TABLE VI

D/l	K	D/l	K	D/l	K	D/l	K
0.	1.	0.45	0.834	0.9	0.711	3.5	0.394
0.05	0.979	0.5	0.818	1.0	0.688	4.0	0.365
0.10	0.959	0.55	0.803	1.1	0.667	4.5	0.341
0.15	0.939	0.6	0.789	1.2	0.648	5.0	0.32
0.2	0.92	0.65	0.775	1.4	0.611	6.0	0.285
0.25	0.902	0.7	0.761	1.6	0.580	7.0	0.258
0.3	0.884	0.75	0.748	2.0	0.526	8.0	0.237
0.35	0.867	0.8	0.735	2.5	0.472	9.0	0.219
0.4	0.850	0.85	0.723	3.0	0.429	10.0	0.203

For a toroidal coil of circular cross section (having only a very small external field),

$$L = 12.57 \times 10^{-3} N^2 [R - \sqrt{R^2 - r^2}] \text{ microhenries} \quad (6)$$

if R denotes the distance from axis to center of the cross section in centimeters, r the radius of the turns of the winding in centimeters, and N the total number of turns. For single-layer or multilayer (long or of disk shape) coils for which the turns touch each other, the formula[1] of Brooks, Morgan, and Turner can be used. It is

$$L = \frac{l^2}{b + c + R} \frac{F' F''}{10^3} \text{ microhenries} \quad (7)$$

[1] *Bull.* 53, University of Illinois.

for the form factors

$$F' = \frac{10b + 12c + 2R}{10b + 10c + 1.4R} \text{ and } F'' = 0.5 \log_{10}\left[100 + \frac{14R}{2b + 3c}\right] \quad (7a)$$

with all dimensions in centimeters, and a the mean radius of the winding, b the axial length of the coil, c the thickness of the winding $(R - r)$, r the internal radius of the winding, R the external radius of the winding, and l the total length of the wire. These formulas hold to a good degree of approximation for low-frequency measurements. The factor F' is unity for very long coils and becomes 1.43 if only a single-turn coil exists (Kirchhoff's formula). All other values lie between these two limits. F'' is for very long coils likewise equal to unity but is still about equal to 1.01 if the axial length of the coil is the largest dimension. But F'' plays an important part if very short coils (disk shape) exist. For

$$a:b:c = 1.5:1.2:1 \quad (7b)$$

the coil gives the *largest* inductance for the smallest length l of the wire. For such a case the inductance increases with the 1.667th power of the total length l of the wire. Since, then, $F' F'' = 1.14$, the optimum inductance can be computed either from the number of turns N by means of

$$L_{\text{opt}} = 2.56 \times 10^{-3}lN \text{ microhenries} \quad (7c)$$

or from $L_{\text{opt}} = 0.2714 \dfrac{l^2}{c\,10^3}.$ Of course, such formulas can be used in the audio-frequency range only.

Example.—The external diameter of a coil is 10 cm, the internal diameter 5 cm, the axial length 3 cm. The number of turns $N = 1868$. Hence $R = 5$ cm, $r = 2.5$ cm, $a = 3.75$ cm, $b = 3$ cm, and $c = 2.5$ cm. The total wire length is

$$l = 2\pi aN = 2\pi 3.75 \times 1868 = 43,990 \text{ cm}$$

Hence $L = 2.56 \times 43,990 \times 1868 \times 10^{-9} = 0.21$ henry. The measurement at 1 kc/sec gave 0.217 henry which is a good check. The computation is therefore simple. If the second expression for (7c) is used, the same result would be obtained by means of $0.2714 \times 10^{-9} \times 43,990^2/2.5$. For simple types of high-frequency coils, H. A. Wheeler[1] has given approximation formulas which are patterned after an empirical formula derived by L. A. Hazeltine. The formulas are derived empirically from inductance formulas and curves in *Circular* 74 of the Bureau of Standards.[2] With reference to Fig. 190, for the multilayer coil,

[1] *Proc. I.R.E.*, **16**, 1398, 1928; discussion by R. R. Batcher and H. A. Wheeler, *Proc. I.R.E.*, **17**, 580, 1929.

[2] At the end of this circular many of the formulas and necessary tables and curves which have been studied by various members of the bureau's staff are given and

$$L = \frac{0.314a^2N^2}{6a + 9b + 10c} \text{ microhenries} \tag{8}$$

which, according to H. A. Wheeler, is correct within about 1 per cent, if the three terms in the denominator are about equal. For the single-layer cylindrical coil

$$L = \frac{0.41a^2N^2}{9a + 10b} \text{ microhenries} \tag{9}$$

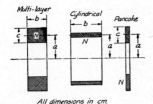

All dimensions in cm.

FIG. 190.—Different coil shapes.

Dimensions in cm.

FIG. 191.—Frame aerial.

which again claims an accuracy within 1 per cent for coils with $b > 0.8a$. Another formula is

$$L = \begin{cases} \dfrac{0.41a^2N^2}{8a + 11c} \text{ single-layer spiral (pancake)} \\[2mm] \dfrac{0.41a^2N^2}{8a + 11b} \text{ single-layer cylindrical} \end{cases} \begin{array}{l} \text{coil in} \\ \text{microhenries} \end{array} \tag{9a}$$

which claims an accuracy within 5 per cent for coils with $c > 0.2a$ and $2a > b > 0.2a$. In the case of frame (coil) antennas, we can distinguish between single-layer axial and single-layer radial (pancake) coils. Each of this type can be used as a multilayer coil, the multilayer of the first type being more customary. For a single-turn coil which forms a polygon of n sides and length s in centimeters for each side and a diameter d in centimeters for the copper wire for $s \gg d$, according to F. W. Grover,[1]

$$L = 2 \times 10^{-3}s\left[2.303 \log_{10} \frac{2s}{d} + A\right] \text{ microhenries} \tag{10}$$

where for a square-shaped single-turn frame $n = 4$, the constant $A = -0.524$ for a hexagon $s = 6$, $A = 0.098$, and for an octagon $s = 8$,

---

represent one of the best compilation of such formulas which have an indirect bearing on high-frequency work. Also formulas for capacitance and other quantities are given. For other Bureau of Standards publications, reference is made to *Circular* 24 (various papers on inductance calculations). For development of inductance formulas, see A. Russell, "Alternating Currents," vol. I, Chaps. II and III, 1914; A. Gray, "Absolute Measurements in Electricity and Magnetism," vol. II, Part 1, Chap. VI. Other references are in *Rayleigh's Collected Papers*, **2**, 15; S. Butterworth, *Phil. Mag.*, **31**, 276, 1916; R. Spielrein, *Arch. Elektrotech.*, **3**, 187, 1915; A. Esau, *Jahrb. d. drahtl.*, **15**, 2, 1920; F. W. Grover, *Bur. Standards, Sci. Paper*, **18**, 451, 1922; **18**, 735, 1923, etc.
[1] *Loc. cit.*

$A = 0.462$. Axial single-layer coils of N turns and of square shape are customary. The coil is then as in Fig. 191 where the pitch p of the winding is to be taken between the centers of the round copper wire of consecutive single-layer turns. The side a of the square is also measured between centers and the width b between centers is equal to $(N - 1)p$. The Bureau of Standards formula[1] is then

$$L = 8 \times 10^{-3}aN^2\left[2.303 \log_{10} \frac{a}{b} + 0.726 + 0.2231\frac{b}{a} \right] - 8 \times$$
$$10^{-3}aN[\gamma + \delta] \text{ microhenries} \quad (11)$$

where the factors γ and δ for different ratios d/p for the diameter d in centimeters of the copper wire and N, respectively, are given in Tables VII and VIII.

TABLE VII

d/p	γ	d/p	γ	d/p	γ	d/p	γ
1.0	+0.557	0.48	−0.177	0.26	−0.790	0.12	−1.563
0.95	0.506	0.46	0.220	0.24	0.870	0.11	1.650
0.9	0.452	0.44	0.264	0.22	0.957	0.10	1.746
0.85	0.394	0.42	0.311	0.20	1.053	0.09	1.851
0.8	0.334	0.40	0.359	0.19	1.104	0.08	1.969
0.75	0.269	0.38	0.411	0.18	1.158	0.07	2.102
0.7	0.200	0.36	0.465	0.17	1.215	0.06	2.256
0.65	0.126	0.34	0.522	0.16	1.276	0.05	2.439
0.6	0.046	0.32	0.583	0.15	1.340	0.04	2.662
0.55	−0.041	0.30	0.647	0.14	1.409	0.03	2.950
0.5	0.136	0.28	0.716	0.13	1.483	0.02	3.355

TABLE VIII

N	δ	N	δ	N	δ	N	δ
1	0.000	9	0.260	45	0.317	200	0.333
2	0.114	10	0.266	50	0.319	300	0.334
3	0.166	15	0.286	60	0.322	400	0.335
4	0.197	20	0.297	70	0.324	500	0.336
5	0.218	25	0.304	80	0.326	700	0.336
6	0.233	30	0.308	90	0.327	1000	0.336
7	0.244	35	0.312	100	0.328		
8	0.253	40	0.315	150	0.331		

Formula (10), when applied to the case of a single turn of square shape, leads to a circuit which can be used for calibration work if too high an accuracy is not required. The inductance is then $L = 8 \times 10^{-3}s$ $\left(\log_{10} \frac{2s}{d} - 0.524 \right)$ μh. If a rectangular single turn of sides s_1 and s_2

[1] *Loc. cit.*

in centimeters which are large compared to d are used, the inductance becomes

$$L = 10^{-3}\left\{4\left[2.303s_1 \log_{10}\frac{4s_1s_2}{d[s_1 + m]} + 2.303s_2 \log_{10}\frac{4s_1s_2}{d[s_2 + m]} - 2(s_1 + s_2 - m)\right] + s_1 - s_2\right\} \text{ microhenries} \quad (12)$$

where $m = \sqrt{s_1{}^2 + s_2{}^2}$. Such rectangular frames were used in the early days for standardizing wave lengths (frequencies) by inserting at the middle of one of the short sides a two-plate condenser whose capacitance could likewise be computed. Such frames are of use when small inductances are required for calibration work. The single circular turn of diameter D in centimeter of the circle between centers of the wire of diameter d in centimeter can also be used for the same purpose and the inductance is computed from

$$L = 2 \times 10^{-3}\pi D\left[2.303 \log_{10}\frac{D}{d} - 0.33\right] \text{ microhenries} \quad (13)$$

which comes from formula (7).

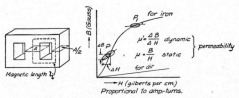

FIG. 192.—Magnetic conditions for a coil with an iron core.

If coils with an iron core are used, the dynamic[1] permeability μ' must be used. In Fig. 192, the inductance is given by $L_e = \mu'kAN^2/l_i$ henries. For the core dimensions in centimeters, $k = 1.256 \times 10^{-8}$ and the dimensions of the core in inches, $k = 3.2 \times 10^{-8}$. The quantity l_i denotes the average length of the iron path, A the cross-sectional area, and N the number of turns. For an air gap of length l, one has $L_e = \dfrac{kAN^2}{\left(\dfrac{l_i}{\mu'} + l\right)}$. From the figure it can be seen that the *dynamic* or incremental permeability $\mu' = \Delta B/\Delta H$ and not the static permeability $\mu = B/H$ must be taken into consideration. As far as the alternating current is concerned, the effective inductance is the change in total flux divided by the change in current, that is, the effective inductance is $L_e = AN \times$

[1] SPOONER, T., *J. Am. Inst. Elec. Eng.*, **42**, 42, 1923; *Phys. Rev.*, **30**, 527, 1925; C. R. HANNA, *J. Am. Inst. Elec. Eng.*, **46**, 128, 1927; D. E. REPLOGLE, *Q.S.T.*, p. 23, April, 1928; C. A. WRIGHT and F. T. BOWDITCH, *Proc. I.R.E.*, **16**, 373, 1928, and the discussion of this paper by W. O. OSBON and C. A. WRIGHT, p. 844; editorial by G. W. O. HOWE, *Exptl. Wireless*, **5**, 49, 1928.

$10^{-8}\Delta B/\Delta I$ if A denotes the cross-sectional area and N the number of turns. With ferromagnetic choke coils used in tube circuits, a superimposed direct-current magnetization cannot always be avoided except theoretically in a push-pull circuit (practically a difference current always exists), for which reasons an air gap of length l in addition to the ferromagnetic length l_i is provided in the core of the coil. For a certain path l_i a definite air gap l exists, for which the dynamic permeability becomes a maximum, that is, for which the effective coil inductance L_e becomes a maximum. For the total increase in magnetomotive force, then,

$$0.4N \ \Delta I = \frac{l_i \ \Delta B}{\mu'} + l \ \Delta B \text{ and } L_e = \frac{0.4 \pi \times 10^{-8} A N^2}{\dfrac{l_i}{\mu'} + l} \text{ henries}$$

if l, l_i, and A are in centimeters and square centimeters, respectively, while for a steady-current magnetization I (amp) the flux density in gausses becomes

$$B = \frac{0.4\pi I N}{\dfrac{l_i}{\mu} + l} \text{ gauss}$$

Introducing the value of N from this expression into the L_e relation,

$$L_e = \frac{A B^2 \left[\dfrac{l_i}{\mu} + l\right]^2}{\left[\dfrac{l_i}{\mu'} + l\right] I^2} \frac{10^{-8}}{0.4\pi} = \frac{B^2 \left[\dfrac{1}{\mu} + \dfrac{l}{l_i}\right]^2 l_i \ A}{\left[\dfrac{1}{\mu'} + \dfrac{l}{l_i}\right] I^2} \frac{10^{-8}}{0.4\pi} \text{ henries}$$

But $l_i A$ is the volume τ of the iron in cubic centimeters and

$$\frac{L_e I^2}{\tau} = \frac{B^2}{0.4\pi \times 10^8} \frac{\left[\dfrac{1}{\mu} + \rho\right]^2}{\dfrac{1}{\mu'} + \rho}$$

for $\rho = l/l_i$. For direct-current magnetization, from the B relation given above,

$$\frac{IN}{l_i} = \frac{B}{0.4\pi}\left[\frac{1}{\mu} + \rho\right]$$

C. R. Hanna[1] used expressions of this type and for certain air-gap ratios ρ plotted curves of $L_e I^2/\tau$ against IN/l_i. The method then leads to a procedure where, by means of curves, the air-gap ratio ρ for the optimum value of L_e can be found.

110. Determination of Low-frequency Inductance.—In order to study skin effect, effect of coil capacitance, etc., at high frequencies, it is necessary to know the static inductance of a coil. With a properly

[1] *Loc. cit.*

designed high-frequency coil, the determination of inductance at 1 kc/sec or a similar audio frequency is then sufficient.[1] The decade-resistance bridge of the General Radio Company or its equivalent is very useful for this work. It is the Wheatstone bridge P_4, P_5, P_6, P_7, P_8, P_9, indicated in Fig. 193. The variable decade resistances R_1 and R_2 are the ratio arms. The arm R_1 consists of four decade resistances 0 to 0.1, 0 to 1, 0 to 10 and 0 to 100 ohms, respectively, giving a total resistance of 1111 ohms. Ratio arm R_2 can be adjusted to 3, 10, 30, 100, 300, and 1000 ohms. The standard resistance R_0 is again variable as R_1 and has 0.1-ohm steps up to 1111 ohms. The decade resistances can be relied upon up to a frequency of about 1.5 Mc/sec. The entire bridge works for the total audio-frequency range when all apparatus except the plug in head set T and the test and standard coils are within a copper shield which is grounded and connected to point P_2 known as "Wagner ground." The Wagner ground avoids the difficulties of unsymmetrical ground capacitances. It can be readily added to the decade box by using a

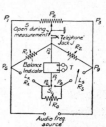

Fig. 193.—Modified Wheatstone bridge with Wagner ground.

5000-ohm dial potentiometer $P_1P_2P_3$ which is connected across the source P_5P_9. The measurement is as follows:

1. The unknown inductance coil L_x, R_x is connected in one arm and the standard inductance L_s,R_s which may be fixed in the other arm.

2. The value of L_x is guessed approximately and the ratio of R_1/R_2 is chosen approximately equal to the ratio L_x/L_s (generally using the largest possible setting of R_2 for this ratio).

3. The single-pole double-throw switch S_1 is connected to point P_6 and R_s is set to its zero value.

4. The variable resistance R_1 is then changed until the sound in the telephone receiver T (which is connected either directly across P_4, P_7 or through an audio-frequency amplifier) passes through a minimum.

5. The setting of R_0 is gradually increased and if the sound becomes louder it shows that the standard L_s has more effective resistance and the switch S_1 must be connected toward P_8.

6. The standard resistance R_0 is then increased until a much better sound minimum is obtained. The residual unbalance is then due to unsymmetrical capacitances of the bridge.

7. The press-button switch S_2 to the Wagner ground P_2 is pushed down and the head set T of the zero-current detector plugged into the telephone jack J and the setting of P_2 varied until zero sound is noticed.

8. The press button is released and the telephone connected back toward bridge points P_4P_7 and the 0.1 settings of R_0, and if necessary the 0.1 settings of R_1 are varied until an absolute zero condition is obtained.

The Wagner ground adjustment is generally affected but little when R_1 is varied by 0.1 ohm and points P_2P_4 remain practically at the same

[1] *Bur. Standards, Tech. Paper* 298.

potential which is that of the ground, although only P_2 is actually connected to ground. If the single-pole double-throw switch S_1 is connected to P_6 for the balanced bridge, for the balanced bridge, the unknown inductance is computed from $L_x = R_1 L_s / R_2$ and the effective resistance of the test coil is $R_x = R_1[R_s + R_0]/R_2$. For the switch S_1 connected to point P_8, the same formula holds for L_x but

$$R_x = \frac{R_1}{R_2} R_s - R_0$$

With properly designed high-frequency coils it may be said that the inductance value measured at 1 kc/sec holds approximately up to about 60 kc/sec.

111. Notes on the High-frequency Inductance of Coils and the Determination of True Inductance.—The effective high-frequency inductance differs from the geometrical inductance because the current distributions along and across the wire are functions of the frequency. The self-capacity of a coil with its dielectric losses also plays an important part and neighboring circuits have an effect. Therefore, high-frequency coils cannot be regarded as a pure reactance with a pure resistance in series. According to experience, for properly designed high-frequency coils the pure inductance L with the pure resistance R may be considered as being shunted by a lumped capacitance C_0 which accounts for the effect of the distributed coil capacitance. Any dielectric losses can then be taken care of by assuming a certain resistance ρ in series with C_0 with the series combination across L, R. The value of C_0 does not vary essentially with the frequency but the effect of $1/\omega C_0$ may be very pronounced. These cases are treated analytically in Sec. 3. From Eq. (9) of that section it is evident that the effective inductance is approximately $L_e = L/(1 - \omega^2 C_0 L)$ if the dielectric resistance ρ is neglected, the exact value being

$$L_e = \frac{L[1 - \omega^2 C_0 L] - C_0 R^2}{[1 - \omega^2 C_0 L]^2 + \omega^2 C_0^2 R^2}$$

It is customary to use coils not close to self-resonance, but far from it. The quantity $\omega^2 C_0 L$ is then generally small compared with unity and

$$L_e \cong L[1 + \omega^2 C_0 L] \tag{13a}$$

If the dielectric resistance ρ is also taken into account, Eq. (12) of Sec. 3 is the formula for the high-frequency inductance if C_0 is used instead of C. Hence if L is expressed in microhenries, C_0 in microfarads, and the frequency f in kilocycles per second, the high-frequency inductance in microhenries can be computed from

$$L_e = L[1 + 3943 \times 10^{-8} \, f^2 C_0 L] \tag{13b}$$

while for coils close to self-resonance which is most undesirable for practical work,

$$L_e = \frac{L}{1 - 3943 \times 10^{-8} f^2 C_0 L} \tag{14}$$

In these formulas the true inductance L can be computed from a theoretical formula as given in the last section or is obtained by the graphical construction given in Fig. 186 which depends upon taking two readings at two different frequencies f_1 and f_2 corresponding to the wave lengths λ_1 and λ_2 for the condenser settings C_1 and C_2, respectively. This construction also gives the value of C_0 required in (13b) and (14). The value of C_0 can also be directly obtained from the frequency readings by the graphical construction of Fig. 194 or by formula (25) in Sec. 105 or any of the other methods described in that section. The true inductance L can be computed by means of (13b) and (14) if L_e is measured by one of the methods described in the next sections. Moreover, the effective coil inductance L_e is also affected by neighboring circuits and shielding. Taking only the case of a pure inductance coil L into consideration, the circuit analysis given in Sec. 4 can be used, where Eq. (29) shows that for a mutual inductance M from the coil L to a closed circuit containing $L_2, C_2,$ and $R_2,$ the inductance L changes to an effective value

Fig. 194.—Determination of coil capacitance.

$$
\begin{aligned}
L_e &= L - \frac{\omega^2 M^2 \left[L^2 - \dfrac{1}{\omega^2 C_2} \right]}{R_2{}^2 + \left[\omega L_2 - \dfrac{1}{\omega C_2} \right]^2} \\
&= L - \frac{\omega^2 M^2 C_2 [\omega^2 C_2 L_2 - 1]}{\omega^2 C_2{}^2 R_2{}^2 + [\omega^2 C_2 L_2 - 1]^2} \tag{15}
\end{aligned}
$$

showing that the effective high-frequency inductance L_e for resonance $(\omega^2 C_2 L_2 = 1)$ in the adjacent circuit only is equal to the true inductance L. For all other values it can be larger or smaller than L, depending upon whether the natural frequency of the disturbing C_2, L_2, R_2 circuit is below or above the resonance frequency. For aperiodic adjacent circuits—such as shielding is, in effect—or a secondary circuit of inductance L_2 and resistance R_2, the effective inductance L_e of coil L is always smaller than the true value L as long as lines of force interlink L and L_2, since according to Eq. (26) of Sec. 4, if applied to this case,

$$L_e = L - \frac{\omega^2 M^2 L_2}{R_2{}^2 + \omega^2 L^2} \tag{16}$$

112. Determination of High-frequency Inductance with the Differential Transformer.—From the above discussion it can be seen that several factors change the geometrical inductance to an effective high-frequency value. Thus, if conventional coils such as used in the broadcast range to cover all frequencies from 500 to 1500 kc/sec are tested, the following results, for instance, are found by direct measurement: All different high-frequency coils at 1 kc/sec were adjusted to exactly the same value, namely, 291 μh, which is of the order of magnitude common in broadcast receivers. Single-layer, honeycomb, basket-weave, bank-wound, and similar coils were used and the effective inductance measured up to 1500 kc/sec. It was found that with such suitable high-frequency coils the 1-kc/sec inductance was correct up to about 300 kc/sec, but from there on all coils increased their effective inductance appreciably. Thus, even with a single-layer coil using No. 28 double-cotton-covered, A.w.g. wire, employing 55 turns on an average diameter of 81 mm with a total winding length of 31.5 mm, the effective inductance was still 291 μh at 300 kc/sec, but 294 μh at 400 kc/sec, 298 at 500, 300 at 580, 304 at 700, 310 at 835, 319 at 1000, 330 at 1160, 340 at 1300, 350 at 1430, and 355 μh at 1500 kc/sec.[1] At 1500 kc/sec, some of the less suitable coils gave values which were as high as 1.5 times the 1-kc inductance and even higher in some cases. From these data, which are characteristic results, it can be seen that the *actual* measurement is the only criterion even when geometrical single-layer coils are under consideration. The method indicated in Fig. 50 is useful if a standard variometer is available. The test coil L_x is inserted in one and the variometer L_s into the other branch. The inductance L_s is varied until a minimum effect is noticed in the zero-current detector, which can be a tuned output branch working through a galena rectifier into a microammeter. The traveling contact K along the slide wire is moved until an absolute balance is obtained. The setting of L_s gives the effective inductance L_x. The disadvantage of this procedure is that both the effective inductance and the effective resistance of the variometer change with both the frequency and the relative position of the movable and stationary coils. Therefore, many calibration curves are required unless the variometer setting L_s is especially calibrated after the setting with one of the other methods. It is then better to employ the simplified differential method[2] shown in Fig. 195. A standard variable-air condenser C_s is then connected in series with the test coil L_x, R_x and in one branch of the differential system, while a decade-resistance box of known variable resistance R is inserted into the other branch. The air condenser is varied until, for a setting C_s, a decided minimum effect is noted on the zero-current detector. The setting of R is varied until a much better balance is noted. The handle of C_s is

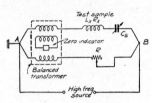

Fig. 195.—Determination of effective inductance L_x and resistance R_x (if standard condenser C_s is shielded, ground B; otherwise ground A.)

[1] For details, consult *Bur. of Standards, Tech. Paper* 298, Fig. 7.
[2] *Elec. World*, **84**, 998, 1924.

then slightly tapped toward each side until an absolute-zero adjustment is found. The high-frequency inductance is computed from

$$L_x = \frac{25{,}345}{f^2 C_s} \qquad (17)$$

with L_x in microhenries, C_s in microfarads, and f in kilocycles per second. It will be found that this is a very rapid method and, besides, there is no difficulty in obtaining reliable standard condensers and frequencies.

113. The Resonance Methods.—The simplest resonance method consists of connecting the test coil L_x across a standard variable-air condenser C_s. The tube generator of Fig. 20 is loosely coupled and set to the desired frequency f either by means of its own calibration or, for more precise work, by means of a loosely coupled standard frequency meter by noting the grid dip. The tube generator is then loosely coupled to the test circuit with L_x and C_s in parallel and C_s varied until a sharp grid dip is noted, for which condition L_x is computed by means of Eq. (17) which refers to another resonance method. The less[1] desirable substitution method can also be used. In it, a variable-air condenser C_s is connected across a suitable standard inductance L_s, and C_s is varied until for a setting $C_s = C_1$ a grid dip is noted in the locsely coupled tube oscillator set to the desired frequency f. The test coil L_x is substituted for L_s and the standard condenser varied again until for a setting $C_s = C_2$ resonance occurs for the same generator frequency f. Since for both determinations $C_1 L_s = C_2 L_x$, the effective inductance is computed from

$$L_x = \frac{C_1}{C_2} L_s \qquad (18)$$

If a variable standard inductance L_s is used in this method, it is unnecessary to have a good calibration for C_s as long as its approximate capacitance is known in order to give the order of the L_s range required for the desired frequency f. The unknown coil L_x is then as above connected across C_s, and C_s is varied until for a setting $C_s = C_2$ resonance occurs. The variable standard inductance L_s is substituted for L_x, and L_s is varied until for a setting $L_s = L_1$ a sharp grid dip is again noted in the tube generator for one and the same $C_s = C_2$ setting. The unknown inductance L_x is then equal to L_1. The method in which L_x is connected in parallel with L_s and C_s, and then L_s and C_s only in parallel, is not recommended because a certain mutual inductance would exist between L_s and L_x even under the best conditions. The series connection of L_x and L_s is more feasible, especially when small inductances are to be measured. The method is then the following: A standard inductance L_s with its setting $L_s = L_1$ near the maximum value is connected across a variable-air condenser C_s which is varied until for $C_s = C_1$ a sharp grid

---

[1] Since, as mentioned in previous sections, many calibration curves are required for the variometer if a wide frequency band is to be covered.

dip is noted on the tube generator, for which condition there is the oscillation constant C_1L_1. The small inductance L_x is connected in series with L_s and the series combination shunted by $C_s = C_1$. Care must be taken that L_s and L_x do not affect each other. The setting $L_s = L_1$ is then decreased until for $L_s = L_2$ resonance occurs again for an oscillation constant $C_1[L_2 + L_x]$ and the effective inductance is computed from $L_x = L_1 - L_2$.

114. The Harmonic Method.—The procedure indicated in Fig. 196 utilizes the fundamental frequency f and one of the higher harmonics of the tube oscillator. The test coil L_x is connected across the standard condenser C_s. The step-over resonator is tuned to the fundamental frequency f of the tube generator noticed by a maximum deflection d of a thermoelectric indicator. Then C_s is varied until for a setting $C_s = C_1$ the deflection d passes through a sharp minimum for which $f = k/\sqrt{C_1L_x}$. Next, the standard inductance L_s is substituted for L_x. The step-over resonator, and hereafter the L_sC_s circuit, is tuned for the second harmonic which is obtained

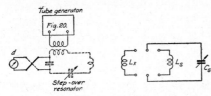

Fig. 196.—Maximum-minimum method utilizing fundamental and higher harmonic currents of a tube generator.

for a setting $C_s = C_2$ and $2f = k/\sqrt{C_2L_s}$. The effective inductance computed from $L_x = 4C_2L_s/C_1$.

115. Determination of Small Inductances.—The method described at the end of Sec. 113 can be used. It is then also possible to employ a separate coupling coil toward the tube generator as in Fig. 197. If L_0 denotes the inductance of this additional coupling coil and of the conductors separating L_x and L_s from each other, there is, for short-circuited terminals 1, 2 for resonance, the oscillation constant $C[L_0 + L_1]$ if L_s is set at some value $L_s = L_1$ near its maximum inductance and the circuit is tuned by the setting $C_s = C$. With the small test coil L_x across 1, 2,

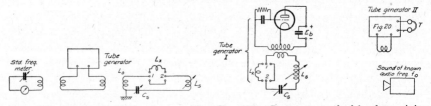

FIG. 197.—Determination of a small inductance L_x.

FIG. 198.—Beat-note method for determining a small inductance L_x

the circuit is tuned for fixed setting $C_s = C$ by decreasing $L_s = L_1$ to some value $L_s = L_2$ for which the oscillation constant $C[L_0 + L_2 + L_x]$. Since the generator frequency f is kept constant, the oscillation constants are equal and L_x is equal to $L_1 - L_2$. The method becomes very sensitive if the beat-note procedure is employed. The arrangement of Fig. 198 can then be used if the measuring circuit of Fig. 197 forms essentially the circuit in Fig. 198 which is responsible for the high frequency f of the tube generator I. The standard L_s is again set to some value $L_s = L_1$ near its maximum value and, for terminals 1, 2 short-circuited, C_s is varied until for the setting $C_s = C$ the desired fundamental frequency f is secured. The loosely coupled heterodyne generator II is increased in frequency until the loud beat tone between the fundamentals of both generators is heard in the receiver T. The frequency of the generator II is then slightly varied until the beat tone is the same as that of the standard audio frequency f_0. Next, the small test inductance is connected across terminals 1, 2 and for unchanged capacity setting $C_s = C$ the variometer setting $L_s = L_1$ somewhat decreased until for a setting $L_s = L_2$ the same beat note of frequency f_0 is again heard and L_x is again computed from $L_1 - L_2$.

In the beat-method procedure one can also make use of the fact that a small added inductance $\Delta L = L_x$ changes the oscillation constant CL of a circuit to $C[L + \Delta L]$ but this can be made equal to the original oscillation constant by decreasing C by a small amount ΔC so that $[C - \Delta C][L + \Delta L] = CL$ from which relation

$$\Delta L = L_x = \frac{L\,\Delta C}{C - \Delta C} \tag{19}$$

which for the determination of small test inductances reduces to

$$L_x = \frac{L}{C}\Delta C \tag{20}$$

since the product $L_x\,\Delta C$ is negligible in comparison with the other terms. Hence, if L and C denote the known values of the entire measuring circuit before L_x is inserted and ΔC the decrease in C setting necessary again to produce the same best tone f_0 as when only C and L act, the unknown small inductance L_x can be computed from Eq. (20). From the relations

$$f = \frac{k}{\sqrt{CL}} \text{ and } f - \Delta f = \frac{k}{\sqrt{C[L + L_x]}}$$

for small values of L_x,

$$f - \Delta f = \frac{k}{[CL + CL_x]^{1/2}} = \frac{k}{\sqrt{CL}\left[1 + \dfrac{L_x}{L}\right]^{1/2}} \cong \frac{k}{\sqrt{CL}}\left[1 - \frac{0.5\,L_x}{L}\right]$$

Subtracting this expression from $f = k/\sqrt{CL}$,

$$\Delta f = \frac{k}{\sqrt{CL}}\frac{L_x}{2L} = \frac{0.5fL_x}{L}$$

or

$$L_x = 2L\frac{\Delta f}{f} \tag{21}$$

where f denotes the natural frequency of the CL circuit and Δf the change in beat note observed when L_x is inserted. This gives a method where L_x is found from the total circuit inductance L before L_x is inserted, the desired high frequency f which is found with a standard frequency meter, and Δf which can be found accurately with a synchro clock and with a good degree of approximation by a calibrated beat-frequency oscillator. If in (20) and (21) the quality L_x is eliminated,

$$\Delta f = \frac{f}{2C}\Delta C \tag{22}$$

which, when solved for ΔC, gives a method for expressing a small capacity change in terms of a change Δf in f produced by a small change in the inductance L.

The Lecher wire method described in Sec. 103 can also be used for the determination of very small inductances L_x. If the quarter wave-length distribution method is used, the unknown inductance L_x must be connected across the open end of the line which differs correspondingly from the length $l = \lambda/4$ for the open line oscillating at the fundamental for one and the same exciting frequency f. The relation $\omega L_x = \sqrt{L/C}$ cotan $\frac{2\pi}{\lambda}\Delta l$ then plays a part, and the unknown inductance is computed from

$$L_x = \frac{L\lambda}{2\pi} \text{ cotan } \frac{2\pi\Delta l}{\lambda} \tag{23}$$

where $\lambda = 3 \times 10^7/f$, if f in kilocycles per second, Δl the change in length of the parallel-wire system in centimeters, and the inductance L of the parallel-wire system per centimeter length is given by Eq. (4) of this chapter if the quantity l in it is put equal to unity. If l denotes the length of the Lecher system in centimeters when the line is open and oscillating in the quarter wave-length distribution $l = \lambda/4$ and l' in centimeters when L_x is across the free end, (23) reduces to

$$L_x = 0.636lL \text{ cotan } 90\frac{\Delta l}{l} \tag{24}$$

This relation simplifies the evaluation of L_x which has the same unit as the *total* inductance lL of the Lecher wire system for the length l. A simple wire antenna can also be used for this work by measuring the resonance frequencies f_0, when no L_x coil loads the antenna at the grounded side, and the fundamental resonance frequency f, when L_x is inserted at the ground side. This is brought out in more detail on pages 393–398.

116. Notes on Antenna and Line Inductance.—As in the case of effective capacitance, the high-frequency inductance can be determined only approximately, since the conditions to ground may change and L_e depends on the current distribution along the aerial system. One must distinguish again between true inductance (geometrical inductance) and effective inductance which is discussed in detail in the introduction of Chap. XV.

117. Determination of Very Large Inductances.—In high-frequency circuits choke coils are required which in the case of battery elimination require values up to 50 henries. The same is true with certain filter coils. Good audio-frequency transformers likewise use effective inductances which may exceed 100 henries. It is then customary to use special laminated iron cores and, if considerable direct-current magnetization is superimposed, air gaps. Formulas given on page 239 in connection with Fig. 192 can then be used to estimate the effective inductance and the considerations brought out at the end of Sec. 109 play a part. Since such large inductances are used at lower frequencies, they are also tested for such frequencies, while high-frequency chokes using subdivided air-coil sections are tested by ordinary high-frequency methods given in the preceding sections. They *must* be tested for the entire high-frequency band for which the coil is to act as a choke and also for self-capacitance. For very large choke coils in the henry range (using ferromagnetic or some other core) the bridge method in Fig. 193 can be used. For coils with an iron core the frequency, as well as the amplitude, affects the effective value L_e of the inductance. Unless the coil is to be used in a push-pull arrangement, the normal direct-current magnetization must also be superimposed while measuring L_e. This leads to difficulties, since the

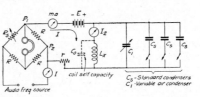

FIG. 199.—Determination of a large inductance L_x using an iron core and superimposed direct-current (I) magnetization.

determination of L_e without direct-current magnetization already leads to only approximate values of L_e, since the effect of iron produces current distortion with a pronounced third harmonic. For a rough inspection of the quality of a large choke coil, the Wheatstone bridge circuit of Fig. 199 can be used. Three arms of the bridge have equal standard resistances R of 1000 to 2000 ohms each. The resistance of the variable battery E and regulating resistance r are both very small compared to R and are provided in order to produce the degree of direct-current magnetization for which the effective inductance is to be measured when a certain direct current I passes the test coil L_x. If no external shunt branch is across $P_1 P_2$, the bridge would balance for $R_s = R$. By connecting the shunt branch across P_1 and P_2, the balance will be disturbed but, by compensating the effect of L_x by means of a variable decade condenser C_s (0.01 μf in steps of 0.001 μf, 0.1 μf in steps of 0.01 μf, 1 μf in steps of 0.1 μf), a sound minimum will be heard again which can be made more decided by decreasing the setting $R_s = R$ to a certain smaller value $R_s = R_1$. The decrease $R - R_1$ is then a measure for the resistance of the external shunt across P_1P_2. The decrease $R - R_1$ will be large for a coil of poor quality, and especially for a coil with short-circuited turns. The effective coil inductance of the choke coil is then computed from

$$L_x = \frac{25{,}345}{f^2 C_s} \text{ henries} \qquad (25)$$

if C_s is in microfarads and f in cycles per second. This gives the formula $7.04/C_s = L_x$ for $f = 60$ cycles/sec. The self-capacitance C_0 of the coil in microfarads is found by the graphical method of Fig. 194. It is then best to tune the inductance for several audio frequencies f_1, f_2, f_3, f_4, f_5, corresponding to the C_s settings C_1, C_2, C_3, C_4, C_5, and see to what extent these points are on a straight line. The intercept with the capacitance axis then gives the coil capacitance. The true inductance of the coil is $L = 25{,}345/[f^2(C_s + C_0)]$. It is the effective value which is of interest in practical work. If large air coils are to be measured, the test coil L_x is connected across a variable decade condenser C_s and a

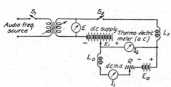

Fig. 200.—The volt-ammeter method for finding L_x.

properly designed tube voltmeter connected across both. A loosely coupled coil carrying a current of desired frequency f is used and C_s varied until the tube voltmeter gives maximum response. The current is then conveniently taken from an output coil of an amplifier to whose input a constant alternating voltage is applied. This method will be found very useful.

Modified[1] volt-ammeter methods can also be used to advantage if a choke coil is to be tested with a superimposed direct current. The inductance L_x is then computed from the voltage current ratio E/I of the test coil by means of $E/I = \sqrt{R_x^2 + \omega^2 L_x^2}$ where in many cases the quadrature term R_x^2 may be neglected. Figure 200 indicates such a method. By means of the shunt circuit with the auxiliary choke coil L_0, a direct-current meter I_1, a variable resistance R, and battery E_0, all of the direct current may be by-passed around the thermometer I_2 so that it does not interfere with the measurement of the small alternating current passing through the test coil L_x. The auxiliary inductance L_0 is chosen large enough so that its reactance is very large compared to the heater resistance of the thermoelectric indicator. The adjustment is as follows:

[1] WRIGHT, C. A., and F. T. BOWDITCH, *Proc. I.R.E.*, **16**, 373, 1928.

1. With switches S_1 and S_2 open, the resistance R is varied until the meter I_1 reads the desired direct current.

2. The switch S_2 is closed, the voltage E_1 of the actual direct-current source is adjusted until the thermoelectric multirange meter I_2 again reads zero, while the reading of meter I_1 is still registering the desired direct current.

3. The meter I_2 is then changed to a more sensitive scale in order to measure the much smaller normal alternating currents for which L_x is to be measured.

4. The switch S_1 is closed and the alternating voltage E varied until the desired alternating current I_2 passes through L_x. The alternating-current voltmeter E then measures $\sqrt{E^2 + e^2} \cong E$, since the potential drop e across the secondary of the input transformer and due to the direct current I_1 is negligibly small because the direct-current resistance of the secondary is small.

In this method the effective resistance of the I_2 meter must be small. A more sensitive method is shown in Fig. 201. A sensitive tube voltmeter which is not affected by steady voltages whose calibration need not be known is used, since the equal-deflection method is employed. The tube voltmeter is connected across a pure resistance of about 10Ω. The thermoelectric-current meter I is connected across P_1P_2 and the impressed alternating voltage varied until the desired alternating current I is obtained. The tube voltmeter will then give a deflection d. The thermoelectric meter is disconnected, terminals P_1P_2 are connected to terminals P_3P_4, and R is adjusted until the desired direct current I_0 flows. The indicator, being of the d'Arsonval type, will

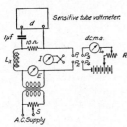

FIG. 201.—Determination of L_x by the impedance method.

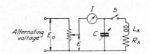

FIG. 202.—The constant-impedance method of H. M. Turner.

not be affected by the alternating component. The slider S on the input potentiometer is moved until the same deflection d is obtained again on the tube voltmeter and L_x computed from the ratio E/I. Figure 202 gives the method due to H. M. Turner.[1] If an alternating voltage E acts across a condenser C and a coil L_x, R_x, the current I flowing to the parallel combination is

$$
\begin{aligned}
I &= E\sqrt{\left[\omega C - \frac{\omega L_x}{R_x^2 + \omega^2 L_x^2}\right]^2 + \left[\frac{R_x}{R_x^2 + \omega^2 L_x^2}\right]^2} \\
&= E\sqrt{\omega^2 C^2 + \frac{1 - 2\omega^2 C L_x}{R_x^2 + \omega^2 L_x^2}}
\end{aligned} \tag{26}
$$

[1] *Proc. I.R.E.*, **16**, 1559, 1928.

Hence if $(1 - 2\omega^2 CL_x) = 0$; that is, the setting of condenser C is equal to $1/(2\omega^2 L_x)$, the current is $I = \omega CE$ and *independent* of the resistance R_x. The unknown inductance L_x is then computed from

$$L_x = \frac{12{,}672}{f^2 C} \text{ henries} \qquad (27)$$

if C is in microfarads and f in cycles per second. The capacitance is therefore only half that required for resonance, which is another inherent advantage of the constant-impedance method. For a 60-cycle source, $L_x = 3.52/C$. Since for this condition it does not matter whether R_x is zero or infinite, the current I must be the same for S open or closed as long as the supply voltage E and the frequency f remain constant. The method is therefore particularly suitable if large choke coils (for battery eliminators, etc.) are to be tested. The voltage E_0 denotes the line voltage of a 60-cycle current and E a suitable portion of it. A decade condenser C with a variable-air condenser in parallel is used and C varied, until for open and closed switch S no permanent change occurs in I,

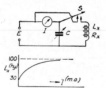

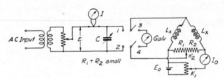

F I G . 2 0 3 . —
Special switch for
the protection of the
I meter.

Fig. 204.—Method which requires two like
test samples L_x.

and L_x in henries is computed from (27) or for this particular case from $3.52/C^{(\mu f)}$. It is to be noted that, with Turner's constant-impedance method, formula (27) does *not* assume that R_x is negligibly small. When L_x, R_x denotes the coil with an iron core (Fig. 203), the effective inductance varies with different supply voltages and care must be taken that the milliammeter I is short-circuited at the moment the inductance L_x is connected across C_x, since, when working near saturation, the meter may burn out owing to a large transient current. For this reason, H. M. Turner provides an extra contact to the switch as in Fig. 203. The same method with superimposed direct-current excitation through the test sample uses, as in Fig. 204, two like choke coils L_x in a Wheatstone bridge.

1. The sliding contact K_1 is moved until the proper direct-current flows through the choke coils.

2. The bridge is then balanced by connecting the double-pole double-throw switch against the terminals 3 and 4 connecting to a portable student galvanometer (about 1-ma full-scale deflection with the zero point at the middle of the scale) and the sliding contact K_2 is moved until direct-current balance is obtained.

3. The double-pole double-throw switch is connected across 1 and 2 and C varied until, for this connection with the switch open, no permanent change in I is noted.

If a 60-cycle current is used, the inductance L_x in henries is $7.04/C$ if the constant-impedance setting occurs for C μf. This is exactly true only if both test coils are exactly alike. Figure 205 shows a modified constant-impedance method used by H. T. Lyman[1] of Yale University.

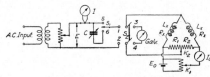

1. The direct-current compensation is as in Fig. 204 but the standard condenser C is now in series with the incoming line instead of across it.

Fig. 205.—Modified constant-impedance method ($R_1 + R_2$ small).

2. After the external direct-current balance is obtained, the double-pole double-throw S_2 switch is connected on 1 and 2 in order to connect the two test coils into the measuring circuit.

3. The single-pole switch S_1 is then connected to terminal 5 and the alternating current I of the thermoelectric meter noted.

The resistances R_1 and R_2 are practically equal and small so that $(R_1 + R_x)^2$ can be neglected in comparison with $(\omega L_x)^2$. The current I passes, then, practically through an external reactance $\omega L_x/2$. If the switch S_1 is connected to 6, the alternating current noted in the thermoelectric meter passes through reactance $1/\omega C$ and then through $\omega L_x/2$; and if C is varied until the current I noted for each position of S is the same, $\dfrac{\omega L_x}{2} = \dfrac{1}{\omega C} - \dfrac{\omega L_x}{2}$ and $L_x = \dfrac{25{,}345}{(f^2 C)}$ henries for f in cycles per second and C in microfarads. For a 60-cycle test, $L_x = 7.04/C$. For the determination of inductances in the henry range, small condensers only are required. Thus for $L_x = 100$ henries the condenser setting required is only 0.00704 μf, while for $L_x = 10$ henries a setting of 0.0704 μf is required.

[1] *Proc. I.R.E.*, **16**, 1567, 1928.

CHAPTER VIII

DETERMINATION OF MUTUAL INDUCTANCE AND COUPLING

The coefficient of mutual inductance is defined as $M = e_2/(di_1/dt)$. Therefore, it is the value of the induced voltage e_2 in a circuit when the current i_1 in a neighboring circuit changes at unit rate. The practical unit is the henry and a mutual inductance of 1 henry exists between two coils when 1 volt is induced across the terminals of one coil by a change of current of 1 amp/sec in the other coil. As in the case of self-inductance, the millihenry (10^{-3} henry) and the microhenry (10^{-6} henry) are more suitable subunits when dealing with high-frequency currents, since the henry is altogether too large a unit for such work. The absolute units in the e.s. and e.m. c.g.s. system are as for self-inductance.

The ability of a circuit to transfer voltage to a neighboring circuit or circuit branch can also be expressed by the coupling factor κ. If L_1 denotes the self-inductance of one branch, L_2 that of the other, and M the mutual inductance between both,

$$\kappa = \frac{M}{\sqrt{L_1 L_2}} \tag{1}$$

If the mutual inductance in one direction is M_{12} and in the other direction M_{21},

$$\kappa = \sqrt{\frac{M_{12}\, M_{21}}{L_1\, L_2}} \tag{2}$$

Multiplying the right sides of (1) and (2) by 100, gives the coefficient of coupling in per cent. The relation of Eq. (1) is generally used.

118. Notes on Formulas for Mutual Inductance.—As with self-inductance, the measurement at the particular high frequency gives reliable values for M only. As in the case of a single coil, the inductance is affected by the self-capacitance so the mutual inductance is affected by the *electric* lines of force passing between two circuit branches. It is known that a broadcast receiver will work to a certain extent on one-point coupling connections, and a thermoelectric indicator when connected to one terminal of a secondary may produce a small deflection. All these effects are due to the displacement currents which have nothing to do with the magnetic lines of force interlinking both circuits and may give rise to a larger or a smaller apparent M value. They can also be such that magnetic and electric lines of force effects compensate each other so that no voltage at all is induced in the secondary. This can be made use of in shielding. Equation (28) on page 345 contains a mutual-inductance term which can be readily computed when the distance between centers of the coupling coil and the loop antenna, with the centers kept on a common axis, is large compared with the dimension of the loop antenna.

119. Determination of Effective Mutual Inductance by Means of a Tube Voltmeter and Ammeter.—The quickest way of finding out whether a coil is completely shielded is by connecting a sensitive tube voltmeter across its terminals and observing whether or not a terminal voltage exists. Hence, if two coils L_1 and L_2, as in Fig. 206, are coupled to each other, the voltage terminals 3 and 4 are a measure for the degree of coupling. The value of mutual inductance M is given by the relation $E = \omega M I$ and computed from

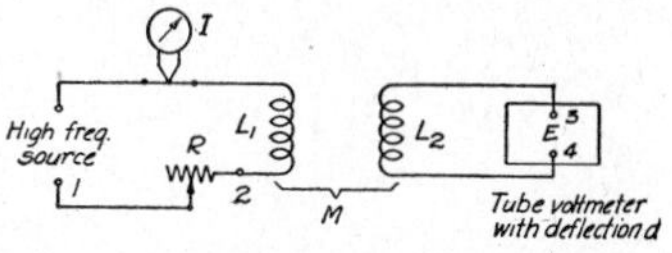

Fig. 206.—Volt-ammeter method for finding M.

$$M = \frac{159.2E}{f\,I} \tag{3}$$

for E in volts, I in amperes, and f in kilocycles per second. A tube voltmeter, as in Fig. 114, will do for measuring E. The calibration of the tube voltmeter is not required if the equal-deflection method is employed. The tube voltmeter is connected across terminals 3 and 4 and the standard resistance R (decade box) is varied until a suitable deflection d is noted on the tube voltmeter for a certain current $I = I_1$ of the desired frequency f in kilocycles per second. The tube voltmeter is then connected across terminals 1 and 2 and R is varied to some value $R = R_1$ ohms for which the same deflection d is secured and the thermo-electric-current meter reads a current $I = I_2$. Then $\omega M I_1 = R_1 I_2$ and M is computed from

$$M = \frac{159.2\,R_1 L_2}{f\,I_1} \tag{4}$$

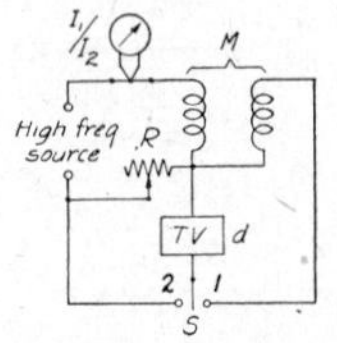

Fig. 207.— Determination of M of interstage transformers and certain filter couplings.

In many circuits terminals 2 and 4 are common as far as the alternating-current flow is concerned. This happens in some filter circuits and when interstage transformers are used in amplifiers. The measuring circuit which must then be used in order to meet the actual working condition is as in Fig. 207. A single-pole double-throw switch S is first connected to 1, and I_1 and the deflection d are noted. The switch is then connected on 2 and for a setting $R = R_1$ corresponding to a current I_2, the same deflection d is secured.

The tube-voltmeter method can also be used to determine the coupling coefficient κ with different kinds of coupling as in Fig. 208. The coupling is then accomplished by means of the branch ab, or branches a_1b_1 and a_2b_2 for a transformer. For the transformer coupling, the source is at first connected across terminals 1 and 2. For open terminals 3 and 4 and negligible coil resistances, the voltages $E_1 = \omega L_1 I_1$ across a_1b_1, and $E_{12} = \omega M_{12} I_1$ across a_2b_2 are measured, giving $L_1 = E_1/(\omega I_1)$ and $M_{12} = E_{12}/(\omega I_1)$. In a similar manner, for open terminals 1, 2 and the source across 3 and 4, the voltages $E_2 = \omega L_2 I_2$ across a_2b_2 and $E_{21} = \omega M_{21} I_2$ across a_1b_1 are measured with a tube voltmeter of suitable input impedance, giving the values $L_2 = E_2/(\omega I_2)$ and $M_{21} = E_{21}/(\omega I_2)$. Upon inserting these results into (2), the currents I_1 and I_2 and the angu-

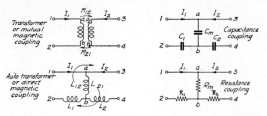

FIG. 208.—Different couplings (I exciting resonance current flowing over input terminals 1, 2 when 3 and 4 are open; I_2 exciting resonance current through 3 and 4 when 1 and 2 are open).

lar velocity ω cancel out and the percentage coupling is computed from

$$\kappa = 100\sqrt{\frac{E_{12}\,E_{21}}{E_1\,E_2}} \qquad (5)$$

where κ is in percentage. This formula holds for all couplings indicated in Fig. 208 if the same procedure of measurement is followed. It is for the direct or autotransformer coupling shown in the figure when the alternating-current source is across 1, 2, and 3, 4 are open as follows:

1. The voltage $E_{12} = \omega L_{12} I_1$ is measured across terminals a and b and the voltage $E_1 = \omega[L_1 + L_{12}]I_1$ across a and 2. The system is then excited by current I_2 through terminals 3 and 4 with terminals 1 and 2 open.

2. The voltage $E_2 = \omega[L_2 + L_{21}]I_2$ is measured across a and 4 and the voltage $E_{21} = \omega L_{21} I_2$ across terminals a and b.

Now, for the direct coupling indicated in the figure, the coupling coefficient κ for the effective to and fro transfer inductance, L'_{12} and L'_{21}, and effective self-inductances, L_1' and L_2', according to the definitions given in Sec. 4, is

$$\kappa = \sqrt{\frac{L'_{12}\,L'_{21}}{L_1'\,L_2'}} = \sqrt{\frac{L_{12}\,L_{21}}{[L_1 + L_{12}][L_2 + L_{21}]}} \qquad (6)$$

From the above measurements,

$$L_{12} = \frac{E_{12}}{\omega I_1}; \quad L_{21} = \frac{E_{21}}{\omega I_2}; \quad L_1 + L_{12} = \frac{E_1}{\omega I_1}; \quad \text{and} \quad L_2 + L_{21} = \frac{E_2}{\omega I_2}$$

which introduced in (6) confirms the formula of Eq. (5). From Sec. 4 one finds that, for the capacity coupling of Fig. 208 with the mutual or transfer capacitance C_m, for the effective mutual capacitances $C'_{12} = C'_{21} = C_m$ and the effective circuit capacitance $C_1' = \dfrac{C_1 C_m}{C_1 + C_m}$ and $C_2' = \dfrac{C_2 C_m}{C_1 + C_m}$,

$$\kappa = \sqrt{\frac{C_1' C_2'}{C'_{12} C'_{21}}} \tag{7}$$

Therefore when the exciting current I_1 flows with terminals 3 and 4 open, and the voltage $E_{12} = I_1/(\omega C_m) = I_1/(\omega C'_{12})$ is measured across a, b, and the voltage $E_1 = I_1/(\omega C_1')$ across a and 2, and in a similar way for the exciting current I_2 flowing into terminals 3 and 4 with terminals 1 and 2 open, the voltage $E_2 = I_2/(\omega C_2')$ is measured across a and 4 and $E_{21} = I_2/(\omega C_m) = I_2/(\omega C'_{21})$ across a and b, the relation (5) again holds. For the resistance coupling R_m for the effective values R'_{12} and R'_{21} of the forward and backward coupling, there is the condition $R_m = R'_{12} = R'_{21}$ and the formula for κ is similar to that of Eq. (6) and is

$$\kappa = \sqrt{\frac{R'_{12} R'_{21}}{R_1' R_2'}} \tag{8}$$

where $R_1' = R_1 + R_m$ and $R_2' = R_2 + R_m$. For the exciting current I_1 flowing with terminals 3 and 4 open, the voltage across a and 2 gives the reading $E_1 = I_1[R_1 + R_m]$ and across a and b the reading $E_{12} = I_1 R_m = I_1 R'_{12}$. With terminals 1 and 2 open and I_2 flowing through 3 and 4, across R_m the voltage is $E_{21} = I_2 R_m = I_2 R'_{21}$ and across a and 4 the reading $E_2 = (R_2 + R_m)I_2$. Inserting these results in (8) again gives the expression of Eq. (5).

120. Differential Methods for the Determination of Effective Mutual Inductance and Coupling Factor.—The method of Fig. 209 requires four measurements.

1. The inductance L_1 of the primary coil only is measured by the balance setting L_{s1} of a standard variometer L_s.

2. In the same manner the secondary inductance $L_2 = L_{s2}$ is found.

3. Both coils are connected in *direct* series, so that the magnetic fields of the coils are additive and the effective inductance $(L_1 + L_2 + 2M)$ of this combination is determined by the balance setting $L_s = L_{s3}$.

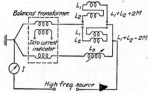

Fig. 209.—Differential method.

Both coils are connected into *opposing* series so that their magnetic fields work against each other and the setting $L_{s4} = L_1 + L_2 - 2M$ is obtained for a balance. The effective mutual inductance M and the coupling factor κ are computed from

$$M = \frac{L_{s3} - L_{s4}}{4} \qquad\qquad \kappa = \frac{L_{s3} - L_{s4}}{4\sqrt{L_{s1}L_{s2}}} 100 \tag{9}$$

where κ is in percentage. If no reliable variometer L_s is available, the differential method described in Sec. 112 in connection with Fig. 195 is used and the various effective inductances are measured by the corresponding balance settings C_1, C_2, C_3, and C_4 on the variable condenser C_s. According to formula (17), there is then for the desired high frequency f in kilocycles per second, C_s in microfarads, L in microhenries, and $K = 25345/f^2$

$$L_1 = \frac{K}{C_1}; \; L_2 = \frac{K}{C_2}; \; L_1 + L_2 + 2M = \frac{K}{C_3}; \; L_1 + L_2 - 2M = \frac{K}{C_4}$$

and

$$M = \frac{6336[C_4 - C_3]}{C_3 \, C_4 f^2} \text{ microhenries } \kappa = \frac{25[C_4 - C_3]\sqrt{C_1 C_2}}{C_3 \, C_4} \quad (10)$$

where κ is in percentage. Other differential methods using the reflection phenomenon are described in Sec. 122.

121. The Constant-frequency and Constant-capacitance Methods.—The constant-frequency method of Fig. 210 is based on the same natural frequency f of the measuring circuit CL when the primary coil L_1 only, the secondary coil L_2 only, both coils in direct series $L_1 + L_2 + 2M$ and both coils in opposing series $L_1 + L_2 - 2M$, respectively, are connected into a resonance circuit which is loosely coupled to the output coil of a tube generator (generator of Fig. 20 with the grid-dip method for resonance can be used). The generator is set to the

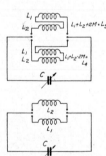

desired frequency f and the corresponding resonance settings C_1, C_2, C_3, and C_4 of the standard condenser C noted. The condition $f = k/\sqrt{C_1 L_1} = k/\sqrt{C_2 L_2} = k/\sqrt{C_3 L_3} = k/\sqrt{C_4 L_4}$ is then satisfied for $k = 159.2$ if f is in kilocycles per second, C in microfarads, and L in microhenries. The various effective inductances are then $L_1 = K/C_1$; $L_2 = K/C_2$; $L_3 = K/C_3$; and $L_4 = K/C_4$ for $K = 25345/f^2$, and the effective mutual inductance M and coefficient κ of coupling are

Fig. 210.—Constant-capacitance and constant-frequency method.

computed again from formulas (10). The constant-capacitance method uses one and the same C setting in Fig. 210 for L_1, L_2, L_3, and L_4, respectively, across C. The measured resonance frequencies are then $f_1 = A/\sqrt{L_1}; f_2 = A/\sqrt{L_2}; f_3 = A/\sqrt{L_3}; f = A/\sqrt{L_4}$ for $A = k/\sqrt{C}$ if C is again in microhenries and k as above. Solving for L in these relations, $L_p = \dfrac{25345}{(f_p{}^2 \, C)}$ for $p = 1, 2, 3$, and 4, respectively, and

$$M = \frac{6336[f_4{}^2 - f_3{}^2]}{C \, f_3{}^2 \, f_4{}^2} \text{ microhenries } \kappa = \frac{25 f_1 f_2 [f_4{}^2 - f_3{}^2]}{f_3{}^2 f_4{}^2} \quad (11)$$

where κ is in percentage, the fixed capacitance C is in microfarads, and the various frequencies are in kilocycles per second. The disadvantage of the constant-capacitance method is that the determination is carried on for different frequencies and M must be the same for this particular frequency range. Other equal-frequency and capacitance methods are also described at the end of the next section. These, however, use the reflection action.

122. Determination of Mutual Inductance and Coupling Factor by Means of the Reflection Effects of the Secondary on the Primary Circuit.—The theory of the air transformer (page 12) shows that the effective resistance R_1 of the primary circuit is increased by an amount $\omega^2 M^2 R_2/(R_2{}^2 + \omega^2 L_2{}^2)$ if M denotes the mutual inductance between the primary coupling coil and the secondary coil of inductance L_2 and R_2 the total effective resistance of the secondary. Hence, if R_2 is chosen large enough to make its square very large compared with $(\omega L_2)^2$, there is an increase $\omega^2 M^2/R_2$. The method is then as in Fig. 211. In one branch of the differential system a variometer L of high-frequency resistance R is connected in series with a standard variable resistance R_s (decade box). The values of L and R need not be known. The unknown mutual induc-

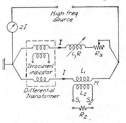

Fig. 211.—Determination of M by means of the reflection effect.

tance (forming an air transformer) is connected across the terminals of the other branch. With the secondary terminals S_1 and S_2 open, the differential system is balanced by means of L and R_s, giving the settings $L = L_1$ and $R_s = R_s{}'$. The resistance of the primary coil of inductance L_1 is then $R_1 = R_s{}' + R$. The secondary terminals $S_1 S_2$ are then connected to a standard resistance R_2 which is large compared with L_2 but not large enough to reduce the reflection effect into the primary too much, and the system is balanced again by decreasing the L setting to some other value L_2 and increasing the R_s setting to some value $R_s = R_s{}''$, for which balance again occurs. The increase of the resistance due to reflection effects is then $\rho = R_s{}'' - R_s{}' = \omega^2 M^2/R_2$ and the mutual inductance is computed from $M = \sqrt{\rho R_2}/\omega$ or

$$M = \frac{159.2\sqrt{\rho R_2}}{f} \text{ microhenries} \tag{12}$$

if f is in kilocycles per second and the resistances are measured in ohms. The simplified differential method of Fig. 195, which for resistance determination is described in Sec. 112, can also be used in finding the value of ρ. The mutual inductance M is then connected in place of L_x, R_x and the respective effective input resistances of the air transformer are found by balancing C_s and R at first for the secondary open and then for R_2 connected across the secondary terminals of M.

The simplified differential system of Fig. 195 can also be used in determining the coupling coefficient κ by means of the reflection of the secondary *inductance* L_2 into the primary of the mutual inductance. The exact adjustment of the phase (by means of C_s)is then most essential. The measurement is as follows:

1. The mutual inductance M with the primary L_1 and the secondary L_2 is connected again in place of L_x, R_x and for open secondary the setting of C_s is varied until for a setting $C_s = C_1$ a decided minimum (resonance $\omega L_1 = 1/(\omega C_1)$) is noted on the zero-current detector. The minimum can be brought to absolute zero by adjusting R in order to balance out the effect of the effective resistance of the primary coil L_1 and again adjusting C_s somewhat in order to obtain the best setting of value C_1. If $\omega/2\pi$ denotes the desired frequency f of the exciting current flowing to the circuit, $f = k/\sqrt{C_1 L_1}$ for $k = 159.2$ if the units are again in kilocycles per second, microfarads, and microhenries. The effective primary inductance with the secondary open is then

$$L_1 = \frac{K}{(f^2 C_1)}$$

for $K = 25345$.

2. The secondary of the mutual inductance is now *short-circuited*, for which the square of resistance of the secondary may be neglected in comparison with $(\omega L_2)^2$ and, according to Eq. (26) in Sec. 4, the primary inductance L_1 with such assumptions will be decreased to a value $L_1 - \frac{\omega^2 M^2 L_2}{R_2{}^2 + \omega^2 L_2{}^2} \cong L_1 - \frac{M^2}{L_2}$. Hence when the differential system is again balanced, it is found from the new capacitance setting $C_s = C_2$, which holds for $\omega\left[L_1 - \frac{M^2}{L_2} \right] = \frac{1}{(\omega C_2)}$, that the same exciting frequency is satisfied by $f = \dfrac{k}{\sqrt{C_2\left[L_1 - \dfrac{M^2}{L_2} \right]}}$, and $L_1 - \frac{M^2}{L_2} = \frac{K}{(C_2 f^2)}$ is obtained. Solving for L_2,

$$L_2 = \frac{f^2 C_1 C_2 M^2}{[C_2 - C_1]K}$$

Inserting the expressions for L_1 and L_2 into Eq. (1), it will be found that the coupling factor can be computed from

$$\kappa = 100\sqrt{\frac{C_2 - C_1}{C_2}} \tag{13}$$

where κ is in percentage. This method may again be called an *equal-frequency* method. If the *equal-capacitance* method is used, the adjustment described under 1, for which the secondary of M is open, is the same, and if the exciting frequency for this case is $f = f_1$ one has from this balance

$$L_1 = \frac{K}{(f_1{}^2 C_1)}$$

3. The secondary is short-circuited *but* the setting $C_s = C_1$ is kept constant and the frequency of the exciting current varied to some value f_2 until a decided minimum effect is noted again on the zero-current indicator. This resonance condition satisfies the formula $L_1 - \frac{M^2}{L_2} = \frac{K}{(C_1 f_2{}^2)}$ which yields

$$L_2 = \frac{f_1{}^2 f_2{}^2 C_1 M^2}{K[f_2{}^2 - f_1{}^2]}$$

Inserting the values for L_1 and L_2 into Eq. (1), the formula

$$\kappa = 100\sqrt{\frac{f_2{}^2 - f_1{}^2}{f_2{}^2}} \tag{14}$$

where κ is in percentage, is obtained, from which the coupling coefficient can be computed.

Instead of the differential system, a resonance circuit together with the calibrated tube generator of Fig. 20 can also be used for the equal-frequency [Eq. (13)] as well as for the equal-capacitance [Eq. (14)] method just described. The mutual inductance M is then connected as in Fig. 212, and the measurement carried on in the same way with the double-pole switch S open and then closed for the settings C_1 and C_2,

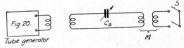

FIG. 212.—Determination of M.

respectively, either when f is constant or for frequencies f_1 and f_2 when C is kept constant. The resonance is then observed by the grid dip or the click noted in the phone of the loosely coupled generator and the factor κ obtained from (13) and (14), respectively. The frequency of the tube generator can be read off by its own calibration or by a loosely coupled frequency meter.

123. Determination of the Coupling Factor by Means of Coupling Oscillations.—This method makes use of the fact that damped wave trains are produced for spark-gap oscillations, and that then the current in the oscillator as well as that in a coupled resonator show two frequencies f_1 and f_2 at the *same time*. The method is as follows: One coil of the mutual inductance M forms the inductance L_1 of the spark-gap oscillator and the secondary coil the inductance L_2 of the resonator which uses a tuning condenser across the secondary. If both circuits are adjusted to the same oscillation constant $C_1L_1 = C_2L_2$, corresponding to a frequency f_0 when acting independently, and then coupled to each other to give the desired relative position of L_1 and L_2, a frequency meter will indicate the resonance frequencies f_1 and f_2, respectively, when the condenser of the frequency meter is varied. These frequencies, according to the theory referred to are $f_1 = f_0/\sqrt{1 + \kappa}$, and $f_2 = f_0\sqrt{1 - \kappa}$. The coefficient of coupling κ is then computed from

$$\kappa = 100\frac{f_2{}^2 - f_1{}^2}{f_1{}^2 + f_2{}^2} \tag{15}$$

when κ is in percentage.

CHAPTER IX

DETERMINATION OF EFFECTIVE RESISTANCE

When steady currents flow through a conductor, the resistance for most materials in the normal range of temperature[1] is a quantity which depends upon the material and dimensions of the conductor. For one and the same material, the resistance becomes smaller, the shorter the length and the larger the cross section of the conductor. Matters are different for the effective resistance offered to the flow of high-frequency currents. The current distribution across the cross section, as well as the distribution along the conductor, then affects the effective resistance. The absorbing effect of neighboring circuits and that due to dielectric resistance of any parasitic condenser actions also increase the resistance. It is not always easy to separate the different components which make up the high-frequency resistance. But in *all* cases, the high-frequency resistance is that quantity which, when multiplied by the square of the effective value of the high-frequency current, gives the energy dissipated in the conductor. Methods based on this relation are fundamentally reliable.

The practical unit of the resistance is the ohm and the absolute unit in the e.m. c.g.s. system has the dimension of a velocity (centimeters per second). It may be derived from Joule's heat law since the centimeters per second electromagnetic unit is that resistance in which 1 e.m.u. of current dissipates 1 erg of heat in 1 sec. For the customary resistance

---

[1] Metals have a positive temperature coefficient. This means they increase their resistance with the temperature, since, according to the classical theory of conduction by *free* electrons, the conductivity is proportional to the number of free electrons in unit volume, proportional to the mean free path of an electron, and inversely proportional to the absolute temperature (273 plus the centigrade temperature). For copper, silver, gold, iron, platinum, and many other metals the positive temperature-coefficient law holds down to the lowest temperatures so far within the experimental reach. But for certain metals such as lead, tin, and mercury (K. Omnes, *Proc. Kon. Akad. v. Wet. Amsterdam*, **17**, 1, 12, 278, 514, 760; see also F. B. Silsbee, Bur. Standards, *Sci. Paper* 307) a superconductivity occurs somewhat above absolute zero somewhere between 1.6 to 6° K. The resistance of mercury disappears at about 4.2° K, at 3.8° K for tin, and at about 6° K for lead. The time constant L/R of a lead coil at such a temperature would therefore have an infinite value, and an induced current in it would, upon removal of the magnetic field, decrease after *days* instead of after a fraction of a second. The conduction, according to K. Omnes, is then proportional to $1/\sqrt{TW}$ where T is the absolute temperature and W the internal energy of the metal. For ordinary working temperatures, most pure metals show an approximate linear relation between specific resistance, and the temperature coefficient is slightly larger than $\frac{1}{273}$. For up-to-date review: W. Meissner, "Supraleitfähigkeit in Ergebnisse der exakten Naturwissenschaften," Vol. XI, Berlin, 1932.

range this unit is altogether too small, while the ohm is of suitable magnitude. The relation is

$$1 \text{ e.m. cm/sec} = 10^{-9} \text{ ohm} \tag{1}$$

The international ohm is the resistance of a mercury column at $0°$ C, 106.3 cm long, of mass 14.4521 g corresponding to a cross-sectional area of 1 mm². For high-frequency work very high resistances are sometimes used or occur. The megohm (10^6 ohms) is then the customary unit. The corresponding "microscopic" unit, the microhm (10^{-6} ohm) is not customary because of the great difficulty which exists when resistance even as low as a large fraction (one-tenth of 1 ohm) are to be determined. The absolute unit in the e.s. c.g.s. system has the dimension of the reciprocal of a velocity, since the ratio of the e.m.u. to the e.s.u. is equal to the square of the velocity of light. There is then the relation

$$1 \text{ e.s. sec/cm} = 9 \times 10^{11} / \text{ohms} \tag{2}$$

Formulas (1) and (2) play a part when deriving expressions from dimensional quantities and taking readings where quantities are partially expressed in e.s.u. and partially in e.m.u.

124. Notes on Formulas for High-frequency Resistance.—As far as computation formulas for the high-frequency resistance for even simple coils are concerned, reference is made to a paper by A. J. Palerno and F. W. Grover.[1] This paper also contains useful references to other workers in the field. It seems best to determine high-frequency resistance by measurement which can be done easily and which leads to reliable values if the measurement is carried on under the actual work conditions. Thin short lengths of constantan and manganin wire have practically the same resistance at 1 Mc/sec as for direct current. For this reason such resistors can be used for slide wires, and in order to produce a known voltage by measuring the current (field-intensity measurements, calibration of tube voltmeters, etc.). Experiment, as well as theory, shows that the increase of resistance due to skin effect is greater in good conductors than in wires with a higher specific resistance. The increase is still more pronounced when the conductor has a magnetic permeability μ larger than unity. Reliable formulas[2] for *straight* isolated conductors of a circular cross section have been derived by Maxwell, Heaviside, Kelvin, and Rayleigh. The high-frequency resistance R can then be computed from the direct-current value R_0 by means of

$$R = \frac{x}{2} R_0 \frac{\text{ber}(x)\,\text{bei}'(x) - \text{bei}(x)\,\text{ber}'(x)}{(\text{ber}'(x))^2 + (\text{bei}'(x))^2} \tag{3}$$

[1] *Proc. I.R.E.*, **18**, 2041, 1930.

[2] Maxwell, *Elec. Mag.*, **2**, Par. 690; O. Heaviside, *Electrician*, 583, 1884; and in *Elec. Papers*, **1**, 353, 429; **2**, 50, 97; W. Thomson, *Math. Phys. Papers* III, 491, 1889; Lord Rayleigh, *Phil. Mag.*, **21**, 381, 1886.

where the factor $x = \pi d\sqrt{2}\, \mu f/\rho$, and d is the diameter of the wire in centimeters, ρ the resistivity in e.m.u. that is in 10^{-9} ohm/cm^3. For copper wire at room temperature $\rho = 1600$ cm^2/sec. The frequency f in the above formulas is expressed in cycles per second. These formulas are derived for a simple periodic current. The ber and bei functions and their differential coefficients ber$'$ and bei$'$, according to Kelvin (W. Thomson, *Math. Phys. Papers* III, 493, 1890) can be found from

$$\left.\begin{aligned}
\text{ber }(x) &= 1 - \frac{x^4}{2^2\,4^2} + \frac{x^8}{2^2\,4^2\,6^2\,8^2} - \cdots \\
\text{bei }(x) &= \frac{x^2}{2^2} - \frac{x^6}{2^2\,4^2\,6^2} + \frac{x^{10}}{2^2\,4^2\,6^2\,8^2\,10^2} - \cdots \\
\text{ber }(x) &= \frac{1}{\sqrt{2\pi x}}\epsilon^{\frac{x}{\sqrt{2}}}\cos\left\{\frac{x}{\sqrt{2}} - \frac{\pi}{8}\right\} \\
\text{bei }(x) &= \frac{1}{\sqrt{2\pi x}}\epsilon^{\frac{x}{\sqrt{2}}}\sin\left\{\frac{x}{\sqrt{2}} - \frac{\pi}{8}\right\}
\end{aligned}\ \right\}\text{for large } x \text{ values} \qquad (3a)$$

and the values of Table IX. This table gives directly the factor $p = R/R_0$

TABLE IX

x	ber (x)	bei (x)	ber$'$ (x)	bei$'$ (x)	$p = R/R_0$
0.0	1.0000	0.0000	0.0000	0.0000	1.0
0.5	0.9990	0.0625	−0.0078	0.2499	1.0003
1.0	0.9844	0.2496	−0.0624	0.4999	1.005
1.5	0.9211	0.5576	−0.2100	0.7303	1.026
2.0	0.7517	0.9723	−0.4931	0.9170	1.078
2.5	0.3999	1.457	−0.9436	0.9983	1.175
3.0	−0.2214	1.938	−1.570	0.8805	1.318
3.5	−1.194	2.283	−2.336	0.4353	1.493
4.0	−2.563	2.293	−3.135	−0.4911	1.678
4.5	−4.299	1.686	−3.754	−2.053	1.862
5.0	−6.230	0.116	−3.844	−4.354	2.043
5.5	−7.974	−2.790	−2.907	−7.373	2.219
6.0	−8.858	−7.335	−0.2931	−10.846	2.394
8.0	20.97	−35.02	38.29	−7.662	3.094
10.0	138.8	56.37	51.37	135.2	3.799
15.0	−2.970	−2.952	86.65	−4.099	5.562
20.0	47.580	115.000	24.330	41.490	7.328

by which the direct-current resistance R_0 of a wire is to be multiplied in order to obtain the high-frequency resistance R. For values of $x > 20$, the formula can be simplified and is

$$R = R_0[0.25 + 0.3536x] \qquad (4)$$

for $x = m\sqrt{8}$, if $m < 1$, the approximation formula is

$$R = R_0[1 + 0.333m^4] \qquad (5)$$

According to J. Zenneck for $1.5 < m < 10$,

$$R = R_0[0.277 + 0.997m] \tag{6}$$

and for very large values of m,

$$R = R_0\left[0.25 + m + \frac{3}{64m}\right] \tag{7}$$

which practically leads to formula (4). An entirely empirical formula for straight conductors is

$$R = R_0[k_1\, d\sqrt{f} + k_2] \tag{8}$$

where, for $d\sqrt{f} > 30$, $k_1 = 0.033$ and $k_2 = 0.5$ if f is again in cycles per second and d in centimeters. The formulas given above hold for sinusoidal currents only. The high-frequency resistance R_d is slightly higher for damped sinusoids and increases with the logarithmic decrement δ according to $R_d = R[1 + 0.0796\delta + 0.0127\delta^2]$. The case of the high-frequency resistance of two parallel cylindrical conductors is more complicated, since the proximity effect must be taken into account. This effect is due to the mutual action of the magnetic field of one conductor in bringing an asymmetrical distribution of current density about the axis of the other. When one conductor is the return branch of the other (parallel-wire system), H. L. Curtis[1] treats it by means of an integral-equation method with the results applying to low frequencies only. S. Butterworth[2] gives a solution which holds whether the currents flow in the same or opposite directions with respect to each other. The Maxwellian method is used for the solution and the formulas apply over the entire useful high-frequency range. There are also the solutions of J. R. Carson,[3] and C. Snow.[4] The formula by Snow for the parallel-wire system is

$$R = \sqrt{\frac{\omega R_0}{1 - (d/a)^2}} \tag{9}$$

where R denotes the high-frequency resistance for each centimeter of the double line, and d the diameter of the wire in centimeters, and a the spacing between centers in centimeters. The direct-current resistance R_0 can be taken out of the above formula as a factor $\sqrt{R_0}$ and for copper (resistivity $\rho = 1600$ e.m. c.g.s. units) one finds for $d = 0.145$ cm, $a = 4.2$ cm,

$$\sqrt{R_0} = \sqrt{\frac{2 \times 1600}{\frac{\pi}{4}\, 0.145^2}} = 440 \text{ e.m. c.g.s. units}$$

[1] *Bur. Standards, Sci. Paper* 374, 1920.

[2] *Phil. Trans. A*, **222**, 57, 1921.

[3] CARSON, J. R., *Phil. Mag.*, **41**, 607, 1921.

[4] SNOW, C., *Proc. Internat. Math. Cong.*, Toronto, 1924.

for the two wires of l-cm length. The high-frequency resistance for unit length of both wires with the above dimensions then becomes.

$$R = 440\sqrt{\frac{2\pi f}{1 - 0.00119}} \; 10^{-9} \text{ ohm}$$

if f is in cycles per second.

For a certain frequency[1] range *Litzendraht* instead of solid wire is better for reducing the skin effect. By *Litz* is meant ideally twisted wires, *each* one having an enamel insulation. The different strands are braided again. It should not be confused with customary stranded wire which is stranded only for flexibility and has only an outside insulation, the various thin wires within the cover being bare copper filaments. The frequency range for which such litz is of advantage depends, strictly speaking, upon the coil used, the number of strands braided together, the number of insulated wires within a strand, and the kind of twisting and braiding. Very many individual insulated copper filaments are of advantage for frequencies below 600 kc/sec, while for frequencies higher than this more than 25 copper filaments give an unfavorable litz. According to Rogowski,[2] a critical frequency f_c exists above which with increasing frequency a solid wire of the same cross section gives again less high-frequency resistance. The value of f_c can be computed from

$$f_c = \frac{13.62}{d^2 \, \rho \, \beta \sqrt[3]{N}} \tag{10}$$

if f_c is in kilocycles per second, d the diameter of the wire of the single copper filament in centimeters, N the number of filaments in the litz, and at room temperature $\rho = 60$ for copper filaments. The quantity β is computed from

$$\beta = \sqrt{\frac{\pi}{4}} \frac{d\sqrt{N}}{p} \tag{10a}$$

if p denotes the pitch of the coil winding in centimeters. The value of β is always smaller than 0.89 and, for a winding in which adjacent turns more or less touch each other, it is practically 0.89.

Example.—A litz with 81 copper filaments of 0.12-mm diameter and a pitch $p = 1.82$ mm for the coil winding gives $d = 0.012$, $\rho = 60$, $N = 81$, and $\beta = 0.52$ and a critical frequency $f_c = 697.3$ kc/sec, above which the litz exhibits a greater high-frequency resistance than a solid wire of the same cross section. The most favorable frequency f_{opt} for which minimum resistance occurs can be found from

$$f_{opt} = \frac{6.71}{d^2 \, \rho \, \beta \sqrt{N}} \tag{11}$$

which gives the above example $f_{opt} = 167$ kc/sec.

[1] LINDEMANN, R., *Verhandl. deutsch. Physik Ges.*, **11**, 28, 682, 1908; *Jahrb. d. drahtl.*, **4**, 561, 1911; W. ROGOWSKI, *Arch. Elektrotech.*, **8**, 269, 1919.
[2] *Loc. cit.*

For a straight piece of litz the critical frequency f_c', above which with increasing frequency solid wire becomes better again, is

$$f_c' = \frac{25}{d^2 \, \rho \, \sqrt[3]{NK^2}} \tag{12}$$

where K denotes the space factor of the litz, that is, the ratio of total copper cross section to the cross section of the litz.

125. Notes on Low-frequency and Direct-current Measurements of Resistance.—To determine the quality of a coil, the ratio of high-frequency resistance to direct-current resistance must be considered. Values as high as 10 and even higher occur and it is then necessary to determine the high-frequency resistance R and the direct-current resistance R_0 by measurement. The latter is conveniently done by use of the ordinary Wheatstone bridge. Since in many cases it is of interest to know the high-frequency time constant L/R of a coil in comparison with the low-frequency time constant L_0/R_0, the latter value is conveniently determined with a 1000-cycle current by the method shown in Fig. 193 and described in Sec. 110. Both values $L_0 \, R_0$ can then be computed from the bridge settings. For a useful high-frequency coil the 1000-cycle resistance R_0 does not differ appreciably from the direct-current value.

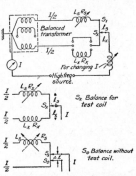

FIG. 213.—Determination of skin effect. (k denotes resistance of slide wire per millimeter length and $R_x = 2k\Delta l$.)

126. Determination of High-frequency Resistance.—If the resistance is purely ohmic, the circuit of Fig. 50 can be used. The unknown resistance R_x is then equal to the setting R_s of the standard if no current is indicated by the zero-current detector. The arrangement shown in Fig. 213 is of especial advantage if the resistance of small inductance conductors is to be determined, since then the resistance of the small variometer is eliminated by the process of measurement and the calibration of the L settings are also unnecessary. The test sample L_x, R_x is connected in one branch and the small variometer in the other branch of the differential transformer. A slide wire of suitable resistance $k(l_s + l_x)$ is used. The total length $(l_s + l_x)$ is in millimeters and the constant k of the wire denotes the resistance per millimeter length.

The slide wire is calibrated either with direct current, if thin constantan or manganin wire is used, or by connecting it in one branch of the differential transformer by short-circuiting the terminals of the test sample and sliding the traveling contact S_x up to position S_1. In place of the standard L_s, a decade-resistance box is used and its setting varied until balance is obtained. The setting of the box then gives the total high-frequency resistance $k(l_s + l_x)$ of the slide wire. The decade re istance must also use either constantan or manganin wire, since the temperature coefficient is then small for the temperature range in a laboratory. The decade boxes of the

General Radio Company are satisfactory up to about 1.5 Mc/sec with a probable error of not more than about 5 per cent, depending upon the magnitude of the resistance. For resistances in 0.1-ohm steps, the accuracy is only a few per cent, since even for direct-current work it is difficult to obtain fractional ohm standards of high precision if the resistance is to be variable. The well-known Ayrton-Perry method (p. 129) of winding resistances with a minimum of self-inductance and self-capacitance is used in such boxes for the normal resistance range (up to 1000Ω). Since such resistances are generally used for measurements in tuned circuits, the frequency error can be made even smaller. Commercial units in 1-ohm steps can then be made with an error of less than 1 per cent even at frequencies as high as 1 Mc/sec, and less then 5 per cent at 2 Mc/sec, while 10Ω units give errors which are less than 1 per cent at 2 Mc/sec and less than 5 per cent for frequencies as high as 4 Mc/sec. If 100-ohm units are used, the error is again greater, giving the values for the 1-ohm unit, while the 0.1-ohm units have errors of less than 1 per cent at 500 kc/sec and less than 5 per cent at 1 kc/sec.

The measurement is as follows:

1. With the test sample of effective resistance R_x in one branch and the variometer of resistance R_s in the other, the small variometer L_s is gradually increased until a decided minimum effect is noted in the zero-current detector. The sliding contact is then moved along the slide wire, until for a position S_x absolute balance is obtained. For this setting $(R_x + kl_x) = (R_s + kl_s)$.

2. The terminals used to connect the test sample are short-circuited with the sample removed and the variometer turned into its minimum position for which only a small residual inductance is left. The sliding contact is moved through a distance Δl mm until for a position S_0 the zero-current detector indicates a decided minimum, for which setting $k[l_x - \Delta l] = R_s + k[l_s + \Delta l]$, since R_s remains about the same for a small inductance.

3. The high-frequency resistance of the test sample is then computed from

$$R_x = 2k\ \Delta l \text{ ohms} \tag{13}$$

If R_0 denotes the direct-current resistance, $R_x - R_0$ gives the apparent increase in resistance.

The simplified differential method of Fig. 195 uses a standard air condenser C_s whose accurate calibration need not be known, since it is

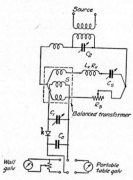

Fig. 214.—Simplified differential method.

necessary to use only a C_s range for which resonance with the test coil is possible. This method is reliable and works for the determination of resistance of straight conductors, and coils of almost any useful size. For very accurate work the more elaborate arrangement in Fig. 214 is suggested, and the secondary S of the differential transformer is tuned by condenser C_1 and a crystal rectifier k used with a block condenser C_0. For the preliminary adjustment a portable tube galvanometer is used to indicate balance, while for the final resistance adjustment the wall-galvanometer connection is employed. The portable table galvanometer may be a Weston Company student galvanometer with the zero at the middle of the scale and about 1.5 ma for the full-scale deflection. The measurement is then:

1. The input coil is tuned to the desired fundamental frequency f by means of C_2.
2. The condenser C_s is varied until for a setting $C_s = C_1$ a decided minimum effect is noted on the table galvanometer.
3. The secondary coil S of the differential transformer is tuned by means of C_1 until a somewhat larger minimum deflection is again obtained.
4. The dial of the decade-resistance box is turned until for a certain resistance R_s a much better minimum deflection is noted.
5. The condenser setting is slightly varied by tapping the handle of the variable-air condenser to either side until almost zero current is produced.
6. The lower steps of the decade box are varied until the table galvanometer registers apparent absolute zero.
7. The double-pole double-throw switch is connected toward a more sensitive wall galvanometer and C_s as well as R_s slightly varied until this galvanometer also indicates absolute zero.

The setting of R_s then measures directly the required high-frequency resistance R_x.

Figure 215 gives the well-known resistance-variation method used in the earlier days of radio by R. Lindemann,[1] C. Fischer,[2] and others. For a sinusoidal current flow I through a low-resistance thermoelectric indicator (about 1Ω resistance), the method is as follows:

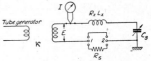

Fig. 215.—Resistance-variation method.

1. The terminals 1 and 2 are short-circuited and C_s is varied until a resonance current $I = I_1$ is indicated. If R_h denotes the heater resistance, r that of the small coupling coil across which the voltage E is induced for the circuit resistance $R_c = R_x + R_h + r$, one has $E = I_1 R_c$.
2. A standard resistance R_s (in the neighborhood of R_c) is inserted across terminals 1 and 2 and the reduced resonance current $I = I_2$ noted, for which condition $E = I_2[R_c + R_s]$. The small standard resistance consists conveniently of a thin constantan wire of short length (about 5 cm long) which is sealed into a glass tube with sealing wax on each end of the tube, using thicker copper-wire terminals through the seals.
3. The entire circuit resistance is then computed from

$$R_c = \frac{I_2}{I_1 - I_2} R_s \qquad 14)$$

The small resistance r of the few coupling turns can usually be neglected; otherwise it is measured with one of the differential methods given before. The coil resistance R_x is found by subtracting the known heater resistance R_h and r from R_c. If in the above determination a variable standard R_s is used and R_s is adjusted until for a value $R_s = R_s'$, the original resonance current I_1 is just reduced to $I_2 = I_1/2$, the setting R_s' gives directly the circuit resistance R_c.

This method is useful for many commercial measurements of *total* circuit resistance but may be considered only as a good *approximation*

[1] *Loc. cit.*
[2] *Ann. Physik.* (4), **28**, 57, 1909.

procedure when coil resistances are determined, since it is assumed that there are no reflection effects between the actual measuring circuit and tube generator, and that E remains constant for *two* determinations which must be carried out at *different times*. With zero methods, the magnitude of E affects only the sensitivity, not the actual readings used in the evaluation of the resistance as in the case of the resistance-variation method. The resistance-variation method also depends upon a very sharp resonance adjustment for two *different* circuit decrements, since in one case the total circuit resistance is R_c and in the other $R_c + R_s$. The logarithmic decrement per cycle for the first measurement is

$$\delta_1 = \frac{R_c}{2fL} = \frac{\pi R_c}{\omega L}$$

and for the second measurement it is the much larger decrement $\delta_2 = \pi[R_c + R_s]/(\omega L)$. In the first measurement (1 and 2 short-circuited) for any slight off position ΔC in the $C_s = C_1$ setting, the measured apparent resonance current I_1 is no longer exactly given by $I_1 = E/R_c$ but is somewhat out of phase with respect to the induced voltage E and equal to $I_1' = E/Z$ for

$$Z = \sqrt{R_c{}^2 + \left[\omega L - \frac{1}{\omega(C_1 + \Delta C)}\right]^2} = R_c\sqrt{1 + \left[\frac{\pi}{\delta_1}\frac{\Delta C}{C_1}\right]^2} = \frac{R_c}{\beta_1} \quad (15)$$

where

$$\beta_1 = \left\{1 + \left[\frac{\pi}{\delta_1}\frac{\Delta C}{C_1}\right]^2\right\}^{-\frac{1}{2}} \quad (16)$$

is a factor smaller than unity as long as a detuning ΔC exists. The current which is actually observed is $I_1' = \beta_1 E/R_c$ and the percentage error η_1 per cent by which the reading is too low is found from $100\,[I_1 - I_1']/I_1$ as

$$\eta_1 = 100[1 - \beta_1]\% \quad (17)$$

For the second adjustment in the resistance-variation method, a resistance R_s is inserted so that the total circuit resistance becomes $R_c + R_s$. This additional resistance increases the original logarithmic decrement δ_1 per cycle to a value $\delta_2 = (R_c + R_s)/2fL$ if f is in cycles per second, L in henries, and the resistances in Ω. It will produce the corresponding factor

$$\beta_2 = \left\{1 + \left[\frac{\pi}{\delta_2}\frac{\Delta C}{C_1}\right]^2\right\}^{-\frac{1}{2}} \quad (18)$$

which is also less than unity but for one and the same detuning ratio $\Delta C/C_1$ larger than β_1 as can easily be seen from the approximation formula

$$\beta \cong 1 - 0.5\left(\frac{\pi}{\delta}\frac{\Delta C}{C_1}\right)^2$$

since $\delta_2 > \delta_1$. This approximation formula is not close enough to apply it for accurate work and (18) should be used for actual checks on the measurements. The actual reading $I_2' = \beta_2 E/(R_c + R_s)$ is therefore

$$\eta_2 = 100[1 - \beta_2]\% \tag{19}$$

lower than the true resonance reading $I_2 = E/(R_c + R_s)$. Both formulas for η_1 and η_2, respectively, show that the errors in the two current readings decrease with increasing logarithmic decrements δ for a certain detuning ratio $\Delta C/C_1$. The resultant error in the determination of R_c may be appreciable, since β_1 and β_2 are unlike and therefore also the percentage deviations of η_1 and η_2. Hence the measured total circuit resistance R_c is not exactly as given in Eq. (14) but

$$R_c' = \frac{I_2'}{I_1' - I_2'} R_s = \frac{\beta_2 I_2}{\beta_1 I_1 - \beta_2 I_2} R_s$$

The percentage error η for *both* measurements, which shows how much the resistance R_c' computed from the I_1' and I_2' readings differs from the actual value R_c, then becomes

$$\eta\% = 100 \frac{R_c' - R_c}{R_c} = 100 I_1 \frac{\beta_2 - \beta_1}{\beta_1 I_1 - \beta_2 I_2}$$

which, expressed in the actual measured current values I_1' and I_2', gives

$$\eta\% = \frac{100 I_1'[\beta_2 - \beta_1]}{\beta_1[I_1' - I_2']} \tag{20}$$

If the percentage values η_1 and η_2 are used,

$$\eta\% = \frac{100 I_1'[\eta_1 - \eta_2]}{[100 - \eta_1][I_1' - I_2']} \tag{20a}$$

That the error can become appreciable may be seen from the following example. Suppose the current I_2' with the standard added resistance R_s is adjusted to a value R_s', for which the apparent resonance reading I_2' is exactly half the reading I_1', when terminals 1 and 2 are short-circuited, formula (20) then reduces to

$$\eta' = 200 \frac{\beta_2 - \beta_1}{\beta_1} \tag{21}$$

and (20a) yields $200[\eta_1 - \eta_2]/[100 - \eta_1]$ per cent.

To test the accuracy, a standard resistance with the coupling turns (across which voltage E is induced, Fig. 215) and a loosely coupled thermoelectric microammeter (coupled to one turn only) was connected across the terminals for the test sample in Fig. 195, and the resistance of this circuit branch measured. It was found to be $R_c = 14.6\Omega$. The measurement was carried out of 500 kc/sec, and the effective inductance of the coupling coil from the C_s setting of 0.000487 μf was found to be $L = 25345/(500^{2'} \times 487 \times 10^{-6}) = 208\ \mu h = 208 \times 10^{-6}$ henry. The test circuit was closed as in Fig. 215 except that the loosely coupled thermoelectric microammeter was used in order to make the two resonance settings such that the resistance reflected into the measuring circuit was small. The loosely coupled tube generator was excited with a frequency $f = 500$ kc/sec and the measuring circuit tuned by means of the setting C_s. The decrement per cycle of the closed circuit, according to the above measurements, is $\delta_1 = R/2fL = 14.6/(2 \times 500 \times 10^3 \times 208 \times 10^{-6}) = 0.0702$. Suppose the original resonance setting of 487 $\mu\mu$f could be set within 5 $\mu\mu$f of the exact resonance point, then $\Delta C/C_1 = 5/.487 = 0.0102$. Inserting this ratio and the value for δ_1 in Eq. (16) gives $\beta_1 = 0.91$. It required a standard resistance of about 15.1 ohms to reduce the original resonance current to half of its value. The logarithmic decrement per cycle, with 15.1 ohms also acting, becomes $\delta_2 = (14.6 + 15.1)/208 = 0.143$. Inserting this result and the above value of $\Delta C/C_1$ into Eq. (18) yields $\beta_2 = 0.976$. Inserting the values for β_1 and β_2 in (21) gives $\eta^1 = 14.5$ per cent error in the total circuit-resistance determination. From this example it can be seen that with the resistance-variation method it is very essential that a *sharp* resonance adjustment is made and that a condenser must be used which allows for a *very accurate* reading of the setting so that $\Delta C/C_1$ becomes a very small quantity.

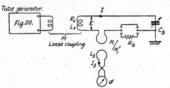

Fig. 216.—Resistance-variation method with coupled indicator.

Instead of the low-resistance thermo-electric indicator in Fig. 215, a single-turn coupling coil as in Fig. 216 can be used. It is loosely coupled to another single-turn coupling turn connected to a sensitive thermocouple which affects a galvanometer. For a fixed coupling the respective resonance deflections d_1 and d_2 for the two determinations are proportional to the square of the respective currents; that is, $d_1 = kI_1^2$ and $d_2 = kI_2^2$ and (14) gives then

$$R_c = \frac{R_s}{\sqrt{\dfrac{d_1}{d_2}} - 1} \tag{22}$$

which, for the resonance deflection $d_2 = 0.25d_1$ with R_s inserted, gives $R_c = R_s$. In this circuit it is again essential that the mutual inductance M is small so that the measuring circuit does not appreciably react back on the tube generator. As far as the back action of the loosely coupled thermoelectric resonance indicator is concerned, the two readings without additional and with additional resistance R_s are carried out first with coupling M_1 which gives by means of Eq. (22), the total circuit resistance

$$m = \frac{R_s}{\sqrt{\dfrac{d_1}{d_2}} - 1} \tag{23}$$

The two measurements are then carried on with a somewhat looser coupling corresponding to transfer inductance M_1' for which the resonance deflections d_1' and d_2' are obtained, and the total circuit resistance becomes

$$n = \frac{R_s}{\sqrt{\dfrac{d_1'}{d_2'}} - 1} \tag{24}$$

The coupled thermoelectric-indicator circuit of effective impedance $Z_3 = \sqrt{R_3{}^2 + (\omega L_3)^2}$ for a coupling M_1 reflects the resistance $\rho = \omega^2 M_1{}^2 R_3/Z_3{}^2$ into the heavily drawn measuring circuit. The true resistance R_c of the closed measuring circuit is increased by this amount and leads to

$$m = \frac{R_s}{\sqrt{\dfrac{d_1}{d_2}} - 1} = R_c + \rho \tag{25}$$

For a somewhat looser coupling corresponding to mutual inductance M_1', the reflected resistance is smaller and equal to $\rho' = (\omega M_1')^2 R_3/Z_3{}^2$ leading to

$$n = \frac{R_s}{\sqrt{\dfrac{d_1'}{d_2'}} - 1} = R_c + \rho' \tag{26}$$

The resonance currents which flow in the *measuring* circuit for the successive adjustments are

$$I_1 = \frac{E}{(R_c + \rho)} \text{ and } I_2 = \frac{E}{(R_c + R_s + \rho)} \quad \begin{array}{l}\text{coupling } M_1 \text{ producing the respective} \\ \text{resonance deflections } d_1 \text{ and } d_2\end{array}$$

$$I_1' = \frac{E}{(R_c + \rho')} \text{ and } I_2' = \frac{E}{(R_c + R_s + \rho')} \quad \text{coupling } M_1' \text{ produces } d_1' \text{ and } d_2'$$

Since the resonance deflections are proportional to the square of the current I_3 passing through the heater of the thermoelectric indicator; that is, $d = kI_3{}^2$ and if i_1, i_2, i_1', and i_2' denote the values of the heater current I_3 which cause the successive resonance deflections d_1, d_2, d_1', and d_2', for the general value I of the resonance current in the measuring circuit of effective total circuit resistance R_c', there is the relation $I = E/R_c'$ and $I_3 = \omega M_3 I/Z_3$ or $I_3 = \omega M_3 E/(R_c' Z_3)$ if M_3 stands for either M_1 or M_1'. The successive heater currents are then

$$i_1 = \frac{\omega M_1 E}{Z_3[R_c + \rho]}; \ i_2 = \frac{\omega M_1 E}{Z_3[R_c + R_s + \rho]}; \ i_1' = \frac{\omega M_1' E}{Z_3[R_c + \rho']};$$

$$i_2' = \frac{\omega M_1' E}{Z_3[R_c + R_s + \rho']}$$

But $\omega^2 M_1{}^2 R_3/Z_3{}^2 = \rho$ and $(\omega M_1')^2 R_3/Z_3{}^2 = \rho'$, in these expressions for $\theta = E\sqrt{\rho/R_3}$ and $\theta' = E\sqrt{\rho'/R_3}$ lead to

$$i_1 = \frac{\theta}{R_c + \rho} = \sqrt{\frac{d_1}{k}}; \ i_2 = \frac{\theta}{R_c + R_s + \rho} = \sqrt{\frac{d_2}{k}}; \ i_1' = \frac{\theta'}{R_c + \rho'} = \sqrt{\frac{d_1'}{k}};$$

$$i_2' = \frac{\theta'}{R_c + R_s + \rho'} = \sqrt{\frac{d_2'}{k}} \tag{27}$$

From these relations, $\sqrt{\dfrac{d_1}{d_2}} = \dfrac{1 + R_s}{(R_c + \rho)}$ and $\sqrt{\dfrac{d_1'}{d_2'}} = \dfrac{1 + R_s}{(R_c + \rho')}$ which, when used in (25) and (26), confirm that $m = R_c + \rho$ and $n = R_c + \rho'$. The values of ρ and ρ' could be computed if M_1, M_1', R_3, and L_3 were known. This procedure, however, requires actual measurements of these quantities and can be avoided by using the relation

$$\rho' = p\,\rho \tag{28}$$

where the value

$$p = \left(\frac{n}{m}\right)^2 \frac{d_1'}{d_1} \tag{28a}$$

is found from the resonance deflections d_1 and d_1' for couplings M_1 and M_1' and no inserted resistance R_s. From the corresponding relations in (27) for i_1 and i_1',

$$i_1 = \sqrt{\frac{d_1}{k}} = \frac{\theta}{R_c + \rho} = \frac{E\sqrt{\rho/R_3}}{m}; \; i_1' = \sqrt{\frac{d_1'}{k}} = \frac{E\sqrt{\rho'/R_3}}{n}$$

and the expression $\dfrac{\rho'}{\rho} = \left(\dfrac{n}{m}\right)^2 \dfrac{d_1'}{d_1} = p$. From this it can be seen that p can also be computed from $p = (ni_1')^2/(mi_1)^2$, if the actual currents i_1 and i_1' are noted on the thermoelectric indicator instead of the deflections d_1 and d_1'. From (25) and (26) the relations $m = R_c + \rho$ and $n = R_c + p\rho$ lead to the formula

$$\rho = \frac{m - n}{1 - p} \tag{29}$$

where m is the apparent circuit resistance computed from (25), which holds for the determination with the transfer inductance M_1 toward the thermoelectric indicator, and n is the apparent circuit resistance computed from (26) for the somewhat smaller transfer inductance M_1'. The correct total circuit resistance is then computed from $R_c = m - \rho$ or

$$R_c = \frac{n - m\,p}{1 - p} \tag{30}$$

The resistance in this method can also be found graphically.[1] The apparent circuit resistance $R_c + \rho$ for different M_1 values toward the coupled thermoelectric indicator is plotted against $\dfrac{d}{k}[R_c + \rho]^2$. A straight line is obtained whose intercept on the ordinate axis gives the average value of the true circuit resistance R_c. The graphical solution of Fig. 217 of H. Pauli[1] does *not* require that the coupling factor $\kappa = \dfrac{M}{\sqrt{L\,L_x}}$ between the high-frequency supply circuit and measuring circuit be very

---

[1] MOELLER, H. G., *Jahrb. d. drahtl.*, **16**, 402, 1920; H. PAULI, *Z. Physik.*, **5**, 376, 1921; **6**, 118, 1921.

loose. The coupling may come even close to the critical value $(1 >> \kappa^2 = \delta/\pi)$ for $\delta = (R_x + R_s)/(\omega L_x)$ as long as it is possible to tune the measuring circuit. For practical reasons, however, it is not advisable to choose κ too close to the critical value, since frequency jumps may occur if the source is a tube generator, as is usually the case.

1. For the determination, a suitable coupling is chosen and the resonance current readings I_1 and I_2 for different values of the standard resistance R_s are observed.

2. The ratio I_1/I_2 is plotted against R_s and the coil resistance R_x found by the intercept of the straight line with the R_s axis.

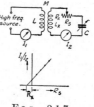

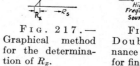

For very accurate work the resistance of the thermoelectric meter I_2 must be subtracted from the R_x value obtained graphically in order to obtain the true coil resistance. The method shown in Fig. 218 depends upon the

FIG. 217.—
Graphical method for the determination of R_x.

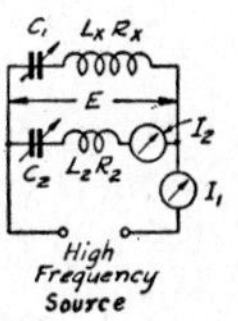

FIG. 218.—
Double-resonance method for finding R_x.

fact that for voltage resonance of both parallel branches $E = [I_1 - I_2]R_x = I_2R_2$ and $R_x = I_2R_2/(I_1 - I_2)$.

There is a reactance-variation method also. The test coil of unknown resistance R_x is connected in series with a variable-air condenser C_s and the circuit is closed through a low-resistance thermoelectric meter. A tube generator is again loosely coupled to the measuring circuit, which is at first tuned by a setting $C_s = C_r$ for a resonance current I_r and then is somewhat detuned for a setting $C_s = C_1$, giving the current reading I_1. For the first adjustment, $I_r = E/R_c$ where R_c again denotes the total resistance of the measuring circuit ($R_c = R_x +$ heater resistance of the indicator). For the second adjustment, $I_1 = \dfrac{E}{\sqrt{R_c^2 + X^2}}$ for $X = \omega L_x - \dfrac{1}{(\omega C_1)}$. Hence $R_c = \dfrac{I_1 X}{\sqrt{I_r^2 - I_1^2}}$. In order to utilize the average value of the sharpness of resonance, that is, both sides of the resonance curve near resonance, the first measurement is carried on as above, giving the current I_r for the setting C_r. Then a somewhat smaller current I is obtained for the respective condenser settings C_1 and C_2 on each side of the C_r value, and the total circuit resistance obtained from

$$R_c = \frac{C_2 - C_1}{2\omega C_1 C_2} \sqrt{\frac{I^2}{I_r^2 - I^2}} \tag{31}$$

or from

$$R_c = \frac{C_2 - C_1}{2\omega C_1 C_2} \sqrt{\frac{d}{d_r - d}} \tag{31a}$$

if the corresponding deflections of the thermoelectric indicator are used. By choosing C_1 and C_2 such that $d = d_r/2$ or $I = I_r/1.41$, the value of the radicals in (31 and (31a) becomes unity. In these formulas all quantities are in practical units, that is, in ohms and farads, and $\omega/2\pi$ is in cycles per second.

High-frequency resistance can also be measured by means of thermic indicators as fully described in Sec. 33, by means of the thermal method (J. A. Fleming) and the calorimeter methods (Sec. 32), the last being the slowest but the most accurate method, since it is independent of wave shape. The circuit is shown in Fig. 219. Use is made of the fact that

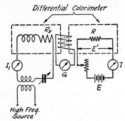

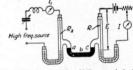

FIG. 219.—Determination of R_x. FIG. 220.—Fleming's differential thermometer for the determination of R_x.

the constant of proportionality, by which the square of the effective current through the test sample is to be multiplied, is equal to the energy dissipated in the test sample. The test sample of the effective resistance R_x is inserted in one calorimeter and the heating current I in the other calorimeter varied until the galvanometer reads zero. The heat dissipated in the resistance R, whose magnitude need not be known, is then equal to that lost in R_x and $R_x = EI/I_1^2$. Fleming's differential-thermometer method conveniently uses a red colored liquid a, b, c, as in Fig. 220, for an indicator. It is especially suitable when the effective resistance of straight wires and thin elongated coils is to be determined. With R_x in one glass tube and a heater resistance R in the other, the direct current I is adjusted until the air expansions in the differential air thermometer are balanced; that is, the indicating liquid stands as in the figure. The effective resistance is computed from the same formula as that obtained for the differential calorimeter above (which can be used more conveniently for any size of test coil and is more accurate than the thermometer method).

127. Substitution Methods.—The simple substitution method is based on two determinations. The test sample R_x, L_x is connected in the measuring circuit of Fig. 221 which is excited by a loosely coupled tube generator. The condenser C is varied until maximum deflection d is obtained. The variable standards L_s and R are now connected in the circuit instead of L_x, R_x, and the circuit is tuned by means of L_s. The setting of the variable resistance is varied until the same resonance deflection d as for the first determination is again secured. The unknown resistance is then $R_x = R + R_s$. If pure resistances R_x are to be determined, the variometer is dispensed with, but for the measurement of coil resistance the variometer L_s plays an important part; otherwise the tuning, for the second determination, would have to be made again by a change of condenser setting. This would give a somewhat different value of condenser resistance. Large errors result then if for one resonance setting the condenser plates are almost turned out. Therefore the con-

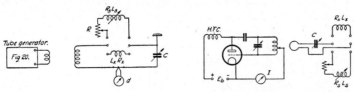

FIG. 221.—Ordinary substitution method.   FIG. 222.—Sensitive substitution method utilizing reflection principle.

denser setting C should be essentially the same for both determinations, especially if the coil resistance R_x is small. Figure 222 shows a more sensitive substitution method where the milliammeter I registers the grid current which is approximately proportional to the voltage amplitude of the high-frequency voltage across the grid and the filament. The measurement is then similar to the above, except that a certain decreased indication of I is noted when the test coil R_x, L_x is in the measuring circuit which is tuned by C. The test coil is replaced by L_s, and R and L_s are varied until about the same value of I is obtained. Hereafter R is adjusted until I reads exactly the same. The resistance then is computed from $R_x = R + R_s$.

128. Notes on the Separation of the Various Resistance Components of a Coil.—The high-frequency resistance of a coil is generally higher than the direct-current value. The direct-current resistance would be preserved if the current density remains the same over the entire cross section and for each cross section of the conductor for the high frequency. Because of the skin effect, the current density near the surface becomes greater and, if the frequency is high enough, for a substance of high conductivity the current flows practically along a thin surface skin only, while most of the cross section is useless. Therefore the resistance of the conductor is increased owing to this effect. When the coil exhibits a certain self-capacitance, the distributed condensers give rise to dielectric losses which are equivalent to another increase of resistance. If an iron core is used for the coil, iron losses due to hysteresis and eddy currents in the iron are produced, which account for a further increase in resistance. If neighboring circuits or shielding affect the coil, a certain resistance is reflected into the coil which accounts for another increase. An increase of resistance is also due to the e.m. radiation effects. With ordinary coils these effects are very small but with coil antennas they may become appreciable. In many cases it is possible to compute the individual resistance contributions or to determine them by measurement. It is always possible to determine the resultant resistance effect (by means of the methods just described) but sometimes difficulty arises if the resistance effect due to distributed coil capacitance is to be found. The resistance due to this varies over a very wide range indeed, up into the high ohmic range (if the coil is tested near its natural frequency). Coils working in the frequency range above natural coil resonance are of interest only for special work and it may be said that for normal conditions a good coil always works well below its natural frequency. As far as the direct-current component is concerned, it is a quantity which depends upon the material and dimensions of the conductor if a normal room-temperature range prevails and the conductor is not very thin (thin platinum wire changes its direct-current resistance appreciably if only a laboratory door is opened). If customary air coils are under consideration, the derivations in Sec. 3 show that, for a self-capacitance C_0 and a true inductance L of the coil, the effective resistance is

$$R_e = \frac{R}{[1 - \omega^2 C_0 L]^2 + \omega^2 C_0^2 R^2} \tag{32}$$

where

$$R = R_0 + k_1 f^2 \tag{33}$$

denotes the high-frequency resistance of the coil of the direct-current resistance R_0. The term $k_1 f^2$ accounts for the increase due to skin effect. The useful range of a good coil is well below self-resonance and the effective coil resistance can then be computed from

$$R_e = \frac{R}{[1 - \omega^2 C_0 L]^2} \cong R[1 + 2\omega^2 C_0 L] \tag{34}$$

while for self-resonance of the coil

$$R_e = \frac{1}{\omega^2 C_0^2 R} = \frac{L}{C_0 R} \tag{35}$$

and the resistance may be in the megohm range. For frequencies above self-resonance, R_e can practically be computed from

$$R_e = \frac{R}{(\omega^2 C_0 L)^2} \tag{36}$$

since the coil acts like a negative reactance, that is, a condenser. From this expression it is evident that with increasing frequency the resistance approaches zero value and that it may happen that the high-frequency resistance R_e becomes smaller than the direct-current value R_0. If the dielectric losses are also taken into consideration, there is obtained, according to Fig. 4 and the corresponding Eq. (11) of Sec. 3 if C_0 is used instead of C, for the useful frequency range (well below resonance frequency) the high-frequency coil resistance

$$R_e' = \frac{R + \rho \omega^4 C_0^2 L^2}{[1 - \omega^2 C_0 L]^2} \tag{37}$$

where ρ denotes a small resistance in series with a pure self-capacitance C_0 and accounts for the dielectric loss. The resistance R is then given again by Eq. (33) in order to account for the skin effect also. The term $\rho\omega^4 C_0{}^2 L^2$ in Eq. (37) is the characteristic factor which takes into consideration the increase of resistance due to dielectric losses. It is in reality proportional to the third power of the frequency $f = \omega/2\pi$ so that (37) can be written in the form

$$R_e{}' = \frac{R_0 + k_1 f^2 + k_2 f^3}{[1 - \omega^2 C_0 L]^2} \qquad (37a)$$

where the divisor $(1 - \omega^2 C_0 L)^2$ shows that the coil capacitance C_0 also causes an increase of resistance in this range until self-resonance occurs. The third-power law can be proved in connection with the vector diagram of Fig. 223. The current through the pure capacitance C_0, because of the fictitious loss resistance ρ, will not lead the applied voltage (which acts also across the actual coil) by *exactly* 90 deg but by an angle which is smaller by the amount $\theta = \tan^{-1}\rho\omega C_0$. Experiments show that $\rho\omega C_0$ is practically equal to a constant K which means that the dielectric resistance ρ must vary inversely with the frequency $f = \omega/2\pi$,

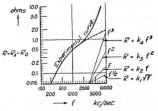

FIG. 223.—Graphical solution for the separation of the different resistance components.

and $\rho = K/(\omega C_0)$. The characteristic factor $\rho\omega^4 C_0{}^2 L^2$ of Eq. (37) for the dielectric loss can then be written as $8\pi^3 K L^2 f^3$, which substantiates the cubic relation in (37a) and shows that $k_2 = 8\pi^3 K L^2$. The constants k_1 and k_2 can also be found experimentally by measuring R_e with any of the methods already described for two different frequencies f_1 and f_2 and solving for k_1 and k_2, since R_0 is known from a direct-current measurement and the coil capacitance C_0 can be found by any of the methods described in Sec. 105. As far as the square law f^2 in (33) and (37a) is concerned, the measurement alone can bring out the law which should be used. The eddy-current losses in the conductor increase as the square of the frequency f, while the skin-effect losses are normally proportional to $\sqrt{f}$. Both of them are responsible for the term $k_1 f^2$ mentioned above and one may become predominant for a certain frequency range, while the other may predominate for another range. Hence, for the general case, any power between these limits is possible. In the practical formulas both effects are included. Thus if a conductor is used for which the radius r is very large compared with the penetration of the current into the wire, there is a resistance ratio $R/R_0 = \pi r \sqrt{\mu f \sigma}$ which means that the increase of resistance is proportional to $\sqrt{f}$. This is the skin-effect law mentioned above. But if the penetration of the current into the conductor begins to play a part in comparison with the radius r of the conductor, the curvature can no longer be neglected and, according to Riemann,[1] the resistance ratio becomes $R/R_0 = 1 + \frac{1}{3}r^4\pi^4\sigma^2\mu^2f^2$ and the effective resistance increases as f^2. A graphical solution as in Fig. 223 is then possible for the separation of the coil resistances. Double logarithmic paper is used to plot the high-frequency resistance $R_x - R_0$ against the frequency. The experimental curve can then be represented by the equation $[R_x - R_0] = k_1f^m + k_2f^n + k_3f^p \cdots$, if the direct-current resistance R_0 has been subtracted from the measured R_x values. By means of tangents at certain points of the experimental curve it is possible to see what power is mostly effective at that frequency. The upper portion of the $(R_x - R_0)$ curve proceeds essentially along the line with a slope giving the third power of f. This means that for the corresponding frequency range the dielectric losses of the coil play a predominating part. The dotted curve is obtained after subtracting this tangent corresponding to steepness $\tan^{-1} 3$. The remaining curve must therefore be essentially due to eddy-current and skin-effect losses. The other tangents show that there are frequency ranges for which a $\sqrt{f}$, a straight f, and an f^2 law prevails. Hence up to 1000 kc/sec it is mostly the eddy-current losses that increase the resistance, and from 1000 to 2000 kc/sec the skin effect predominates, while for the uppermost portion dielectric losses are most significant.

For the effect of the reflected resistance from neighboring circuits, reference is made to Sec. (4) and the derivation of Eq. (29) of Sec. 126. From these references it is evident that, for an effective coil inductance L_x, an inductance L of the pick-up coil of an adjacent closed circuit of effective impedance Z, and a mutual inductance M between L_x and L, the resistance reflected into the L_x branch is ω^2M^2R/Z^2 if R denotes the total resistance of the adjacent circuit.

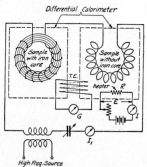

FIG. 224.—Good but slow method for determining iron losses and effective coil resistance.

129. Determination of the Increase of Coil Resistance Due to Iron Losses and Neighboring Circuits.

—The less convenient but more reliable method of Fig. 224 with the differential calorimeter can be used. Two like coils, one with and the other without an iron core are connected in series, each coil located in a separate calorimeter.

1. Before any current is switched on, the respective calorimetric liquids are brought to exactly the same temperature noted by a zero deflection on the galvanometer G.

2. The high-frequency current of the desired magnitude I_1 and frequency f is sent through both coils, after a while producing a certain steady deflection on G.

[1] "Webers," vol. 2, p. 518, 1929.

3. The direct current due to voltage E is varied until for some value I the galvanometer deflection is again zero.

4. The total iron loss of the coil is then $W = EI = R_x I_1^2$.

5. In place of the test coil with the iron core, insert the like coil from the other calorimeter, leaving in that calorimeter the compensating heater unit and the thermo-element only. Send the same high-frequency current I_1 through the coil, with air or some other nonmagnetic core and adjust the heater current to some value I' which is smaller than I, and for which the galvanometer again reads zero. The relation $EI' = R_x' I_1^2$ is then the expression for the power dissipated in the coil without iron. The increase in resistance due to the iron losses is then

$$R_x - R_x' = \frac{E}{I_1^2}[I - I'] \tag{38}$$

The increase of the coil resistance when a neighboring current affects it is determined by means of the arrangement in Fig. 195. It consists of determining the resistance of the inductance when the neighboring circuit is not present. The standard condenser is varied until the zero-current detector indicates a decided minimum. The standard resistance in the other branch is varied until, for a value R_1, an absolute balance is obtained. The neighboring circuit is now put in the desired position with respect to the coil and the processes of measurement repeated. Final zero balance is then obtained for a setting R_2 of the standard resistance. The difference $R_2 - R_1$ is then the increase of the resistance due to the neighboring circuit.

130. Determination of Very High Resistances.—If the high resistance is noninductive, the circuit of Fig. 178 can be used if C_x now denotes a variable-air condenser and R the unknown resistance. The measurement is exactly the same as described in Sec. 101 in connection with this figure and the unknown resistance R found from Eq. (17) of that section.

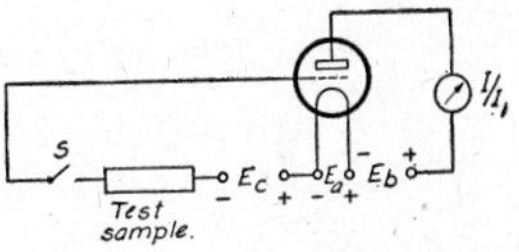

Figure 225 gives a means of measuring very high leak resistances, such as insulators, etc.

Fig. 225.—Determination of insulator resistances.

1. The deflection I of the indicator is noted when the switch S is open.

2. The test sample is connected into the circuit and the deflection of the plate meter noted after a few minutes.

If the sample has an appreciable conductivity, a smaller current I_1 will be obtained, since the voltage of about $E_c = -45$ volts charges the grid negatively and decreases the plate current. For very good insulators only, a very small decrease in the plate current will be noted. The insulation resistance R_x can be computed from

$$R_x = \frac{t}{C[\log_\epsilon E - \log (E - e)]} \text{ ohms} \tag{39}$$

where

$$e = E[1 - \epsilon^{-\frac{t}{CR_x}}] \tag{39a}$$

A good condenser C in this case is connected across the grid and the filament. Its capacitance must be much larger than the interelectrode capacitance. The capacitance is expressed in farads and the voltages in volts. The voltage which is obtained after t sec can be read off from the grid-voltage plate-current characteristic of the tube. Another method which depends upon a similar formula is shown in Fig. 226. The unknown resistance R_x acts as a grid leak and R_x is determined by means of the relaxation oscillations which start and stop the high-frequency oscillations due to the tube circuit. The coupling between the grid and plate coils is chosen so that the two clicks for starting and stopping the high-frequency oscillations are heard as only one click. The variable grid voltage e_g then rapidly charges the grid condenser C. There is then the relation

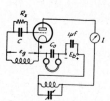

Fig. 226.—Oscillator for the determination of R_x.

$$t = CR_x \log_\epsilon \frac{E_1}{E_2}$$

if E_1 is that grid voltage for which high-frequency oscillations *just* start up again and E_2 the grid voltage for which the oscillations *just* stop, t is the time in seconds during which $C^{\text{(farads)}}$ discharges itself over R_x ohms to a voltage E_1. Since for a single click the entire time during consecutive clicks is equal to the discharge period, it is easy to read off the voltages at any instant of this period. The voltage E_3 is then noted at instant t_3, and the voltage E_4 at instant t_4, and the unknown resistance R_x is found from

$$R_x = \frac{t_4 - t_3}{C \log_\epsilon \dfrac{E_3}{E_4}} \tag{40}$$

The last two methods are not high-frequency tests in the true sense.

Figure 227 shows an arrangement where the resistance R_x is again tested with high-frequency currents. Use is made of the fact (for details, Sec. 3) that a pure condenser C_1 with a high ohmic resistance R_x in parallel can be substituted by another pure condenser C_2 with a low resistance R in series. Therefore it is possible to determine a very high resistance by means of a small resistance and *vice versa*, if the values of C_1 and C_2 as well as the frequency f are known. A resistance range from about 10^4 to 5×10^6 ohms, can be readily covered with such a method. Two good

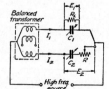

Fig. 227.—Differential method for determining a high-resistance R_x.

air condensers C_1 and C_2 and a variable resistance R (a short slide-wire resistance of constantan wire will do in many cases) are connected in the differential system of Fig. 227 as indicated, and the test resistance R_x

across C_2. The condensers C_1 and C_2 are varied until the zero-current indicator shows a decided minimum indication. R is then varied until absolute balance is obtained and the unknown resistance computed from

$$R_x = \frac{1}{\omega^2 C_1 C_2 R} \tag{41}$$

where the capacitances are in farads, the resistances in ohms, and the frequency $\omega/2\pi$ in cycles per second. Formula (41) is based on the final balance of the differential system which requires that the respective currents I_1 and I_2 have the same amplitude and the same phase. The phase for the upper branch is $\tan \varphi_1 = \omega C_1 R_x$ and of the lower branch is $\tan \varphi_2 = 1/(\omega C_2 R)$ and (41) is obtained from $\tan \varphi_1 = \tan \varphi_2$. The measurement can also be carried out with the substitution method shown in Fig. 228 and with one and the same variable-air condenser C_s. The first measurement is carried on with switches S_1 and S_2 closed and C_s is varied until for a setting $C_s = C_1$ resonance deflection d is obtained.

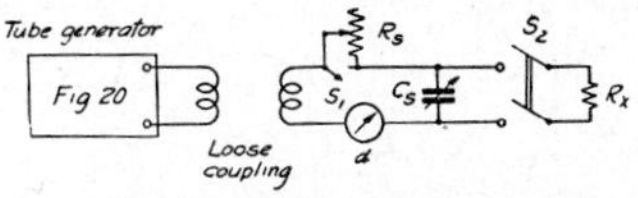

FIG. 228.—Substitution method.

Both switches are opened and R_s as well as C_s is varied until for settings $C_s = C_2$ and $R_s = R$ the same resonance deflection d is again obtained. The unknown resistance is computed from (41) or from the approximation formula $R_x \cong 1/(\omega^2 C_1^2 R)$, since in most cases $C_2 = C_1$, because, according to Eqs. (5) and (6) of Sec. 3, the effective-series capacitance of C_1 and R_x in multiple is $C_e = C_1\left[1 + \dfrac{1}{\omega^2 C_1^2 R_x^2}\right]$ and the effective-series resistance R_e of the equivalent-series circuit is $R_x/(1 + \omega^2 C_1^2 R_x^2)$. But $\omega^2 C_1^2 R_x^2$ is large compared with unity; hence $C_2 = C_e \cong C_1$ and $R = R_e \cong 1/(\omega^2 C_1^2 R_x)$.

The methods so far described do not take into account the phase angle of the unknown high resistance R_x. However, it is known that even short leak resistances show capacitance effect at very high frequency, since the inductive effects are small compared with it. The phase angle will take either effect into consideration. The method of Fig. 227 can then be used again in order to account, for instance, for any self-capacitance C_0 which is imagined in shunt with R_x and produces the phase angle φ_x for R_x. The measurement is as described in connection with Fig. 227 and the unknown resistance R_x and its self-capacitance C_0 are computed from

$$R_x^{\text{(ohms)}} = \sqrt{\frac{1 + \omega^2 A^2}{B}}; \qquad C_0^{\text{(farads)}} = A\sqrt{\frac{B}{1 + \omega^2 A^2}} - C_1 \tag{42}$$

and the phase angle φ_x from

$$\varphi_x = \tan^{-1} \omega C_0 R_x \text{ deg} \tag{43}$$

The frequency $\omega/2\pi$ is again in cycles per second. The factors A and B in the above formulas are

$$A = \frac{1}{RC_2\omega^2} \quad \text{and} \quad B = \frac{C_2{}^2\omega^2}{R^2C_2{}^2\omega^2 + 1} \tag{44}$$

where for most determinations $B \cong \omega_2{}^2C_2{}^2$, since $\omega^2C_2{}^2R^2$ is generally negligibly small compared with unity. Since φ_x is small, there is the approximation $\varphi_x \cong \omega C_0R_x$ for Eq. (43). The proof for (42) and (43) according to Fig. 227, if C_0 is imagined in parallel with R_x, is as follows:

For the I_1 branch

$$\tan \varphi_1 = \omega R_x[C_1 + C_0] \quad \text{and} \quad I_1 = E_1\sqrt{\frac{I}{R_1{}^2} + \omega^2[C_1 + C_0]^2}$$

and for the I_2 branch

$$\tan \varphi_2 = \frac{1}{\omega RC_2} \quad \text{and} \quad I_2 = \frac{E_2}{\sqrt{R^2 + \dfrac{1}{(\omega C_2)^2}}}$$

Since for the final balance of the differential system $\varphi_1 = \varphi_2$; $E_1 = E_2$ and $I_1 = I_2$,

$$\omega R_x[C_1 + C_0] = \frac{1}{\omega RC_2} \tag{45}$$

and

$$\frac{1}{R_x{}^2} + \omega^2[C_1 + C_0]^2 = \frac{1}{R^2 + \dfrac{1}{(\omega C_2)^2}} \tag{46}$$

Since only C_1, C_2, and R are known, R_x and $(C_0 + C_1) = C_x$ are the unknowns in (45) and (46). From (45), one has $R_xC_x = 1/(RC_2\omega^2) = A$ and

$$C_x = \frac{A}{R_x} \tag{47}$$

From (46),

$$\frac{1}{R_x{}^2} + \omega^2C_x{}^2 = \frac{\omega^2C_2{}^2}{R^2C_2{}^2\omega^2 + 1} = B \tag{48}$$

From (47) and (48), one obtains

$$\frac{1 + \omega^2A^2}{R_x{}^2} = B \text{ or } R_x = \sqrt{\frac{1 + \omega^2A^2}{B}}$$

and $C_x = A\sqrt{\dfrac{B}{1 + \omega^2A^2}}$. That means the self-capacitance $C_0 = C_x - C_1 = A\sqrt{\dfrac{B}{1 + \omega^2A^2}} - C_1$ and $\tan \varphi_x = \omega C_0R_x$.

Formulas (42) also hold for the substitution method shown in Fig. 228. All these methods described can also be used to measure plate resistance, rectifier resistance, insulator resistance, grid leaks, etc. The resistance of grid leaks, especially when used as plate resistors in high-efficiency voltage amplifiers, should be determined under the actual operating conditions. The measurement with a Wheatstone bridge is by no means satisfactory. The test is then carried out with the method of Fig. 229. A multirange meter of the Weston Company (30, 3, 0.3, and 0.03 ma) or its equivalent is conveniently used in series with a B battery of adjustable voltage E and the primary of an input transformer of a two-stage audio-frequency amplifier. The resistance of the primary, that of the battery, and that of the meter can be neglected in comparison with the high resistance in customary grid leaks. Such a voltage E is chosen in volts so that the current I is about the actual current for which the high resistance

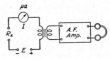

Fig. 229.—Determination of grid-leak resistances.

is to operate. If I is expressed in microamperes the ratio E/I gives the resistance R_x directly in megohms. The audio-frequency amplifier is used in order to test for any microphonicness of the leak.

131. Determination of the Resistance of a Thermoelement.—The alternating-current bridge of Fig. 230 is used and for a balance the resistance is computed from $R_x = l_1R/l_2$. A direct-current measurement would require the compensation of the current generated by the thermoelement.

132. Determination of the Effective Resistance[1] of a Circuit in Current Resonance.—The procedure indicated in Fig. 231 measures the resonance resistance L/CR across terminals 1 and 2 in terms of the nega-

Fig. 230.—Determination of the resistance of a thermocouple.

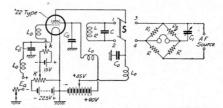

Fig. 231.—Determination of resistance L/CR for current resonance by means of negative resistance. (L_0 = high-frequency chokes and C_0 = 0.5-μf by-pass condensers.)

tive resistance r_p of a vacuum tube in the dynatron or pliodynatron connection. A shield-grid tube can be used with great advantage, although for some resistance ranges an ordinary three-element tube will do. Using a 222 type tube, for instance, the negative dynamic plate resistance which exists across the terminals of switch S can, for a filament current of 0.135 amp, a plate potential of about $+45$ volts, and a shield-grid potential of about $+90$ volts, be varied from about 15,000 to 10^6 ohms, if the bias of the control grid varies from zero to about -22.5 volts. Choosing other shield-grid and plate potentials, the lower limit

---

[1] Methods of this type have been developed in various laboratories. For publications, reference is made to C. E. Worthen, *Gen. Radio Experimenter*, **4**, May, 1930; P. D. Zotter, *Q.S.T.*, **14**, 39, 1930; H. Iinuma, *Proc. I.R.E.*, **18**, 537, 1930.

may be extended to about 7000 ohms negative.   For the measurement it is convenient to choose suitable plate and shield-grid voltages for a suitable filament current (usually normal current).   The negative resistance is then roughly varied by the traveling contact K and in small amounts by the contact k.   It is then possible to determine the point for which dynatron oscillations just begin if the test circuit C, L, R is connected across the switch S, and for which condition the negative plate resistance r_p just compensates the effective resonance resistance experienced across terminals 1 and 2.   In Sec. 9 it is shown that with a good degree of approximation

$$r_p = \frac{L}{CR} \tag{49}$$

where r_p and R are in ohms, C in microfarads and L in microhenries. The frequency of the dynatron oscillations is then given approximately by $f = 159.2/\sqrt{CL}$ kc/sec.   Hence, if r_p is found by a separate measurement or from the dynatron characteristic by means of $(E_{p1} - E_{p2})/(I_{p1} - I_{p2})$, that is, by the increment method, the resistance R can be computed from (49) if the high-frequency capacitance C is measured by one of the methods of Chap. VI.   The determination is as follows:

1. The switch S is connected against terminals 1 and 2 of the test sample, and with the aid of a near-by heterodyne generator (Fig. 20) it is observed whether dynatron oscillations exist.   They are noticed by means of a beat tone in the phones of the heterodyne if its fundamental frequency is close to the fundamental frequency of the dynatron oscillations.   (Beat tones with respect to higher harmonics are also possible although much weaker.)   If no dynatron oscillations exist, the grid bias of the control grid is made more negative by means of the slider K until oscillations set in.

2. With the heterodyne far enough away so that no back action on the CL circuit is produced, the respective sliders K and finally k are moved toward less negative control-grid potentials until the dynatron oscillations just break off, noted by the disappearance of the beat note.

3. The slider k is then moved toward a more negative potential until oscillations begin again and the heterodyne is adjusted to zero beat in order to read off the frequency f either by means of its own calibration or for more accurate work by means of the grid dip of a frequency meter coupled to the heterodyne.

4. The slider k is again moved toward less negative grid potentials and until the dynatron oscillations just stop.

5. The switch S is connected against the audio-frequency bridge with input terminals 3 and 4 and R_2 is varied until a sound minimum is noted.   Next, the small condenser C_1 is varied until a better sound minimum is observed and then R_2 is set for final balance.   Since r_p acts in parallel with R_1 and equal ratio arms exist for balance, one obtains from $\dfrac{R_1 r_p}{(R_1 + r_p)} = R_2$ the relation

$$r_p = \frac{R_1 R_2}{R_1 - R_2} \tag{50}$$

133. Notes on the Effective Resistance of a Condenser and Its Determination.

—This resistance is understood to be the small resistance R_x which may be imagined in series with the pure capacitance C of a condenser to account for *all* of its losses. According to the considerations in Sec. 3 and the discussion in connection with Fig. 227, a very high resistance in parallel with the pure capacitance may also be used in accounting for the losses. The values for the pure capacitance for series and the parallel resistance are not exactly alike but are nearly so. It is the action of a high ohmic parallel-loss resistance and that of a low series resistance which is utilized in the determination of condenser resistance. The series resistance R_x, also known as the equivalent resistance, if multiplied by the capacitance admittance ωC, for many condensers practically gives a constant value for the entire high-frequency range and is approximately equal to the low-frequency value of $\omega C R_x$. The constancy of $\omega C R_x$ explains why it is so difficult accurately to determine the equivalent condenser resistance R_x at a high frequency. As the frequency $\omega/2\pi$ is increased, R_x must decrease inversely with the first power of the frequency. Thus resistance values of a fraction of 1 ohm may occur for the upper high-frequency range. Even a high-loss condenser, for instance, using glass as a dielectric may, for a capacitance of 0.002 μf, have an equivalent resistance as low as 1 ohm at 500 kc/sec. The causes of the equivalent resistance may be dielectric losses, surface leakage, poor contacts, resistance of the leads and the conductive layers (plates in the case of air condensers). Losses due to mechanical vibrations are not likely to happen in the high-frequency range unless modulated currents occur. For a well-designed air condenser the equivalent resistance is small and more or less due to surface leakage, poor contact, and losses in the conductive layers. Therefore it can be seen why it is so difficult to give much weight to the accuracy of a measurement of a very good air condenser. Surface leakage is a function of humidity, temperature, and other causes which may take place in the average laboratory, and it is therefore necessary to take great care

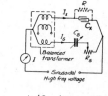

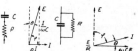

Fig. 232.—Loss determination of an imperfect condenser. ($C_s = C$ and $R_s = \rho$ for balance.)

with precision air condensers and enclose them completely and in such a way that the enclosure acts as a screen without contributing variable losses.

The method in Fig. 232 can be used for the determination of R_x. The lower diagrams indicate the vector diagrams for the variable standards and the test sample for balance. For simplicity, it is assumed that the effective value $C_s = C$ is exactly equal to that of C_x. The dotted resistance R is the imagined loss resistance acting in multiple with the pure capacitance C_x of the test sample, which may be a Leyden jar, as indicated, or any other condenser with losses. The losses of C_s for all settings are negligibly small. The determination then exists in varying C_s until for some value $C_s = C$ a pronounced minimum effect is noted in the zero-current detector. The slider along the slide wire R_s is then moved until for a setting $R_s = \rho$ final balance is obtained. The value ρ then denotes the equivalent resistance of the test sample. A similar determination can also be carried out with the simple substitution method shown in Fig. 233. The test condenser C_x is connected in the measuring circuit and C is varied until a resonance deflection d, occurs with the desired fundamental frequency of a loosely coupled tube generator. C should be a low-loss condenser. The standard condenser C_s with the variable standard series resistance is connected into the circuit in place of C_x, and C_s and R_s are varied until the same resonance deflection d is obtained. The setting of R_s is equal to the equivalent-loss resistance

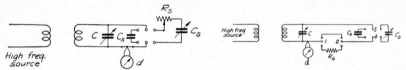

FIG. 233.—Simplified substitution method.   FIG. 234.—Resistance-variation method for determining equivalent condenser resistance.

and the setting of C_s equal to the true high-frequency capacitance. The resistance-variation method shown is a more complicated substitution method and was used at one time at the Bureau of Standards for the determination of equivalent-condenser resistance.[1] Again it makes the assumption that the resistance of the standard air condenser C_s is negligible compared with the resistance of the test condenser to be determined. The method is then essentially as in Fig. 234. The total circuit resistance R_1 is determined with the test condenser C_x in the measuring circuit, and the total resistance R_2 when the standard condenser C_s is in the circuit. The equivalent resistance of C_x is then $R_1 - R_2$. The details of the determination are as follows:

1. Terminals 1 and 2 are short-circuited and C_x connected across terminals 3 and 4. The setting of the variable-air condenser C is changed until the resonance deflection d_1 for the desired fundamental frequency of the loosely coupled tube generator is obtained.

2. A short straight resistor (thin constantan wire sealed in a glass tube) of suitable known resistance R_s is connected across terminals 1 and 2 and the reduced resonance deflection d_2 noted. The magnitude of R_s is conveniently chosen in the neighborhood of the expected total circuit resistance.

3. The total circuit resistance is computed from $R_1 = \dfrac{R_s}{\sqrt{\dfrac{d_1}{d_2}} - 1}$.

4. The standard air condenser C_s is connected across terminals 3 and 4 and terminals 1 and 2 are again short-circuited. The circuit is tuned by means of C_s until a resonance deflection d_3 is noted.

[1] *Bur. Standards, Circ.* 74; J. H. DELLINGER, *Proc. I.R.E.*, **7**, 27, 1919; J. H. DELLINGER and J. L. PRESTON, *Bur. Standards, Sci. Paper* 471, 1923.

5. The standard resistance R_s is again connected across terminals 1 and 2 and the reduced resonance deflection d_4 is noted.

6. The circuit resistance is computed from $R_2 = \dfrac{R_s}{\sqrt{\dfrac{d_3}{d_4}} - 1}$ and $(R_1 - R_2)$ is

the desired equivalent resistance of C_x.

The last method, although simple in operation, has the inherent disadvantage of the resistance-variation method already discussed in Sec. 126. The method is reliable only when the circuit is tuned *sharply*, when the standard resistance is accurately known, and when care is taken that the induced voltage in the measuring circuit is exactly the same with 1 and 2 short-circuited and R_s across these terminals and that there is no action of the measuring circuit on the tube generator. The simple substitution method of Fig. 233 and the differential method of Fig. 232 have the disadvantage that either the maximum-current or the zero-current deflection, respectively, in the *final* and *determining* adjustment must correspond to a *small* resistance component which is in quadrature to the reactive component $1/\omega C$ if the circuit is slightly off tune. The reactive component is large at high frequencies and any slight detuning may drown out altogether a slight difference in the resistance setting, since while making the adjustment the *impedance* (including both quadrature components) plays a part. The resonance indicator d of Fig. 233 and the zero-balance indicator of Fig. 232 do not have a great resolving power for the small resistance component, although the method of Fig. 232, for proper circuit conditions, is more sensitive than that in Fig. 233. This difficulty can be avoided by using a method which, for the final resistance adjustment, can be made responsive only to the quadrature resistance component. This is done in the differential method shown in Fig. 235, where the dis-appearance of the zero current is observed by means of a thermocross bridge or a vacuum-tube bridge (Sec. 40). The deflections d of this bridge are proportional to $I_1 I_0 \cos \psi$ where ψ is the phase angle between I_1 and I_0. Hence, if the auxiliary current I_1 is so chosen

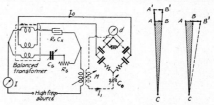

Fig. 235.—Determination of the loss resistance of a condenser.

that it is ± 90 deg. out of phase with respect to the current I_0 coming from the secondary, no indications are possible, while for any other phase angles deflections occur and maximum response for $\psi = 0$. Therefore it is only necessary to adjust the phase of I_1 by means of C and M in such a way that, for almost zero balance, very small variations in the R_s setting are effectively indicated by d. For such a sensitive adjustment, the component of I_0 which is due to a change of R_s has a phase angle of zero with respect to I_1, while any unbalancing due to a slight incorrect setting of C_s does not affect the indicator.

Reference is made to the vector diagram of Fig. 235 for details. The phase of the current I_0 depends upon how much the adjustment of C_s deviates from the true balance setting and how much the resistance balance R_s is met. AB denotes the watt component and AC the wattless quadrature component of current I_0. The wattless component is produced by an off setting of C_s and therefore for high-frequency work is always very large compared with AB which is produced by the off setting of R_s. The hypotenuse BC then gives the actual phase and magnitude of I_0. Hence, if the resistance balance R_s only is correct and the setting C_s somewhat off, the wattless component is either longer or shorter by the piece AA', and BB' denotes the current difference caused in I_0. For such measurements it is nearly equal to AA'. But if C_s is exactly adjusted and the R_s setting somewhat off, the vector triangle $AB'C$ is obtained instead of the balance triangle ABC and BB' is the variation in I_0. The variation BB' is therefore practically 90 deg. out of phase with respect to the variation AA' for the incorrect R_s setting, and it is possible by means of the indicator bridge of Fig. 235 to balance very small equivalent-condenser resistances.

134. Note on Ground, Radiation and Aerial Resistance and Their Determination.—The determination of ground resistance is not an easy matter, since the frequency determines to what extent ground acts as a conductor and to what extent as a condenser. The conductivity σ and the dielectric constant of κ vary through a wide range as can be seen from Table X, taken from recent measurements.[1] That both quantities play a part can be seen from the formula

TABLE X

f, cycles/sec	10^{-14} e.m.u. σ
23	3.61
47	3.86
100	4.29
435	4.6
870	4.7
1,740	4.73
3,480	4.76
6,960	4.74
13,920	4.78
8.1×10^4	4.82
1.5×10^5	4.86
2.5×10^5	4.9
5×10^5	4.9

$$\kappa_e = n^2 = \kappa - j18 \times 10^{17} \frac{\sigma}{f} = \kappa - j18 \times \frac{10^8}{f\,\rho} \qquad (51)$$

for the index of refraction n from air toward ground if f is in kilocycles per second, the dielectric constant κ expressed in e.s., σ in e.m. c.g.s. units, and ρ the resistivity per centimeter cube. κ and σ are the values for ground

[1] Strutt, M. J. O., *E.N.T.*, **10**, 387, 1930.

and κ_e denotes the complex dielectric constant of ground. κ_e plays the same part with respect to the conducting medium as κ for a nonconductive medium. The index of refraction is used because the ground is of most importance as far as direct-wave propagation is concerned. The radiation resistance of an aerial, as well as the energy lost in the ground, depends upon n^2. A general statement that the ground acts toward electromagnetic waves as an insulator (very high resistance) is not correct. Also the general statement that it behaves as a good reflector (mirror) is true only for a certain frequency band. For ground which acts as a good semiconductor, the radiation resistance may be computed by assuming that the ground is almost a perfect reflector for frequencies below 300 kc/sec, since, for instance, for $\sigma = 5 \times 10^{-14}$; $\kappa = 10$, and $f = 100$ kc/sec, one finds $n \to \infty$. Above 300 kc/sec and dry ground, the ground can no longer be considered a good reflector. Hence, if the radiation resistance were calculated for the ground as a good mirror toward electromagnetic waves (as a fairly good conductor), for a high-frequency current of 3 Mc/sec flowing into a tuned horizontal antenna 10 m long and 10 m above ground, the radiation resistance would be about 3 ohms, while for values of $\kappa = 4$ and $\sigma = 10^{-15}$ it would come out higher than 30 ohms. For frequencies above 20 Mc/sec, the ground begins to act as a condenser. Hence both quantities σ and κ must be taken into account, especially when wave propagation along the ground surface is of interest. For perfect ground there would be the simple law that the field strength of the wave decreases inversely with the distance, while actually the field intensity of the ground wave for distances which are not too close to the sender is inversely proportional as the square of the distance.

One can distinguish between direct and indirect methods for the determination of σ. The former use either two parallel plates with the ground as a resistance material or a parallel system (Lecher wires). The indirect methods determine σ and κ indirectly and the forward tilt of the wave front with respect to the normal to ground can be used for the determination. The simple parallel-plate method can be used only for the lower high-frequency range (up to about 300 kc/sec), the upper limit being set by the capacity effect of the ground. The first term of Eq. (51) represents the displacement and the second the conduction term. The parallel-plate method can also be used only to measure ground resistance when the first term is comparatively small. Hence, if very dry ground of low value for σ is to be tested, the upper-frequency limit may be only as high as 200 kc/sec. The method is then as in Fig. 236 where E denotes a tube voltmeter and I a thermoelectric-meter reading up to about 25 ma. If the dimensions of the volume of ground between the parallel plates are known, the conductivity and its reciprocal, the resistivity ρ in ohms per centimeter cube, can be found from the E and I readings.

With respect to the measurement at higher frequencies where the dielectric constant κ also enters, reference is first made to Fig. 237 where the space below the XY plane denotes the ground and the space above it

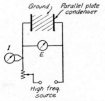

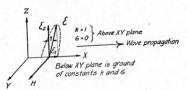

FIG. 236.—Determination of ground resistance.

FIG. 237.—Showing forward tilt τ of the electric vector $\mathcal{E}$ due to ground.

ordinary atmosphere (air). A plane e.m. wave moves in the X direction producing the tilt τ in the electric-field vector $\mathcal{E}$, while the magnetic vector is parallel with the Y-axis. For the direct surface wave,

$$-\frac{\mathcal{E}_x}{\mathcal{E}_z} = \frac{1}{\sin 90 \sqrt{\kappa_e}} = \frac{1}{\sqrt{\kappa_e}} = \tan \tau \tag{52}$$

since the direct wave sweeps along the ground and the angle of incidence is 90 deg and there can be no reflected wave from the ground. The *measured* angle τ is the *apparent* forward tilt, since a time phase θ exists between the horizontal component $\mathcal{E}_x$ and the vertical component $\mathcal{E}_z$ of the resultant field vector $\mathcal{E}$. Substituting the value for the apparent dielectric constant κ_e from (51) in (52), for $S = 18 \times 10^8/(\rho f)$,

$$\tan^2 \tau = \frac{1}{\kappa - jS} = \frac{\kappa}{\kappa^2 + S^2} + j\frac{S}{\kappa^2 + S^2} = A + jB$$

for $A = \kappa/(\kappa^2 + S^2)$ and $B = S/(\kappa^2 + S^2)$. But $A + jB = \epsilon^{j2\theta}\sqrt{A^2 + B^2}$ for $2\theta = \tan^{-1}(B/A) = \tan^{-1}(S/\kappa)$ and

$$\tan \tau = \epsilon^{j\theta}\sqrt[4]{A^2 + B^2} = \epsilon^{j\theta} \tan \tau_0 \tag{53}$$

where τ_0 denotes the forward tilt which would exist if $\theta = 0$ and $\mathcal{E}_x$ and $\mathcal{E}_z$ had the *same* time phase which is generally *not* at all the case. Then

$$\tan \tau = \frac{\epsilon^{j\theta}}{\sqrt{\kappa}} \sqrt[4]{\frac{[\rho\kappa f/(18 \times 10^8)]^2}{1 + [\rho\kappa f/(18 \times 10^8)]^2}} \tag{54}$$

where

$$\theta = 0.5 \tan^{-1}\left[\frac{18 \times 10^8}{\rho\kappa f}\right] \tag{54a}$$

where ρ is the resistivity of ground in ohms per centimeter cube, κ the dielectric constant of ground giving its numerical value with respect to that of air which is the conventional unity, and f is in kilocycles per second. From (53) it can be seen that the apparent tilt τ is smaller than the angle

τ_0 for no time-phase displacement. The expression of (54) confirms the wave-tilt formula of J. Zenneck.[1]

The tilt formula can also be found by means of the Maxwellian curl equation leading to the expressions

$$
\left.
\begin{aligned}
\frac{1}{c^2}\frac{\partial^2 H}{\partial t^2} &= \frac{\partial^2 H}{\partial x^2} + \frac{\partial^2 H}{\partial z^2} \quad \text{above ground in air} \\
\frac{\partial^2 Hg}{\partial x^2} + \frac{\partial^2 Hg}{\partial z^2} &= \frac{\kappa}{c^2}\frac{\partial^2 Hg}{\partial t^2} + \frac{4\pi}{\rho}\frac{\partial Hg}{\partial t} \quad \text{below surface of ground}
\end{aligned}
\right\} \quad (55)
$$

since for air $\kappa = 1$, $1/\rho = 0$, and $\mu = 1$, and for ground as expressed in the second equation. H_g denotes the magnetic-field vector in ground and H in air, and the above relations are the outcome of $\dfrac{\partial H}{\partial z} = \dfrac{1}{c^2}\dfrac{\partial \mathcal{E}_x}{\partial t}$ and $\left(-\dfrac{\partial H}{\partial x}\right) = \dfrac{1}{c^2}\dfrac{\partial \mathcal{E}_z}{\partial t}$ for air, and $\dfrac{\partial H_g}{\partial z} =$ $\dfrac{\kappa}{c^2}\dfrac{\partial \mathcal{E}_{g_x}}{\partial t} + \dfrac{4\pi}{\rho}\mathcal{E}_{g_x}$ and $\left(-\dfrac{\partial H_g}{\partial x}\right) = \dfrac{\kappa}{c^2}\dfrac{\partial \mathcal{E}_{g_z}}{\partial t} + \dfrac{4\pi}{\rho}\mathcal{E}_{g_z}$ for ground. The solutions for (55) are then the same as for the well-known telegraph equation and are $H_1 = H_0 \epsilon^a$ and $H_g = H_0 \epsilon^b$ for $a = -px - p_1 z + j\omega t$ and $b = -px + p_2 z + j\omega t$ giving $\mathcal{E}_x = \dfrac{-c^2}{j\omega}p_1 H$ and $\mathcal{E}_z = \dfrac{c^2}{j\omega}pH$ and $\tan \tau = \mathcal{E}_x/\mathcal{E}_z = p_1/p_2$. This solution has the advantage of giving expressions for the damping for each centimeter length along ground in the direction X of propagation, for the damping along the positive Z direction, that is, upward in the ground, and for the damping in the negative Z direction, that is, along the depth. The case for damping along each centimeter of depth is most important when underground communication is of concern. The general case in all three directions is solved in Breisig's book.[2] It is shown for instance, that for a 160-kc wave sweeping over ocean water, for $\kappa = 80$ and $\sigma = 10^{-10}$ for the conductivity there is a space damping of 1.475×10^{-11} for each centimeter length along the ocean water, which is considerably less damping than would be experienced along a copper wire or any commercial overhead line. For the damping component in the water upward a value of 7.02×10^{-8} per centimeter length is obtained. It compares with a decay along a thin telephone line. For the decay along the depth direction 7.93×10^{-3} is obtained for each centimeter depth so that in about 3-m depth the amplitude is only one-tenth for that at the surface. When the 160-kc wave sweeps along dry ground $\kappa = 4$ and $\sigma = 10^{-15}$, one finds $p = 32.9 \times 10^{-6}\epsilon^{j88°}$; $p_1 = 9.46 \times 10^{-6}\epsilon^{-j57°}$; and $p_2 = 114 \times 10^{-6}\epsilon^{j53°}$. The damping along the ground is then of the order as found for telephone currents which flow along a cable.

Since the horizontal and vertical components of $\mathcal{E}$ have a phase difference of θ, a rotating electric field is produced and, for the amplitudes $\mathcal{E}_x$ and $\mathcal{E}_z$, there are the relations $\mathcal{E}_x \sin \Omega$ and $\mathcal{E}_z \sin (\Omega + \theta)$ if $\Omega = 2\pi$ ft. The resulting field has the instantaneous value

$$
\mathcal{E}_t = \sqrt{\mathcal{E}_z{}^2 \sin^2 \Omega + \mathcal{E}_x{}^2 \sin^2 (\Omega + \theta)} =
$$
$$
\sqrt{0.5[\mathcal{E}_z{}^2 + \mathcal{E}_x{}^2 - \cos 2\Omega(\mathcal{E}_z{}^2 + \mathcal{E}_x{}^2 \cos 2\theta) + \sin 2 \Omega \mathcal{E}_x{}^2 \sin 2\theta]}
$$

and during each cycle a maximum and a minimum value occurs for $2\Omega = \tan^{-1}$ $[(-\mathcal{E}_x{}^2 \sin 2\theta)/(\mathcal{E}_z{}^2 + \mathcal{E}_x{}^2 \cos 2\theta)]$. For the above 159.2-kc wave sweeping over dry

[1] *Ann. Physik*, **23**, 846, 1907. Such a formula was also used by A. Bailey, S. W. Dean, and W. T. Wintringham, *Proc. I.R.E.*, **16**, 1645, 1928, for the finding of ground resistance by means of wave antennas in the lower high-frequency range.

[2] BREISIG, F., "Theoretische Telegraphie," F. Vieweg & Sohn, Braunschweig, 1924, pp. 482–487.

ground $\kappa = 4$ and $\sigma = 10^{-15}$, there are obtained the ratio numbers $\mathcal{E}_z = 32.8$ and $\mathcal{E}_x = 9.37$ and $\theta = 37.7°$ from which the maximum value $\mathcal{E}$ occurs for $\Omega = 87.8°$ with a value 33.6 if the same arbitrary scale is used as for $\mathcal{E}_x$ and $\mathcal{E}_z$. The apparent tilt τ is then about 77 deg.

For the actual measurement and the determination of ρ, according to (53), one must distinguish between the forward tilt τ as found by *measurement* and the tilt τ_0 for $\theta = 0$, since for the actual case for a time displacement θ the angle τ of the forward tilt of the major axis of the ellipse traced by the electric vector is less than the absolute magnitude of the ratio of the horizontal and vertical components $\mathcal{E}_x$ and $\mathcal{E}_z$ of $\mathcal{E}$. From the $\tan \tau_0$ value of (53) and (54a), there are the formulas

$$\rho = \frac{18 \times 10^8}{f} \frac{\tan^2 \tau_0}{\sqrt{1 - \kappa^2 \tan^4 \tau_0}} \quad \text{and} \quad \theta = 0.5 \cos^{-1} [\kappa \tan^2 \tau_0] \quad (56)$$

f in kilocycles per second, ρ in ohms per centimeter cube, κ numeric.

Therefore the procedure for the finding of ground resistance depends upon the measurement of the *apparent* angle τ of the forward tilt. This can be done conveniently by means of a Hertzian rod which may be rotated anywhere in space about its mid-point. The rod is rotated about a horizontal axis which is perpendicular to the direction of wave propagation and located a few miles away from a sender. If the rod is turned until the received energy gives a maximum response, it will be along the resultant $\mathcal{E}$ vector (large axis of ellipse). However, it is more convenient to turn the rod through 90 deg from this position, that is, into a direction for which minimum effect (only minimum since elliptically polarized) is noted in the receiver. The angle which the rod then makes with the *horizontal* is the apparent forward tilt τ with respect to the normal to ground. From τ must be found first the corresponding angle τ_0 which would hold for $\theta = 0$, that is, for equal time phase for $\mathcal{E}_x$ and $\mathcal{E}_z$, and the specific resistivity ρ is computed from Eq. (56). To find τ_0 a value for κ must be assumed which varies from 2 to 15 for ground, the values above 6 referring to wet ground, and up to 80 for ocean water. Having selected a value for κ, a value for τ_0 must be chosen so that (53) is satisfied. This means a value of τ_0 must be used for which $\epsilon^{j\theta} \tan \tau_0$ is equal to the tangent of the measured forward tilt. This is conveniently done graphically by means of plots of $\epsilon^{j\theta}$ against τ_0 for certain fixed values of κ, say for $\kappa = 2, 5, 10, 15,$ and 80. On the same curve sheet $\tan \tau_0$ is plotted. It is then necessary to pick out points on the $\epsilon^{j\theta}$ and $\tan \tau_0$ curves for which the multiplication of their ordinates satisfies $\tan \tau$. The computations for many cases can be greatly simplified by realizing that κ is often small compared with the j term in (51), especially when the frequency f, which is in kilocycles per second in that formula, and the resistivity ρ are not too high. In many cases where the second term in (51) is prominent, there is in the formula for θ in (56) a value for $\kappa \tan^2 \tau_0$ which is nearly zero, making $\cos 2\theta \cong 0$ or $\theta = 45°$. Plotting θ against τ_0 for certain fixed values of

κ, say 2, 5, 10, 15, and 80, it will be found that for angles $\tau_0 \leqq 2.5°$, the value of θ does not fall much below 45 deg if ground (land) resistance is concerned ($R = 2$ to 15). If the square of the j term in Eq. (51) is *large* compared with κ^2, condition for $\theta \cong 45°$ is satisfied, for which $\epsilon^{j\theta} \cong$ $\cos 45 + j \sin 45 = (1 + j)/\sqrt{2}$. From (53), $\tan \tau = \epsilon^{j\theta} \sqrt[4]{A^2 + B^2} \cong$ $\dfrac{\sqrt{B}}{\sqrt{2}}$ and $\tan^2 \tau = 0.5 B = \dfrac{0.5S}{\kappa^2 + S^2} \cong \dfrac{1}{2S}$. But $S = 18 \times \dfrac{10^8}{(\rho f)}$ and the resistivity ρ of the ground in ohms per centimeter cube can then be computed from the simplified formula

$$\rho = \frac{36 \times 10^8 \tan^2 \tau}{f} \text{ ohms/cm}^3 \tag{57}$$

if the frequency is again in kilocycles per second. The simplified formula shows also that the wave tilt is proportional to the square-root value of the ground resistance as well as to the square root of the frequency.

As far as the measurement goes, care must be taken that no indirect sky wave is superimposed on the direct ground wave. It can be avoided, for instance, up to and into the broadcast range and even for higher frequencies by taking the readings during the hours of daylight for which no reflections from the ionized layer can exist.

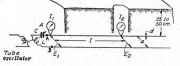

Fig. 238.—Determination of ground resistance. (Spacing between wires about $a = 2$ cm., diameter of wires $d = 0.15$ cm.; total length of parallel-wire system about 10^4 cm.)

For very high frequencies for which indirect-ray transmission is partially possible, the forward tilt is to be measured closer to the transmitting station.

The parallel-wire method of Fig. 238 in its simplest form consists of two parallel copper wires buried about 30 cm deep into the ground to be tested. The distance between centers of the wires is a cm and the diameter of the wire d cm. Without the input circuit (C, L) and the current indicators (I_1 and I_2), the input terminals A and B are connected across the test terminals X, X of the circuit shown in Fig. 50 and the settings of the variable standard (mainly a decade box) changed until a balance is obtained. The setting R ohms of the decade box then measures the effective resistance of the double line of length l cm experienced at the input terminals A and B. For this measurement the ground connection at the mid-point of the differential transformer is removed. If the capacity current across the two wires is neglected, the conductivity of the ground in e.m.u. per centimeter cube can be found from $\sigma = \dfrac{4000f}{R^2} \log_\epsilon \left(\dfrac{2a}{d}\right)^2$ where $\log_\epsilon = 2.303 \log_{10}$ and f is in kilocycles per second. Since the resistivity is $1/\sigma$, $1/\sigma$ must be divided by 10^9 in order to obtain the resistivity in ohms per centimeter cube. The specific resistance ρ per centimeter cube is then computed from

$$\rho = \frac{1085 \times 10^{-16} R^2}{f \log_{10} [2a/d]^2} \tag{58}$$

If the resistance-variation method is employed to determine the effective input resistance, the input circuit (C, L) is connected across terminals A and B and a thermoelectric indicator I_1 inserted as shown in Fig. 238. The circuit is tuned, giving the reading $I_1 = I_1$. Then a known standard resistance R_s is inserted and the reduced resonance current $I_1 = I_1'$ noted and the circuit resistance R_c found from $\dfrac{R_s \, I_1}{I_1 - I_1'}$. The resistance R_h of the thermoelectric indicator and that of the coupling coil R_1 is subtracted from R_c to obtain R. The resistance $(R_h + R_1)$ can be determined with the same method by short-circuiting the AB terminals and connecting the indicator I_1 into the CL branch.

For high-frequency currents traveling along a parallel-wire system buried in the ground as indicated in Fig. 238, practically only a wave train $I_1\epsilon^{-nl}$ will be traveling toward the open end, since the ground losses are so pronounced that practically zero line current is produced at places before the open end is reached. There can be no appreciable reflected wave train traveling back toward the source. One can then use the line equations $E_2 = E_1\epsilon^{-nl}$ and $I_2 = I_1\epsilon^{-nl}$ where E_1 and I_1 denote the current and voltage at the input side of the parallel-wire system and the propagation constant n is

$$n = \frac{2\pi}{\lambda}\sqrt{\frac{-\kappa + \sqrt{\kappa^2 + [6 \times 10^{10}\lambda/\rho]^2}}{2}}$$

if the wave length λ is in centimeters, the dielectric constant κ of the ground again the ordinary numerical value, and the resistivity ρ in electromagnetic centimeters per second units per centimeter cube of the ground. This formula was originally derived by M. Abraham[1] for such work. If the frequency is introduced in kilocycles per second, and the resistivity is expressed in ohms per centimeter cube, the formula

$$n = \frac{2\pi f}{3 \times 10^7}\sqrt{\frac{-\kappa + \sqrt{\kappa^2 + \left[\dfrac{18 \times 10^8}{(\rho\,f)}\right]^2}}{2}} \tag{59}$$

is obtained. If the effect of the dielectric constant κ is negligibly small compared with the effect due to the ground resistance, the above formula reduces to

$$n \cong 2\pi \times 10^{-3}\sqrt{\frac{f}{\rho}} \tag{60}$$

---

[1] ABRAHAM, M., H. RAUSCH V. TRAUBENBERG, and J. PUSCH, *Physik. Z.*, **20**, 145, 1919. Such a method was also employed by M. J. O. Strutt, *loc. cit.*

For very high frequencies for which κ plays the most prominent part,[1] n approaches zero value, and theoretically no ground attenuation takes place. The capacitance of the ground, so to speak, then by-passes the loss resistance. If now, as in Fig. 238, another current indicator I_2 is placed a distance l cm away from the input side A and B, its reading is $I_2 = I_1 \epsilon^{-nl}$, and, if the currents are measured with low ohmic indicators or the corresponding voltages E_1 and E_2 are noted with a suitable tube voltmeter, there is for the ratio value $p = I_2/I_1 = E_2/E_1$

$$n = -\frac{\log_\epsilon p}{l} = -\frac{2.303 \log_{10} p}{l} \qquad (61)$$

where l is in centimeters. From this relation ρ and κ can be found. Hence, if the effect of κ is very small, there is, by means of (60) and (61), the formula

$$\rho = \frac{4\pi^2 \times 10^{-6} l^2 f}{[\log_\epsilon p]^2} \qquad (62)$$

with f in kilocycles per second and p either the voltage or the current ratio of the values measured at a distance l cm from the input end and at the input, respectively. If a distance $l = 1/n$ is chosen, then $\epsilon^{-nl} = 1/2.718$ and the measured current or voltage at distance $1/n$ cm is 0.368 times the value measured at the input side. It is not practical to move the measuring meter for noting E_2 or I_2, respectively, along the line, since it is buried in ground and requires an opening toward the surface of the ground to make the observation. But from a preliminary measurement the approximate distance can be located and the frequency f is then varied until the reading of the meter at the approximate distance l is only $0.368I_1$ or $0.368E_1$, respectively. The specific resistance is then computed from

$$\rho = 4\pi^2 \times 10^{-6} l^2 f \qquad (63)$$

since $\log_\epsilon p = 1$. If, however, the first term of (51) is not negligible with respect to the j term including ρ, Eq. (59) must be used, for which a suitable value of κ is to be assumed in order to find ρ from (59) and (61).

Reference is made to Chap. XV where methods are given for determining the total aerial resistance. It can be seen from the beginning of that chapter that the current distribution along the aerial wire must be taken into account. With respect to radiation or useful aerial resistance, reference is made to page 398. It must be remembered that Eq. (51) gives a means of finding to what extent the ground affects this resistance and to what extent the ground acts as a reflector. The total aerial resistance which is measured with methods given in Chap. XV

---

[1] At about 20 Mc/sec, the displacement component of average ground is of about the order of the conduction component. Hence, for frequency much above 20 Mc, κ plays only a part.

consists essentially of three portions, of which the useful component R_1, the radiation resistance, is in many cases proportional to the square of the frequency.   The second component R_2 includes the effective resistance of the aerial wire itself, including the losses due to eddy currents in ground and surrounding objects.   This component varies in many cases about as the square root of the frequency.   The third component R_3 accounts for the losses in the surrounding dielectric and varies about inversely as the frequency.   There is then for total resistance measured

$$R = R_1 + R_2 + R_3 = k_1 f^2 + k_2 \sqrt{f} + \frac{k_3}{f} \qquad (64)$$

Therefore, if R is found experimentally for three different frequencies the constants k_1, k_2, and k_3 can be found, and with them the three components.

135. Determination of Negative Resistance.—Negative resistance can be obtained from the slope (tangent) of the static voltage-current characteristic for a particular operating point.   Since negative resistance (Sec. 9) shows valuable features only when current variations prevail, it is best to determine it dynamically, that is, with currents of the desired frequency.   In many cases tests with a 1000-cycle source is sufficient. Since for a negative resistance R_x a small voltage *increase* across it produces a corresponding current *decrease* and *vice versa*, it can be readily determined by connecting a standard resistance in series with it.   If the negative resistance R_x is numerically equal to the standard resistance R_s, the total series resistance must vanish.   For a parallel combination of both, infinite resistance occurs for equality.   Hence, if in the one branch of the balanced transformer (using an iron core) of Fig. 50 a negative resistance R_x is connected in series with a fixed standard R_1 and another standard resistance inserted in the other differential branch is varied until for a value R_2 a decided sound minimum is noted in a telephone receiver connected across the secondary of the transformer, one has $R_1 - R_x = R_2$ or $R_x = R_1 - R_2$, if R_1 happens to be numerically greater than R_x.   It is then convenient to excite the differential system with a small sinusoidal voltage taken from a 1000-cycle source.   A Wheatstone bridge arrangement can also be used.   The method is then similar to the one described in Sec. 132.   If inaudible currents are impressed upon the system, the air transformer of Fig. 50 is used with any suitable zero-current detector.   A tube voltmeter can be used also.   For another method, the negative resistance R_x is connected in multiple with a standard resistance R_1.   For a sinusoidal voltage E impressed upon the parallel combination, a current I will flow to the combination and $E = -IR_xR_1/(R_1 - R_x)$.   Next, the standard parallel resistance is varied until for the same input voltage E half the current flows to the system, and $E = -0.5IR_xR_2/(R_2 - R_x)$.   These two relations give the formula $R_x =$

$-R_1R_2/(R_2 - 2R_1)$ for the negative resistance.   Still another procedure uses the standard resistance R in series with the negative resistance R_x. For a sinusoidal voltage E_1 (measured with a high-impedance voltmeter) applied to the series combination the current reading I is noted.   The relation is then $I = E_1/(R - R_x)$.   Next, the negative-resistance device is short-circuited and the input voltage changed to a value E_2, for which the same current I flows through the standard resistance R.   For this condition $I = E_2/R$ and the negative resistance is computed from $R_x = -R(p - 1)$ for $p = E_1/E_2$.   The balance method shown in Fig. 239 is essentially the same as described by E. N. Dingley.[1]   For minimum effect in the telephone receiver, the curren display is as in the figure, since the negative-current variation I_3 through $(-R_x)$ occurs as indicated.   Inasmuch as P_1 and P_2 are essentially of the same potential, $R_1I_1 = R_3I_3$ and, according to Kirchhoff's law for balance, $I_3R_3 +$ $(I_1 + I_3)R_2 - R_xI_3 = 0$ around the circuit $P_1P_3P_4P_1$.   For the numerical value of the negative resistance both expressions give the formula $R_x = (1 + m)R_3 + R_2$ for $m = R_2/R_1$.

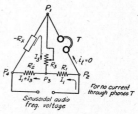

FIG. 239.—Determination of negative resistance.

For negative-resistance measurements it must be understood that a negative resistance is a current-carrying circuit and that blocking condensers and chokes, etc., must be used to keep direct and variable currents in the respective branches to which they belong.

[1] *Proc. I.R.E.*, **19**, 1948, 1931; F. HORTON and A. C. DAVIS, *Proc. Roy. Soc. (London)*, 23–43, 1920.

CHAPTER X

DETERMINATION OF HIGH-FREQUENCY POWER AND LOSSES

Ordinary wattmeters used for low-frequency work cannot be used for higher frequencies because of their inductive and capacity effects. For high frequency, special constructions[1] are needed. The simplest way of determining high-frequency power is by multiplying the effective resistance of the test apparatus by the square of the effective current. If it is difficult to obtain the effective resistance, as, for instance, for coils using iron cores, the rate of heat dissipation in the sample can be measured and the electrical equivalent in watts computed from it. The *watt* is the *power* dissipated in a resistance of 1 ohm when 1 amp flows through it. The *joule* is the *energy* (work) expended in 1 sec by a flow of 1 amp through 1 ohm. Therefore, the practical unit of the power is a derived unit. For smaller values of power the milliwatt (10^{-3} watt) and the microwatt (10^{-6} watt) are used, while for larger values the kilowatt (1000 watts) is the customary unit. In the electrostatic as well as in the electromagnetic c.g.s. system, the power is in ergs per second, and 1 watt is equal to 10^7 ergs/sec.

$$1 \text{ watt} = 1 \text{ volt} \times 1 \text{ amp} = 10^7 \text{ ergs/sec} \tag{1}$$

with the international watt = 1.0005×10^7 ergs/sec. Hence, if the electric vector $\mathcal{E}$ of a *direct* surface wave has at a certain place a forward tilt τ with respect to the normal to ground (see Sec. 134 and Fig. 237), the component $\mathcal{E} \cos (90 - \tau)$ is responsible for the energy which passes across each square centimeter of the surface of the ground. The power absorbed in c.g.s. units is then $(3 \times 10^{10} \, \mathcal{E}^2 \sin \tau)/(4\pi)$, and in the practical system $(3 \times 10^3 \, \mathcal{E}^2 \sin \tau)/(4\pi)$ watts. For circuit problems it is often convenient to express the numerical magnitudes of two powers P_1 and P_2 in logarithmic units (Sec. 36). This is especially useful for changes of voltages or currents due to successive changes in a circuit. The common logarithmic unit is the decibel. It is also known as the transmission unit (TU) and the number N_1 is given by

$$N_1 = 10 \log_{10} \frac{P_1}{P_2} \text{ decibel} \tag{2}$$

---

[1] M. Eastham (*Jahrb. d. draht.*, **11**, 266, 1916) gives a special design of a torsion wattmeter which uses the dynamometer principle. H. Chireix (Radio-électricité, *Bull. tech.* 57, 1924) describes a hot-wire-type wattmeter the deflection of which is due to the expansion of two hot wires.

Hence, a large power ratio can be expressed by a comparatively small value for N_1. Thus, if $P_1/P_2 = 10^6$, one finds $N_1 = 10 \times 6 = 60$ db. A unit ten times larger than the decibel is the bel. The natural logarithmic unit is the neper, given by

$$N_2 = 0.5 \log_\epsilon \frac{P_1}{P_2} \text{ nepers} \tag{3}$$

Then

$$10 \text{ TU} = 10 \text{ db} = 1 \text{ bel} = 1.15 \text{ nepers} \tag{4}$$

From (2) and (3) it can be seen that a power gain exists for $P_1/P_2 > 1$, and a loss for a value smaller than unity (see Table XV at the end of the book). A reliable method for power gain and loss measurement is described in Sec. 163. For a relation for the total iron loss in a laminated iron core, reference is made to the formula[1]

$$W = \frac{a\omega^2}{4m\rho} \frac{\alpha \sinh 2\,ma\alpha - \beta \sin 2\,ma\beta}{\cosh 2\,ma\alpha - \cos 2\,ma\beta} B^2 \tag{5}$$

$2a$ is the thickness of the laminations, $m = \sqrt{2\pi\mu\omega/\rho}$; $\alpha = \sqrt{1 + \sin \gamma}$; $\beta = \sqrt{1 - \sin \gamma}$; μ the permeability, ρ the resistivity, γ the hysteresis angle, $\omega/2\pi$ the frequency in cycles per second, and B the apparent flux density. The hysteresis angle γ is then conveniently determined with a 60-cycle current flowing through a reactance coil which uses a closed core made up of the laminations. At such a low frequency practically only the hysteresis losses play a part and the power factor $\cos \varphi = \sin \gamma$. It will be found that the angle γ for very thin laminations is larger than for thick laminations. For laminations used in high-frequency work the thickness $2a$ of the laminations is about 5×10^{-3} cm and even less (Hausrath foil used in Lorentz high-frequency apparatus). The resistivity is about 30 μ ohms/cm^3 and $\sin \gamma$ about 0.4.

136. The Cathode-ray Tube as a High-frequency Wattmeter.—If the voltage across the test sample which dissipates energy is applied to one deflection condenser and the drop across condenser C, which is proportional to the current of the test sample, is connected

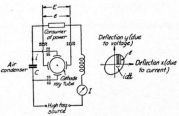

Fig. 240.—Cathode-ray watt-meter. (E and I are effective voltage and current of test sample and e and i, instantaneous values.)

across the other deflection condenser, a Lissajous-Ryan[2] power diagram is traced on the screen of the tube as shown in Fig. 240. The closed-area dia-

[1] LATOUR, M., *Proc. I.R.E.*, **18**, 220, 1920.

[2] H. J. Ryan used such traces for the first time for high-voltage measurements and J. P. Minton applied it to the determination of dielectric losses in transformer coils at commercial frequencies (60 cycles/sec).

gram is proportional to the voltages applied to the respective deflection condensers which are mounted at right angles to each other, and it represents
the power diagram. That the enclosed area A is proportional to the
average power for one period $T = 1/f$ can be seen from

$$\dot{y} = k_1 e; \quad dx = \frac{k_2}{C} i dt \quad \text{and} \quad dA = \frac{k_3}{C} e \, i dt \quad \text{for} \quad k_3 = k_1 k_2$$

Comparing $A = \dfrac{k_3}{C} \displaystyle\int_0^T e \, i dt$ with $W = \dfrac{1}{T} \displaystyle\int_0^T e \, i dt$, for $\dfrac{1}{k_3} = k$,

$$W = 10^{-3} k f A C \text{ watt} \tag{6}$$

if k is in square volts per square millimeter, f in kilocycles per second,
C in microfarads, and A in square millimeters. The constant k of the
circuit is found as follows. Suppose for a certain high-frequency current
I, which flows through the sample, the area $A = 50$ mm^2 is found by
means of a planimeter for a frequency $f = 500$ kc/sec and a condenser
$C = 0.002$ μf. Suppose 100 volts across the voltage-deflection condenser
produces the deflection[1] of 10 mm and 30 volts across the current quadrants the same deflection. Then 100 mm^2 area corresponds to 3000 volts^2
and $k = 3000/100 = 30$ volts^2/mm^2 area. The power read off from the
above diagram is then $W = 10^{-3} \times 30 \times 500 \times 0.002 \times 50 = 1.5$ watts.
It should be remembered that pure sinusoidal voltages of about the same
frequency should be used to determine the constant k if measurements
are made at very high frequencies. For the lower high-frequency range
direct voltages can be used to find k.

137. The Thermocross Bridge as a Wattmeter.—The arrangement
of Fig. 59 can also be used as a high-frequency wattmeter, if one voltage
terminal is connected to the bridge point B and the other through a high
resistance with the bridge point C. Bridge points A and D are used as
current terminals and the power computed from $W = d/k$, where d is the
deflection of the galvanometer in divisions or in millimeters (when a wall
galvanometer is used), and k denotes the bridge constant in deflection
units per square ampere. For a power factor cos φ, the deflection is
$d = kI \, i \cos \varphi = k \, W$. The constant k is then conveniently determined
by two known currents I_1 and I_2 which flow into the bridge at A and C,
respectively. The deflection is then $d_1 = k I_1 I_2$ if I_1 and I_2 are in phase
or if I_1 and I_2 denote direct currents. Then $k = d_1/(I_1 I_2)$.

138. Tube Wattmeters.—The circuit shown in Fig. 245 can also be
used to indicate power.[2] The determination is then as described in Sec.
146 in connection with Fig. 245. If E_g and E_p denote the effective volt-

---

[1] A cold Braun tube is used with less voltage sensitivity or a hot-cathode-ray tube
with indicated series condensers (dotted) in order to cover a wider power range.
External-deflection condensers can also be used for cutting down the sensitivity.

[2] TRAUTWEIN, F., *Inaug. Diss. Karlsruhe*, 16, 1921; H. M. TURNER and
F. T. McNAMARA, *Proc. I.R.E.*, **18**, 1743, 1930; E. O. PETERSON, 1926 (U. S. patent
1,586,553).

ages for the grid and plate circuits, the plate current I is a measure for $E_g E_p \cos \varphi$. One of the two voltages is made proportional to the current of the test sample whose wattage is to be found. The tube wattmeter of H. Hausrath[1] requires only two determinations instead of three. If in Fig. 245 for fixed-voltage amplitudes E_1 and E_2, on the grid and the plate, respectively, the plate current is I_1, and for the phase of E_1 displaced by 180 deg the plate current is I_2, one has $I_1 = k[E_2 + \mu E_1]$ and $I_2 = k[E_2 - \mu E_1]$ if the characteristic is linear. If E_g and E_p are the corresponding effective values, the relation $I_1{}^2 - I_2{}^2 = 4\mu k E_g E_p \cos \varphi = K E_g E_p \cos \varphi$ is obtained.

Figure 241 shows a tube wattmeter independently suggested by H. M. Turner and F. T. McNamara[2] as well as by E. O. Peterson.[2] Two tubes connected in push-pull act as a balanced modulator and, by using a microammeter μa, the circuit is suitable for measuring power in the microwatt range. The purpose of the balanced modulator is to keep undesired components from affecting the microammeter. In the case of the tube voltmeters described above, two input voltages with one proportional to the load voltage and the other to the load current are applied. The component which is proportional to the load current I is

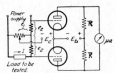

Fig. 241.—Tube wattmeter.

taken off as voltage e_2 across low resistances, while a suitable fraction e_1 of the load voltage is used as the other component. As can be seen from the figure, the sum of the instantaneous values e_1 and e_2 is impressed on one tube and the difference $e_1 - e_2$ on the other tube. Working as a modulator along the curved portion of the tube characteristic, one finds that the plate current is proportional to the square of the lumped tube voltage, that is, for $E = E_b - \mu E_c$, one has $i = k[E + \mu(e_1 + e_2)]^2$. The plate current in one plate branch is then $i_1 = k[E^2 + 2\mu E(e_1 + e_2) + \mu^2[e_1{}^2 + e_2{}^2] + 2\mu^2 e_1 e_2]$ and for the other plate branch $i_2 = k[E^2 + 2\mu E(e_1 - e_2) + \mu^2[e_1{}^2 + e_2{}^2] - 2\mu^2 e_1 e_2]$. For balanced circuits the reading of the microammeter is proportional to $(i_1 - i_2) = 4\mu k[E e_2 + \mu e_1 e_2]$. For a sinusoidal input current I which is φ deg out of phase with respect to the terminal voltage of the load, for $\theta = \omega t$ and $2\mu k = K$, the microammeter will read $i = K[2EE_2 \sin \theta + 2E_1 E_2 \sin \theta \sin (\theta + \varphi)]$. The first term cannot affect the meter, since the average value of $\sin \theta = 0$. Hence $i = 2KE_1 E_2 \sin \theta \sin (\theta + \varphi) = KE_1 E_2 [\cos \varphi - \cos (2\theta + \varphi)]$ where the average value of $\cos (2\theta + \varphi)$ is zero, and $i = KE_1 E_2 \cos \varphi$ which shows that the indication of the microammeter is proportional to the power dissipated in the load.

[1] TRAUTWEIN, F., *Inaug. Diss. Karlsruhe*, 16, 1921; H. M. TURNER and F. T. McNAMARA, *Proc. I.R.E.*, **18**, 1743, 1930; E. O. PETERSON, 1926 (U. S. patent 1,586,553).

[2] *Loc. cit.*

139. The Differential Transformer as a Wattmeter.—The test sample (in Fig. 242 an aerial) is connected in one branch and the variable standards in the other of the differential system. By means of C_s, L_s, and R_s, the circuit is balanced (noted by zero current in the secondary of the transformer). The power transferred to the aerial system is then

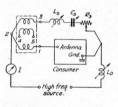

$W = 0.25RI^2$ if R in ohms denotes the balance setting of the variable resistance R_s and I the high-frequency current flowing for balance to the differential system. The differential system is then grounded as indicated in the figure. For small amounts of antenna power, the high-frequency resistance R_1 of L_s must be taken into account and W is computed from $0.25[R -$

Fig. 242.—Balanced-transformer wattmeter.

$R_1]$ I^2. For the determination of large powers the design of the differential transformer is much simpler. The two primary windings then are formed by the open loop 1-2-3 in the shape of a copper cylinder with a wide-open slit. The arcs 1-2 and 3-2 are symmetrically arranged with respect to another copper ring 4-5 made of litz.

140. Determination of Dielectric Losses.—In the cathode-tube circuit of Fig. 240, the test condenser represents the consumer and the inductor L_0 is omitted. The area A braced by the spot of the cathode ray is then proportional to the dielectric loss, since the vertical deflection is $y = k_1 E \sin \theta$ and the instantaneous horizontal deflection $x = k_2 I \cos (\theta + \varphi)$, since the condenser current for an air condenser leads its terminal voltage by 90 deg. The angle φ denotes the lead of the current of the test condenser with respect to its voltage. The area of the ellipse is then

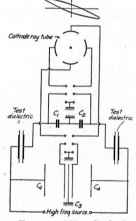

$$A = \int y dx = \int [k_1 E \sin \omega t] \, [-k_2\omega I \sin (\omega t + \varphi) dt]$$
$$= -\pi k_1 k_2 EI \cos \varphi$$

The area is proportional to the power dissipated in the condenser; that is, $A = K W$ where $K = \pi k_1 k_2$ and is found as described in Sec. 136. The circuit shown in Fig. 243 is more accurate since a symmetrical system is used. The disadvantage is that two test samples are required. The voltages impressed on the test samples act at the same time across the variable condenser C_4, C_4. This may be a space condenser which consists of hollow metal cylinders with rounded ends.

Fig. 243.—Cathode-ray tube for the determination of dielectric loss.

The circuit of Fig. 232 can also be used for the determination of dielectric losses. The test condenser C_x is connected in one branch and a variable-air condenser C_s with a short piece of slide wire R_s in series is connected in the other branch of the differential system. For balance the dielectric loss is $W = 0.25\rho I^2$. The balance by means of the small resistance R_s is best carried out with the scheme described in connection with Fig. 235. With respect to the balance adjustment indicated in Fig. 476 the expression $W = \dfrac{\rho(\omega C)^2}{1 + \rho^2\omega^2 C^2}E^2$ can be used for the study of dielectric loss W dependent upon the impressed voltage E. This voltage can be computed by means of the balance current $0.5I$. If the loss is to be found dependent upon the capacitance C_x, there is the formula $W = \rho\omega^2 C C_x E^2$ where C_x, strictly speaking, is theoretically slightly different from C (for details, see Sec. 3).

141. Determination of Iron and Coil Losses.—This method is conveniently carried out with the slow but reliable calorimeter method shown in Fig. 224 and described in Sec. 129. If ordinary air coils are to be tested, the calorimetric method can also be used, but the procedures described in Sec. 126 for the determination of high-frequency resistance are more rapid, since by a knowledge of the effective coil resistance it is only necessary to multiply the resistance by the square of the effective high-frequency current in order to obtain the loss of the coil. In the earlier days of radio the loss was usually determined from the logarithmic decrement.

CHAPTER XI

DETERMINATION OF LOGARITHMIC DECREMENT, POWER FACTOR, PHASE DIFFERENCE, AND SHARPNESS OF RESONANCE

The amplitudes of successive maxima are the same for ordinary tube oscillations, since enough power is being supplied to cover circuit losses. But if a condenser is charged and left to discharge its energy freely over a suitable inductance L of resistance R so that self-oscillations are possible, the successive amplitudes will become smaller and smaller, the decrease depending on both R and L. The successive amplitudes of the same polarity then decrease according to a logarithmic, straight-line, or other law. If I_1 and I_3 denote any two successive amplitudes of the same polarity for very pronounced spark damping, a linear law $D = (I_1 - I_3)/I_1$ can exist where D is known as the "linear decrement." Normally oscillations die off logarithmically and the logarithmic decrement per cycle is $\delta = \log_\epsilon \dfrac{I_1}{I_3} = 2.303 \log_{10} \dfrac{I_1}{I_3}$. The logarithmic decrement can be determined from any two instantaneous values of current which are one period out of phase. Hence

$$\frac{i_t}{i_{t+T}} = \frac{I\epsilon^{-\alpha t} \sin 2\pi ft}{I\epsilon^{-\alpha[t+T]} \sin 2\pi ft} \text{ and } \log_\epsilon \frac{i_t}{i_{t+T}} = \alpha T = \frac{R}{2L}T = \frac{R}{2fL} = \delta \quad (1)$$

from which $\alpha T = \delta$. The factor α is then known as the "damping factor" and denotes the decrease of oscillation intensity per second while δ is the decrease for a complete period. Taking $f = 1/(2\pi\sqrt{CL})$, one finds $\delta = \pi R\sqrt{C/L}$. For one cycle we also have

$$\frac{\text{Joulean heat loss}}{\text{Magnetic-field energy}} = \frac{\frac{1}{2}I^2RT}{\frac{1}{2}I^2L} = 2\alpha T = 2\delta \quad (2)$$

142. Relations between Logarithmic Decrement, Power Factor, Phase Difference, Sharpness of Resonance and Their Determination by Means of a Tube Generator.—Sharpness of resonance, phase difference, and power factor appear in many places in this text, since it seems more convenient to use them with sinusoidal currents instead of the decrement as used in the past. If φ denotes the angle between the terminal voltage of an apparatus and its current, $\cos \varphi$ is known as the "power factor." The angle $(90 - \varphi) = \Psi$ is known as the "phase difference" which plays an important part with condensers. If the quantities are expressed in the customary practical units, that is, ohms, henries, farads, and cycles per second, there is the interrelation

$$\delta = \frac{R}{2fL} = \pi R \sqrt{\frac{C}{L}} = \frac{\pi R}{\omega L} = \pi \cos \varphi = \pi \sin \Psi \tag{3}$$

This means that the power factor $\cos \varphi$ is equal to the logarithmic decrement divided by π. There is also $\cos \varphi = \sin \Psi \cong \Psi$, since Ψ is usually very small. The sharpness S of resonance is equal to $\omega L/R$ and $S = \frac{\pi}{\delta} = \frac{1}{\cos \varphi}$. Therefore it does not matter whether the power factor, the sharpness of resonance, or the logarithmic decrement per cycle is used; all express the same circuit quality.

The loss angle of a condenser is $\Psi = (90 - \varphi)$. It changes but little with the frequency and it is better to use it instead of the phase angle φ for this particular case. At 100 cycles/sec, the phase difference Ψ is seldom more than two to three times the value at 1 kc/sec. The changes are much smaller within the range of high frequencies. Since the sine Ψ is equal to the power factor of the condenser, there is often $\Psi \cong \cos \varphi$ where Ψ is expressed in radians (1 radian = $180/\pi$). Therefore, for small values of Ψ, the power factor can be used like Ψ.

According to Sec. 5 for an induced sinusoidal voltage E in a closed CLR circuit for any C setting, there is the current

$$I = \frac{I_r}{1 + jS\left[\rho - \dfrac{1}{\rho}\right]}$$

for the resonance current $I_r = E/R$, the sharpness of resonance $S = 2\pi f_r L/R$ where f_r is equal to the resonance frequency $1/(2\pi\sqrt{CL})$ and $\rho = f/f_r$ and f denotes the frequency for any C setting, while f_r corresponds to the resonance setting of the tuning condenser. Since $S = \pi/\delta$, one has

$$\delta = \pi \frac{\rho - \dfrac{1}{\rho}}{\sqrt{(I_r/I)^2 - 1}}$$

and with the approximation made in Sec. 5, according to Eqs. (41), (42), and (43) of that section,

$$\delta = 2\pi \frac{f_r - f}{f_r} \sqrt{\frac{I^2}{I_r^2 - I^2}} = 2\pi \frac{f_r - f}{f_r} \sqrt{\frac{d}{d_r - d}} \tag{4}$$

Hence, if the resonance deflection d_r and the deflection d for a slight detuning are noted, the logarithmic decrement δ per cycle can be computed with above formula. The radical in the formula becomes unity if the deflection d is equal to half of the resonance deflection. Such a method is convenient when the total decrement of any resonator (frequency meter, for instance) is to be determined and the power factor and the sharpness of resonance are computed from

$$\cos \varphi = \frac{2(f_r - f)}{f_r} \text{ and } S = \frac{1}{\cos \varphi}.$$

A similar determination consists in finding at first the resonance frequency f_r of the resonator by means of a loosely coupled driver and a frequency meter. The condenser of the resonator is then changed to values f_1 and f_2, one being higher and the other lower than f_r but such as to produce half-resonance deflection corresponding to $0.709 I_r$, and the decrement and the power factor are computed from

$$\delta = \pi \frac{f_2 - f_1}{f_r} \quad \text{and} \quad \cos \varphi = \frac{f_2 - f_1}{f_r}$$

143. Determination of the Decrement and Power Factor of Individual Apparatus.—If, for instance, the decrement of a condenser is to be determined, the method of Figs. 232, 233, 234, and 235 can be used. If C_s and R_s denote the setting of the equivalent air condenser with a standard resistance R_s in series in order to account for the losses (phase angle) of the actual condenser, the decrement is computed from $\delta = 1973 \times 10^{-5} C_s R_s f$ where f is in kilocycles per second, C_s in microfarads, and R_s in ohms.

Example.—Suppose, for the final balance in Fig. 235, the current $I/2 = 0.0045$ amp flows through the test condenser and $C_s = 0.00192$ μf and $R_s = 0.31 \Omega$. The frequency $f = 770$ kc/sec. The power lost in the condenser is therefore $0.0045^2 \times 0.31$ watt and the decrement $\delta = 1973 \times 10^{-5} \times 0.00192 \times 0.31 \times 770 = 0.0091$.

144. The Cathode-ray Tube as a Power-factor Meter.—As indicated in Fig. 244, the area of the E, I trace is $A_\varphi = \int_0^{2\pi} y dx = KEI \cos \varphi$. For a sinusoidal current there is generally the indicated inclined ellipse. If the power factor $\cos \varphi = 1$, there is the dotted ellipse, that is, an area $A_0 = KEI$. If a' and b' are the main axes of the resonance ellipse and a and b the principal axes for any phase angle φ between E and I, $\cos \varphi = A_\varphi / A_0 = (ab)/(a'b')$. Therefore the determination requires three photographic exposures (or traces by hand on the rear face of the tube).

1. The inclined ellipse is photographed which gives the actual conditions of the test sample, since the respective quadrature deflections (see also Fig. 240) are proportional to terminal voltage E and the current I through the sample.

2. Only voltage E acts, giving the linear trace $2a'$.

3. Only the current I acts on the other deflection quadrant, giving the linear trace $2b'$.

4. The axes a and b are then drawn and $\cos \varphi$ is computed from $ab/a'b'$.

145. The Thermocross Bridge as a Phase Meter.—If two sinusoidal currents I and i flow in the circuit of Fig. 59, the galvanometer will give a deflection $d = kIi \cos \varphi$. The method consists of using at first two in-phase currents I_1 and i through the respective terminals $A\ D$ and $B\ C$. The deflection is then $d_1 = kI_1i \cos 0 = k_1I_1$. Hereafter the actual current I_2 is made to flow in place of I_1, and the deflection $d_2 = kI_2i \cos \varphi$ $= k_2I_2$ is noted. The power factor is found from $\cos \varphi = k_2/k_1$, where $k_1 = d_1/I_1$ and $k_2 = d_2/I_2$.

Fig. 244.—Power ellipse

Example.—$I_1 = 0.25$ amp and $I_2 = 0.1$ amp with the corresponding deflections $d_1 = 75$ mm and $d_2 = 26.5$ mm. Hence $k_1 = 75/0.25 = 300$ and $k_2 = 26.5/0.1 = 265$ and $\cos \varphi = 265/300 = 0.8825$ and $\varphi = 28°3'20''$.

146. Tube-phase Meters.—The circuit of Fig. 245 gives a means of determining the phase φ between two sinusoidal currents. One current

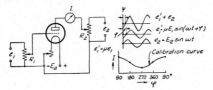

FIG. 245.—Tube phasometer.

affects the grid and the other the plate circuit. The corresponding voltages are e_1 and e_2. By means of the potentiometers R_1 and R_2, suitable voltages are impressed on the grid and the plate. Both voltages affect the plate current I which also depends upon the phase displacement. The tube is calibrated by means of known alternating grid and plate voltages, and I plotted against the known phase angle φ. If the tube is then used as the phasometer, the same grid and plate voltages are to be adjusted by means of the potentiometers R_1 and R_2. The phase angle φ is then read off from the calibration curve for the value I obtained. The same voltages are obtained by having only e_1 acting and noting the plate current, or by having only e_2 acting and noting the plate current as in any direct-reading tube voltmeter. The respective plate currents must be the same as the values $I = I_1$ and $I = I_2$ obtained when the respective calibration voltages act independently. The push-pull modulator circuit of Fig. 241 described in Sec. 138 can also be used as a phasometer. The same circuit, but as in Fig. 246, then gives a very

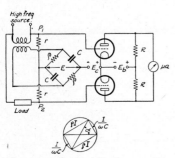

FIG. 246.—Push-pull phase meter.

sensitive meter for the measuring of small voltages across points P_1 and P_2, since by means of the well-known phase shifting bridge $\rho C \rho C$, the phase α between the auxiliary voltage E_0 and the outgoing voltage E of the same amplitude can be adjusted to a value which brings E in phase with the drops across $P_1 P_2$.

147. Determination of Phase Angle by Means of a Recurrent Network.—In the arrangement of Fig. 247 a long single-layer coil is connected at equal distances through condensers to a common conductor. If a sufficient number of sections is chosen, the voltage impressed at one end

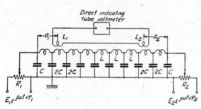

FIG. 247.—Determination of phase difference by means of a recurrent network.

will give practically zero-voltage effect at the other end of the coil with respect to the common conductor. Suppose a voltage $E_1 \sin(\omega t + \varphi_1)$ is impressed at one end and a voltage $E_2 \sin(\omega t + \varphi_2)$ at the other end, and the potentiometer sliders along R_1 and R_2 are so adjusted that equal voltage amplitudes are impressed. Then if two equal small coils L_1 and L_2 are moved within the long coil until the indicated tube voltmeter gives no response, the difference $(a_2 - a_1)$ is a measure for the phase difference $\varphi_2 - \varphi_1$. The same method can also be used to calibrate a recurrent network for phases. The calibration holds for a certain frequency band only.

CHAPTER XII

FERROMAGNETIC MEASUREMENTS

If a coil uses an iron core, copper and iron losses are dealt with A portion of the former are the same as for direct current if the increase of resistance due to iron losses, dielectric losses, and skin-effect action of the conductor is subtracted. This is evident because the heat loss in the iron core requires a certain amount of current flow through the coil. The core losses are divided into hysteresis and eddy-current losses in the iron. The hysteresis loss can be computed from the area of the hysteresis loop. For test samples it is often of advantage to have the iron core occupy about 70 per cent of the average area of the coil, since then about a 1 per cent change in the terminal voltage occurs due to the air space which is left within the coil. This is evident if it is realized that the voltage due to the cross section of air is displaced about one-quarter period with respect to the voltage due to the cross section of iron.

For ferromagnetic relations in coils there are analogous expressions as in the ordinary electric circuit. The magnetic permeability μ corresponds to the electric conductivity σ, the magnetomotive force (m.m.f.) to the electromotive force (e.m.f.), the magnetic flux density B to the current density i, the magnetic reluctance (magnetic resistance) R_m to the ohmic resistance R, and the magnetic flux Φ to the current I. If H denotes the magnetic-field strength in gilberts per centimeter, A_{cm^2} the magnetic as well as the electric cross section, and l cm the length for magnetic as well as for the analogous electric circuit, e.m.f./$I = R$ and m.m.f./$\Phi = R_m$. The first relation is in volts, amperes, and ohms and for the second expression the m.m.f. is in gilberts, Φ in maxwells, and R_m in oersteds. For N turns with the magnetizing current I_m, one has m.m.f. $= Hl = 0.4\pi N I_m$ gilbert $= N I_m$ amp-turns. For the magnetic reluctance $R_m = l/(\mu A)$, and there is the analogy $\mu = \dfrac{\Phi/A}{\text{m.m.f.}/l} = \dfrac{B^{(\text{gauss})}}{H^{(\text{gilbert/cm})}}$ and $\sigma^{(\text{mhos})} = \dfrac{I/A}{\text{e.m.f.}/l} = \dfrac{i^{(\text{amp/cm}^2)}}{\text{volt/cm}}$.

Reference is made to page 239 and Fig. 192 for the incremental permeability and loops superimposed on hysteresis loops. In many ferromagnetic determinations, the change in magnetic flux must be measured. There are essentially two methods for doing this. In one method the change in flux is noted in a relatively short air gap. The other method, which is more customary for high-frequency work, is based upon the use of a separate coil (search coil) surrounding the iron core and finding the value of the time integral of the voltage induced across the terminals of the separate coil which may be the secondary if a transformer core is to be tested. For static iron measurements, the first throw of a

311

ballistic galvanometer is used as an integrating instrument.   For high-frequency work it is more convenient to integrate by means of a purely electrical circuit.[1]   The integrating circuit then consists of combinations of capacitance, resistance, and inductance, since such elements can be used to obtain the cyclic integral of a current and therefore also that of a voltage.   If (as done with a cathode ray oscillograph) the hysteresis loop is traced, the terminals of an exploring coil surrounding the test core are connected across a series combination of a condenser and a resistance. This is followed up in more detail with one of the methods in the next section.

148. Determination of Magnetic Hysteresis and of B and H.—If, as in Fig. 248, an open core consisting of a bundle of straight iron wires is to be tested, the stray field which is proportional to the magnetic induction will cause an upward and downward deflection, while a suitable voltage E_1 which is proportional to the current I passing through the coil will by means of the deflection condenser C_1, C_1 produce

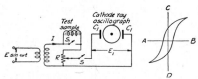

FIG. 248.—Cathode-ray oscillograph for tracing the hysteresis loop for an open-core sample.

a to and fro deflection proportional to the magnetic field.   Hence, if the switch S is closed, the indicated hysteresis loop is traced by means of the fluorescent spot of the cathode ray. The axis AB is obtained by short-circuiting the test coil with switch S_1. The axis CD is obtained by opening S_1 and S.   The area of the hysteresis loop for such a determination may be taken as an approximate measure for the hysteresis loss per cycle since the stray field does not give exactly the true conditions all along the open core (stray field is nonuniform owing to the demagnetizing effects of the poles).   If a cathode-ray tube with two internal deflection condensers is employed, the deflection condenser which is not used, and in space quadrature with respect to C_1C_1, must be short-circuited and connected to the grounded plate C_1 of the deflection condenser C_1, C_1.   Figure 249 shows an arrangement where, for more accurate work, a closed core is used. The respective quadrature deflections are produced by symmetrical deflection coils L_1, L_3 and L_2, L_4.   A large air choke L_0 with a large time constant is used, so that the current through coils L_2L_4 is proportional to the flux density B.   The current through L_1L_3 is again a measure of the magnetizing force.   In the circuit of Fig. 250 an exploring coil S is used to produce the B deflection by means of one deflection condenser and deflection coils again to produce the H component of the hysteresis

[1] KAUFMANN, W., *Z. Physik*, **5**, 316, 1921; W. KAUFMANN and E. POKAR, *Physik. Z.*, **26**, 597, 1925; E. L. BOWLES, *J. Am. Inst. Elec. Eng.*, **42**, 849, 1923; O. E. CHARLTON and J. E. JACKSON, *J. Am. Inst. Elec. Eng.*, **44**, 1220, 1925; K. KRUEGER and H PLENDL, *Z. Hochfreq.*, **27**, 155, 1926; J. B. JOHNSON, *Bell System Tech. J.*, **8**, 286, 1929

loop to be traced. It is necessary to have R large in comparison to $1/(\omega C)$ and the number N of the turns of the exploring coil must be such that i_2 is small and cannot react back appreciably on i_1. The instantaneous voltage across the integrating condenser C is

$$e_1 = 10^{-8} \int \frac{NA}{RC} \frac{dB}{dt} = \frac{NA}{RC} B \times 10^{-8} \text{ volts}$$

if A denotes the cross-sectional area of the sample and B the flux density. The voltage e_1 is amplified to a value e_2, producing a deflection d cm/volt along the B-axis of the loop. A knowledge of the amplification is not

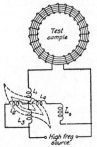

FIG. 249.—Employs deflection coils for tracing hysteresis loop for a closed-core sample.

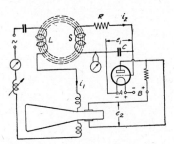

FIG. 250.—Tracing of magnetizing loop.

required, since the calibration constant can be found by noting the deflection d cm for a known voltage e_1 across the input of the amplifier. Hence any ordinate d_x (parallel with the B-axis) on the traced hysteresis loop then gives a flux density

$$B_x = \frac{d_x B C}{d N A} \text{ gauss} \tag{1}$$

The calibration for the H ordinates is obtained by measuring the deflection produced by a known direct current i_1 and the magnetizing field of the test sample is computed from the dimensions of the coil for the current reading i_1.

149. Determination of Flux Density and Permeability.—The above methods using the cathode-ray oscillograph give the flux density and the permeability by means of B/H, since H can also be found from the trace and a separate calibration if the H deflection only is produced. If the substitution method of Fig. 251 is used, the test sample is compared with a standard variometer L_s in series with a standard resistance by connecting either the sample or the standard into a resonator. The sample should not contain too much iron so that the effective inductance L_x does not come out unreasonably high and the iron must occupy almost the entire space within the turns, so that L_x depends mostly upon the permeability of the core to be tested. At first the circuit containing L_x, R_x is tuned by means of the variable condenser and the variable inductance (which always stays in the circuit) and the resonance current I_r is noted. Next, the test sample is removed and the standards are used instead. The settings of the standard variometer and resistance are varied until for a setting L_s and R_s the same resonance current I_r is again obtained. Then $L_x = L_s$ and

$$B_{max} = 1.415 \frac{L_s \times 10^8}{N\,A} I_r \text{ lines of induction per cm}^2 \text{ (in gauss)} \qquad (2)$$

if the inductance is in henries, the resonance current I_r in amperes, the cross section of the iron in square centimeters, and N denotes the number

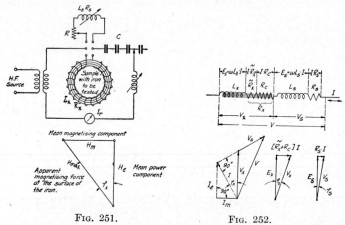

Fig. 251.

Fig. 252.

Fig. 251.—Substitution method for finding B and μ. (Cos φ_x is power factor of sample.)

Fig. 252.—Voltmeter method (R_s, high-frequency resistance of the air coil; $\tilde{R}_x$, high-frequency resistance of the test coil; R_x, apparent resistance of test coil; R_c, apparent increase of high-frequency resistance due to the iron core; I_c, power component of coil current; I_m, magnetizing component; φ_s, phase angle of air coil; φ_x, phase angle of test coil; cos φ_x, power factor of test coil).

of turns. The permeability is then $\mu = B_{max}/H_{max}$ and the resulting magnetic-field strength H_{max} of the sample given by

$$H_{max} = \frac{4\pi}{10}\sqrt{2}\,\frac{NI_m}{l} \text{ gilberts/cm} \qquad (3)$$

if the mean length l of the magnetic path is in centimeters. The magnetizing component I_m of the total current I_r passing through the sample is

$$I_m = I_r \frac{\omega L_s}{\sqrt{(R_. + R_s)^2 + (\omega L_s)^2}}$$

so that

$$H_{max} = \frac{11.14\ NfL_sI_r}{\sqrt{(R + R_s)^2 + (\omega L_s)^2}}$$

and the effective permeability

$$\mu = 1.27 \times 10^7 \frac{\sqrt{(R + R_s)^2 + (2\pi f L_s)^2}}{A N^2 f} \tag{3a}$$

where l is in centimeters, A in square centimeters, f in cycles per second, the resistance in ohms, and L_s in henries. The maximum field strength H_{max} which exists at the surface of the core consists of a watt and a perpendicular wattless component which magnetizes. Since the phase as well as the amplitude of the magnetizing force are different at different places within the core, H_{max} must be regarded as an average value.

A voltmeter method can also be used if the arrangement of Fig. 252 is employed. The coil L_x then contains the test core and the air coil L_s in series has enough turns so that its terminal voltage for the desired current I is about equal to that of the test sample. The measured coil current I through L_s then lags practically one-quarter period the terminal voltage of the air coil. L_s must be known (measured with any of the high-frequency methods of Chap. VII), as well as its effective resistance R_s. The high-frequency voltage V impressed on the system must be sinusoidal. The action of R_s can be neglected in comparison with ωL_s. For the desired high-frequency current I the terminal voltage across the air coil is then (vectorially) $E_s = \omega L_s I = V_s - I R_s \cong V_s$. The inductance of the coil is

$$L_s = \frac{0.4 \times 10^{-8} \pi N^2 A}{l}$$

where L_s is in henries, the effective cross section of the coil A in square centimeters, and the mean magnetic length l in centimeters, for N turns. The counter e.m.f. of the air coil is then $E_s = \omega \dfrac{0.4\pi 10^{-8} N^2 A I}{l} = \omega N H A$

for $H = \dfrac{0.4\pi N I}{l}$ gilbert/cm where I is in amperes. For the test sample of effective cross section A' cm^2 (which has about the same over-all coil area as L_s) the number of magnetic lines of induction are increased by $\mu A'$ if μ denotes the high-frequency permeability. The correct reactive voltage E_x of the test coil is then $E_x = \omega N H[A + \mu A']$. The magnitude of E_x can be obtained by geometrical subtraction of the voltage drop in $\tilde{R}_s$ and its apparent increase R_c due to the iron losses. The ratio $E_s/E_x = A/(A + \mu A')$ gives the effective permeability

$$\mu = \frac{A}{A'}\left[\frac{E_x}{E_s} - 1\right] \tag{4}$$

for any frequency $f = E_s/(2\pi L_s I)$. The graphical solution in Fig. 252 shows that the voltages E_x and E_s can also be computed from

$$E_x = \sqrt{V_x{}^2 - [I(\tilde{R}_x + R_c)]^2} \text{ and } E_s = \sqrt{V_s{}^2 - (IR_s)^2} \qquad (5)$$

where R_s, R_c, and R_x are found by suitable methods described in Chap. IX, and V and V_s by means of a tube voltmeter.

There is also a volt-ampere meter method. The terminal voltage E and the current I passing through the coil with the test core are measured. There are then the formulas

$$\mu = \frac{B_{\max}}{H_{\max}}; \ H_{\max} = \frac{0.4\pi\sqrt{2}NI}{l} \text{ gilberts/cm and } B_{\max} =$$

$$\frac{10^8 E}{4.44 f N A} \text{ gauss} \qquad (6)$$

This method is the oldest procedure and rather inaccurate, since no distinction is made between resulting and magnetizing current.

150. Determination of the Power Factor of a Coil with an Iron Core.— The circuit in Fig. 252 is used. From the measurements of the terminal voltages, V, V_x, and V_s by means of a tube voltmeter, the voltage triangle is constructed. The current vector I is then drawn perpendicular to vector V_s, since for the air coil at high frequencies practically 90-deg phase displacement exists between the terminal voltage and the current. The cosine between V_x and I is the power factor; that is, $\cos \varphi_x = I/V_x$. From the vector diagram,

$$V^2 = I^2 + \{V_s + \sqrt{V_x{}^2 - I^2}\}^2 \text{ that is, } I = \frac{V}{2V_x}\sqrt{V^2 - 4V_x{}^2}$$

If the air coil is chosen such that its terminal voltage $V_s = V_x$, the power factor can also be computed from

$$\cos \varphi_x = \frac{V\sqrt{V^2 - 4V_x{}^2}}{2V_x{}^2} \qquad (7)$$

151. Determination of the Magnetizing and Power Current of a Coil with an Iron Core.—Figure 252 gives the circuit. A sinusoidal voltage V is impressed on the series combination. The test core is inserted in one coil and the number of turns of the air coil chosen so that V_s is about equal to V_x for the desired high-frequency current. The watt and wattless components can then be determined with a fair degree of accuracy. By means of a tube voltmeter the voltage triangle $V_x V_s V$ is obtained, where the current vector I is again perpendicular to V_s. For the measured current I the length of I gives the scale for the current triangle. The watt component I_e which is mostly due to the iron loss is relatively small and is parallel with V_x. The perpendicular vector I_m then gives the magnetizing current where, for the millimeter as the unit for the length of the current vectors, the current scale in amperes is $I_{\text{amp}}/I_{\text{mm}}$.

152. Notes on the Determination of Core Losses.—The arrangement shown in Fig. 253 may be used if no very accurate results are required.

The total loss of the coil is $W = E_{\min} \times I_{\max}$. A circuit of this type can also be used to determine the permeability.[1] If the circuit of Fig. 251 is used, the test sample is first inserted and the circuit tuned by means of the coupling and the condenser setting, in order to obtain the desired resonance current which is equal to the current for which the coil is to be tested. The same current setting is repeated with the standard variometer and variable resistance in the circuit instead of L_x, R_x until the same resonance current flows again. The total circuit loss is then $I_r{}^2[R + R_s]$. The process of measurement is repeated but without the iron core. If a balance setting $R = R_1$ is obtained, then $R_1 + R_s$ must be equal to the total circuit resistance and $(R + R_s) - (R_1 + R_s)$ the resistance due to core loss only. Therefore the core loss is

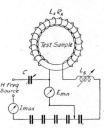

FIG. 253.—Simple but less accurate method for the determination of iron losses.

$(R - R_1)I_r{}^2$. In the method of Fig. 254 the test sample R_x, L_x is connected across terminals 1 and 2 and the resonance current I_2 and generator current I_1 noted for the setting $C = C_1$ and with the standard resistance R at its zero value. Terminals 1 and 2 are short-circuited and C as well as R is varied until for values $C = C_2$ and $R = R$ the same exciter current I_1 and the same resonance current I_2 is again obtained. The loss resistance R_x is then equal to R and to the total coil loss equal to $I_2{}^2R$. The correctness can be seen from the impedance values. For the first determination $Z = R_x + j\left[\omega L_x - \dfrac{1}{\omega C_1}\right]$ and for the second $Z = R + \dfrac{j}{\omega C_2}$.

From this relation it can also be seen that

$$L_x = \frac{1}{\omega^2}\left[\frac{1}{C_1} - \frac{1}{C_2}\right]$$

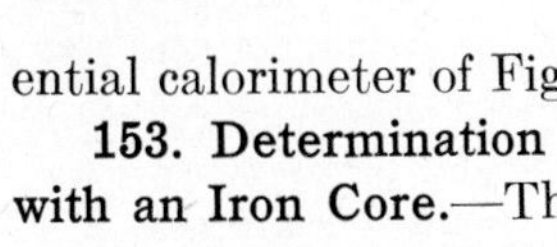

FIG. 254.—Determination of the resistance and reactive components of a choke coil.

with L_x in henries, C_1 and C_2 in farads, and $\omega/2\pi$ in cycles per second.

The slowest but most accurate procedure of determining core loss is by means of the differential calorimeter of Fig. 224. It is fully described in Sec. 129.

153. Determination of Reactance and Effective Resistance of Coils with an Iron Core.—The method described in connection with Fig. 254 gives the value of L_x and the reactance as $X = \dfrac{C_2 - C_1}{\omega C_1 C_2}$, if the capacitances are in farads, $\omega/2\pi$ in cycles per second, and X in ohms. The

---

[1] E. F. W. Alexanderson (*J. Am. Inst. Elec. Eng.*, **30**, 2433, 1911) with a circuit of this kind investigated ferromagnetic properties up to 200 kc/sec. L. T. Wilson (*Proc. I.R.E.*, **9**, 56, 1921) followed up the work from 100 to 1500 kc/sec; N. W. McLachlan (*J. Inst. Elec. Eng. (London)*, **54**, 480, 1916) investigated properties up to 1000 kc/sec with arc oscillations and the voltmeter method.

resistance is $R_x = R$. In the same way, the effective reactance and resistance experienced with an interstage transformer or any other transformer can be found. The primary of the transformer is then connected to terminals 1 and 2 of Fig. 254, while the secondary is con-

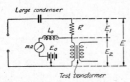

Large condenser

Test transformer

FIG. 255.—Test of an iron-core transformer.

nected to a tube as in the actual circuit and the determination carried on as is described in connection with Fig. 254. Another procedure is by means of the well-known triple-voltage method shown in Fig. 255, where the voltages E_1, E_2, and E are measured with the tube voltmeter. The proper direct-current is superimposed by means of the battery E_0. The solution is then as for Fig. 252. The tube voltmeter must be such that a voltage due to a direct current cannot affect it. Either a sufficient negative bias is used to just balance the direct-current drop or a grid condenser must be used.

154. Determination of Slope Inductance.—This inductance plays a part in large choke coils, interstage transformers, and the like. Hence, for the determination, the method described in Sec. 152 in connection with Fig. 254 can be used. For quick work where not much accuracy is required, the voltmeter method of Fig. 255 or Fig. 256 can be used. The resistance R is adjusted until, for the desired direct-current excitation of the choke coil L_x, the same alternating voltages $E_1 = E_2$ are noted. Then for the negligible coil resistance $L_x = R/2\pi f$ if L_x is in henries, R in ohms, and f in cycles per second. The coils L_0 in Fig. 256 are auxiliary choke coils to reduce the alternating current as much as possible in this branch. The tube volt-

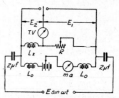

FIG. 256.—Determination of slope inductance of coils with an iron core.

meter must again use a grid condenser or sufficient negative bias, respectively, to eliminate the effect of the superimposed drop due to the direct current. Reference is made to Sec. 117 for the determination of the slope inductance of very large coils.

CHAPTER XIII

TUBE MEASUREMENTS

The characteristic of a vacuum tube generally depends upon the relative position of the electrodes, their material and potential, and the degree of the vacuum. The mean free distance d_m plays an important part in the vacuum. It is the average path between collisions for any given condition of a gas. By very high vacuum is understood such a low pressure of a gas, for instance, 10^{-6} mm of mercury, that the mean free distance d_m is so large compared with the distances between electrodes that for normal operating potentials practically no collisions can take place. The mean free distance of a molecule of a certain gas can be computed from

$$d_m = 12.86 \frac{\nu}{p} \sqrt{\frac{T}{M}} \tag{1}$$

where ν is the viscosity of the gas in c.g.s. units, p is the pressure in millimeters, T the absolute temperature ($273+$ centigrade temperature), and M the molecular weight. Hence helium at atmospheric pressure ($p = 760$ mm) with a molecular weight of 4.0 has at room temperature ($T = 293°$ K) a mean free distance of only 25.2×10^{-6} cm, for $p = 1$ mm of 19.2×10^{-3} cm, and for $p = 10^{-6}$ mm 19,200 cm. For nitrogen and oxygen at atmospheric pressure with $M = 28$ and 32, respectively, one finds 9.3×10^{-6} and 9.9×10^{-6} cm and for a vacuum as good as $p = 10^{-6}$ mm, $d_m = 7100$ and 7600 cm. For air under a fairly good vacuum—and better—nitrogen plays the most important part; hence for $p = 10^{-6}$ mm the value of d_m is 7100 cm as for nitrogen and for $p = 1$ mm it would be 7.1×10^{-3}. When dealing with mean free distances of an electron, it is greater than for the atoms themselves, since the electron is very small compared with any of the atoms which may occur, and the mean free distance can be computed from

$$d_\epsilon = \frac{1}{\pi N D^2} \tag{2}$$

if D denotes the diameter of the atom in centimeters and N the number of atoms per cubic centimeter. Hence, for high-speed electrons, d_ϵ is about 40,000 cm, if the air under a bulb is exhausted to 10^{-6} mm of mercury. In spite of such low pressure, there would still be about several billions of molecules left for each cubic centimeter of space. The speed of the electron must be taken into consideration in the above case, since it has mass by virtue of its motion and the effective mass ascribed to energy W is

$$M_e = \frac{W}{c^2} \tag{3}$$

if c is the velocity of light. This relation is the outcome of Einstein's law which shows that electromagnetic energy has momentum and acceleration. This relation plays an important part in electron tubes. For instance, if a cathode-ray tube is used for very high accelerating voltages, for example, 50 kv (Fig. 36), the formula for the deflection PP_1 would not be $PP_1 = \dfrac{b\ lE}{2aV}$, where E is the voltage applied across the deflection plates and V denotes the accelerating voltage, but

$$PP_1 = \frac{b\ lE}{aV}\ \frac{V + c^2\dfrac{m_0}{q}}{V + 2c^2\dfrac{m_0}{q}} \tag{4}$$

where all geometrical dimensions are in centimeters, m_0 denotes the mass of a slowly moving electron, and q its charge. Therefore $c^2\dfrac{m_0}{q} = \dfrac{9 \times 10^{20}}{1.77 \times 10^7} = 5.08 \times 10^{13}$ e.m.u. For $V = 50$ kv accelerating voltage,

$$\frac{V + c^2\dfrac{m_0}{q}}{V + 2c^2\dfrac{m_0}{q}} = \frac{0.5 \times 10^5 + 5.08 \times 10^5}{0.5 \times 10^5 + 10.16 \times 10^5} = 0.53$$

and the formula for the dimensions PP_1, a, b, and l in centimeters, the deflection and accelerating voltage E and V in volts, is

$$PP_1 = \frac{0.53blE}{aV},$$

while in the lower voltage range V is negligibly small compared to c^2m/q and for twice this value, the factor 0.5 is obtained, confirming the formula of Sec. (24). Therefore, it can be seen that if very high accelerating voltages exist, as, for instance, used to produce rays passing through a Lenard window (see page 84), it is necessary to use formula (4), that is, to utilize the Einstein-Lorentz equation

$$m_0c^2\left[\frac{1}{\sqrt{1 - \beta^2}} - 1\right] = \frac{Vq}{300} \tag{5}$$

which gives the effective mass[1] m_e of an electron which is

---

[1] The energy given to an electron in falling through a difference of potential V is

$$\int_0^v v\ d[m_ev] = m_0c^2\left[\frac{1}{\sqrt{1 - \beta^2}} - 1\right] = \frac{qV}{300}$$

According to H. A. Lorentz (*Verst. Kon. Akad. u. Wet. Amsterdam*, 1904) one must also

$$m_e = \frac{m_0}{\sqrt{1 - \beta^2}} = \frac{8.99 \times 10^{-28}}{\sqrt{1 - \left[\dfrac{v}{2.9982 \times 10^{10}}\right]^2}} \tag{6}$$

if m_e in grams, v denotes the velocity of the electron in centimeters per second due to the accelerating voltage V in volts. Table XI shows that, for accelerating voltages V higher than 300 volts, errors of more than one-half of 1 per cent occur if the nonrelativistic velocity $v = 0.6 \times 10^8 \sqrt{V^{\text{(volts)}}}$ cm/sec according to $0.5 m_0 v^2 = Vq/300$ were used. For accelerating voltages higher than 8000 volts the error would be larger than 1 per cent and if a tube is operated at 50 kv the nonrelativistic velocity would give $v = 0.6 \times 10^8 \sqrt{5 \times 10^4} = 1.34 \times 10^{10}$ cm/sec which if compared with the corresponding relativistic velocity of Table XI (which gives 1.24×10^{10} cm/sec) shows that an error would exist as high as 8.1 per cent if the

distinguish between longitudinal and transverse mass. With respect to the ratio of the charge q to the mass m_0 of an electron, it has been determined with methods observing the effects of *free* electrons, such as occurring, for instance, in cathode-ray tubes (H. Busch, *Physik. Z.*, **23**, 438, 1922; F. Wolf, *Ann. Physik.*, **83**, 849, 1927) or by means of spectroscopic measurements where one deals with *bound* electrons *within* atoms. Methods using high-frequency fields are due to E. Wiechert, *Wied. Ann.*, **69**, 739, 1899, and E. L. Chaffee, *Phys. Rev.*, **34**, 474, 1912; F. Kirchner, *Physik. Z.*, **30**, 773, 1929 (using more or less Chaffee's procedure and C. T. Perry and E. L. Chaffee, *Phys. Rev.*, **36**, 904, 1930). E. Wiechert carried on direct measurements of the velocity of cathode rays by timing their travel between two points by means of *damped* high-frequency oscillations. In the method of Chaffee, the cathode rays (electrons) were accelerated by means of potentials from 10 to 20 kv. *Undamped* high-frequency oscillations are used in order to determine the velocity directly by timing the passage of electrons between two localized electric fields (transverse high-frequency fields, using two deflection condensers of a specially designed cathode-ray tube). The two deflection condensers were in the Perry-Chaffee experiments 75 cm apart. The velocity obtained, together with the expression for the energy imparted to the electron while falling through a measurable potential difference, gives the ratio q/m_0 which in the Perry-Chaffee experiments came out

$$\frac{q}{m_0} = (1.761 \pm 0.001)10^7 \text{ e.m. c.g.s. units}$$

and is in agreement with the values obtained by spectroscopic methods, as, for instance, obtained by H. D. Babcock (*Astrophys. J.*, **58**, 149, 1923, and **69**, 43, 1929) who finds

$$\frac{q}{m_0} = (1.706 \pm 0.0012)10^7 \text{ e.m. c.g.s. units}$$

as a mean value for certain selected lines in the spectra of chromium, zinc, cadmium, and titanium. The value is not in agreement with the most accurate previous values obtained for free electrons, for instance $(1.769 \pm 0.002)10^7$ as found by Wolf, *loc. cit.* In the Perry-Chaffee paper a possible explanation is given for the disagreement between the values of q/m_0 obtained by methods using either free or bound electrons, respectively.

TABLE XI

V, in volts	$\beta = \dfrac{v}{2.9982 \times 10^{10}}$	Relativistic velocity $v \times 10^{10}$ cm/sec	V, volts	β	$v \times 10^{10}$ cm/sec	V, volts	β	$v \times 10^{10}$ cm/sec
1	0.001984	0.00595	1,000	0.06267	0.188	60,000	0.4474	1.34
10	0.006266	0.0188	2,000	0.08849	0.265	80,000	0.5037	1.51
20	0.008875	0.0266	3,000	0.1082	0.324	100,000	0.5486	1.64
40	0.01255	0.0376	5,000	0.1393	0.418	200,000	0.6966	2.09
60	0.01537	0.0461	8,000	0.1754	0.526	300,000	0.7777	2.33
80	0.01774	0.0532	10,000	0.1956	0.586	400,000	0.8289	2.49
100	0.01984	0.0595	20,000	0.2227	0.817	500,000	0.8638	2.59
200	0.02806	0.0841	30,000	0.3293	0.987	600,000	0.8888	2.66
300	0.03436	0.103	40,000	0.3751	1.12	800,000	0.9215	2.76
500	0.04434	0.133	50,000	0.4138	1.24	1,000,000	0.9416	2.82

Einstein relation were not used.   In high-voltage tubes, as experimented with by G. Breit, M. A. Tuve, L. R. Hapstad, and O. Dahl,[1] the relativity relation must be used, since according to Table XI for one million volts almost the velocity of light is reached.

One may distinguish between tube measurements for the determination of fundamental tube properties and measurements dealing with tube factors as utilized in high-frequency engineering.   Methods for the former are considered first because they have a direct bearing on the methods used in determining tube characteristics which should always be obtained for the actual tube condition.   Several methods are based on bridge methods such as originally suggested by J. M. Miller[2] and by S. Ballantine.[3]   Methods dealing with characteristic tube factors are described according to the tentative suggestions made by the various committees on measurements of the Institute of Radio Engineers.

155. Experiments on the Richardson Equation and Determination of the Work Required to Liberate One Electron from a Hot Cathode.—The saturation current i_s is given by the expression $i_s = KT^2 \epsilon^{-\frac{B}{T}}$, where K is equal to the surface of the hot cathode in square centimeters multiplied by a factor $60{,}200$ ma/(cm deg)^2, i_s is in milliamperes, T the absolute temperature of the hot cathode, and $B = \dfrac{q}{k}\Phi$ for $q = 1.592 \times 10^{-19}$ coulomb for the elementary charge, the Boltzmann constant $k = 1.372 \times 10^{-16}$ erg/deg and Φ the work function per unit charge.   Its value is then $\Phi = 8.62 \times 10^{-5} B$ volt where the value of B is given on page 40 for different materials.   From the above exponential law,

[1] *Phys. Rev.*, **36**, L 1261 and 1576, 1930.
[2] *Proc. I.R.E.*, **6**, 144, 1918.
[3] *Proc. I.R.E.*, **7**, 129, 1919.

$$\log_\epsilon i_s = \log_\epsilon K + 2 \log_\epsilon T - \frac{B}{T}$$

which, when changed to the logarithm of base 10, yields

$$\log_{10} i_s - 2 \log_{10} T = \log_{10} K - 0.4343\frac{B}{T} \qquad (7)$$

It has the form

$$y = a - bx \qquad (7a)$$

The saturation current i_s is measured with a milliammeter and the temperature T with an optical pyrometer. The quantity y is then plotted as in Fig. 257 against x. If a *straight drooping* line is obtained, Richardson's equation is valid. According to (7a), the intercept a on the y-axis gives the value $a = \log_{10} K$, while the slope $b = a/c = 0.4343B = 0.4343q\Phi/k$ is a way of finding the amount of work required to liberate one electron. The quantity $q\Phi$ represents the work expended in removing one electron of charge q from the hot cathode. This work can be computed from the slope $b = a/c$ by means of $W = q\Phi = 2.303kb = 2.303 \times 1.372 \times 10^{-16}b$, by using the formula

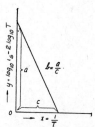

Fig. 257.—Test on Richardson's equation.

$$W = 3.16 \times 10^{-16}b \text{ ergs} = 3.16 \times 10^{-23}b \text{ joules} \qquad (8)$$

Since the *work function* Φ or the *electron affinity* represents the work done per unit charge (*not* electronic charge), it is found from $\Phi = W/q$ for $q = 1.592 \times 10^{-19}$ coulomb, if W is expressed in joules. Hence,

$$\Phi = 199 \times 10^{-6}b \text{ volts} \qquad (9)$$

156. Determination of the Equation of a Tube Characteristic.—Section 12 shows how the equation for an experimental curve can be found.

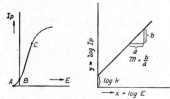

Fig. 258.—Determination of the exponent m of Eq. (10).

The characteristic of ordinary electron tubes follows the law

$$I_p = kE^m \qquad (10)$$

where I_p denotes the plate current and E the anode potential with respect to the negative end of the hot cathode. The exponent m is different for different portions of the tube characteristic. If an ordinary three-element tube is considered, one may distinguish between two important types of static characteristics

$$\left.\begin{array}{l} I_p \text{ as a function of } E_p \text{ for } E_g = \text{cons} \\ I_p \text{ as a function of } E_g \text{ for } E_p = \text{cons} \end{array}\right\} \qquad (11)$$

For one, the plate current is read off in dependence upon the plate potential with the grid potential fixed. For the other, the plate current is noted with respect to the grid potential E_g, and E_p is constant. In each case normal filament excitation is used. From the curve plot I_p as a function of the plate potential E (Fig. 258), it is noted that the small portion AB which corresponds to currents which flow against small negative-electrode and zero-electrode potential follows Maxwell's distribution law, as can be computed from Eq. (92) on page 41. Hence, if log (I_p) is plotted against log $(-E)$, a straight line with a slope giving the exponent will be obtained. For a pure electron discharge, the portion B to C follows essentially the three-halves-power law for which $m = 1.5$ in Eq. (10), if E is below values for which I_p reaches saturation current. Instead of Eq. (10) for the logarithm of any base, one can also write

$$\log I_p = \log k + m \log E \tag{12}$$

Therefore, there is an equation of the form $y = c + mx$ if $c = \log k$ and m denotes the slope. If the significant portion BC of the characteristic

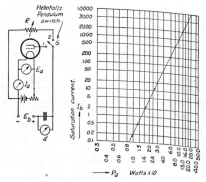

Fig. 259.—Emission chart.

is plotted to a logarithmic scale as in Fig. 258, the slope $m = b/a$ will give the exponent of E in Eq. (10) and from the intercept $c = \log k$ on the y-axis, the factor k can be found.

In many laboratories it has become customary to plot I_p against E_p for E_g = cons. Several plots for different values of constant grid bias gives then a means for estimating the proper resistance load line.

157. Determination of the Total Electron Emission.—For ordinary three-element tubes, the grid and the plate are connected together and sufficient positive potential is applied with respect to the negative end of the filament to measure the total electron emission. Since for normal filament power $(E_a\,I_a)$, the total emission would be so much that the tube would be injured, the standardization committee of the Institute of Radio Engineers suggests that about 25 volts positive potential be applied to the grid and plate and readings taken for the reduced filament power $P_a = E_a\,I_a$ for which the total emission is 0.1, 0.2, 0.5, and 1.0 ma. If the four points are plotted on the special power-emission chart of Fig. 259, they should lie on a straight line, and the normal emission is obtained by extending the straight line to the point for normal filament power. If the points tend to fall below a straight line with the larger currents, it indicates that too low a positive potential has been used and the experiment is repeated with 30 volts instead of 25 volts. On the other hand, if the points tend to lie above a straight line with larger currents, the vacuum of the tube is not good enough for a test in this manner. This procedure is due to C. J. Davisson who proposed the special coordinate system of Fig. 259, for which the abscissas are curved. The values of the abscissas may also be taken on a reduced scale, the heating power of the cathode for each square centimeter of surface and the values along the ordinate denote the corresponding saturation current. The coordinate system is so chosen that, if the emission follows Richardson's equation and the heat radiation of the filament is given by the Stefan-Boltzmann law, a straight-line relation must exist.

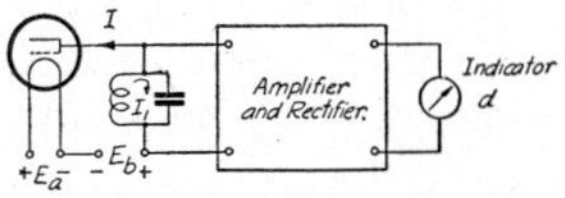

Figure 259 shows also a method which follows essentially a scheme suggested by B. J. Thompson.[1] It may be called an "instantaneous method," since, with the switch S on 1, a deflection d is obtained when a Helmholtz pendulum (page 62) closes a switch for about 10^{-3} sec. The switch S is then connected on 2 and R varied until the same deflection d is obtained when the pendulum switch operates. The emission current is computed from E_b/R.

153. Determination of the Shot Effect.—W. Schottky has shown that the emission current in a vacuum tube actually consists of a multitude of energy quanta reaching the plate. Therefore the energy quanta arriving at the plate of the tube shown in Fig. 260 occur in jerks and will produce oscillations in the CL circuit by the method of impact. The electronic charges q arriving at the plate can then be computed from $q = 2RCI_1{}^2/I$. The mean square value of the variable current I_1, according to A. W. Hull and N. H. Williams,[2] can be measured by the corresponding potential variations impressed on a shield-grid amplifier with a detector tube as the final stage. The deflection d of the indicator of the detector stage is then a measure for the I_1 fluctuations. It is essential that the E_b battery have sufficient voltage so that all electrons emitted by the filament reach the plate and that the period of the CL circuit correspond to the rate of electron bombardment usually existent in electron tubes of this type. The natural frequency lies in the broadcast range. In the Hull-Williams experiments it was at 750 kc/sec and the value of q obtained was the electronic charge.

Fig. 260.—Determination of shot effect.

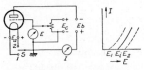

Fig. 261.—Determination of ionization potential.

159. Determination of Ionization and Radiation Potentials in Electron Tubes.—A critical positive accelerating potential exists for which electrons will just begin to collide inelastically with neutral gas particles and produce ions. The current-voltage relation of the

[1] In a letter to *Phys. Rev.*, **36**, 1415, 1930.
[2] *Phys. Rev.* **25**, 148, 1925.

tube from this critical potential on, which is also known as the "minimum ionization potential," will show a quicker increase of current. If a three-element tube is used, as in Fig. 261, the grid is connected across a potentiometer with the *positive* end against the grid. The power is supplied by a battery $E_c = 45$ volts, while the ordinary B battery with about 12 volts is connected with its *negative* terminal toward the plate. The common return to the filament is first made by closing switch S on 1. If sufficient positive grid potential $E = E_1$ is chosen, some of the electrons will pass through the openings of the grid and ionize the remaining gas molecules between the grid and the plate, and a current I will flow, carrying the positive nuclei toward the negative plate. The same will be observed for a positive grid potential $E = E_2$ when S is on 2, and 0.5 $[E_1 + E_2]$ will be the minimum ionization potential.

If the potential in an electron tube containing traces of gases is raised to a critical value so that an electromagnetic radiation of a characteristic frequency (giving a spectral line) just occurs, a radiation potential is dealt with, since the momentum of the electron is not sufficient to knock off an electron from an atom but will raise it to some higher energy level.

160. Determination of the Degree of Vacuum in Electron Tubes.— The succeeding methods are based on the fact that the plate current is in reality the result of two currents which flow in opposite directions. One current is the electron current I_ϵ which for good tubes is considerably larger than the positive-ion current I_+ produced by I_ϵ. The plate current is then $I_p = I_\epsilon - I_+$. The positive current is produced by electrons which have sufficient speed to liberate other electrons from the gas molecules and leave the positively charged nuclei free to move in the opposite direction toward the filament. Since positive ionization increases with the number of gas molecules in the evacuated bulb, the positive-ion current is proportional to the pressure of the residual gas. Since the number of impacts is proportional to the number of electrons emitted from the hot cathode, the current I_+ must also increase with the thermionic emission. Since the positive ionization depends directly on the space between the hot cathode and the plate, I_+ must increase with the distance d between these electrodes. Therefore, there is the empirical formula $I_p = k\,d\,p\,I_g$ where I_g denotes the negative current which flows to a positively charged grid and I_p the positive-ion current attracted toward a negatively charged plate, and p denotes the pressure of the residual gas in the bulb. The method of Fig. 262 in principle is the same as used in Fig. 261 for the determination of the ionization potential. Between the grid and the negative end of the filament a voltage $E = 150$ to 200 volts is impressed with the *positive* terminal toward the *grid*. A *negative* plate potential $E_1 = -10$ to -20 volts with respect to the filament is put on the plate. Therefore, the grid will act as the collector of electrons, and I_2 measures the electron current. Most of the positive ions formed by impact of electrons with sufficient speed will pass toward the negatively charged plate, and I_1 is a measure for the positive-ion current. Since the distance d between the plate and the filament is fixed, it can be combined with the constant k of the formula given above, making $K = kd$. The quality Q of the vacuum can then be computed from

$$p = K\frac{I_1}{I_2} = KQ \qquad (13)$$

and Q must be as small as possible for a good vacuum. For the measurement of the positive current I_1, a sensitive mirror galvanometer is conveniently used. A tube socket should not be used but the connections made directly to the prongs of the tube, in order to avoid any leakage currents. The method indicated in Fig. 263 is convenient if the quality of the vacuum is to be determined for tubes of the same kind. E_1 is 100 to 200 volts and E_2 about 20 volts. With such voltages the currents I_1 and I_2 can be read off directly with milliammeters. If a high degree of vacuum does not exist, positive-ion and electron currents flow. The electron current passes from filament to grid and the positive-ion current from grid to the plate. The I_2 meter indicates therefore in the negative sense, while the I_1 meter registers in the conventional way. But if the vacuum is very good so that practically pure electron emission exists only, the current will pass from plate to grid and grid to filament and the deflection of the I_2 meter also occurs in the conventional way. The vacuum is better, the larger the pure electronic current which passes through the I_2 meter, if E_1 and E_2 are fixed and tubes of the same type are tested. The quality of the vacuum can also be found by means of the static grid-potential plate-current characteristic for increasing and decreasing positive grid potentials. The readings must be taken into the saturation region, since for a poor vacuum apparent saturation occurs but for somewhat higher positive grid potentials the plate current rapidly increases again. For a good vacuum, the increasing E_g, I_p characteristic coincides with the decreasing characteristic. But if the vacuum is not very good, a sort of hysteresis loop is obtained, the decreasing portion falling somewhat lower than the increasing portion. The residual gas in this case lowers the saturation. For a vacuum which is still poorer, the first part of the decreasing characteristic falls below the increasing portion of the characteristic; then the decreasing characteristic intersects the increasing characteristic in order to proceed above it toward the zero value. The positive ionization is then pronounced enough to neutralize somewhat the negative space charge.

F I G. 262.— Determination of the degree of a high vacuum.

FIG. 263. Comparison of the degree of high vacuum of several tubes of the same type.

161. Experiments on Secondary-electron Emission and the Test on Power Tubes.—Secondary electrons can be produced by the impact of primary electrons with a metal surface. They play an important part in the dynatron of A. W. Hull[1] and may account for strange tube characteristics in ordinary tubes and especially in multiple-grid tubes. Secondary-electron emission begins with about 10 volts and reaches a maximum for electrode potentials between 250 and 800 volts. Lenard[2] finds that this happens between about 400 and 500 volts, while Lange[2] gives 600 to 800 volts and A. Gehrts finds 220 volts. Figure 264 gives the characteristic if either a dynatron (with a perforated anode due to A. W. Hull) or an ordinary three-element tube with more positive grid

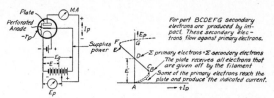

Fig. 264.—Action of an apparatus giving negative resistance (dynatron).

potential than for the plate is used. The characteristic is obtained by choosing a fixed positive grid potential E_g and plotting the plate-current reading I_p against the positive plate potential E_p. Figure 265 shows the characteristics for a pliodynatron which uses two grids, or one grid and perforated additional anode. A suitable positive potential E_{g2} is kept constant as well as the positive potential E_{g1}, and I_p is plotted against the plate potential. It is evident that negative resistance $(-r_p)$ can be readily changed by means of additional grid voltages ΔE_g and $\Delta E_g + \Delta E_g'$ on the first grid. In the case of the tube constants, such as the negative plate resistance $(-r_p)$, one must distinguish between static and dynamic values. The latter play a part when dynatron oscillations are excited or $(-r_p)$ is used to neutralize the circuit resistance either partially or entirely (for instance, in the method of Sec. 132). Characteristics as in Fig. 266 are sometimes obtained for transmitter tubes. It will be noticed that the grid current decreases from P_1 to P_2, which may be due to secondary-electron emission on the grid or primary-electron emission on the grid if the temperature of this electrode becomes sufficiently high. It may also be due to gases excluded from an overheated plate. In order to find out whether secondary-electron emission exists

[1] *Proc. I.R.E.*, **6**, 5, 1918; for other work on secondary electrons, P. Lenard, *Ann. Physik*, **8**, 149, 1902; **12**, 449, 1903; **15**, 485, 1904; A. Gehrts, *Ann. Physik*, **36**, 995, 1911; H. Starke and M. Baltruschat, *Physik. Z.*, **23**, 403, 1922; F. Tank, *Jahrb. d. drahtl.*, **20**, 82, 1922; B. van der Pol, *Physica*, **3**, 325, 1923; H. Salinger, *Z. tech. Physik*, **5**, 96, 1924; H. Lange, *Jahrb. d. drahtl.*, **26**, 38, 1925; H. G. Moeller, "Die Elektronenröhren," Vieweg & Sohn, Braunschweig, 1929, p. 245.

[2] *Loc. cit.*

or whether the two other conditions are present, a contact finger is rapidly rotated so that the grid is not cooled fast enough or any gas given off by the plate absorbed quickly enough during the short intervals during which the contact maker sweeps from segment 1 to segment 2. Hence, if gases

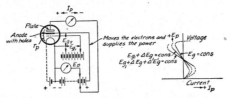

Fig. 265.—The magnitude of the negative resistance can be varied by means of grid voltage.

are given off on the plate or primary electrons are emitted from the grid, both milliammeters I_1 and I_2 would indicate the same negative grid current corresponding to point P_2. But if the grid gives off secondary electrons, the meter I_1 registers a positive grid current corresponding to point P_1, and the meter I_2 a negative current according to point P_2. If the tube is well
evacuated, tube characteristics as in Fig.
266 are generally due to the secondary-
electron emission. Such a condition is not
always undesirable, since the grid-circuit
losses in circuits with such tubes can be

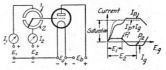

Fig. 266.—Test for secondary electrons.

made small and the tube can be used to produce oscillations of much higher frequency.

162. Determination of Static and Dynamic Tube Characteristics.— Usually static tube characteristics are taken and dynamic tube constants, such as the plate resistance r_p and mutual conductance g_m, found by the increment method from this characteristic. The dynamic tube characteristic can either be derived from the static characteristic or obtained with the cathode-ray oscillograph. The static tube characteristic of a two-element tube is obtained by noting the plate current I_p as a function of the plate potential E_p. If an ordinary three-element tube is to be tested, several characteristics are dealt with, all generally having reference to normal filament excitation. The most important static characteristics give the plate and grid currents, respectively, in dependence upon the grid potential. The plate potential is kept constant. Sometimes it is also convenient to plot the plate current depending upon the plate potential for a fixed grid potential. In a similar way the various static characteristics are obtained for multigrid tubes. It is customary in the case of two-grid tubes to keep one grid voltage constant, while the other grid voltage is varied, thus giving two different grid-characteristic curves for one tube. If the plate-current plate-voltage characteristic of a double-grid tube is taken, both grids are at suitable fixed potentials during the test. The characteristic giving the filament current as a function of the filament voltage is taken with floating grid and plate potentials. (Grid and plate are not connected in a circuit.) For many purposes lumped tube characteristics are of value. It is the plot of the plate current as a function of the plate potential plus the grid potential multiplied by the amplification factor. If the cathode-ray

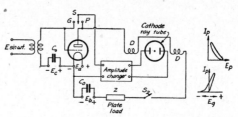

Fig. 267.—Dynamic-tube characteristics by means of the cathode-ray oscillograph.

tube, as in Fig. 267, is used to obtain the dynamic I_p, E_p and I_p, E_g characteristics, a sinusoidal voltage is impressed on the grid which is properly biased so that the amplified actions in the plate circuit vary about the desired operating point. If switch S_2 is closed and S connected to G, the I_p, E_g characteristic is traced. The coordinate axes are obtained by alternately opening switches S and S_2. The I_p, E_p characteristic is obtained when S_2 is closed and S connected toward P. The impedance of the deflection coils D, D must be small compared with the impedance Z of the plate load. The plate load Z must be the actual load for which the tube is to be used.

163. Notes on Important Tube Constants and Power Gain and Loss Determination.—The theory of electron tubes shows that dynamic values of internal plate resistance r_p, mutual conductance g_m, and amplification factor μ are interrelated by

$$\mu = r_p \, g_m \tag{14}$$

A knowledge of any two, fixes the value of the third tube factor. The static values R_p and G_m can be obtained for a certain portion of the static characteristic by choosing a suitable point on the characteristic and computing from $G_m = I_p/E_g$ and $R_p = E_p/I_p$. It is the dynamic values $r_p = \partial e_p/\partial i_p$ and $g_m = \partial i_p/\partial e_g$ which are of most concern. They can be obtained either from the tube characteristic or by direct measurement. The first method, which is also known as the "increment method," is not so precise and rapid as the procedures commonly carried out with a balance which uses an audio-frequency supply and a telephone receiver with or without an amplifier as a zero indicator. However, the increment method has the inherent advantage that different portions of the tube characteristic can be used to find out to what extent the tube factors change along the characteristic. The increment method notes the current values I_1 and I_2 for slightly different values of electrode potential E_1 and E_2. Hence, if r_p is to be determined, two values E_1 and E_2 of the plate potential are read off near the operating point, as well as the corresponding plate currents I_1 and I_2, and the internal plate resistance is computed from $r_p = (E_1 - E_2)/(I_1 - I_2)$. Closer analysis shows that μ^2/r_p denotes the quality of tube for amplification work. This can be understood also from Eq. (14). Suppose any device, a tube or any other apparatus capable of power amplification, then $\mu = g_m r_p$ may be taken as the generalized expression with μ as the amplification factor, g_m the steepness of the work characteristic, and r_p the internal-output impedance of the device. Suppose for one device $\mu = 10$, $g_m = 1000$ μ mhos, and $r_p = 10{,}000\Omega$. If the device is for a constant value of g_m changed to one which has an amplification factor μ of only 0.1, it will still work satisfactorily if $r_p = 100\Omega$. Of course, in each case it is necessary to have both the input and output properly terminated and matched for maximum power transfer. This brings up the often difficult problem of how to ascertain whether or not one actually has power amplification. Some engineers prefer a reference power output P_r, of some 6 mwatts, and refer other power outputs to this. Hence, if an amplifier shows an output P larger than P_r, it is assumed that a gain occurs, while for $P/P_r < 1$ a power loss is assumed. No doubt a reference value P_r leads to simplification for certain comparison work, but it can *never* be used to determine whether a device actually amplifies in power. Figure 268 gives a test for power gain. The power transferred

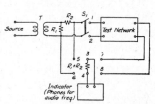

FIG. 268.—Test for power gain in a network.

by transformer T for S_1 open and 5 on 3 and 6 on 4 is fed into the indicator (for audio-frequency test, a set of phones). It is noted that the resistance $(R_1 + R_2)$ across the indicator is matched for maximum power transfer and the indicator must respond most. Next S_1 is closed on 1 and 2, and the connections 3 on 7 and 4 on 8 are made. If the response in the indicator is more than before, power amplification exists. For much of the work, R_1 is chosen as low as 100Ω and $R_2 = 500\Omega$ in order to make the customary 600Ω termination.

164. Determination of the Amplification Factor.—The method given in Fig. 269 uses two voltmeters to note the negative grid potential e and the positive plate potential E. The current meter d in the plate circuit is used only as an equal-deflection meter and a calibration is not needed. The tube voltages are chosen for the actual operation condition, normal grid bias $e = e_1$, and normal plate voltage $E = E_1$. These values are read off on the respective voltmeters and the deflection d of the plate meter is noted. The plate voltage E is now increased to a value E_2 by means of the traveling contact K along the E_b battery and to about a value which is 10 per cent higher than E_1. An increased deflection on the plate meter will be obtained. The traveling contact k along the grid potentiometer is moved toward more negative potentials until,

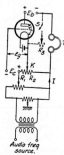

for a voltage $e = e_2$, the same deflection d is again obtained, and the static amplification factor computed from $\mu = \dfrac{E_2 - E_1}{e_2 - e_1}$. The static amplifica-

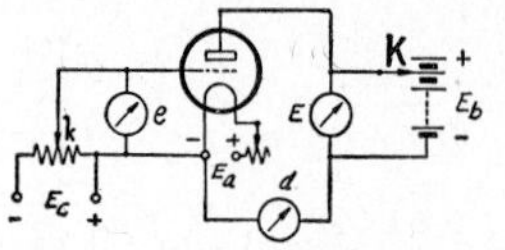

FIG. 269.—Determination of the static amplification factor.

tion for a fixed plate voltage E can also be obtained by increasing the negative grid bias e until the plate current just disappears, for which condition $E - \mu e = 0$ or $\mu = E/e$. Since μ varies somewhat for different values of E, it is better to find μ for several values of E and use the average value.

The method of Fig. 270 is used to determine the dynamic value of the amplification factor μ. The method is due to J. M. Miller.[1] A nearly sinusoidal current I of about 500 to 1000 cycles/sec is supplied to the potentiometer $R_1 + R_2$. The telephone receiver T should have a fairly low resistance. The procedure is as follows: The filament voltage is chosen for normal rating and the grid and plate voltages at their proper values. If e_g denotes the sinusoidal voltage which is impressed on the grid, the alternating-voltage drop across R_2 must be equal to $e_g R_2/R_1$ and is 180 deg out of phase with respect to the alternating plate voltage $e_p = \mu e_g$. The traveling contact K is moved until silence is observed in T, for which condition $e_g R_2/R_1 = \mu e_g$. The dynamic amplification factor is then computed from $\mu = R_2/R_1$. With such balance methods a single value only is determined for the desired normal grid and plate voltages E_c and E_b. The magnitude of the alternating grid voltage must be such that the grid

FIG. 270. Determination of the dynamic amplification factor (dotted branch only for r_p measurement; otherwise S is open).

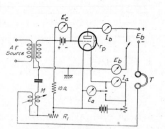

FIG. 271.—Determination of dynamic amplification factor. (Phase compensation is provided.)

never goes positive in the cycle of the impressed alternating voltage. In the method of Fig. 271 a small variable mutual inductance M is provided to compensate any small difference in phase of currents caused by interelectrode capacitances or by slight residual reactances in the grid and plate branches. The filament, grid, and plate voltages are again set for the desired steady voltages. The resistance R_1 and the mutual inductance M are adjusted for balance (silence in T) and the

[1] *Proc. I.R.E.*, **6**, 144, 1918.

amplification factor is computed from $\mu = R_1/10$. For an external plate-load impedance Z, the voltage and current amplification factors $\mu Z/(Z + r_p)$ and $\mu/(Z + r_p)$ are obtained, which for a resistance load $Z = R$ give the voltage and current amplifications $A_e = e_p/e_g = \mu R/(R + r_p)$ and $A_i = \mu/(R + r_p)$. These expressions give the alternating-voltage and alternating-current output per volt input. For the power output per volt squared input, $A_p = \mu^2 R/(R + r_p)^2$.

The ratio of the watts output to the square of the effective voltage input is generally known as the "power sensitivity" of a tube. It has also been suggested (by S. Ballantine and H. L. Cobb) that the square root of the power output divided by the effective value of the sinusoidal voltage applied to the grid be defined as power sensitivity. Such a definition seems to be of advantage if loud-speaker tests are under consideration, since the sound pressure from a loud-speaker is proportional to the square root of the power rather than directly proportional to the power. With such a sensitivity definition it is then possible to compare directly the equivalent gains of two different types of output tubes of the same power capacity.

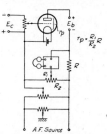

FIG. 272.—Determination of dynamic grid resistance r_g.

165. Notes on the Determination of Grid Resistance.—The grid resistance varies very much and therefore should be determined near the operating point of the grid-voltage grid-current characteristic by noting the small grid current I_1 for a grid bias E_1 and the current I_2 for the bias E_2, where the fixed grid bias E_c is about halfway between E_1 and E_2. Then $r_g = (E_1 - E_2)/(I_1 - I_2)$. This resistance is generally very high if a proper grid bias is chosen and the amplitude of the impressed alternating voltage e_g is comparatively small. From the above formula

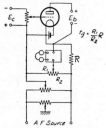

FIG. 273.—Determination of dynamic plate resistance.

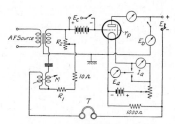

FIG. 274.—Determination of r_p.

it is evident that for the saturation region $I_1 = I_2$ and $r_g = \infty$ or nearly so, a fact which is important for certain work. The dynamic grid resistance can also be found with the ordinary bridge method of Fig. 272. The bridge must then be carefully designed, since high resistances are to be determined. For many cases the input resistance must be measured under the actual conditions, that is, at high frequency, and a suitable method in Chap. IX should be used.

166. Determination of Plate Resistance.—The increment method for the determination of the dynamic plate resistance r_p has already been described in Sec. 163. Figure 273 gives the simple Wheatstone bridge method. The bridge balance is again made for the desired steady operating voltages of the tube. Figure 274 gives the bridge method with a small mutual inductance M which is also provided for the compensation of any slight difference in phase of the currents due to interelectrode capacitances and residual reactances in the plate and grid circuits. The voltages E_a, E_c, and E_b are set at the desired values and R_1 at the value found in the test of Fig. 271, for which μ is determined. The settings of R_2 and M are varied until silence is noted in T for which condition $r_p = 100R_2$. If the circuit of Fig. 270 is used, the dotted branch is also employed by closing the switch S. The alternating plate-current component is then $i_p = \mu e_g/(r_p + R_3)$ and when the telephone receiver indicates balance (silence)

$$i_p R_3 = \frac{\mu e_g}{r_p + R_3} R_3 = \frac{R_2}{R_1} e_g$$

since the voltage drop in R_3 and R_2 compensate each other. Then

$$r_p = \left[\frac{\mu R_1}{R_2} - 1 \right] R_3$$

and for $R_1 = R_2$ the formula $r_p = [\mu - 1]R_3$.

167. Determination of the Mutual Conductance of a Tube.—According to (14), this quantity can be computed after the r_p and μ of a tube have been determined. It can also be determined by the increment method from the I_p curve as a function of the grid voltage E_g by using the two values E_1 and E_2 of the grid bias in the neighborhood of the operating point and the corresponding plate currents I_1 and I_2 and computing $g_m = (I_1 - I_2)(E_1 - E_2)$. If a number of plate-characteristic curves (I_p as a function of E_p and each curve for a different grid bias) are

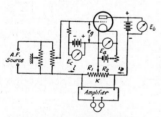

Fig. 275.—Determination of the dynamic mutual conductance g_m.

available, the difference in plate current between two neighboring curves for the desired plate potential to the corresponding difference of grid bias will give the value of g_m as above. With the circuit of Fig. 275, the dynamic value of the mutual conductance can be found directly. The traveling contact K is moved along the potentiometer $(R_1 + R_2)$, which may be a slide wire, until the sound in T disappears. The alternating-current components i and i_p are then such that the voltage drop across $(R_1 + R_2)$ is zero; that is, $iR_1 = i_pR_2$. But $g_m = \partial i_p/\partial e_g$ and for the linear portion $i_p = g_m e_g = g_m R_3 i$ and $g_m = R_1/(R_2 R_3)$ in mhos, if the resistances are in ohms. Figure 276 gives a circuit for the determination of g_m for screen-grid tubes. The proper direct voltages E_a, E_b, and E_{sg}, as well as E_c, are applied and R_1 is varied until the telephone receiver T registers silence. The mutual conductance is computed from $g_m = R_1/(R_2 R_3)$. It is then customary to make $R_2 = 1000$ ohms and $R_3 = 100$ ohms and compute from g_m(mhos) $= 10R_1$ if R_1 is in ohms.

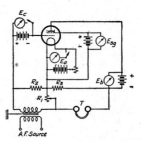

FIG. 276.—Determination of the dynamic value g_m of a double-grid tube.

168. Determination of the Detector Action of a Three-element Tube. The method shown in Fig. 277 is based upon the application of a completely modulated high-frequency voltage. The audible voltage in the plate circuit is compared with a known voltage of the same frequency. A detector separates the high-frequency from the audio-frequency component. Therefore the detector action is better, the larger the audible output component. For many detectors the audio current in the plate branch increases with about the square of the impressed grid voltage unless linear detection is provided. The square law holds only for a limited voltage region. The resistance R is low, about 10 to 30 ohms (short piece of constantan wire sealed in a glass tube). The impressed voltage e_g can then be computed from the current reading by means of $i R$. The resistance R_1 denotes a decade resistance box (0 to 1000Ω)

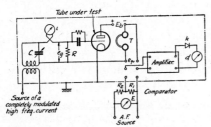

FIG. 277.—Determination of the detector action of a tube.

and R_2 a decade box (0 to 10,000Ω). E denotes a tube voltmeter 0 to 150 volts. The voltage across R_1 can then be computed. An ordinary contact rectifier k and a milliammeter (about 1 = ma full-scale deflection) is used to note the amplified audio-frequency voltages coming from either the output of the tube under test or the comparator circuit. An output transformer is used in the plate branch of the two-stage amplifier. The audio-frequency source which gives the known voltage of the comparator is also used to modulate completely the input voltage of the tube. The tube generator which supplies the modulated high-frequency voltage uses an 800- or a 1000-cycle voltage in the plate circuit of the high-frequency generator. An effective voltage of about 100 volts is used and by means of a step-down transformer about 25 volts is applied to the input terminals. Screening is very essential in this work and the high-frequency generator, which is not shown, should also be under a screen and at least a few meters from the test circuit. The process of measurement is as follows:

1. The modulated high-frequency voltage is applied and the effective grid voltage computed from $e_g = iR$. This voltage occurs when the input circuit is tuned by means of C, for which condition a maximum deflection d is obtained with the output indicator connected against the e_p terminals.

2. The double-pole double-throw switch is then connected toward the comparator and R_1 and R_2 are varied until the same deflection d is obtained. The voltage across the telephone receiver is then $e_p = ER_1/(R_1 + R_2)$ and the detector action equal to e_p/e_g^2.

The telephone receiver T is used only if it represents the actual load of the detector tube. It is essential that the actual load be used because the action of the detector also depends upon the external plate load. The same method can also be used for the power detector. The square law no longer holds then and a very large voltage range can be covered. If the detector action of several tubes is to be compared, a suitable modulated high-frequency voltage E_1 is impressed on the detector and the audio-frequency output voltage E_2 noted. The ratio E_2/E_1 is a measure for the detector effect. It has become customary to use a 30 per cent modulated high-frequency voltage. It should be understood that for a fair comparison the tubes must work at the most suitable operating point. If a linear detector is under test, the output voltage E_2 should be substantially proportional with the carrier voltage for the entire useful range. If the tube works along a nonlinear portion of the characteristic curve, the modulated high-frequency current producing the input voltage is converted into a modulated direct current.

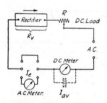

Fig. 278.—Determination of degree of rectification.

169. Determination of the Form Factor and the Rectification Action of a Two-element Tube.—In Fig. 278, I_e denotes a dynametric type of current meter and I_{av} a direct-current meter. The form factor is then found from $F = I_e/I_{av}$ and the rectification action from $\xi = I_{av}/I_e$. This method no longer holds when the tube capacitance plays a part.

170. Determination of the Efficiency and Rectification Action of a Loaded Rectifier Tube.—The efficiency η in percentage is given by

$$\eta = 100\frac{\text{d-c power in output}}{\text{a-c power in input}}$$

The power $W = EI \cos \varphi$ delivered to the input can be found by a suitable wattmeter. The form factor F and the load resistance R give the power output $[I_{av}F]^2R$ and

$$\eta = \frac{100[I_{av} \, F]^2 R}{W} \qquad (15)$$

For the rectification action ξ of a rectifier (in percentage),

$$\xi = 100\frac{\text{useful current in d-c circuit}}{\text{possible alternating current in this circuit}} = 100\frac{I_{av}}{I} \qquad (16)$$

The quantity I_{av} is read off on the direct-current meter in the output branch and I denotes the reading of the I_e meter of Fig. 278 if the tube is short-circuited, that is, the valve resistance R_v encountered by the rectified current is equal to zero and no rectification occurs. In the most general case (of an imperfect rectifier) with a small inverse current I_2 in addition to the desired current I_1 (which is in some way true in electron tubes, since a current flow is possible against small decelerating potentials), the ratio of useful current to possible current is

$$\xi = \frac{I_{av}}{I} = \frac{I_{av}}{I_{max}/\sigma} = \frac{\dfrac{0.5[I_1 - I_2]}{\sigma F}}{I_{max}/\sigma} = \frac{I_1 - I_2}{2F I_{max}} \qquad (17)$$

where σ is the peak factor of the rectified current. Hence, for an imperfect rectifier, the rec*'*ification ability is computed from the ratio I_{av}/I. Moreover, $I_{max} = E_{max} \, R$ and $I_1 = E_{max}/(R_v + R)$, since $I_{max} = I\sqrt{2}$ denotes the maximum value of alternating current for the tube short-circuited, and I_1 the maximum positive fluctuation of the rectified current which is dependent upon R_v. The I_2 effect is very small and if neglected

$$\xi = \frac{I_1}{2F I_{max}} = \frac{E_{max}/(R_v + R)}{\dfrac{2F \, E_{max}}{R}} = \frac{1}{2F\left[1 + \dfrac{R_v}{R}\right]}$$

Since $F = I_e/I_{av}$ we have the formula

$$\xi = \frac{50 I_{av}}{I_e\left[1 + \dfrac{R_v}{R}\right]} \qquad (18)$$

from which ξ can be computed, since I_{av} and I_e are read off and R_v can be measured.

171. Determination of Interelectrode Capacitances.—Reference is made to Secs. 12, 93, and 106 for details. The direct interelectrode capacitance between grid and plate is C_{gp}, between grid and filament C_{gf}, and between plate and filament C_{pf}. These capacitances are the values determined on a tube without tube socket. Then

$$C_g = C_{gp} + C_{gf}; \; C_p = C_{gp} + C_{pf}; \; C_f = C_{gf} + C_{pf} \qquad (19)$$

where C_g, C_p, and C_f denote the grid, plate, and filament capacitances, respectively. C_g then denotes the sum of the direct capacitances between the grid and all other conductors of the electron tube, C_p the sum of the direct capacitances between the plate and all other conductors, and similarly for C_f. One method of finding the values of C_{gf}, C_{gp}, and C_{pf} is described in Sec. 12. The Committee on Standardization of the Institute of Radio Engineers recommends that the direct capacitances rather than the total capacitances be measured. In order to avoid one electrode's floating in potential, circuits as in Fig. 279 are used. No direct voltages are present and the filament is not lighted. In the bridge method of Fig. 279 the most important direct capacitance, namely, C_{gp}, is determined. A 1000-cycle source is employed. The resistance R balances the capacitance C_{gf} which is in parallel with R_2 and corrects any other disturbing phase shift which may exist in other branches of the bridge. For balanced bridge $C_{gp} = CR_1/R_2$. In connection with Fig. 172 another bridge method is described. Tube manufacturers often carry out the measurements without tube sockets, since the kind of socket to be used is not known. However, in the laboratory, the capacitances should be determined with the tube socket to be used in the actual work.

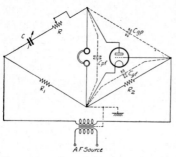

Fig. 279.—Determination of grid-plate capacitance.

172. Notes on Testing Receiving Apparatus.—Tubes must be tested in the actual circuit and it is therefore necessary to take transmission characteristics of circuits including tubes. Such circuits then combine stages of high-frequency amplification, a rectifier or detector stage, and stages of audio-frequency amplification. Many receivers utilize complete battery elimination besides, which makes a test on alternating-current hum necessary. Distortion may be due to nonlinear portions of the dynamic work characteristics. It is necessary to test for high-frequency amplification, for audio-frequency amplification, and detector action under the actual conditions. In many cases it is also desirable to have methods for obtaining the transmission characteristics of input, interstage, and output coupling.

The determination in *physical* terms of the sound output of a receiver is by no means simple, as can be readily understood from the diagram of Figs. 280 and 281 which are the outcome of investigations by H. Fletcher and R. L. Wegel[1] on the normal ear. It can be seen that one must distinguish between a limit for which sound can just be heard and a limit for which it is so intense that pain is caused in the ear and that the respective limits vary with the audio frequency. Fechner's law for the sensation S of loudness (relative sensitivity of the ear) is

$$S = a \log_{10} p + b \tag{20}$$

if p is the excess pressure. The factor a depends upon the frequency and b upon both

[1] *Phys. Rev.*, **19**, 553, 1922.

the frequency and the threshold pressure. For very loud sounds, $S \cong a \log_{10} p$ and practically a logarithmic law exists. According to D. MacKenzie,[1] the above relation is more convenient in the form

$$\log_{10} p_1 = K_1 + K_2 \log_{10} p_2 \tag{21}$$

giving

$$\left.\begin{array}{l} 20 \log_{10} p \text{ as sensation unit} \\[4pt] 20 \log_{10} \dfrac{p}{p_t} \text{ as sensation level} \end{array}\right\} \tag{22}$$

if p_t denotes the threshold pressure. By sensation level is meant the number of sensation units needed to reduce the loudness to the threshold value. From (22) it

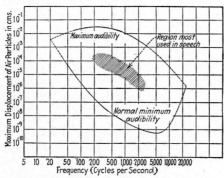

Fig. 280.—Air displacement due to sound waves.

can be seen that the sensation level can be expressed in decibels. The decibel in this case then gives the *physiological* response of the ear and corresponds closely to the minimum perceptible change in loudness if the sound wave is *pure* harmonic. For complex sounds, as is usually the case, probably 2 to 3 db corresponds to the minimum change observed by the normal ear. For this reason, it is also convenient to express the output characteristics of the final tube stage in decibels rather than in voltages. Moreover, if p denotes the sound pressure in dynes per centimeter squared at a certain place in air, the flow of energy in ergs per centimeter squared during each second is p^2/R_a where $R_a = \rho v$ is the specific acoustic resistance in grams per sec cm²). The quantity $v = 343.3 \times 10^2$ cm/sec is the ve-

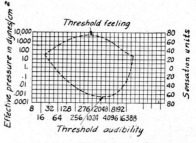

Fig. 281.—Threshold feeling and audibility for sound waves of different pitch.

locity of sound in dry air at room temperature (20° C) for atmospheric pressure (760 mm of mercury) and $\rho = 12 \times 10^{-4}$ g/cm³ is the density of the air for these conditions.

[1] *Phys. Rev.*, **20**, 331, 1922; also G. W. Stewart and R. B. Lindsay, "Acoustics," D. Van Nostrand Company, New York, 1930, p. 224. V. O. Knudsen, *Phys. Rev.*, **19**, 261, 1922, and **21**, 84, 1923, published experimental data on the Fechner-Weber law. Fechner's law is based on Weber's law that the increase of stimulus to produce the minimum perceptible increase of sensation is proportional to the stimulus which existed before. Hence having a certain sound intensity the increase is $\delta S = k \delta I / I$ if I is the intensity of stimulus and S the magnitude of sensation. Hence $S = k \log_e I$. $\delta I / I$ is a function of intensity I and can be found experimentally but it is not possible to measure S directly.

Hence $W = p^2/R_a = 243 \times 10^{-4}$ erg $= 243 \times 10^{-11}$ watt, and

$$W = 243 \times 10^{-5}p^2 \tag{23}$$

where W is expressed in microwatts and p in dynes per square centimeter. This is a very useful relation for electroacoustic work. If materials other than air are concerned, the numerical factor is different and can be computed from v and ρ for the particular material. Assuming that a pressure change $p = \pm 1.5 \times 10^{-3}$ dyne/cm² can be observed by the normal ear, then according to (23) this would be equivalent to only $243 \times 10^{-5} \times 1.5^2 \times 10^{-6} = 5.46 \times 10^{-9} \mu$ watt. Moreover, it is necessary to distinguish between the absolute and practical value of the efficiency of an electroacoustic device connected in a tube circuit. The absolute efficiency is an expression either in percentage or in decibels, found from the ratio of the output of the electroacoustic apparatus to be tested to that of a perfect electroacoustic device. Since the latter is practically not attainable, the standardization committee of the Institute of Radio Engineers suggests the practical efficiency with respect to a reference electroacoustic device. Thus, if the efficiency of a telephone receiver is to be determined, the ratio $\dfrac{E_2}{E_1}\sqrt{\dfrac{R_1}{R_2}}$ is used to find the efficiency either in percentage or in decibels, respectively. E_1 is the voltage in series with the test telephone receiver and a resistance R_1 which is equal to the impedance for which the receiver is designed. E_2 is the voltage in series with the reference receiver and the resistance R_2 in series for which the reference telephone receiver is designed. The voltage E_1 is adjusted in the experiment until the same intensity of sound is observed as for the reference receiver employing a voltage E_2. It is important that a suitable point in the sound field be chosen. In the same way, if an électroacoustic transmitter, for instance, a microphone, is to be tested for the practical efficiency, the test transmitter is at first connected to the input tube of the actual audio-frequency amplifier and the voltage E_1 noted which is produced by the transmitter across the grid and the filament when a desired pure sound affects the transmitter. A reference transmitter is then connected to the amplifier and the voltage E_2 noted across the grid and the filament of the input tube if the same sound conditions prevail, and the ratio E_1/E_2 is used for computing the efficiency in percentage or in decibels. The number of decibels are found from $20 \log_{10} \dfrac{E_1}{E_2}$. In determining the gain of an audio-frequency amplifier the ratio ρ of the voltage output to voltage input is measured for different frequencies and the decibels computed from $20 \log_{10} \rho$ as described in Sec. 174.

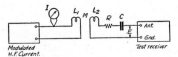

Modulated
H.F Current.

Fig. 282.—Lumped aerial L_2RC and input set up for a receiver test.

As input circuits for receiver tests the standardization committee of the Institute of Radio Engineers recommends a lumped dummy antenna made up of $L_2 = 20$ μh, $C = 200$ $\mu\mu$f, and $R = 25$ ohms, as shown in Fig. 282, for the broadcast range. The voltage E impressed on the set can then be readily adjusted by either the current I, the mutual inductance M between L_1 and L_2, or both. The equivalent electric field strength is then

$$\mathcal{E} = \frac{6.28\,fMI}{h_e} \ \mu\text{volts/m} \tag{24}$$

if f is the high frequency in kilocycles per second, M measured with one of the methods in Chap. VIII and expressed in millihenries, the current I through primary coil L_1 in microamperes, and $h_e = 4$ m the equivalent effective height of the dummy antenna. Hence, $E = 6.28fMI$ equal to 4 μ volts would correspond to a field strength of 1 μv/m, which is a value only sufficient for very sensitive receivers. (For urban areas 5 to 30 mv/m are considered necessary in order to raise the signal level

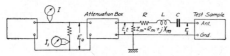

FIG. 283.—Input set up using an attenuator.

sufficiently above a high static and other noise levels. In rural districts 100 μv/m is sufficient.) Figure 283 shows a standard input circuit for which CLR again denotes the dummy aerial. Instead of the variable transfer inductance M of Fig. 282, an attenuation box (for details see Sec. 36 and Fig. 53) with a load impedance Z_m is used as a coupling. For the broadcast range $R + R_m = 25$ ohms if R also includes the resistance of $L = 20$ μh and $C = 200$ $\mu\mu$f and

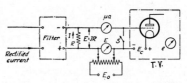

$$\mathcal{E} = \frac{\alpha Z_m I}{h_e} \ \mu\text{volts/m} \qquad (25)$$

FIG. 284.—Determination of the degree of pulsation in a rectified and filtered current.

where α is the attenuation factor of the attenuator, I in microamperes, and h_e again equal to 4 m. If the attenuator is calibrated in terms of voltage and includes the impedance Z_m, then

$$\mathcal{E} = \frac{\alpha E_0}{h_e} \ \mu\text{volts/m} \qquad (26)$$

if E_0 is the measured voltage in volts. Hence $E = \alpha E_0 \ \mu$ volts.

173. Tests for the Smoothness of Rectified Current and for Output Hum.—Oscillographic records are not sufficient, since it is impossible to notice pulsations of less than a few per cent if the rectified current coming out of a filter is investigated. The tube-voltmeter method of Fig. 284 is simple and has sufficient analyzing power. By means of the

FIG. 285.—Distortion test.

auxiliary voltage E_0 and the potentiometer, the steady voltage E can be determined by the compensation method, while any superimposed variable voltages e are measured with the tube voltmeter. The tube voltmeter is then best calibrated in maximum values of e and the ratio $100e/E$ gives the percentage effect of any superimposed ripples with respect to the desired steady voltage E. The procedure is then as follows: Switch S is closed and the traveling contacts along the potentiometer moved until the microammeter reads zero. The reading E is then proportional to the direct current I. The switch S is then opened and e found by means of the tube voltmeter. Figure 285 gives a well-known method for the determination of the distortion factor D of a 60-cycle supply line. The resistance R is chosen equal to $1/(6.28 \times 60C)$ if C is in farads and R in ohms, and such that the 110-volt supply gives a suitable reading on the current meter I. If no harmonics are present, the reading of I must be the same whether S is on 1 or on 2. But, with a higher harmonic content, the reading $I = I_1$ for S on 1 is somewhat larger than the reading $I = I_2$ for S on 2 and $D = I_1/I_2$ denotes the distortion factor which should not be appreciably larger than 1.05. As can be understood from the remarks in Sec. 172 (acoustic effects on the ear), the output voltage existing across the terminals of the final tube

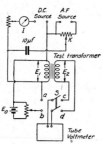

stage is not an indication of the quantitative effect on the ear. The electroacoustic response characteristic shows that higher harmonics of the 60-cycle hum are emphasized.

FIG. 286.—Transmission-characteristic test.

174. Tests of Transformers Used in Tube Circuits.—Input, interstage, and output transformers in tube circuits must be tested under actual conditions. Therefore it is necessary to provide a superimposed direct-current magnetization as in Fig. 286 if it exists in the actual case. A tube voltmeter, as indicated, can be used or a cathode-ray tube as a voltmeter utilizing one deflection condenser. The switch S is connected to a and b, and the primary voltage E_1 measured. The steady voltage due to the superimposed direct current I is balanced out by means of the potentiometer across the auxiliary voltage E_0. The switch S is connected on c and d, and the output voltage E_2 measured. The measurement is carried out over the entire audio-frequency band and it is convenient to have the input voltage E_1 constant. This can be readily done with the traveling contact K along the potentiometer across the audio-frequency source. The ratio E_2/E_1 for input and interstage transformers should be essentially constant, which, of course, can only be approximately obtained for a certain frequency range. If two stages of audio-frequency amplification with transformers are employed, it is best to determine the voltage ratio for both stages including the tube effects with a method similar to that shown in Fig. 288. For an output transformer the sensation units [Eq. (22)] must be taken into account if a telephone receiver or a loud-speaker forms the load. The transmission characteristic should then be plotted in decibels against the audio frequency. If E_1 denotes the voltage between the grid and the filament of the output tube and E_2 the voltage acting across the telephone receiver or the loud-speaker the number N of decibels for the entire stage is $N = 20\log_{10}\dfrac{E_2}{E_1}$. If, for the entire useful audio-frequency band 50 to 10,000 cycles/sec, the number N does not vary by more than about 3 db, it may be said that the output stage is very well designed, since for complex sounds which come from loud-speakers 2 to 3 db are about the smallest change noticed by the average ear. Of course, such a good frequency characteristic will not always happen, but it can often be obtained without the redesign of a fairly good output transformer by connecting suitable resistances either across the input, or the output coil (depending upon the transformer), or across the grid of the last tube. A peaked characteristic may then be flattened out. The number of decibels are given in Table XVII at the end of the book. If the ratio $E_2/E_1 <$

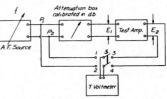

Fig. 287.—Determination of amplification by means of an attenuation box.

1 as for dynamic loud-speaker outputs, the ratio E_1/E_2 is used. It is of no concern whether E_2/E_1 or its reciprocal is used, since the change of the ratio only is of interest. Table XVII can be readily extended. Thus, if the voltage amplification of an audio-frequency amplifier is 6540, then $6540 = 6.54 \times 10^3$. From the table, the voltage ratio 6.54 gives 16.31, and 10^3 according to $N = 20\log_{10}\dfrac{E_2}{E_1}$ gives the value 3×20 and the number of decibels is $60 + 16.31 = 76.31$ db. The test can be simplified by using circuit of Fig. 287. The attenuation setting is varied until for a setting N db the same deflection d is produced on the tube voltmeter whether switch S is on 1 and 2 or on 3 and 4. The

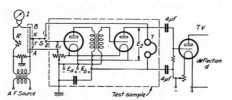

Fig. 288.—Determination of audio-frequency amplification. (AB is a slide wire.)

voltage across P_1P_2 is then equal to E_2 and the gain in the amplifier is equal to the loss N in the attenuator. The attenuator then gives directly the number of decibels for the particular audio frequency.

175. Determination of Audio-frequency Amplification.—In the method of Fig. 288, an audio source whose frequency can be varied is used and the audio current I adjusted by means of R in order to apply about $E_1 = 0.1$ volt to the grid when the switch S is on 2. A deflection

d is then produced on the tube voltmeter. If $I = I_1$ and the resistance $r = r_1$ of the input potentiometer is used, the input voltage is $E_1 = I_1 r_1$. The switch S is now connected on 1 and r is increased to some value r_2 and I to some value I_2 until the same deflection d is again obtained. The product $I_2 r_2$ then gives E_2 and the voltage amplification is $E_2/E_1 = I_2 r_2/(I_1 \ r_1)$. If only one stage of amplification is to be determined in this way, for which the amplification is not so large, the constant current method can be used. It consists of choosing the traveling contact K along the slide wire AB close to A and so that AK is equal to a length l_1. The resistance R is varied until with S on 2 a suitable deflection d on the tube voltmeter is obtained. The switch S is then connected on 1 and K moved more toward B until for $AK = l_2$ the same deflection d is again obtained. The ratio l_2/l_1 then denotes the stage amplification. The determination is carried on over the entire audio-frequency range. A somewhat different method is shown in Fig. 289. The tube voltmeter is connected across c, d and I is varied until a suitable deflection d is obtained. The tube voltmeter is now connected across the output a, b of the audio-frequency amplifier and R is varied until the same deflection d is obtained. The voltage amplification of the amplifier is computed from

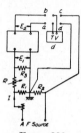

FIG. 289.—Determination of voltage amplification.

$$A_e = \frac{R_2(R + R_1 + R_3)}{R_1 R_3} \tag{27}$$

Since $\dfrac{E_2}{E_1} = \dfrac{R_2}{\dfrac{R_1[R + R_3]}{R + R_1 + R_3} \cdot \dfrac{R_3}{R + R_3}}$. For R_1 and R_3 about 0.1 ohm,

that is, negligible in comparison with the comparatively large variable resistance (decade box) R, there is the total voltage amplification $A_e = kR$ for $k = R_2/(R_1 R_3)$. The circuit of Fig. 287 can also be used to find the voltage amplification E_2/E_1 of the amplifier from the relation $N = 20$ $\log_{10} \dfrac{E_2}{E_1}$ if N denotes the number of decibels used in the attenuation box to produce the same deflection d for S on 1 and 2 or S on 3 and 4. For this work it is more convenient if the attenuation box (for theory see Sec. 36) is calibrated in terms of damping α. Since for equal deflections the voltage across $P_1 P_2$ is E_2, for a corresponding damping setting of the attenuator, $E_2 = E_1 \epsilon^\alpha$. Since the voltage amplification $A_e = E_2/E_1$, this ratio can be computed from $\log_{10} A_e = \alpha/2.303$. The fixed and variable attenuation-box method shown in Fig. 79 and described in Sec. 54 in connection with the determination of very small currents can also be used. Whenever an attenuation box is used, it is necessary to load it with a resistance equal to the characteristic resistance of the box. For speech amplifiers the input of the amplifier is often either 500 or 600 ohms and standard attenuation boxes can be inserted in the circuit as shown in Fig. 287. If the input impedance is, however, different, it is necessary to insert an unsymmetrical network between the attenuation box and the amplifier in order to avoid reflection losses. Unsymmetrical networks may be either a special transformer or, for instance, an unsymmetrical T-section (Sec. 36). A vacuum tube can also be used as an unsymmetrical network. In all cases the transmission loss in the unsymmetrical network is known and forms a part of the added attenuation by means of which the amplification is determined.

176. Determination of High-frequency Amplification.—A modulated high-frequency voltage is applied to the test receiver. For broadcast receivers it is customary to do it by an artificial field intensity which is 30 per cent modulated at 400 cycles/sec. Oscillators as described in Sec. 14 can be used.[1] If the degree of modulation is of importance for a certain test, it should be *measured*, since, for instance, an audio-frequency modulation of 1 kc/sec with the ordinary method of having an audio-frequency generator acting on a high-frequency source may give a considerably different degree of modulation for different carrier frequencies from that anticipated. Modulations of carrier frequencies which are low (for instance, 25 to 50 kc/sec) for modulation frequencies

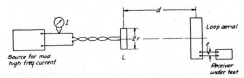

Fig. 290.—Production of a small known input voltage *e*.

as high as 1.5 kc/sec and higher give entirely different results from those met with in the broadcast band with customary signal generators. It is then best not to use tuned plate loading for the final circuit which delivers the modulated high-frequency current.

The high-frequency voltage *E* applied to a test receiver may be applied as indicated in Figs. 282 and 283 or by means of a frame aerial as in Fig. 290. The modulated high-frequency current is noted by the *I* reading in microamperes. If *d* denotes the distance (large compared with the dimensions of the loop) in centimeters, *N* the number of turns of coil *L* of diameter 2*r* in centimeters, and θ the angle between the axis of the loop antenna and the line between coil centers, the equivalent high-frequency field intensity is

$$\mathcal{E} = \frac{18,850NIr^2}{\sqrt{[r^2 + d^2]^3}} \cos\theta \;\mu\text{volts/m} \tag{28}$$

[1] Portable signal generators for broadcast frequencies are commercially available. A good design is also described by R. S. Kruse, *Electronics*, **1**, 295, 1930.

This is the circuit recommended by the Standardization Committee of the Institute of Radio Engineers and is especially useful when used as a comparator for the determination of received signal currents. It is then customary to couple the coils as shown in Fig. 290 for which $\cos \theta = 1$. If an attenuation box is used (with resistances along and across the line) with a terminating impedance Z_m as in Fig. 283, the high-frequency voltage is transformed into the frame aerial by connecting the transfer impedance Z_m in series with the loop at a point of ground potential. The equivalent field intensity is then

$$\varepsilon = \frac{E_t}{A} \ \mu\text{volts/m} \tag{29}$$

where

$$A = 2Nh \ \sin \frac{\pi a f}{3 \times 10^5} \tag{30}$$

for N turns of the loop with a height h and width a in meters, and f in kilocycles per second. The quantity E_t denotes the transfer voltage acting across the terminating impedance Z_m of the attenuator. The voltage can also be transferred to the loop by a small resistance (about $1\,\Omega$) inserted at the mid-point of the loop.

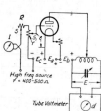

High freq source
$r = 400-500\,\Omega$.

Tube Voltmeter

FIG. 291.—Determination of high-frequency amplification.

If only small voltage amplifications (for a single stage, for instance) are to be determined at a high frequency, the method is essentially the same as for audio frequency. A potentiometer arrangement can be used or a reliable attenuation box, respectively. The measurement is then, for example, as follows: A high-frequency voltage is produced across a pure resistance of a few hundred ohms which is connected across the input terminals as in Fig. 291. Regeneration does not as a rule take place for such a resistance input. If the amplification is much more than about twentyfold, screening should be used and proper grounding. If the entire test circuit is in a good copper cage, the tube voltmeter should not give a reading for short-circuited input terminals. Tube voltmeters as shown in Fig. 114, or a two-stage tube voltmeter as in Fig. 116, are suitable. The circuit of Fig. 114 works well up to voltage amplification as high as 500 fold. With this method a calibration of the tube voltmeter is not required.

1. The voltmeter is first connected across the slider S_1 and the negative terminal of the grid bias and S_1 moved to a point for which practically the entire resistance r acts on the input side. Let the resistance be r_1.

2. The slider S is then moved to a point until the tube voltmeter gives a suitable deflection d.

3. The tube voltmeter is connected across the plate load as indicated in the figure.

4. The slider S_1 is moved to the negative terminal of the grid bias and the tube voltmeter should read zero if the screening is satisfactory.

5. The slider S_1 is moved until for a value $r = r_2$ the same deflection d is obtained. The voltage amplification per stage is then

$$A_e = \frac{E}{e} = \frac{r_1}{r_2}$$

If very large amplifications are to be determined, the method with a suitable attenuation box (described in Sec. 36) may be used. With this procedure the small input voltage e can be computed from the current passing into the attenuation box, since the current I, passing through r, for amplifications, as high as 5000 is altogether too small to be read off on a microammeter. By means of the attenuation box, the current I can be computed as well as $e = I r$. The output voltage E in this case is measured with a calibrated tube voltmeter. The following method does not require the knowledge of I. Suppose there are three stages of tuned high-frequency amplification and the entire amplification is about 5000. According to the method suitable for a single stage for which $E = I r_1$ and $e = I r_2$, the resistance r_1 would have to be $5000r_2$. This would not lead to an accurate determination. Therefore it is necessary to use a smaller current I_1, for the production of input voltage $e = I_1 r_2$ than is used to find $E = I r_1$. In order to avoid this also, the four following determinations are made:

1. The tube voltmeter is connected across the entire resistance r and S is moved along R until a suitable deflection d is obtained for a current I which is measured with the indicated thermoelectric indicator of Fig. 291. Any amplified voltages which produce the same deflection d are then given by $E = I r$.

2. Only one stage of high-frequency amplification, as in Fig. 291, is at first tested, giving the voltage amplification $A_1 = E/e_1$ by noting the setting r_1 of the input resistance for the same deflection d of the tube voltmeter across the plate load of the first tube. Hence $e_1 = I r_1$.

3. The high-frequency current I is now greatly reduced by means of slider R to some value I_1 and such that for the entire input resistance r the deflection d is again obtained on the tube voltmeter when connected across the plate load of the first tube. Hence $e_1 = I_1 r$.

4. The tube voltmeter is now connected across the output load of the last tube (third tube in this particular example) and the slider S_1 moved toward smaller values of r until for an input resistance r_2 the same deflection d is obtained. The voltage impressed on the grid of the first tube is then $e_2 = e = I_1 r_2$. The total voltage amplification of all three stages therefore is

$$\frac{E}{e} = A_e = \frac{E}{e_1} \frac{e_1}{e_2} = A_1 \frac{r}{r_2}$$

Therefore it is possible to express the total amplification in terms of the amplification A_1 of the first tube by multiplying A_1 by r/r_2. Since $A_1 = E/e_1 = r/r_1$ one finds the total amplification from $r^2/r_1 r_2$.

177. Determination of High-frequency Amplification with Regeneration Input.[1]—Many high-frequency amplifiers do not work from a resist-

---

[1] Friis, H. T. and A. G. Jensen, *Bell System Tech. J.*, **3**, 181–205, 1924.

ance input. If a few hundred ohms were inserted in a tuned filament-grid input, any back feed into this branch (regeneration) is negligible, while for regeneration the effective input voltage is larger than the actual grid voltage initially applied to the amplifier. If the back-feed factor k_b is known, this factor, multiplied by the voltage amplification A_e measured, gives the voltage amplification which is only due to the straightforward action (from input toward output end) of the amplifier. In many cases it is difficult to determine the voltage amplification due to the final conditions at the input and output end of the amplifier. For this reason it is essential that the voltage-supply system at the input side does not appreciably change the actual conditions under which the test device must actually operate. Figure 292 shows a tuned input amplifier coupled to an antenna which induces a small voltage in the *CL* branch. If the terminals 1-2 across which a small resistance r can also be inserted are short-circuited, the actual circuit conditions exist. At first, the filament of the test circuit is not heated. The tube

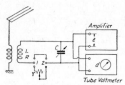

F I G. 292.—Determination of the back-feed factor of a high-frequency amplifier.

voltmeter indicates a certain deflection d if a certain modulated high-frequency wave is received. The filament current is now switched on and, for no back feed, the deflection d must be the same as before; otherwise a larger or a smaller deflection is obtained. For a larger deflection the back feed is positive, that is, additive to the input-grid voltage, since the resistance of the input (*CL*) circuit then becomes smaller in effect. By means of a suitable resistance r inserted across terminals 1 and 2, the original deflection d can be again obtained and r is a measure for the back feed. If R denotes the circuital resistance of the *CL* loop when terminals 1 and 2 are short-circuited, the resistance $(R - r)$ denotes the effective circuit resistance if r is connected across 1 and 2 and regeneration takes place. Since the voltage e across the grid of the first tube increases inversely with the circuit resistance of the *CL* loop, for the back-feed factor $k_b = R/(R - r)$ is obtained. Hence if A_e denotes the voltage amplification of an amplifier measured as described in connection with Fig. 291, the true forward amplification is $A_t = k_b\,A_e$. If the signal is received with a loop instead of an open aerial, there is the circuit shown in Fig. 293. The procedure is as just described. The resistance r is then inserted at the center of the loop and the determination carried on only for one-half of the loop.

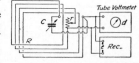

F I G. 293.—Determination of the back-feed factor with a frame aerial.

For the determination of very large high-frequency amplifications, the signal generators of Figs. 128 and 129 can be used to advantage, since then only high-frequency voltages of the proper small input value are produced and any stray fields from the actual high-frequency generator cannot affect the tube-voltmeter readings. This is practically true, since the input voltage has then twice the frequency of the fundamental carrier current of the signal generator. If Fig. 128 is used, the high-frequency current I of double frequency is computed from M and the reading of a direct-current meter which is always very sensitive. The circuit of Fig. 129 is even more simple and very small input voltages e can be produced. It is computed from the direct-current meter in the grid branch, the mutual inductance M, and the resistance of the I circuit. The frequency f is determined with a frequency meter, since a small voltage e is obtained by means of M and κ. The fundamental frequency of the generator is apt to change somewhat while e is being adjusted.

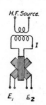

H.F. Source

E_1 E_2

Fig. 294.—Mutual-inductance method for the determination of high-frequency amplification.

Figure 294 gives a mutual-induction method which can be used for the determination of high-frequency amplification for which the voltage gain is not too large. A modulated high-frequency current I is impressed on a stationary primary coil. Two secondary coils with induced voltages E_1 and E_2, respectively, are mounted at right angles to each other and can be turned as a whole with respect to the primary coil. Hence, if the coil with voltage E_1 is perpendicular to the primary coil, then E_1 gives a minimum reading (theoretically zero), while E_2 gives an optimum indication. E_1 is impressed on the amplifier whose voltage amplification is to be determined and the secondary system tuned until E_2 gives the same deflection on a tube voltmeter as the output voltage of the amplifier. The voltage amplification is then E_2/E_1, which can be found from M_2/M_1 where M_2 denotes the mutual inductance of the E_2 coil with respect to the primary and M_1 the mutual inductance of the E_1 coil with respect to the primary.

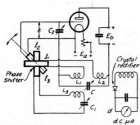

Fig. 295.—Determination of phase of a back-feed voltage.

178. Determination of Phase of a Back Feed.—In Fig. 295, L_1L_2C is an adjustable oscillation circuit. It also includes one coil l_1 of a phase shifter. A resonator $C_1L_3l_2$ is tuned to the frequency generated by the $CL_1L_2l_1$ circuit. The coil l_3 can be turned in the revolving field of the phase shifter and is connected across the filament and the grid which is also shunted by a tuning condenser C_2. Therefore the phase of the induced voltage e can be adjusted and read from the angle l_3 makes with the stationary-coil system of the phase shifter. The effect of the phase of e can be found from the deflection d of the coupled aperiodic circuit.

179. Notes on Distortion Measurements.—If audio-frequency amplifiers are to be tested for distortion, the method indicated in Fig. 296 can be used.   A condenser microphone with a tube circuit whose transmission characteristic is known and good is connected to the audio-frequency amplifier under test.   The audio current of the output is sent through

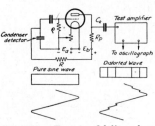

an ordinary oscillograph. If pure tones affect the condenser, a good amplifier should not show any distortions in the oscillograph record.   It is unnecessary to photograph the sine wave or to delineate it, since for a pure sine-wave output, the vibrating spot will trace out a rectangular area as indicated. For distortions, lines similar to spectral lines

Fig. 296.—Test for fidelity of an   will be observed.   However, this method is
audio-frequency amplifier.   unsatisfactory for some work, since
an oscillograph record cannot show distortions of much less than about 1 per cent.   In acoustic measurements, for instance, for the determination of the absorption and reflection factor of different building materials, currents which have a harmonic content of much more than 0.1 per cent cannot be used.   Indeed, the wave form must be even better, since in some methods the sound intensities at the pseudonodal points of stationary sound waves are measured and compared with the readings of materials for which practically zero intensity exist at such points. This is only possible if very pure sine currents are used.   The methods described in Secs. 56 and 76 are then satisfactory.   If T in Fig. 297 denotes the output tube, the harmonic content can then be found with a tube voltmeter and a sinusoidal search frequency.   The value of R is

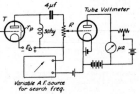

Fig. 297.—Determination of the fidelity of the variable-output current of an amplifier.

chosen equal to the plate resistance r_p.   But if the actual tube circuit uses an output transformer, $R = r_p/\rho^2$ denotes the reflected value of the tube resistance where ρ is the ratio of primary to secondary turns.   The test is carried out by applying pure sinusoidal voltages of different audio frequencies to the input stage and sweeping over the harmonic range with the search frequency.   This is described in detail in Sec. 56.   It is essential that the search-frequency oscillator have a good wave shape.

180. Notes and Tests on Special Tubes.—Photoelectric cells, glow-discharge tubes, thyratrons, etc., belong to this class.   For light-sensitive cells, it must be realized that their sensitivity changes with the frequency of the light which affects it.

The human eye can perceive only radiations of one octave of frequencies corresponding to wave lengths between $(4 \text{ to } 8)10^{-5}$ cm or 4000 to 8000 Å.U.   As with sound, in the case of the eye sensation units are dealt with.   The eye is not very suitable for estimating the intensity of light, since the brighter the light, the more change in intensity is needed in order that a change in brightness can be observed. The reason is that for certain intensity the change of intensity required to produce an effect upon the eye is proportional to the intensity itself. There is also a different sensitivity for different colors. At about 5550 Å.U., the normal eye is most sensitive. It requires about 10^{-8} erg/sec light intensity or the equivalent of 10^{-3} $\mu\mu$watt to just affect a normal eye.

The *lumen* is the quantity of light due to a source of 1 cp 1 ft distant and affecting an area of 1 sq ft during 1 sec. The intensity of illumination is called the *foot-candle*. For photoelectric cells, photons for any illumination are given off symmetrically about the normal of the emitting surface. Such an emission also exists for any angle of inci-dence and any direction of vibration of the electric vector of the light, and Lambert's cosine law $I = K$ 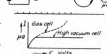 $\cos i \cos \dfrac{r}{d^2}$ gives the distribution of electrons in numbers for a fixed plane, if i is the angle of inci-dence, r the angle of reflection, and d the distance from source to plane. If a high-vacuum photoelec-tric cell is exposed to light for a certain plate po-tential E, a certain emission current will be

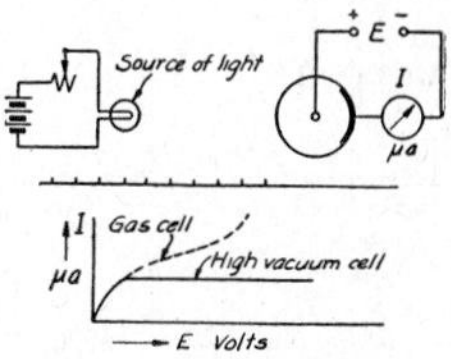

Fig. 298.—Illumi-nation test for a photo-electric cell.

noted. The plot of microamperes per lumen against the plate potential denotes one characteristic of a photoelectric cell. It is obtained by the method in Fig. 298 where the light source and the photoelectric cell are mounted in a box so that no other light may affect the light-sensitive cathode. The light flux in lumens is $l = \dfrac{C_p A}{d^2}$ if C_p denotes the candlepower of the light source affecting an area of A sq ft at a distance of d ft. In the characteristic for a high-vacuum cell, saturation takes place as in a high-vacuum thermionic tube. The plate current I is then no longer dependent upon the plate voltage if E is within the saturation region, which is of advantage for certain work. Since, according to theory, the number of emitted electrons is directly proportional to the intensity of the light source, a straight-line character-istic for the plate current as a function of the light flux in lumens is obtained for a high-vacuum cell. This can likewise be obtained by means of the circuit in Fig. 298 by changing the light intensity and taking I readings in microamperes for a certain fixed plate potential E. For a gas-filled cell the linearity holds for a limited portion only, and only approximately. However, it is good enough for many applications. The quality Q of a photoelectric cell is given by the relation

$$Q = \frac{1}{l}\frac{dI}{dE} = \frac{g}{l}$$

that is, by the conductance of the tube per lumen.

By dynamic response of a photoelectric cell is meant the changes in space current of a cell produced by changes in light flux. It is generally measured by light-flux variation in the audio-frequency range and for vacuum cells it does not vary with the frequency. As in the case of ordinary electron tubes, the interelectrode capacitance of a photoelectric cell must be taken into account within the range of very high frequencies.

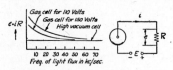

FIG. 299.—Output voltage in dependence of light variations.

The dynamic sensitivity of gas-filled cells decreases with increasing frequency of the light-flux modulation (Fig. 299). The sensitivity S is determined from the slope of the space-current lumen characteristic and is $S = dI/dl$, which shows that for the straight-line relation of the high-vacuum cell S is a constant as mentioned above, and the instantaneous space current $i = S l$. It should be understood, however, that the sensitivity S varies somewhat with the plate voltage but remains constant within the saturation region of a high-vacuum cell. The conductance of a photoelectric cell is therefore obtained by choosing two values I_1 and I_2 and their corresponding plate potentials E_1 and E_2 near the operating point of the space-current plate-voltage characteristic and computing $g = (I_1 - I_2)/(E_1 - E_2)$. In a similar way, the sensitivity is obtained for a given operating point by choosing two near-by points on the space-current lumen characteristic such as I_1 and I_2 with the corresponding light fluxes l_1 and l_2, and computing $S = (I_1 - I_2)/(l_1 - l_2)$. Figure 299 gives characteristic output-voltage curves for light-flux variations.

181. Notes on Certain Types of Tubes.—At different places in the text it has been necessary to mention certain types of tubes or their equivalent in order to give useful magnitudes of circuit constants. The few types of tubes mentioned are tabulated in Table XII.

TABLE XII

Type	Filament		Amplifier B battery, volts	Amplifier, negative C (battery) bias, volts	Plate current, ma	Alternating-current plate resistance, ohms	Mutual conductance g_m, μmhos	Amplification factor
	Voltage	Current, amp						
112A	5	0.25	135; 157.5; 180	9; 10.5; 13.5	7; 9.5; 9.5	5,000; 4,700; 4,700	1,600; 1,700; 1,700	8; 8; 8
201A*	5	0.25	90; 135	4.5; 9	2.5; 3	11,000; 10,000	725; 800	8; 8
222†	3.3	0.132	135	1.5 (control grid)	1.5	850 000	350	300
240	5	0.25	135; 180	1.5; 3	0.2; 0.2	150,000; 150,000	200; 200	30; 30
171A	5	0.25	90; 135; 180	16.5; 27; 40.5	10; 16; 20	2,500; 2,200; 2,000	1,200; 1,360; 1,500	3; 3; 3

* .01 is used at places in the list to denote a 201-A, 301-A, or 401-A tube.

† 222 tube has reference to a high-frequency amplifier and is a double-grid tube with 45 volts on the outer grid and 15 ma shield-grid current.

CHAPTER XIV

MODULATION MEASUREMENTS

Since a high-frequency current is characterized by its amplitude, frequency, and phase, such a current can be modulated by amplitude and frequency as well as by phase changes. Though procedures for amplitude and frequency modulation were already known in the earliest days of radio, they are again being discussed[1] because it has been thought that the width of the frequency channel for the transmission of speech and music could be made narrower if frequency modulation were employed. Phase modulation is usually an undesirable by-product, although there is no reason why it should not be used to advantage. A thorough knowledge of the underlying principles and the actions of the three types of modulations is important and methods are given whereby all types of modulations can be determined from measurements under actual conditions.

Addition of harmonic currents for a linear characteristic $(i = k_0 + k_1 e)$ where $e = E_1 \sin \lambda t + E_2 \sin \omega t$ (Only components of i of original frequencies λ (and ω) and no modulation.

Curved characteristic $(i = k_0 + k_1 e + k_2 e^2$ gives besides other terms for $p = k_2 E_1 E_2$ also the modulation term $2p \sin \lambda t + \sin(\lambda + \omega)t = p[\cos(\lambda - \omega) - \cos(\lambda + \omega)t]$

FIG. 300.—Addition of harmonic currents for a linear and a curved characteristic.

182. Circuits and Theory for Amplitude Modulation.—

Modulation is a process whereby amplitude, frequency, or phase of a high-frequency carrier is generally varied by means of an audible current. Sometimes two kinds of modulations are present and it may happen that all three types of modulations occur. By double modulation is understood a carrier current of a particular high frequency which is at first modulated by a signal wave and is then made to modulate another high-frequency current of different frequency. The degree of modulation is generally expressed in percentage and denotes the variation in amplitude of a modulated current from its mean value expressed in percentage of the mean value. The device which is used at the sender end for producing modulation is called the "modulator," and the device which is used in the receiver for extracting the modulation (signal wave) is called the "demodulator." As a rule, the modulator and demodulator operate (Fig. 300)

[1] CARSON, J. R., *Proc. I.R.E.*, **10**, 57, 1922; R. BOWN, DeLOSS K. MARTIN, and R. K. POTTER, *Bell System Tech. J.*, **5**, 143, 1926; H. SALINGER, *E.N.T.*, **9**, 1929; A. HEILMANN, *E.N.T.*, **6**, 1, 1930; W. LOEST, *Z. Hochfreq.*, **36**, 188, 1930; T. L. ECKERSLEY, *Exptl. Wireless*, **7**, 482, 1930; C. H. SMITH, *Exptl. Wireless*, **7**, 609, 1930; B. VAN DER POL, *Proc. I.R.E.*, **18**, 1194, 1930; W. RUNGE, *E.N.T.*, **7**, 488, 1930; J. C. SCHELLENG, *Proc. I.R.E.*, **18**, 913, 1930; A. HEILMANN, *E.N.T.*, **8**, 469, 1931.

along a *nonlinear* characteristic. For this reason, it is customary to utilize either the curved portion of a tube characteristic or the magnetization curvature in the case of a ferromagnetic modulator. It must be understood, however, that there are also cases where the parabolic portion of the tube characteristic will not produce demodulation. For instance, this happens when an arriving electromagnetic wave is modulated in frequency only and equivalent to the carrier wave of the high frequency F and an infinitude of side bands, separated in frequency by integral multiples of the modulating frequency f, whose amplitudes are given by Bessel functions of increasing orders. At first inspection, it would appear that a detector tube produces an audio current of frequency f but this is not the case because of the phase relationship between the side bands. It *is* the *phase relationship* and *not the width of the band* where frequency modulation differs fundamentally from amplitude modulation. Therefore, it is necessary that a circuit be inserted between the receiving aerial and the tube with a curved work characteristic which translates frequency modulation partially into amplitude variation.

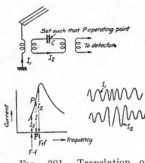

FIG. 301.—Translation of frequency modulation in I_1, into amplitude variation in I_2.

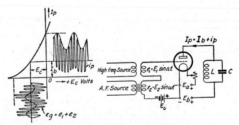

FIG. 302.—Grid modulation.

This can be readily done by using a CL circuit which is *not* tuned to resonance with the carrier frequency F about which frequency modulations $\pm f$ take place, but on a suitable point P of the ascending or descending portion of the resonance curve (Fig. 301). The current in the CL circuit will then fluctuate between a maximum and a minimum value about the value I, corresponding to the unmodulated carrier frequency F. Of course, this can also be done directly in the sender arrangement or in the sender as well as the receiver. The general case of amplitude modulation has been dealt with in Sec. 8. Amplitude modulation can be done by means of grid modulation (Fig. 302) or plate modulation (Fig. 304). For grid modulation the negative grid bias is so chosen that the square law for the variable plate current holds with a good degree of approximation and $i_p = k_1 e_g + k_2 e_g{}^2 +$ terms which are neglected. If $\Omega/2\pi = F$, the frequency of sinusoidal high-frequency voltage e_1 impressed on the grid, and $\omega/2\pi = f$, the frequency of audio voltage e_2, there is obtained for this characteristic curvature

$$i_p = k_1[E_1 \sin \Omega t + E_2 \sin \omega t] + k_2[E_1{}^2 \sin^2 \Omega t + E_2{}^2 \sin^2 \omega t +$$
$$2E_1 E_2 \sin \Omega t \sin \omega t] \quad (1)$$

Since the steepness of the work characteristic is

$$g_m = \frac{\partial i_p}{\partial e_g} = k_1 + 2k_2 e_g + \underbrace{3k_3 e_g{}^2 + 4k_4 e_g{}^3 + \cdots}_{\text{negligible}} \quad (2)$$

it can be seen that g_m can only be a linear function of $e_g = e_1 + e_2$ if both amplitudes E_1 and E_2 of e_1 and e_2 are not very large. Therefore grid modulation cannot be applied to cases where the tube is worked to full capacity; otherwise considerable distortion will take place.

Expanding (1) gives

$$i_p = k_1[E_1 \sin \Omega t + E_2 \sin \omega t] + 0.5k_2[E_1{}^2 + E_2{}^2 + 2E_1 E_2 \cos (\Omega - \omega)t$$
$$- 2E_1 E_2 \cos (\Omega + \omega)t + E_1{}^2 \cos 2\Omega t - E_2{}^2 \cos 2\omega t] \quad (3)$$

There are, therefore, four high frequencies, $F = \Omega/(2\pi)$, $2F$, $(F + f)$, and $(F - f)$, and two low frequencies, $f = \omega/(2\pi)$ and $2f$. Since the CL circuit in the plate branch is tuned to the carrier frequency F only, components of such a frequency predominate in the plate current and, according to (1) and (3),

$$i_p = \underbrace{k_1 E_1 \sin \Omega t}_{\substack{\text{carrier current} \\ \text{only}}} + \underbrace{2k_2 E_1 E_2 \sin \Omega t \sin \omega t}_{\text{modulation term}}$$

$$= \underbrace{k_1 E_1 \sin \Omega t}_{\substack{\text{term of frequency} \\ F}} + \underbrace{k_2 E_1 E_2 \cos (\Omega - \omega)t}_{\substack{\text{current of frequency} \\ F - f}} - \underbrace{k_2 E_1 E_2 \cos (\Omega + \omega)t}_{\substack{\text{current of frequency} \\ F + f}} \quad (4)$$

which is drawn in detail in Fig. 303. If such an amplitude-modulated wave is radiated and received with an aerial, the received voltage of frequencies F, $F - f$, and $F + f$ must be again impressed on a square-law detector (demodulator) in order to extract the audio current of frequency f. In the demodulator, if single side-band reception (F and $F + f$ only) is chosen, there is obtained the summation oscillation of frequency $2F + f$, which cannot be heard, and the difference oscillation of the desired audio frequency f. If the plate-current variations vary over a portion of the dynamic characteristic for which the cubic term is also to be considered, $i_p = k_1 e_g + k_2 e_g{}^2 + k_3 e_g{}^3$, and additional current components of high frequencies $F + 2f$ and $F - 2f$ will appear, requiring a double side-band width of $4f$. For amplitude modulation, according to Fig. 17, the instantaneous value of the modulated high-frequency current is obtained as

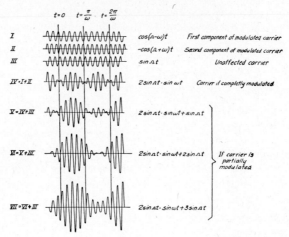

FIG. 303.—$\Omega/2\pi$ = frequency of carrier current. $\omega/2\pi$ = frequency of audio current which modulates.

$$I_t = I_m \sin \Omega t + i_m \sin \Omega t \sin \omega t = I_m[1 + K \sin \omega t] \sin \Omega t \qquad (5)$$

where $K = i_m/I_m$ denotes the degree of modulation. According to Eq. (52) of Sec. 8,

$$I_t = I_m[\sin \Omega t + 0.5K \cos (\Omega - \omega) - 0.5K \cos (\Omega + \omega)] \qquad (5a)$$

showing that the carrier current of high frequency F has an amplitude I_m, and $KI_m/2$ is the amplitude of the lower and upper side frequency $F - f$ and $F + f$, respectively.

For the case of plate modulation as in Fig. 304, more modulated power can be obtained than with grid modulation, especially when the

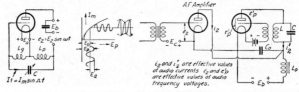

FIG. 304.—Plate modulation.

audio-frequency voltage e_2 is first amplified before it is connected into the plate branch of the high-frequency oscillator CL of frequency $\Omega/2\pi$. A common B battery of voltage E_b is provided for both the audio-frequency amplifier and the high-frequency oscillator and C_0 offers a low-impedance branch to the high-frequency currents, while L_0 is a large iron choke.

If i_2 denotes the audio-current fluctuation in the plate branch of the amplifier tube, and i_2' the audio fluctuation in the plate branch of the high-frequency oscillator, the voltage variation across L_0 is $j\omega L_0[i_2 + i_2']$ if the resistance of L_0 is small compared with ωL_0. The more variable current the amplifier tube draws from the common B supply, the larger is the voltage drop across L_0 and the smaller the voltage available in the plate of the oscillator tube of the internal plate resistance r_p', and it is smaller the more the high-frequency current is modulated (decreased in this particular case), since for the mean plate current i_2' with respect to the high-frequency current $i_2' = -j\omega L_0[i_2 + i_2']/r_p'$ and $i_2 = [\mu e_g - j\omega L_0[i_2 + i_2']/r_p$. These two expressions lead to

$$\frac{e_p'}{e_g} = \frac{j\omega L_0[i_2 + i_2']}{e_g} = \frac{j\mu\omega L_0}{r_p[1 + j\omega L_0\left[\dfrac{1}{r_p} + \dfrac{1}{r_p'}\right]}$$

making the audio-frequency voltage variations e_p' on the plate of the oscillator a maximum value if ωL is very large compared with the plate resistance of either tube. The approximation $e_p'/e_g = \mu/(1 + \rho)$ then holds if $\rho = r_p/r_p'$; from which it is evident that e_p'/e_g is large if the plate resistance of the oscillator tube is larger than that of the amplifier tube and becomes equal to the amplification factor of the amplifier tube if r_p/r_p' is negligible compared with unity. Moreover, from the i_2' expression given above, $i_2 = -\left[1 + \dfrac{jr_p'}{\omega L_0}\right]i_2' \cong -i_2'$ if $r_p' \ll \omega L_0$ showing that L_0 should be large. The audio-frequency components are then equal in both plate branches.

From the above discussion for the amplifier-modulated oscillator current and the characteristics of the amplitude of the high-frequency current in the CL_gL_p branch against the plate potential (Fig. 304), $I_m = gE_p$ if g denotes the steepness of the work characteristic. Therefore, $I_t = gE_p \sin \Omega t$. But $E_p = E_b + e_2 = E_b + E_2 \sin \omega t$, and the expression

$$I_t = g[E_b \sin \Omega t + E_2 \sin \Omega t \sin \omega t]$$
$$= gE_b[1 + K \sin \omega t] \sin \Omega t \qquad (6)$$

is obtained. Exactly the same relation as in equations (5) and (5a) is obtained for $gE_b = I_m$. It does not matter whether grid or plate modulation is employed for modulation measurements. However, it is of

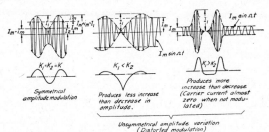

FIG. 305.—Symmetrical and unsymmetrical amplitude modulation.

importance whether symmetrical or unsymmetrical amplitude modulation exists (Fig. 305). Hence there generally are two significant influence factors K_1 and K_2 which express modulation so that the maximum instantaneous value of the modulated current is $I_1 = I_m[1 + K_1]$ and the minimum value $I_2 = I_m[1 + K_2]$. For the symmetrical case both influence factors are equal and $K_1 = K_2 = (I_1 - I_m)/I_m = (I_m - I_2)/I_m$

$= i_m/I_m = K$. For the second case, shown in Fig. 305, the maximum instantaneous value I_1 of the modulated current is less above than the minimum instantaneous value I_2 is below the I_m line. Therefore the influence factor K_1 is smaller than K_2. The opposite is true for the third diagram of Fig. 305 and $K_2 > K_1$. The average value $0.5[K_1 + K_2]$ can then be used to obtain an idea of the modulation K and

$$K = \left[\frac{I_1 - I_m}{I_m} + \frac{I_m - I_2}{I_m} \right] = \frac{I_1 - I_2}{2I_m} \qquad (7)$$

Therefore it can be seen that the degree of amplitude modulation can be found by measuring I_1, I_2, and I_m or the corresponding voltages E_1, E_2, and E_m. For symmetrical amplitude modulation it is necessary only to measure the amplitude without modulation and the amplitude when modulation exists. A vacuum-tube voltmeter is fundamentally a device which measures maximum voltage and lends itself readily for the measurement of E_1 and E_m corresponding to I_1 and I_m, and to finding K. It is a method which has been employed in most laboratories since the advent of the electron tube.

183. Determination of Amplitude Modulation.—Using the scheme just described, which consists of measuring with a tube voltmeter across a portion of a circuit, the maximum voltage E_1 when a wave is modulated with a sinusoidal current and the maximum voltage E_m for no modulation and computing, according to Fig. 17 (if voltages instead of currents are used), the percentage modulation from $K = 100[E_1 - E_m]/E_m$. As simple as this method seems to be, it has the following disadvantages:

1. It requires symmetrical modulation ($K_1 = K_2 = K$, Fig. 305).

2. It is assumed that the carrier amplitude has the same value with and without modulation.

3. It is necessary to take one reading without modulation which can be done only at the sender end and not at the receiver unless the sender and receiver stations experiment together.

Therefore the errors with this method can be considerable, unless the above precautions are taken. The objection that the method cannot be used with a received high-frequency wave is not serious, since the intensity of the sound heard at the receiver end also depends upon the demodulator of the receiver as well as upon the selectivity used in the stages of high-frequency amplification. If the selectivity is too high, only poor quality in sound reproduction can be expected, since the pass band may not be wide enough to accommodate the width of half the band width required owing to the gravest modulation frequency at the sender end. It is then best to test the receiving set with a local high-frequency source, which can be readily modulated or used without modulation. In the case of local modulation objection 2 can be almost avoided if the plate-current (Heising) modulation is properly adjusted.

If an ordinary oscillograph with two vibrator elements is available, the case of unsymmetrical modulation (objection 1) may be observed and objection 2 with respect to a change of the carrier amplitude is avoided, since an oscillogram is taken under actual conditions. One way of using the oscillograph is by coupling a few turns to the circuit which carries the modulated current. The few turns of the coupling coil work over a rectifier (demodulator) and through one vibrator element of the oscillograph. The other vibrator element is set in such a way that the image on the ground glass coincides with the image of the other vibrator when no current affects it. If modulated high-frequency current flows in the measuring circuit, one image will give a steady deflection and trace a line on the revolving drum which is produced a distance d_m from the zero line traced by the other vibrator (which is not connected in any circuit). The distance d_m is a measure for the rectified amplitudes I_m of the unmodulated high-frequency current. If modulation exists, according to Fig. 305, the image spot of the vibrator affected by the rectified current gives the values d_1 and d_2 corresponding to I_1 and I_2. The mean value $0.5[d_1 + d_2]$ of the extreme swings of the sinusoidal-amplitude trace is taken as the amplitude d_m of the carrier. The degree of modulation is then [according to (7)] computed from $K = 0.5[d_1 - d_2]/d_m = [d_1 - d_2]/[d_1 + d_2]$. There-fore it is necessary only to take the readings d_1 and d_2 under the actual (modulated) condition. The method[1] shown in Fig. 306 is simpler than the oscillograph procedure and requires but two thermionic rectifier tubes. Ordinary three-element tubes with the grid and plate tied to-gether will then also do. This method again takes into account the actual condition and can

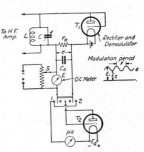

FIG. 306.—Determination of amplitude modulation.

therefore also be used to determine the degree of modulation of a received wave where, as mentioned above, it must be realized that because of circuit tuning (CL branch of Fig. 306) the degree of modulation may be decreased. The tube T_1 acts as demodulator where $r_0 = 3 \times 10^5 \Omega$ and $C_0 = 500 \ \mu\mu$f acts practically as a short circuit for the carrier current, but as an open circuit for the modulation component. Therefore the voltage e across C_0 has the form indicated in the figure. By means of another recti-fier tube (T_2) and a sensitive direct-current meter, the voltage E_1 and E_2 can be measured by an auxiliary adjustable voltage E. The double-pole switch is first connected toward 1 and the potentiometer slider S moved until the microammeter just reads zero. The voltmeter then gives the value $E = E_1$. The double-pole double-throw switch is connected on 2 and by means of zero-current balance the reading $E = E_2$ is obtained.

[1] Van der Pol, B., and K. Posthumus, *Exptl. Wireless*, **4**, 140, 1927.

The percentage modulation is then computed from $K\% = 100[E_1 - E_2]/[E_1 + E_2]$. If the modulation of a received wave is determined, the CL branch is also used and C tuned to the carrier frequency. The supply from the amplifier is so chosen that about 10 volts exists across C. Figure 307 gives the method of E. Mauz[1] which determines the degree of modulation with a cathode-ray tube. This method applies the audio-frequency modulation voltage across one deflection condenser of the cathode-ray tube, and the high-frequency output with its modulation is impressed

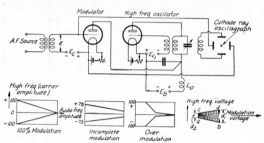

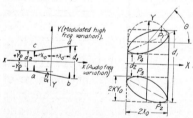

Fig. 307.—Cathode-ray oscillograph for finding degree of amplitude modulation (*abd* cathode-ray pattern for incomplete modulation).

across the other deflection condenser. Since the high frequency and the audio frequency generally have no harmonic relation, a fluorescent area as indicated in the figure will be seen on the screen of the tube. The long vertical side d_1 indicates the large double amplitude $2I_1$ (Fig. 305) and d_2 the smallest double amplitude $2I_2$ and $0.5[d_1 + d_2]$ is the average value, that is, equal to the double amplitude of the carrier. Therefore the percentage modulation can be computed from $K\% = 100[d_1 - d_2]/[d_1 + d_2]$. For complete modulation $d_2 = 0$. The amplitude traces ab and cd are straight but curved for distorted modulation. According to Fig. 308, one must distinguish between a trapezoid and an equivalent trapezoid for which a phase angle θ for the audio-frequency deflection exists. The variation along the X-axis is due to the audio-frequency variation of a demodulated current (Fig. 309) and the variation along the Y direction of the cathode-ray pattern is due to the modulated high-frequency current in the CL circuit. The spot along the Y-axis then follows the law $y = \pm Y_0[1 + K \varphi(t)]$ where $\varphi(t)$ is the time function of the audio-frequency variation and, according to Eq. (5), $Y_0 = Y_m \sin \Omega t$. The time function $\varphi(t)$ varies between ± 1. The tube demodulator

Fig. 308.—*abdca* area as traced by fluorescent spot; XX and YY lines traced if only audio frequency or if only modulated carrier voltages act.

[1] Mauz, E., and J. Zenneck, *Jahrb. d. drahtl.*, **19**, 256, 1922; *Western Elec. Instruction Bull.* 176; M. v. Ardenne, *E.N.T.*, **7**, 80, 1930.

produces a low-frequency variation in the plate branch which produces the deflection $x = X_0\,\varphi(t)[1 + 0.5K\,\varphi(t)]$. For K small, $x = X_0\,\varphi(t)$ as an approximation and $X_0 = \text{cons } K$. These two relations give a trapezoid with the two straight lines $y = \pm Y_0[1 + \text{cons } x] = \pm Y_0[1 + x\tan\alpha]$ of constant spread and the parallel boundary lines are given by $x = \pm X_0$. For the left diagram of Fig. 308 there is no phase shift of the audio-frequency modulation in the modulator and the branch connected to the cathode-ray tube. If a choke coil is connected between terminals 1 and 2 of Fig. 309, a phase shift θ is produced as is shown in Fig. 308. The same also happens when a demodulator with succeeding stages of audio-frequency amplification is used before connecting the audio-frequency voltage to the cathode-ray tube.

The stationary patterns as indicated in Figs. 307 and 308 will not appear when the modulation K is not constant (for voice and other variable modulation). It is then necessary to use the deflection of the

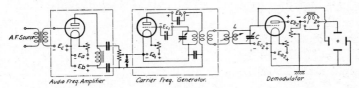

Audio Freq. Amplifier   Carrier Freq. Generator.   Demodulator

FIG. 309.—Circuit for the fluorescent trace shown in Fig. 308.

modulated high-frequency current only, that is, the Y deflection, and use either a revolving mirror to view the modulations or a revolving film to photograph them. A linear time-axis device can also be used for this purpose.

Another method for determining modulation utilizes the fact that, for a current meter which responds to the heat effect (thermoelectric indicator, hot-wire meter), the measured modulated current is larger than for no modulation and even for symmetrical modulation. This can be seen from the following. For no modulation, the instantaneous value of the carrier current is $I_t = I_m \sin \Omega t$ and a thermoelectric indicator gives the effective current reading

$$I_1 = \sqrt{\frac{1}{2\pi}\int_0^{2\pi} I_m{}^2 \sin^2 \Omega t\, dt} = \frac{I_m}{\sqrt{2}}$$

For the modulation $K = i_m/I_m$, the effective current reading becomes

$$I_2 = \sqrt{\frac{1}{2\pi}\int_0^{2\pi} I_m{}^2 \sin^2 \Omega t[1 + K \sin \omega t]^2 dt} = \frac{I_m}{\sqrt{2}}\sqrt{1 + 0.5K^2}$$

and the two readings give the relation $I_2 = I_1\sqrt{1 + 0.5K^2}$. The percentage

$$K = 141\sqrt{\left[\frac{I_2}{I_1}\right]^2 - 1} \qquad (8)$$

where K is in percentage. For 100 per cent modulation $I_2 = 1.224I_1$. It is then possible to design a direct-indicating modulation meter which gives the percentage modulation directly. The deflections of the meter must then be chosen such that the indications between 1 and 1.224 utilize a large portion of the scale. This can be easily done by making the maximum deflection of the indicator 1.224. In place of the currents, $K\%$ is engraved. Hence the maximum deflection is marked 100 and the deflection 1 is $K = 0$. The thermoelectric meter is then connected to a coil of a few turns which are coupled to a high-frequency circuit, which at first carries an unmodulated carrier current of the desired high frequency $\Omega/2\pi$. The coupling is then varied until the modulation indicator just reads $K = 0$. The high-frequency carrier is then modulated and a larger deflection will be noted which gives the percentage modulation directly. The calibration of the meter can be carried on either with known calibrations or by means of Table XIII and the graphical solution of Fig. 310. It is based upon Eq. (8) by writing $[0.707K]^2 = [I_2/I_1]^2 - 1$. For $K = 1$, that is, 100 per cent modulation, the height h of the triangle of Fig. 310 is 0.707, the base is unity, and $I_2/I_1 = 1.2247$. For no modulation $K = 0$ there is $I_2/I_1 = 1$ which is the base line and the other extreme. This method is applicable in finding approximately the degree of modulation, or where it is necessary to keep a check upon a certain degree of modulation. In the same way

Fig. 310.—Graphical construction for finding degree of amplitude modulation.

TABLE XIII

K, per cent	$I_2/I_1 = \sqrt{1 - 0.5K^2}$	h
100	1.2247	0.707
90	1.1853	0.636
80	1.1489	0.565
70	1.1158	0.495
60	1.0863	0.424
50	1.0606	0.353
40	1.0392	0.283
30	1.0222	0.212
20	1.0099	0.1414
10	1.0025	0.0707

a voltmeter giving the effective voltage reading can be used for a direct-reading modulation meter. Such modulation meters should, however, not be confused with, for instance, meters, used often in broadcast stations, which merely indicate the relative magnitude of audio-frequency voltage. Another form of modulation meter has been developed by

K. W. Jarvis.[1] It makes use of the audible-current components in the plate branch of a demodulator and employs a tube voltmeter to determine the effective audio current by means of the voltage drop across a known resistance in the plate branch of the demodulator. The action of the method is based upon the expression

$$i_p = e_g \frac{\partial I_p}{\partial E} + \frac{e_g{}^2}{2} \frac{\partial^2 I_p}{\partial E^2} + \frac{e_g{}^3}{6} \frac{\partial^3 I_p}{\partial E^3} + \cdots \tag{9}$$

This relation holds for the change in current in an ordinary three-element tube of lumped control voltage E in the relation

$$I_p = F\left(\frac{E_p}{\mu} + E_g\right) = F(E)$$

for the voltage function F and the relation $I + i_p = F(E + e_g)$ if a variable voltage e_g across the grid and the filament produces the variation e_p in the plate current, where it must be understood that $\partial I_p/\partial E$ depends upon the load in the external plate branch. Now, if the carrier voltage $E_m \cos \Omega t$ is modulated and the voltage $e_g = E_m \cos \Omega t[1 + K \cos \omega t]$ is applied to the grid of a demodulator for which only the terms with $\partial I_p/\partial E$ and $\frac{\partial^2 I_p}{\partial E^2}$ play a part, and if all high-frequency terms are omitted, the change i_p in plate current becomes

$$i_p = \underbrace{\frac{E_m{}^2}{4} \frac{\partial^2 I_p}{\partial E^2}}_{\substack{\text{increase in plate} \\ \text{current } I_p \text{ due to} \\ \text{rectification}}} + \underbrace{\frac{K^2 E_m{}^2}{8} \frac{\partial^2 E_p}{\partial E^2}}_{\substack{\text{increase in plate} \\ \text{current } I_p \text{ due} \\ \text{to side band}}} +$$

$$\underbrace{}_{i_1 = \text{d-c component of } i_p}$$

$$+ \underbrace{\frac{K E_m{}^2 \cos \omega t}{2} \frac{\partial^2 E_p}{\partial E^2}}_{\substack{\text{useful audio-frequency} \\ \text{modulation}}} + \underbrace{\frac{K^2 E_m{}^2 \cos 2\omega t}{8} \frac{\partial^2 I_p}{\partial E^2}}_{\substack{\text{double audio-frequency} \\ \text{modulation since both} \\ \text{side currents beat with} \\ \text{each other}}} \tag{9a}$$

$$\underbrace{}_{i_2 = \text{a-c component of } i_p}$$

The first term $\frac{E_m{}^2}{4} \frac{\partial^2 I_p}{\partial E^2}$ denotes the rectification effect. Hence, if the detector action $\partial^2 I_p/\partial E^2$ is known or found experimentally, and if the audio current i_p and the maximum voltage E_m are measured, the modulation K can be found from (9). This method then has the inherent advantage that $\partial^2 I_p/\partial E^2$ changes with the external plate load of the demodulator and, if an impedance is used for load, it becomes also a function of the frequency. Besides, the carrier voltage is modulated and it is difficult to measure E_m accurately. For these reasons Eq. (9a)

[1] *Proc. I.R.E.*, **17**, 697, 1929.

is split into a direct-current component i_1 and an alternating-current component i_2, giving

$$i_1 = 0.5E_m{}^2\frac{\partial^2 I_p}{\partial E^2}[0.5 + 0.25K^2]; \quad i_2 = 0.5E_m{}^2\frac{\partial^2 I_p}{\partial E^2}[K\cos\omega t +$$
$$0.25K^2\cos 2\omega t] \quad (10)$$

If the $e_g = E_m\cos\Omega t\ [1 + K\cos\omega t]$ is so adjusted that a constant direct-current change i occurs in the value of I_p noted by a direct-current meter in the plate branch and irrespective of the value of modulation K, then $i_1 = i$ and the first expression of (10) gives $0.5E_m{}^2\partial^2 I_p/\partial E^2 = 4i/(2 + K^2)$, which, inserted in the second expression of (10), gives for the remaining audible alternating-current components

$$i_2 = \frac{4i}{2 + K^2}[K\cos\omega t + 0.25\cos 2\omega t]$$

or

$$I_2 = \frac{4iK}{2 + K^2}\sqrt{1 + 0.0625K^2} \quad (11)$$

since the effective current I_2 in this case is due to two currents of frequency $\omega/2\pi$ and ω/π and equal to the square-root value of the sum of their squares. In many cases the square-root factor may be put equal to unity, since the effect of the double audio frequency even for $K\%$ = 100, that is, $K = 1$, is only about 4 per cent. Taking other errors into account, the total error is about 5 per cent. The approximation formula is then $I_2 = 4iK/(2 + K^2)$, from which K can be found, since I_2 can be

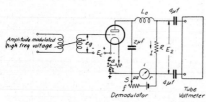

Fig. 311.—Determination of modulation (L_0 is high-frequency choke and R load resistance.)

measured with a tube voltmeter which determines only the effective alternating voltage E_2 across a known resistance R in the plate branch of the modulator and i is the constant direct-current shift in the plate current. The circuit is then as in Fig. 311. With no modulated voltage e_g acting on the grid, the slider S is moved until the direct-current micro-ammeter i reads zero. The modulated voltage e_g is impressed and the deflection of the direct-current meter noted, and i is computed by means of ρ and r. The tube voltmeter which measures the effective voltage E_2 gives the value I_2 by means of R. K is then found from (11) or the simplified expression.

184. Notes on Frequency and Phase Modulation.—Frequency modulation may be produced by varying either the capacitive or inductive reactance of an oscillator. This can be done, for instance, by using a condenser microphone as the capacitance value C of the CL circuit, which practically determines the frequency of the oscillation. The value of C is then no longer a constant but a time function $C_t = C + \Delta C \cos \omega t$. Solutions for the case of a non-dissipative oscillator have been given by J. R. Carson[1] and by B. Van der Pol.[1]

Suppose $\Omega/2\pi = F$ is the frequency of the carrier, that is, the high frequency produced by the CL oscillator and $\omega/2\pi = f$ the modulating frequency. For no modulations, there is the ordinary simplified resonance relation $\Omega = 1/\sqrt{CL}$, while, for the presence of modulations, there is a variable high frequency of instantaneous value $F_t = \Omega_t/2\pi$ and the relation $\Omega_t = 1/\sqrt{C_t L}$. In the relation $C_t = C + \Delta C \cos \omega t$, the quantity C denotes the constant capacity value about which the value of C_t fluctuates with a comparatively small amplitude ΔC, since $m = \Delta C/C$ is small compared with unity. Hence,

$$\Omega_t{}^2 = \frac{1}{CL[1 + m \cos \omega t]} \cong \Omega^2[1 - m \cos \omega t] = \Omega^2[1 + 2p \cos \omega t]$$

if $p = \Delta\Omega/\Omega$, since $\Delta C/C = -2\Delta\Omega/\Omega$ and $\Delta\Omega$ is the maximum deviation of the angular velocity from its mean value Ω. The relation $niL + \dfrac{i}{nC} = 0$ for $n = \dfrac{d}{dt}$ and $\dfrac{1}{n} = \int dt$ expresses that the voltage drop around the non-dissipative characteristic CL loop is zero. Multiplying the equation by n and dividing it by L leads to $n^2 i + \dfrac{i}{CL} = 0$.

For the time function C_t instead of C, the relation $n^2 i + \dfrac{i}{C_t L}$ is obtained. But $\dfrac{1}{C_t L} = \Omega_t{}^2 = \Omega^2[1 + 2p \cos \omega t]$ and, realizing that $n^2 i = d^2 i/dt^2$, the differential equation

$$\frac{d^2 i}{dt^2} + \Omega^2[1 + 2p \cos \omega t]i = 0 \tag{12}$$

is obtained, which is a typical equation of the Mathieu function.[2] The solution is then $i = A \cos \left(\Omega t + \dfrac{\Delta\Omega}{\omega} \sin \omega t \right)$ which can be used to find the component frequencies by spectral analysis. The spectral solution in Carson's paper[3] gives an expression of the form

$$\sum_{-\infty}^{+\infty} B_q \cos [(\Omega + q\omega)t + \theta_q]$$

and the frequencies present in the frequency-modulated wave are an *infinite* series spaced at the interval $\omega/2\pi = f$ and are F, $F + f$, $F - f$, $F + 2f$, $F - 2f$, $F + 3f$, $F - 3f$, etc., and the *frequency channel* must be at least *just as wide* as for amplitude modulation. Van der Pol's solution leads to the same conclusion. For unity amplitude in $i = A \cos \left(\Omega t + \dfrac{\Delta\Omega}{\omega} \sin \omega t \right)$ one finds for $\beta = \Delta\Omega/\omega$

[1] *Loc. cit.*

[2] Humbert, "Fonctions de Lamé et fonctions de Mathieu," Paris, 1926; or Whittaker and Watson, "Modern Analysis," p. 402.

[3] *Loc. cit.*

$i = \cos [\Omega t + \beta \sin \omega t]$

$= J_0\beta \cos \Omega t$ term of carrier frequency F

$\quad -J_1\beta\{\cos (\Omega - \omega)t - \cos (\Omega + \omega)t\}$ ⎱ term giving the first two side frequencies ⎰ $F + f$ and $F - f$

$\quad +J_2\beta\{\cos (\Omega - 2\omega)t + \cos (\Omega + 2\omega)t\}$ ⎱ giving side frequencies $F + 2f$ and ⎰ $F - 2f$

$\quad -J_3\beta\{\cos (\Omega - 3\omega)t - \cos (\Omega + 3\omega)t\}$ for side frequencies $F + 3f$ and $F - 3f$

$\quad + \cdots$ \hfill (13)

From the above discussion it is evident that a *frequency*-modulated current is equivalent to a carrier wave of frequency F and an infinitude of side frequencies separated in integral multiples of the modulating frequency f. The amplitudes of the side-frequency currents are partially given by Bessel functions of increasing order J_0, J_1, J_2, J_3, etc., and the factor $\beta = \Delta\Omega/\omega = \Delta F/f$ which is the ratio of the absolute frequency deviation ΔF to the modulation frequency f. For a *small* value of β, as often occurs in high-frequency work, for instance, $\beta = 0.2$, the *spectrum practically consists* of the *carrier frequency* F only and the *first two side frequencies* $F + f$ and $F - f$ and the instantaneous value of the modulated current of unit amplitude ($I_m = 1$) becomes

$$i = I_t = \cos \Omega t - \beta \sin \Omega t \sin \omega t \qquad (14)$$
$$\text{(for \textit{frequency} modulation)}$$

for which either amplitude of the side frequencies $F + f$ and $F - f$ is 0.5β times the amplitude of the carrier. Comparing this result with

$$I_t = \sin \Omega t - \beta \sin \Omega t \sin\omega t \qquad (15)$$
$$\text{(for \textit{amplitude} modulation)}$$

shows that the same double-band width $2f$ exists for both kinds of modulations (with the assumption that β is a small value) *but* that there is a phase shift of 90 deg between carrier and modulation component in the case of frequency modulation. For the sinusoidal modulation of frequency f of a carrier of frequency F, it may be said that the width of the channel is practically $2f$ as long as ΔF is smaller than f, and practically $2\Delta F$ as long as f is smaller than ΔF. Hence the larger value of the quantities ΔF and f, respectively, determines the width of the frequency channel which accommodates the double side band. Therefore the phase relation of 90 deg which occurs in (14) is where frequency modulation (with the above assumptions β small) differs from amplitude modulation [Eq. (15)] and *not the width* of the channel. For this reason a current which is purely frequency modulated *cannot* produce an audio-frequency output in customary parabolic demodulators but requires first some form of amplitude translation as described in connection with Fig. 301.

Frequency modulation may give rise to errors if selectivity curves of a radio receiver are taken with poorly designed signal generators. It may happen that the selectivity curve of the receiver is somewhat bent out on one side of resonance and very much pushed in on the other side.

That an unsymmetry of this kind may be due to a modulated signal generator, rather than to the test set, can be understood from the following: Suppose plate modulation is produced with a customary tube oscillator, for instance, by means of a 400-cycle audio-frequency source. Both the amplitude and the frequency of the output current of the generator will vary over a definite range. If the receiver is tuned to the average value of the carrier frequency, the frequency modulation cannot seriously affect the reading on the output meter. But if readings are noted for one side of resonance, the amplitude modulation due to frequency modulation increases the value of the true amplitude variation. On the other side of the resonance curve, the frequency modulation which is translated into amplitude modulation subtracts from the value of the true amplitude variation. The translation of frequency into amplitude modulation is all the more pronounced, the more selective the receiver. It may happen that the added and subtracted translated modulation is of the order of the true amplitude modulation. To find to what extent frequency modulation affects the test curve, it is only necessary to take a selectivity curve without modulation, or by generating the modulated high-frequency current by applying the modulation to a separately excited amplifier.

Moreover, it can be seen that sinusoidal frequency modulation at frequency $\omega/2\pi = f$ about a carrier frequency $\Omega/2\pi = F$ gives the instantaneous angular velocity $\Omega_t = \Omega + \Delta\Omega \sin \omega t$ where $\Delta\Omega$ denotes the maximum deviation from Ω. The instantaneous value of the high frequency then varies between the limits $F + \Delta F$ and $F - \Delta F$ and does this f times per second. For an unmodulated carrier current of instantaneous value $I_m \sin \Omega t$, there is then found for *frequency* modulation for $\beta = \Delta\Omega/\omega = \Delta F/f$ a small value, the instantaneous value for the current

$$I_f = I_m \sin [\Omega t - \beta \cos \omega t]$$
$$= I_m\{\sin \Omega t + \cos [\beta \cos \omega t] - \cos \Omega t \sin [\beta \cos \omega t]$$
$$\cong I_m\{\sin \Omega t - \cos \Omega t \, \beta \cos \omega t\}$$
$$= I_m \sin [2\pi F t] - 0.5\beta I_m \cos [2\pi(F + f)t] - 0.5\beta I_m$$
$$\cos [2\pi(F - f)t] \quad (16)$$

in comparison with the instantaneous value, from Eqs. (5) and (5a),

$$I_a = I_m \sin \Omega t [1 + K \sin \omega t]$$
$$= I_m \sin \Omega t - 0.5K I_m \cos [2\pi(F + f)t] + 0.5K I_m \cos [2\pi(F - f)t] \quad (17)$$

for *amplitude* modulation. These two relations show clearly that for *frequency* modulation the phase of *one* side current is shifted by 180 deg, and with the above assumptions (β small) the width of the frequency channel required for faithful transmission of the modulation is just as wide for either kind of modulation. For either type of modulation the respective amplitudes of the side currents have the same value. For frequency modulation the ratio of side-current amplitude to carrier amplitude is 0.5β, while this ratio for amplitude modulation is $0.5K$ where K denotes the degree of modulation. Since $\beta = \Delta F/f$, for large values of f, the frequency modulation is very small and for certain small values of the modulating frequency f the value $\beta = K$ is approached. If then frequency and amplitude modulation exist simultaneously, one side current cancels out. For still smaller values of the modulating frequency, the frequency modulation is more predominant than the amplitude modulation. This is discussed in detail under measurements.

Upon inspection of the significant factor for unit amplitude ($I_m = 1$) in Eq. (16), one sees that $\sin[\Omega t - \beta \cos \omega t]$ has the form $\sin[\Omega t - \theta_t]$. This means it is a sinusoidal variation, whose phase θ_t also varies with the time. But a variable phase and a corresponding change of frequency are interrelated, since the frequency variation is equal to the rate of change of phase of a periodic function. Now, the argument in the function $\sin[\Omega t - \beta \cos \omega t]$ is $\Omega t - \beta \cos \omega t$ and the time rate of it gives

$$\frac{d[\Omega t - \beta \cos \omega t]}{dt} = \Omega + \omega\beta \sin \omega t = \Omega + \Delta\Omega \sin \omega t$$

which confirms the term used to obtain the first expression in Eq. (6). From the interrelation between the variable phase and corresponding frequency variation, it is evident that any variations in phase must produce frequency modulation. It happens as an undesirable additional modulation, producing distortion in long-distance transmission when direct and indirect waves arrive at a receiver station, since the sky and direct wave have traveled through different distances, of which one distance may vary (will be discussed later). It also happens in intermediate circuits coupling, for instance, tube generators with aerials.

In phase modulation there is for sinusoidal phase variation $\theta_t = \theta \sin \omega t$, for which $\omega/2\pi = f$ denotes frequency with which the phase changes and θ the maximum value of the phase change. The maximum value for the corresponding frequency change is then θf and the frequency change at any time is $\theta f \cos \omega t$. This is true because a phase-modulated carrier current of frequency $\Omega/2\pi = F$ at any instant has the value

$$I_p = I_m \sin[\Omega t + \theta \sin \omega t] \tag{18}$$
$$= I_m \sin \gamma$$

The high frequency of the modulated current at any instant then has the value

$$F_t = \frac{1}{2\pi}\frac{d\gamma}{dt}$$

or

$$F_t = \frac{\Omega}{2\pi} + \underbrace{\theta f \cos \omega t}_{\text{change in frequency due to phase change}} \tag{19}$$

Since $F_t - F$ denotes the change ΔF in frequency and for this particular time function is $\theta f \cos \omega t$, one has generally only to solve for the time rate of the phase. Hence, for the general case of phase modulation given by

$$I_p = I_m \sin (\Omega t + \theta_t) \tag{20}$$

There is the corresponding change in frequency

$$\Delta F = \frac{d\theta_t}{dt} \text{ and the phase shift } \theta_t = \int \Delta F dt \tag{21}$$

Hence a sinusoidal time variation of phase angle θ_t gives a cosinusoidal frequency variation, while the time slope relation of (21) gives for the θ_t variation of Fig. 312 the indicated frequency variation.

Eq. (18) can be expanded into

$$I_p = I_m \{ \sin \Omega t \cos [\theta \sin \omega t] + \cos \Omega t \sin [\theta \sin \omega t]$$

leading to a general expression

$$I_p = I_m \sum_{-\infty}^{+\infty} J_q(\theta) \sin (\Omega + q\omega)t \tag{22}$$

which is the relation for the frequency spectrum and where $J_q(\theta)$ is the Bessel function of the first kind and order q. This result indicates that a series of side currents of frequencies $(\Omega \pm q\omega)$ are also produced by phase modulation. Compared with frequency modulation, the modulation index in this case does *not* depend upon the modulation frequency $f = \omega/2\pi$ but upon the magnitude of the phase displacement θ only. Figure 313 shows a case of phase modulation. The frequency is kept constant by means of a piezo-electric oscillator. In the oscillation circuit two high-frequency currents of the same frequency are superimposed on each other, so that the phase displacement be-

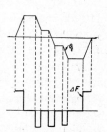

Fig. 312.—Phase and corresponding frequency variation.

tween both currents can be varied by means of modulation. The circuits with L_1 and L_2 are so connected and adjusted that the phase angle between the currents in the respective branches is 180 deg, and no current exists in the $C_2L_3L_4$ circuit. If a sound affects the differential condenser microphone C, the phases of the currents through L_1 and L_2, respectively, will be simultaneously displaced with respect to each other and amplitude variations occur which correspond to the phase displacements.

Equation (20) for phase modulation is of the same form as $I_f = I_m$ $\sin [\Omega t + \beta \sin \omega t]$ if the high frequency F_t fluctuates cosinusoidal about the mean value $F = \Omega/2\pi$; that is, $F_t = F + \Delta F \cos \omega t$. In order to see this, it is only necessary to put $\theta_t = \beta \sin \omega t$. In many cases phase and frequency modulations mean therefore the same thing. The original cause of frequency modulation is often produced by phase modulation, although a distinction must be made between frequency and phase modulation. The production of frequency modulation normally consists of changing either the capacitive or the inductive reactance of an oscillator so that $\Omega = 1/\sqrt{CL}$ is no longer a constant but either $\Omega_t = 1/\sqrt{C_tL}$ or $= 1/\sqrt{CL_t}$. This means that the phase angle of the circuit branch is rhythmically changed and the frequency changes accordingly again to produce in-phase condition.

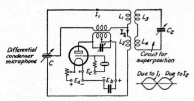

Fig. 313.—Arrangement for producing amplitude variations due to phase effects.

Since for such a case the frequency change always compensates any phase change which would otherwise exist, it may be called a frequency modulation in the true sense, because it happens directly in the source which produces the oscillations. If an alternator is used, frequency modulations may be due to irregularities in the speed (hunting), irregularities in the slots and windings, etc., and there is again true frequency modulation. True frequency modulation also happens in tube generators when amplitude modulation (either grid or plate modulations), because of back action during the modulation period, produces sufficient changes in the effective plate voltage of the oscillator to give variations in the high frequency of the produced tube oscillations. This can be practically avoided by using a properly designed piezo-electric oscillator and also by using master oscillators. By phase modulations may be understood variable phase shifts which cannot vary the generator frequency. Such phase shifts take place in intermediate circuits sometimes a large distance from the source. They can take place in high-frequency amplifiers (Fig. 314) which are connected between a high-frequency source and an aerial.

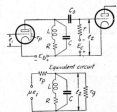

Fig. 314.—Explaining why high-frequency amplifiers may give rise to phase modulation.

Phase shifts may occur during the hour when the ionized layer, so to speak, "fluctuates" and the paths of the indirect rays vary in length. Cases similar to the Doppler effect in sound are then dealt with. They may also occur on long electrical high-frequency lines or for synchronized broadcast stations. Interference patterns at some point of reception due to variable phase shifts will then cause distortion on account of undesired modulations. In such cases as for the Doppler effect in sound, the frequency of the source may be absolutely constant and, nevertheless, variable phase variations at the receiver end will produce frequency variations and thereby undesired frequency modulations. The case of an undesirable phase modulation in a stage of high-frequency amplification is indicated in Fig. 314. The grid voltage e_1 is a sinusoidal voltage taken from a piezo-electric oscillator. A tuned plate circuit with a coupling condenser C_0 to the next tube is used. Since the effect of this condenser may be neglected, the equivalent variable current circuit is as shown in the figure. The resistance r_g denotes the effective resistance across the grid filament of the succeeding tube, therefore also including the effect of resistance r. If the grid should go somewhat positive, r_g will change considerably, since the internal resistance of grid to variable current is de_g/di_g. Assuming plate tuning and r_g very high, say practically infinitely high, the voltage applied to the following grid, for the abbreviation $\rho = L/(CR)$ is $e_2 = \dfrac{e_1\rho}{r_p + \rho - \dfrac{j}{\omega C}}$ with a phase angle $\theta_1 =$

$$\tan^{-1}\left[\frac{R}{\omega[r_pRC + L]}\right]$$ while for any finite value of r_g

$$e_2 = \frac{e_1\rho}{r_p + \left[1 + \dfrac{r_p}{r_g}\right]\left[\rho - \dfrac{j}{\omega C}\right]}$$

with a phase angle of

$$\tan^{-1}\left\{\frac{R\left[1 + \dfrac{r_p}{r_g}\right]}{\omega\left[r_pRC + L\left(1 + \dfrac{r_p}{r_g}\right)\right]}\right\}$$

For small values of r_g the angle $\theta_2 = \tan^{-1}[R/\omega L]$ is approached. Then the phase angle never varies by more than 90 deg. The value of ρ is often in the neighborhood of the tube resistance r_p and the phase may vary over a maximum value as much as 45 deg.

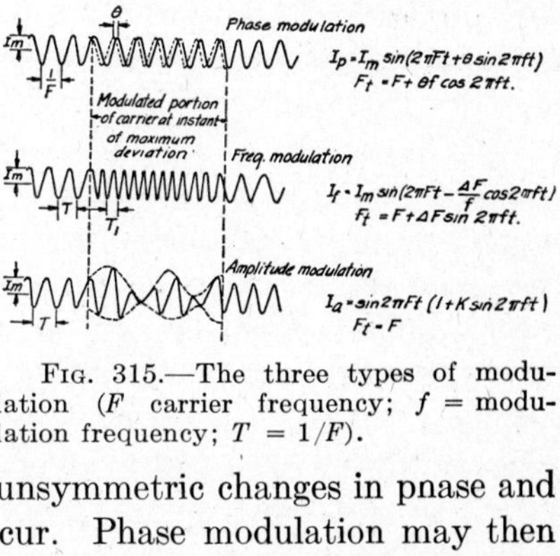

There seems to be a certain amount of confusion concerning phase modulation. If frequency deviations occur at the receiver which *cannot* be attributed to similar frequency fluctuations in the high-frequency source, phase modulation is the cause of it. Phase modulation may then be due to poor tuning of the carrier-current circuits so that unsymmetric changes in phase and amplitude of the side frequencies occur. Phase modulation may then also be due to a nonlinear work characteristic of certain portions of circuits, as, for instance, brought out in connection with Fig. 314, or in the case of coils using an iron core (impedances which depend upon the amplitude), etc.

Fig. 315.—The three types of modulation (F carrier frequency; f = modulation frequency; $T = 1/F$).

Figure 315 shows the three types of modulation. The modulated portion of the carrier is shown at the instant of maximum deviation. This means that θ gives the maximum value of phase shift during the periodic change $\theta \sin \omega t$ and ΔF the maximum frequency deviation for the frequency-modulated wave, respectively. Since $T_1 = 1/F_1$ denotes the smallest period during the periodic frequency modulation, $\Delta F = \dfrac{1}{T_1} - \dfrac{1}{T}$. For both phase- and frequency-modulated waves, the characteristic terms $\sin (\Omega t + \theta \sin \omega t)$ and $\sin (\Omega t - \beta \cos \omega t)$ appear and both terms have the form $\sin (\Omega t + \theta_t)$, as already mentioned above, if in one case $\theta_t = \theta \sin \omega t$ and in the

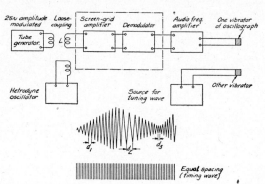

FIG. 316.—Determination of frequency modulation for an amplitude-modulated carrier by means of a heterodyne variation.

other case $\theta_t = -\beta \cos \omega t$. The wave form in either case is therefore the same for sinusoidal modulation in either case except for the amplitude of the modulation, which is in one case θ and in the other case β. This is, however, not true for any other modulation variations, since the frequency variation due to variable phase shifts is $\dfrac{1}{2\pi} \dfrac{d(\text{phase})}{dt}$. Hence for a square-topped modulation in frequency, the frequency is equally varied all along the square-top portion. For the phase modulation this holds also as far as the phase shift θ is concerned, while no corresponding frequency modulation can exist for the flat-top portion of the phase modulation, since the time derivative is zero. Thus if a phase modulation θ_t, as in Fig. 312, prevails, the corresponding frequency changes give an entirely different wave shape.

185. Determination of Frequency Modulation.—This is essentially the procedure as used in the classical experiments by R. Bown, DeLoss K. Martin, and R. K. Potter[1] and recently by A. Heilmann,[1] who has also developed a stroboscopic method, and is as indicated in Fig. 316. A low modulation frequency, about 25 cycles/sec is used to modulate a tube generator. This generator is very loosely coupled to a high-frequency shield-grid amplifier which is carefully screened except the small input coil L. It is also affected by a loosely coupled heterodyne oscillator to produce about a 1000-cycle beat note with the mean carrier frequency of the tube generator. A demodulator is used between the high-frequency and the audio-frequency amplifier. The audio-frequency amplifier is designed so that it transmits a 25-cycle variation very poorly.

[1] *Loc. cit.*

The output current affecting one vibrator of an ordinary oscillograph will then show a variation of a 1000-cycle signal with a 25-cycle modulation in amplitude. By means of the timing wave below, any unequal distances such as d_1, d_2, and d_3 can be expressed in time and the corresponding change ΔF in carrier frequency F for a modulation period to be found.

186. Determination of Phase Modulation.—If, for instance, at a receiving station, tests are to be carried out for phase modulation which produce distortion due to corresponding frequency variations, it is possible to find the frequency variations which can be determined with the method in the last section. The generator which is modulated in amplitude is then part of a sender station, while the coil L of the receiving set is coupled to a coil in a receiving aerial. The oscillogram indicated in Fig. 317 then represents the fluctuations of the beat tone, which is produced by the superposition of a sinusoidal high-frequency current due to the heterodyne oscillator and the received current of desired amplitude modulation. The distances along the t axis are scaled off and expressed in seconds by means of the timing wave. The corresponding frequency changes are then computed and plotted as the ΔF curve. According to (21) the phase change $\Delta \theta$ is

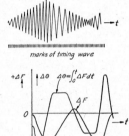

marks of timing wave

Fig. 317.—Determination of phase change $\Delta \theta$ by means of graphical integration.

obtained from the frequency variation $\Delta F = F_t - F$ by means of graphical integration. The stroboscopic effect can also be used in the determination of phase and frequency modulation (Fig. 318). If only amplitude modulation prevails and no voltage impulses e_2 are

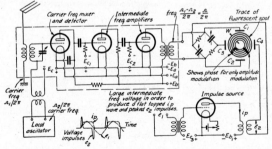

Fig. 318.—Determination of phase modulation utilizing the stroboscopic effect of a cathode-ray trace. (Curved dark region shows that phase modulation is superimposed while for only amplitude modulation a straight dark radial trace shows up in the concentric ring pattern.)

impressed, the fluorescent spot of the cathode ray traces out a ring-shaped illuminated area, the width w of which depends upon K, the degree of amplitude modulation. If synchronized voltage impulses e_2 also act (frequency of these impulses equal to or an integer multiple of the intermediate frequency $(\Omega_1 - \Omega_2)/(2\pi) = \Omega/(2\pi)$, an illuminated circular area with a dark *radial* trace (dotted in Fig. 318) is described. If the amplitude-modulated antenna current is also modulated in phase, the dark trace appears curved.

For details, reference is made to Fig. 319. The upper diagrams show the case of an unmodulated carrier ($E_m \epsilon^{j\Omega t}$) and an amplitude-modulated carrier $E_m \epsilon^{j\Omega t}[1 + K \sin \omega t]$. For the former, the well-known circle is traced by the fluorescent spot if equal voltages of the carrier produce a circular polarization across the deflection quadrants $C_1 C_2$ and $C_3 C_4$, as in Fig. 318 for $e_2 = 0$. For pure amplitude modulation the circular-ring area is described by the fluorescent spot and the degree of modulation is computed from $K = (E_1 - E_2)/(E_1 + E_2) = w/(2E_m)$. Hence, as long as the carrier frequency $\Omega/(2\pi)$ remains constant, the radius vector describes equal angles in equal times. If the carrier frequency fluctuates, however, different angles are produced. To observe any such angular changes, the timing impulse e_2 (Fig. 318)

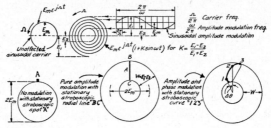

Fɪɢ. 319.—Vector traces on the fluorescent screen of a cathode-ray tube for no modulation, pure amplitude modulation, and phase modulation $\Delta\theta$, superimposed on amplitude modulation.

is impressed so that two consecutive e_2 impulses (produced by a large e_1 input) are equal to the period $2\pi/\Omega$ of the unaffected carrier. According to the stroboscopic effect, the e_2 impulse will then produce a quick "sweep off" of the fluorescent spot always at the same point and mark a darkness spot A as indicated in Fig. 319. If

$II+I$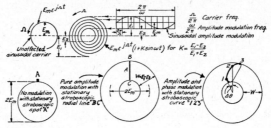

II

I

Fɪɢ. 320.—Amplitude modulation produced if two frequency-modulated waves of constant amplitude are superimposed.

pure amplitude modulation exists, the spot will trace the darkness line $ABACABA$, etc. But, for superimposed frequency or phase modulation, the synchronized timing point A has a component which moves it up and down owing to amplitude modulation and a component which moves it back and forth to each side because of phase changes. Hence, a curved dark timing trace 123 must appear as indicated in Fig. 319. Similar to the method described in connection with Fig. 316, the arrangement of Fig. 318 carries on the determination by means of a difference frequency. It is then essential that the intermediate frequency current produced by interference of the antenna current, to be examined with that due to the local oscillator, preserves the same degree of amplitude and phase modulation as exists in the aerial current. To assure this, the amplitude due to the local oscillator must be large compared with the amplitude due to the aerial current. Such an operating point on the rectification characteristic of the frequency mixer must be chosen so that the modulation of the corresponding amplitude fluctuations occur along a linear portion of the characteristic. Hence, if the voltage due to the antenna current has the form $E_1 \sin (\Omega_1 t + \theta \sin \omega t) (1 + K$

sin ωt) and the local oscillator superimposes the *pure* sinusoidal voltage $E_2 \sin \Omega_2 t$, for which the amplitude E_2 is large compared with E_1, for the amplitude of the mixture,

$$\sqrt{\{E_1^2(1 + K \sin \omega t)^2 + E_2^2 + 2E_1 E_2 (1 + K \sin \omega t)\}\{\cos[(\Omega_1 t + \theta \sin \omega t) - \Omega_2 t]\}} \cong$$

$$E_2\sqrt{1 + 2\frac{E_1}{E_2}(1 + K \sin \omega t) \cos[(\Omega_1 t + \theta \sin \omega t) - \Omega_2 t]}$$

since E_1^2 is negligibly small compared with all other terms. Hence, there is an expression of the form $E_2\sqrt{1 + 2\delta}$ where 2δ is small compared with unity. There is then obtained the approximation $E_2\left\{1 + \frac{E_1}{E_2}(1 + K \sin \omega t) \cos[(\Omega_1 - \Omega_2)t + \theta \sin \omega t]\right\}$.

Hence, if the rectifier operates linearly between the limits $E_2\left[1 + \frac{E_1}{E_2}(1 + K)\right]$ and $E_2\left[1 - \frac{E_1}{E_2}(1 + K)\right]$, the above relation is also the expression for the intermediate frequency variation with the same amplitude and phase modulation as the aerial current.

187. Notes on the Superposition of Two Frequency-modulated Currents of Constant Group Phase Shift.

—With the method described in connection with Fig. 301, a wave in space of constant amplitude but with frequency variations about a mean frequency can be changed to a current of variable amplitude. This means frequency modulation is partially translated into amplitude modulation. Now, if as in Fig. 320 two frequency-modulated waves I and II, which are as a whole shifted against each other, are added (I + II), they will in addition produce amplitude variation. The resultant is the characteristic fading record. The frequency variations may be due to inconstancy of the frequency of the generator at the sender end (as reported in the paper by R. Bown, etc.),[1] or due to rapid fluctuations of the path of the indirect ray (in reality indirect rays). The same thing happens for synchronized stations sending out the same program at the same time and being received by one and the same set. This case is then somewhat more involved, since any frequency modulations due to frequency fluctuations at the respective sender stations will not happen in the same manner and the unmodulated carrier waves arriving at the receiver will generally not have the same amplitude. Undesirable distortion will then occur, owing to superimposed frequency modulation and the effect on the amplitude of the resultant wave. Whether one deals with synchronized broadcast transmitters or the one sender only where for simplicity's sake it is assumed that only one sky ray interferes with a direct ray at the receiving station is immaterial. Taking therefore two transmitters, according to the relations leading to Eq. (16), for a frequency modulation at the sender stations, the instantaneous value of the high frequency is $F_t = F + \Delta F \sin \omega t$, if ΔF denotes the maximum frequency variation about the unmodulated carrier frequency F and sinusoidal variation of modulation frequency $\omega/2\pi = f$ is assumed.

[1] *Loc. cit.*

Suppose the case is taken where F_t denotes the frequency of two synchronized senders and d_1 and d_2 denote the respective distances to a receiving station. If c is the velocity of wave propagation, the instantaneous frequencies of the currents induced due to the arriving waves are $F_1 = F + \Delta F \sin 2\pi f\left(t - \dfrac{d_1}{c}\right)$ and $F_2 = F + \Delta F \sin 2\pi f\left(t - \dfrac{d_2}{c}\right)$, if the frequencies are in cycles per second, t in seconds, the distances in centimeters, and $c = 3 \times 10^{10}$ cm/sec. The phase difference between the arriving waves can be found from the instantaneous frequency values F_1 and F_2, since these frequencies give the rate of change of phase of the periodic function. Hence the instantaneous value φ_1 for the phase of the wave arriving over the path d_1 is obtained from $\varphi_1 = \displaystyle\int_0^t 2\pi F_1 dt$, and for the other wave $\varphi_2 = \displaystyle\int_0^t 2\pi F_2 dt$ denotes the instantaneous values of the phase at the receiving station. For the resultant current induced in the receiving aerial, the phase difference $\varphi_1 - \varphi_2$ is used. Since $\varphi_1 - \varphi_2$ continually changes, the resultant received current will experience amplitude changes which produce distortion.

188. Effects of All Three Types of Modulation.—If a high-frequency current $I_m \sin \Omega t$ is modulated in amplitude as well as in frequency and at the same modulation frequency $\omega/2\pi = f$, the instantaneous value of the current is

$$I_{af} = I_m \sin [\Omega t + \beta \sin \omega t][1 + K \sin (\omega t + \psi)]$$

$$= I_m \sum_{-\infty}^{+\infty} [J_q(\beta) \sin (\Omega + q\omega)t - 0.5KJ_q(\beta) \cos \{[\Omega + (q + 1)\omega]t + \psi\}$$

$$+ 0.5KJ_q(\beta) \cos \{[\Omega + (q - 1)\omega]t - \psi\}] \quad (23)$$

where $J_q(\beta)$ is again a Bessel function of the first kind and order q. If β is taken small so that the first two side frequencies only are of concern, there is for unity amplitude if expressed in cosine terms

$$\cos [\Omega t + \beta \cos (\omega t + \varphi)][1 + K \cos \omega t] = \cos (\Omega t + \beta) \cos (\omega t + \varphi) -$$

$$\underbrace{- 0.5K \cos \{(\Omega + \omega)t + \beta \cos (\omega t + \varphi)\}}_{\text{one side current}} \underbrace{+ 0.5K \cos \{(\Omega - \omega)t +}_{\text{frequency affected carrier current}}$$

$$\underbrace{\beta \cos (\omega t + \varphi)\}}_{\text{other side current}} \quad (24)$$

The carrier as well as the two side currents are no longer of constant frequency but change as in Fig. 321 over a range $\beta\omega/2\pi = \Delta\Omega/2\pi = \Delta F$. The amplitudes of the two side currents are $0.5K$ and the carrier as well as the two side frequencies, "vibrate" as a whole to and fro with a maximum swing ΔF. Hence at any instant the difference frequency between the carrier and each side current is the same constant. Figure

322 gives the measured values of W. Runge[1] here expressed in terms of the theoretical Eqs. (5a), (16), (17), and (18) and (22). The representation for amplitude and frequency modulation only (only K and ΔF modulation) confirms exactly the theory brought out by the respective side-current relations

$$\left. \begin{array}{l} 0.5KI_m\{- \cos[2\pi(F+f)t] + \cos[2\pi(F-f)t]\} \text{ for amplitude} \\ 0.5\beta I_m\{- \cos[2\pi(F+f)t] - \cos[2\pi(F-f)t]\} \text{ for frequency} \end{array} \right\} \text{modulation}$$

(25)

as taken from (16) and (17) where K is the ratio of the amplitude i_m of the modulating current of frequency f to the amplitude I_m of the carrier current of high frequency F and β the ratio of the maximum frequency variation ΔF from the carrier frequency F to the frequency f of the modulating current. Since the cosine terms have opposite signs for the side current of frequency $(F - f)$; that is, the currents $0.5KI_m$ cos $(\Omega - \omega)t$ and $0.5\beta I_m$ cos $(\Omega - \omega)t$ are in antiphase, they must produce a differential action. Therefore the value of the effective modulation K_e on the left side of the carrier line (F line) falls below the K line for different values of the frequency f which is used in connection with the

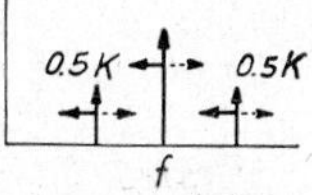

Fig. 321.—Showing that carrier and two side bands are no longer constant in frequency.

constant ($K = 20\%$) *amplitude* modulation. A value $f = f_1$ must exist for which this side current must vanish altogether, since for a condition of this kind

$$0.5I_m[\beta - K] \cos(\Omega - \omega)t = 0$$

yields $K = \beta = \Delta F/f = \Delta F/f_1$, and the maximal frequency deviation ΔF of the frequency modulation can be computed from

$$\Delta F = Kf_1$$

(26)

In the diagram of the figure, $f_1 = 100$ cycles/sec and, since 20 per cent amplitude modulation gives $K = 0.2$, the amplitude of the frequency

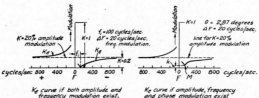

Fig. 322.—Experimental curves for amplitude and frequency as well as all three types of modulations.

modulation is $\Delta F = 20$ cycles/sec. According to (25) the degree of effective modulation K_e for different frequency values for f is for the left side of the F line larger than $K = 0.2$ if frequency modulation is also present.

[1] *Loc. cit.*

From the K_e curves in the other diagram representation of Fig. 322, it can be seen that if phase modulation is also present still more distortion takes place and the K_e curve for the lower side band falls to a minimum value M only, as is proved in connection with Eqs. (30) and (31) in the next section.

189. Determination of the Maximum Value of Periodic Frequency and Phase Modulation.—The explanation just given in connection with Fig. 322 gives a method for finding the maximum frequency deviation ΔF if frequency modulation is present in addition to amplitude modula-

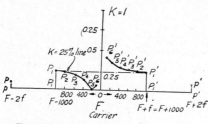

Fig. 323.—Determination of frequency modulation by means of the experimental $P_1P_2P_3P_4P_5P_6$ and $P_1'P_2'P_3'P_4'P_5'P_6'$ or K_e curves.

tion. It is then only necessary to determine the K_e curves for different modulation frequencies f within the side-band region. If pure amplitude modulation exists for a constant amplitude ratio i_m/I_m of modulation to high-frequency amplitude, the dotted K line is obtained for different values of f. But if frequency modulation also exists, the heavily drawn K_e curves of Fig. 322 for the effective modulation will be obtained. Therefore the procedure consists in modulating the carrier in *amplitude*, with a fixed ratio $K = i_m/I_m$, for instance, equal to 0.25, and determining the amplitudes P_1P_1 and $P_1'P_1'$ of Fig. 323 with a sinusoidal search current (Sec. 56, using, for instance, the method of Fig. 90) of known amplitude and known variable frequency F_s if $f = 1000$ cycles is the frequency of i_m which modulates I_m to 25 per cent in amplitude. Since $f = 1000$ cycles is a high-modulation frequency compared with undesirable periodic-frequency modulations, for carrier frequencies F which are not too high, it will be found that P_1P_1 is practically equal to $P_1'P_1'$ as would be expected from the theory for pure amplitude modulation. If the demodulator is not strictly parabolic and if the term $\partial^3 I_p/\partial E^3$ [Eq. (9)] of the work characteristic plays also a part, the search-frequency method will also locate two additional side currents of frequencies $F \pm 2f$ with amplitudes pp and $p'p'$. Section 56 gives the description of several methods for determining the harmonic content of a distorted current. They all are applied to cases for different currents having frequencies which are harmonically interrelated. This is not the case here, since a spectrum of frequencies F, $F \pm f$, $F \pm 2f$, etc., for different values of f is being dealt with. The effective K_e curve for $F \pm f$ as a function of f on each side of the carrier frequency F is of utmost interest here. The method of Fig. 90 can then be used if the indicator of the spectrum analyzer gives a deflection proportional to the amplitude product of the search current and that of the particular side current [Eq. (28)].

The modulated current, together with the search current of frequency F_s, is squared in this procedure and affects a low-frequency indicator which is tuned to a frequency f_b which is smaller than the smallest difference frequency of the carrier and the side current. If F_s is varied over both side-frequency regions, the indicator gives a deflection proportional to the amplitude of the particular side current whenever F_s is close to the respective values $F \pm f$. Since the frequency F_s and the amplitude of the search current are known, as well as the frequency to which the indicator responds, both the amplitude of the side current and its frequency $F \pm f$ can be computed from experimental data. It is then convenient to work with beat frequencies $F_s - (F \pm f)$ not much higher than 20 cycles/sec. For this reason a low-pass filter with a cut-off at 20 cycles/sec is used in Fig. 90. A transformer-coupled audio-frequency amplifier then follows this filter in such a way that the primaries of the amplifier transformers are bridged with condensers of a magnitude (a few microfarads) which gives a selective amplification, for instance, at about 15 cycles/sec. It is now to be proved that the beat frequency f_b of 15 cycles/sec for $F_s - (F \pm f)$ or $F_s - F$, if the carrier intensity is to be determined, does not give rise to incorrect readings when a current is modulated.

In considering the general case of an amplitude- and frequency-modulated current, there is the general expression $A \sin (2\pi Ft + B)$ where A and B are continuous functions of the modulation frequency f, since $A \sin (\Omega t + B) = a \sin \Omega t + b \cos \Omega t = \sqrt{a^2 + b^2} \sin \left(\Omega t + \tan^{-1} \dfrac{b}{a} \right)$, that is, $A = \sqrt{a^2 + b^2}$; $B = \tan^{-1} \dfrac{b}{a}$ and $a = A \cos B$ and $b = A \sin B$. Hence, if only amplitude modulation occurs, the phase B cannot vary and must be constant. If the heterodyne generator superimposes a harmonic current $D \cos 2\pi(F - f_b)t$ on the modulated current and f_b denotes the low frequency (15 cycles in the above case) on which the indicator of spectrum analyzer of Fig. 90 gives maximum response, the square-law detector gives

$$[A \sin (\Omega t + B) + D \cos 2\pi(F - f_b)t]^2 = [D \cos 2\pi(F - f_b)t + a \sin \Omega t + b \cos \Omega t]^2$$

The useful terms of solution give $2aD \sin (2\pi f_b t) + 2bD \cos (2\pi f_b t) =$

$$2AD \sin [2\pi f_b t + B].$$

From this discussion it is found that a current modulated in both amplitude and frequency enters the spectrum analyzer in the form

$$A \sin (2\pi Ft + B) \tag{27}$$

and affects the indicator of the analyzer in the form

$$2AD \sin [2\pi f_b t + B] \tag{28}$$

This means that neither A nor B, which are the continuous functions of the modulation, has been changed, but the frequency F has been changed to the beat frequency f_b, to which an indicator can be readily tuned (using a vibration galvanometer, the General Radio oscillograph, etc.).

From this it is also evident that, for superimposed frequency modulations for which B is no longer a constant but equal to $\beta \sin 2\pi ft$, the low-frequency current, after heterodyning and detector action, becomes

$$2AD \sin\left(2\pi f_b t + \frac{\Delta F}{f} \sin 2\pi ft\right) \tag{29}$$

and a variable audio frequency will be heard in a telephone receiver connected to the output of the rectifier. But, for small values of $\beta = \Delta F/f$, this is not true unless the variations are so low that the ear can follow them and the frequency of the sound observed at any instant is $f_s = \dfrac{1}{2\pi}\dfrac{d}{dt}\left[2\pi f_b t + \dfrac{\Delta F}{f} \sin 2\pi ft\right] = f_b + \Delta F \cos 2\pi f$.

Comparing (27) and (28), it is evident that the factor 2 enters and that K is equal to the double ratio of the amplitude noted for the side current divided by the amplitude noted for the unmodulated carrier. Hence, if the deflection noted for the unmodulated carrier is d_c and that for the particular side current is d_s, then $K_e = 2d_s/d_c$ is the degree of effective modulation. This is done as in Fig. 323 for several values of modulation frequency f, for instance, for 800, 600, 400, and 200 cycles/sec. When frequency modulation is also present, the deflections obtained for spectrum frequencies $(F - f)$ will come out smaller than for the corresponding values of frequency $F + f$. The reason for this is given in the preceding section in connection with Eqs. (25) and (26); that is, the experimental points P_2, P_3, P_4, P_5, P_6 are below the K line and form the K_e curve for the lower side band, while the experimental points P_2', P_3', P_4', P_5', P_6', lying above the K line, form the K_e branch for the upper side band, giving rise to distortion at the receiving end. According to Eq. (26) the maximum frequency deviation ΔF from the mean value is computed from $\Delta F = K f_1$ where K in this particular case is 0.25 and $f_1 = 200$ cycles found from the K_e curve where $K_e = 0$ is obtained. Hence $\Delta F = \pm 50$ cycles/sec.

For the determination of phase modulation, one must distinguish between the procedure with frequency modulation present and for only phase and amplitude modulation. According to (18) for small values of maximum phase displacement θ for phase modulation,

$$
\begin{aligned}
I_p &= I_m \sin\left(\Omega t + \theta \sin \omega t\right] \\
&= I_m\{\sin \Omega t \cos\left(\theta \sin \omega t\right) + \cos \Omega t \sin\left(\theta \sin \omega t\right)\} \\
&\cong I_m\{\sin \Omega t + \cos \Omega t\,\theta \sin \omega t\} \\
&= \underbrace{I_m \sin \Omega t}_{\text{carrier current}} + \underbrace{0.5\theta I_m \sin\left(\Omega + \omega\right)t}_{\text{one side current}} + \underbrace{0.5\theta I_m \sin\left(\Omega - \omega\right)t}_{\text{other side current}}
\end{aligned}
\tag{30}
$$

Comparing only the characteristic side currents occurring for amplitude, frequency, and phase modulation,

$$
\left.
\begin{aligned}
&0.5K I_m\{- \cos\left[2\pi(F + f)t\right] + \cos\left[2\pi(F - f)t\right]\}\,\text{amplitude} \\
&0.5\beta I_m\{- \cos\left[2\pi(F + f)t\right] - \cos\left[2\pi(F - f)t\right]\}\,\text{frequency} \\
&0.5\theta I_m\{+ \sin\left[2\pi(F + f)t\right] + \sin\left[2\pi(F - f)t\right]\}\,\text{phase}
\end{aligned}
\right\}\text{modulation}
\tag{31}
$$

Hence, for small values of θ, which is the assumption for the last expression of (31), the side currents due to phase modulation occur *at right angles* to the side currents due to amplitude modulation as well as the side currents due to frequency modulation. The same can also be seen from the corresponding expressions

$$\left.\begin{aligned} F_t &= F + \theta f \cos (2\pi f t) \text{ for phase} \\ F_t &= F + \Delta F \sin (2\pi f t) \text{ for frequency} \end{aligned}\right\} \text{modulation} \qquad (32)$$

for the instantaneous value of the high frequency. The effect is that the degree of modulation computed from the amplitude ratio comes out somewhat larger than the measured value. A difference would then be noted only for considerable phase modulations, since rectangular addition is made. Therefore the method just described for finding ΔF, if frequency and amplitude modulation only exist, is unsuitable. But if frequency modulation and amplitude and phase modulation are present, the phase-quadrature effect due to phase modulation can be recognized by the minimum value k, obtained at M in Fig. 322 on the K_e curve, instead of the absolute-zero value of K_e for which the respective side currents due to frequency and amplitude modulation cancel out in the lower side-band region. From Eq. (31) for the lower side band,

$$\underbrace{[0.5\beta I_m - 0.5KI_m]}_{\text{vanishes at point } M \text{ (Fig. 322)}} \cos (\Omega - \omega t) + 0.5\theta I_m \sin (\Omega - \omega)t = kI_m \sin (\Omega - \omega)t$$

where k denotes the small value $K_e = k$ of modulation left due to phase modulation. Hence $0.5\theta \sin (\Omega - \omega)t = k \sin (\Omega - \omega)t$. The maximum value θ of phase modulation can then be computed from the formula

$$\theta = 2k \qquad (33)$$

For the case shown in Fig. 322, the value of k is 0.025; that is, $\theta = 0.05$ radian $= 0.05 \times 57.3 = 28.7$ deg.

If phase modulation but no frequency modulation exists at the same time, the same method is possible if a known frequency modulation is superimposed and the current *amplitude* also modulated for the constant value $K = i_m/I_m$. The values of K_e found with the spectrum analyzer of Fig. 90 are plotted as in Fig. 322 against the modulating frequency f of the amplitude modulation and θ computed from the minimum value of $K_e = k$ by means of Eq. (33).

If also a fixed phase angle ψ exists, for a current whose amplitude and phase are modulated sinusoidally and for small maximum phase-angle amplitude θ,

$$\begin{aligned} I_{ap} &= I_m\{[1 + K \cos \omega t] \cos [\Omega t + \theta \cos (\omega t + \psi)]\} \\ &= I_m\{\cos \Omega t - 0.5K \theta \cos \psi \sin \Omega t \\ &\quad + 0.5K \cos (\Omega + \omega)t - 0.5\theta \sin [(\Omega + \omega)t + \psi] \\ &\quad + 0.5K \cos (\Omega - \omega)t - 0.5\theta \sin [(\Omega - \omega)t - \psi] \\ &\quad - 0.25K\theta \sin [(\Omega + 2\omega)t + \psi] \\ &\quad - 0.25K\theta \sin [(\Omega - 2\omega)t - \psi]\} \qquad (34) \end{aligned}$$

Distortion therefore takes place, since additional terms appear and only for $\psi = 0$ does the upper first-order side current equal in amplitude that of the lower side current.

190. Notes on the Modulation Frequency in Television Work.—Present-day experiments on television are based on scanning. If a Nipkow disk is employed, the number of apertures N which are spirally arranged and the speed S in revolution per second of the disk determine the modulation frequency f with which a carrier is to be modulated. It is computed from

$$f = 0.5SP \text{ cycles/sec} \tag{35}$$

where P denotes the number of picture elements per frame. The factor 0.5 appears in this formula, since the maximum rate of change in light intensity happens from light to darkness from one picture element to the next and causes one alternation. For one revolution of the spiral-apertured scanning disk, the field of view is divided in as many parallel lines (slightly curved) as there are openings N in the Nipkow disk. The smallest area which is scanned is called a "picture element" and its size is determined by the smallest part of the picture which should be distinguishable. If the field of view is of square shape, there are for N apertures in the disk $P = N^2$ picture elements per frame which, for 50 openings in the disk running at $S = 20$ r.p.s. according to (35), would give a modulation frequency of 25 kc/sec and for double side-band transmission a channel as wide as 50 kc/sec, in spite of the fact that 50 lines would make a face only recognizable without details, while such details, as, for example, wrinkles, would require at least 75 apertures in the disk, giving a modulation frequency of $f = 0.5 \times 20 \times 5625 = 56.25$ kc/sec. The speed S must be at least 16, since objects in motion, as is well-known from the technique used in moving pictures, require such a repetition per second. When large scenes as outdoor life, etc., are to be televised, very many line elements per frame are required for good reproduction and the modulation frequency required becomes almost unreasonably high. If the field of view is not of square shape but has a vertical to a horizontal edge as 4 to 5, there is for $N = 80$ apertures in the disk from $n{:}80 = 5{:}4$ the value of $n = 100$, and the number of picture elements per frame is $P = 80 \times 100$ which, for $S = 20$ r.p.s. according to (34), gives the modulation frequency $f = 80$ kc/sec.

CHAPTER XV

DETERMINATIONS ON AERIALS AND LINES

When dealing with high-frequency lines and aerial systems, static constants of capacitance, inductance, resistance, etc., must be distinguished from correct effective constants. This is even more the case when dealing with natural line oscillations which occur in tuned aerial systems where voltage and current distribution are known. There are also apparent effective constants.

1. The static or true constants C_A, L_A, and R_A of capacitance, inductance, and resistance of an aerial presuppose that the potential and current distributions along the conductor are uniform. Therefore the static constants may be considered as geometric quantities of the aerial system.

2. The correct effective values C_e, L_e, and R_e take the actual distributions of potential and current along the line into consideration. They determine the effective decrement $\delta_e = \pi R_e \sqrt{C_e/L_e}$ as well as the effective oscillation constant $C_e L_e$. For any inductive aerial loading L_0, for instance, at the grounded end (as customary), for the generalized hyperbolic angular velocity $n = \alpha \pm j\omega$, there is the relation[1] $n[L_e + L_0] + \dfrac{1}{(nC)} = 0$. If a high-frequency line which is open at the free end is excited with an audio-frequency voltage, one has practically $C_e = C_A$; $L_e = L_A/3$ and $R_e = R_A/3$, since the aerial system behaves toward the currents of such a low frequency as a short electrical conductor producing essentially constant potential distribution along the conductor. The effective audio-frequency current falls off practically linearly toward the open end.

3. The apparent correct aerial constants C_e, L_e, and R_e assume sinusoidal and cosinusoidal current and potential distributions along the conductor. However, the equivalent lumped aerial made up of lumped values of C_e, L_e, and R_e will only confirm the true fundamental-resonance frequency of the antenna but as a rule not give the correct value for the resonance current. This means only the product $C_e L_e$ is confirmed, but the ratio L_e/C_e which is basic in the decrement formula is *not* always satisfied.

The correct effective aerial constants defined under 2 are of utmost importance.

191. Notes on Formulas Used for High-frequency Lines.—The impedance experienced at the generator end, if looking into a line which is terminated through an impedance Z at the far end, is

$$Z_1 = Z_0 \frac{Z + Z_0 \tanh \Omega}{Z_0 + Z \tanh \Omega} \tag{1}$$

[1] For long horizontal aerials with a relatively short lead-in to the station, the relation $\omega(L_e + L_0) - \dfrac{1_e}{\omega C_e} = \omega L_0 - \sqrt{\dfrac{L_A}{C_A}} \cot \omega \sqrt{C_A L_A} = 0$ holds to a good degree of approximation if sinusoidal excitation prevails.

if $Z_0 = \sqrt{r + j\omega L}/\sqrt{g + j\omega C} \cong \sqrt{L/C}$ denotes the surge impedance, $\Omega = nl$ the electric length of the line of geometrical length l. The quantity $n = \alpha + j\beta$ is the propagation constant, with the real term α as the space attenuation and the imaginary term β as the wave-length constant per unit length. The quantities r, g, L, and C are the line constants for unit length for resistance along the line, conductance across the line, inductance, and capacitance, respectively. The surge impedance Z_0 in many high-frequency cases can be considered as a pure resistance, since $\sqrt{L/C}$ is in ohms and a real quantity. It is the impedance measured at the generator end if the line is infinitely long or is terminated at the free end with a resistance equal to $\sqrt{L/C}$. The line then acts as if aperiodic. For a parallel-wire system of spacing a between centers of the cylindrical conductors of diameter d, it is

$$Z_0 = 120 \log_e \frac{2a}{d} = 276 \log_{10} \frac{2a}{d} \tag{2}$$

which does not hold for very small spacings, since the proximity effect $(d/a)^2$ is neglected in comparison with unity. For a 600Ω line $a = 74.2\,d$. For high-frequency work for the attenuation per unit length,

$$\alpha = 0.5\sqrt{\frac{C}{L}} + 0.5g\sqrt{\frac{L}{C}} = \frac{0.5r}{Z_0} + 0.5gZ_0 \cong \frac{r}{2Z_0} \tag{3}$$

This is a very useful formula. The wave-length constant is $\beta = 2\pi f/c'$ if c' denotes the velocity of propagation along the line. If it is assumed equal to the velocity of light, $c' = c = 3 \times 10^{10}$ cm/sec, if f is in cycles per second, and the unit length of the line is 1 cm. If the line is short-circuited at the far end ($Z = 0$), Eq. (1) gives the impedance measured at the generator end

$$Z_{sc} = Z_0 \tanh \Omega \tag{4}$$

For the far end open, $Z = \infty$ and

$$Z_{oc} = Z_0 \coth \Omega \tag{5}$$

The results of (4) and (5) are very useful formulas for finding the values of natural-line frequencies. They are obtained for Z_{oc} and Z_{sc} equal to zero. Combining (4) and (5) results in another expression for the surge impedance, namely,

$$Z_0 = \sqrt{Z_{oc} Z_{sc}} \tag{6}$$

This means that it is only necessary to measure the input voltage E_1 and current I_1 for the open-ended line and the E_2 and I_2 for the free end short-circuited and compute Z_0 from $\sqrt{E_1 I_2/(I_1 E_2)}$. The propagation constant n of the line is

$$n = \frac{1}{2l} \cosh^{-1} \frac{Z_{oc} + Z_{sc}}{Z_{oc} - Z_{sc}} \tag{7}$$

It can also be found from

$$n = \frac{1}{2l} \log_\epsilon \frac{1 + \sqrt{Z_{sc}/Z_{oc}}}{1 - \sqrt{Z_{sc}/Z_{oc}}} \qquad (7a)$$

where l denotes the unit length of the line.

G. W. O. Howe and L. W. Austin have given formulas for the static antenna capacitance. Howe's formula is

$$C_A = \left\{ 3.6\sqrt{A} + 0.58\frac{A}{h}\left[1 + 0.0375\frac{l}{b} \right] \right\} \left[1 + 0.0375\frac{l}{b} \right] 10^{-5} \qquad (8)$$

where C_A is in microfarads, and Austin's formulas are

$$C_A = \begin{cases} \left[4\sqrt{A} + 0.885\frac{A}{h} \right] 10^{-5} \text{for aerials which are not too long and} \\ \qquad\qquad \text{distance between wires not too large} \\ \left[4\sqrt{A} + 0.885\frac{A}{h} \right]\left[1 - 0.015\frac{l}{b} \right] 10^{-5} \text{ if the length } l \text{ is more} \\ \qquad\qquad\qquad \text{than eight times the breadth } b \end{cases} \qquad (9)$$

where C_A is in microfarads. The quantity A denotes the area in square meters, h the height, l the length, and b the breadth in meters. Howe's theoretical formula gives about the same values as Austin's empirical formulas. The error is about 10 per cent in each case.

In the case of the formulas on the effective height of aerial systems, it must be understood that the index of refraction of the ground plays a part. Since the effective height of a loop aerial can be readily computed from its dimensions and the frequency employed, it is often used to determine the effective height of complicated aerial systems. The effective height of a loop aerial is

$$h_e^{(m)} = 2Nh \sin 1.045 \times 10^{-5} a\,f \qquad (10)$$

if a rectangular loop of width a m, height h m with N turns is used for a frequency f in kilocycles per second. If the width a is smaller than about one-sixth of the wave length in meters ($\lambda^{(m)} = 3 \times 10^5/f^{(kc/m)}$), the sine of the angle becomes equal to the angle itself and

$$h_e \cong 209 \times 10^{-7} ANf \qquad (10a)$$

if $A = a\,h$ denotes the area of the loop in square meters. The form factor F of a loop aerial is then $F = 209 \times 10^{-7}\ afN$, since the actual height h of the frame multiplied by F gives the effective height.

192. Determination of Surge Impedance and Propagation Constant.— For good one-sided direction effect of a Beverage antenna as in Fig. 324, it is necessary to ground the far end of the long horizontal aerial over a resistance equal to the surge impedance; that is, R must be equal to $\sqrt{L/C}$. Therefore it is necessary to determine experimentally the value of R. This is done by plotting the impedance ratio E/I as obtained from the volt and ammeter readings against the frequency for certain fixed R settings. For the value $R = \sqrt{L/C}$, which in this particular case is about 400Ω, the aerial system acts as an ohmic resistance for all frequencies. For a short-circuited far end $(R = 0)$ the heavily drawn

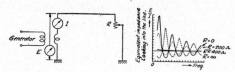

FIG. 324.—Determination of the surge impedance of a line aerial.

space resonance curve is obtained, while for the far end open $(R = \infty)$ the dashed multiresonance curve is obtained. For $R = 200\Omega$ the dotted resonance curve exists. According to Eq. (6), the heavy line is the geometrical mean for the curves obtained for $R = 0$ and $R = \infty$. It is not always necessary to take the voltage readings (E) also, but R is varied until the reading of the current meter I remains essentially constant, while the frequency f is varied for constant-input voltage. The value of R could also be found by taking the voltage and current reading $E = E_1$ and $I = I_1$ for the free end open and the readings $E = E_2$ and $I = I_2$ for the free end short-circuited to ground and computing $R = \sqrt{E_1 I_2 / (I_1 E_2)}$. This is also the method often used with the double line. Instead of taking voltage and current readings, an impedance bridge can be used which gives the value $Z_{oc} = E_1/I_1$ and $Z_{sc} = E_2/I_2$ for the open and short-circuited line. As an impedance bridge, the differential system of Fig. 50 is convenient employed for higher frequencies. The ground of the balanced transformer is then omitted. The test line goes between terminals XX if a double line is to

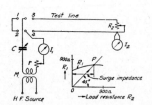

FIG. 325.—Determination of surge impedance. (R_1 is resistance of the line experienced across input terminals 3 and 4.)

be tested; otherwise the aerial wire is connected to the X terminal next to the P_2 coil and the ground is connected to the other X terminal. A variable standard reactance X_s and a decade resistance R_s are connected in series and form the variable standard. If the balance settings $R_s = R_1$ and $X_s = X_1$ for the line open at the free end are expressed as the impedance $Z_1 = \sqrt{R_1{}^2 + X_1{}^2}$ and, for the far end short-circuited, the balance settings R_2 and X_2 given as $Z_2 = \sqrt{R_2{}^2 + X_2{}^2}$, the surge impedance is computed from $Z_0 = \sqrt{Z_1 Z_2}$. According to Eq. (7), the propagation constant n is computed from

$$n = \frac{1}{2l} \cosh^{-1} \frac{Z_1 + Z_2}{Z_1 - Z_2}$$

Figure 325 shows the method due to C. A. Boddie[1] for measuring surge impedance on power lines used for high-frequency work. It again makes use of the fact that for a loading $R_2 = \sqrt{L/C}$ the resistance of the line, when looking into terminals 3 and 4, is also equal to $\sqrt{L/C}$.

1. The switch is connected on 1 and 2, and the circuit is tuned by means of C to the desired frequency with r cut out, giving a suitable resonance reading I_1 for a proper coupling M.

2. The resistance r (decade box) is gradually cut in until the resonance current falls to $I_1/2$ for the setting $r = r_0$, which is the effective resistance of the closed circuit.

With a certain load resistance R_2 and r cut out, the switch is connected on terminals 3 and 4 and C again varied until the current-meter reading I_1 gives a resonance setting. The resistance r is gradually cut in until for a value $r = r_1$ half the resonance current is obtained. The value $R_1 = r_1 - r_0$ then denotes the input resistance. The R_1 characteristic is plotted for different values of load resistance R_2 for equal abscissa and ordinate scales. The intersection of the 45-deg line with the R_1 characteristics gives point P whose ordinate or abscissa gives the surge resistance of the line.

The method described in connection with Fig. 324 can also be used to find the surge impedance by measuring the input impedance Z_1 and Z_2 for open and closed line at the far end by means of a volt and ammeter or a suitable impedance bridge. However, it will be often found for long electrical lines (as a result of tuning) that values are obtained which are either very large or very small. It is then better to take the input readings Z_a and Z_b for two suitable terminations R_a and R_b at the far end and compute the surge impedance Z_0, according to Eq. (1), from

$$Z_0 = \sqrt{\frac{r\,Z_a\,Z_b + \rho\,R_a\,R_b}{r + \rho}} \text{ ohms} \tag{11}$$

where $r = R_a - R_b$ and $\rho = Z_b - Z_a$. The propagation constant per unit length is then

$$n = \frac{1}{l} \tanh^{-1}\left[Z_0 \frac{r + \rho}{Z_0 R_a - Z_b R_b} \right] \tag{12}$$

For very high frequencies the methods described so far are not very reliable. The arrangement of Fig. 326 is then useful. The line is tuned for resonance by means of C_1. Next, the line is shortened by a distance d equal to $\lambda/8$. The line angle corresponding to this distance is then

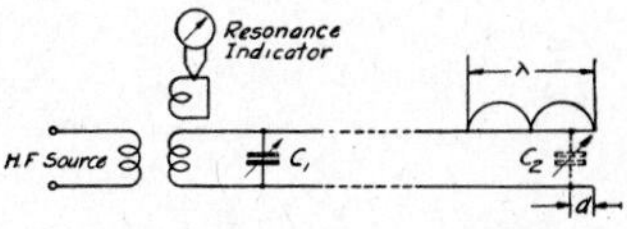

Fig. 326.—Determination of a large impedance at high frequencies.

$$\beta d = \frac{2\pi}{\lambda}d = \frac{\pi}{4}$$

For sinusoidal excitation and such a short distance d there is for the reactance of the short piece d the value

$$j\sqrt{\frac{L}{C}} \cot \frac{\pi}{4} = jZ_0$$

[1] *Proc. I.R.E.*, **15**, 559, 1927.

Hence, by inserting a condenser C_2 at a distance d from the free end and making its reactance $1/j\omega C_2$ equal to $X_d = jZ_0$, one finds

$$Z_0 = \frac{1}{(\omega C_2)} \tag{13}$$

This is done by varying the condenser until for a setting C_2 resonance is again established.

193. Determination of Impedance and Reactance of a Line and Aerials.—To determine the impedance of a line or an aerial, it is only necessary to measure the input current I for a certain input voltage E and compute the input impedance from $Z = E/I$. It can also be done by using an impedance bridge, for instance, the balance-transformer method of Fig. 50. It consists of connecting the line across terminals X, X and a variable reactance X_s in series with a decade resistance box in series in place of the standard. The ground on the mid-tap of the balanced transformer is omitted. Either a variable condenser or a variable inductance acts as the standard reactance X_s, depending upon the voltage distribution along the line. The variable reactance X_s is varied until a minimum deflection is observed on the zero-current detector and the setting $X_s = X$ noted. The variable resistance R_s is varied until for $R_s = R$ final balance is secured. The value $Z = \sqrt{R^2 + X^2}$ is the effective impedance and $\tan^{-1}\dfrac{X}{R}$ the phase angle. For antennas, the aerial is connected to the terminal X next to P_2 and the other terminal X is grounded. The reactance of a line is the setting $X_s = X$. Another method of finding the reactance of the line is by using the circuit of Fig. 325. The switch is closed on 1 and 2 and the circuit is tuned for the desired frequency (with r short-circuited) by means of C. The resonance condition occurs for a maximum reading on meter I_1. If C_1 denotes the resonance setting of C, its reactance $X_1 = 1/(\omega C_1)$

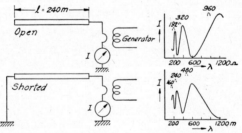

Fig. 327.—Determination of the velocity of propagation by means of equivalent voltage and current resonance. (Full drawn curve for $v < c$; dotted curve for $v = c$.)

is just equal and opposite to that of the coil. The switch is thrown on terminals 3 and 4 and, for a certain loading R_2 or the open line (whichever is the desired line condition), the combination is again tuned until for a setting $C = C_2$ the meter I_1 gives a maximum response. The reactance of the variable condenser is then $X_2 = 1/(\omega C_2)$ and the line reactance is computed from $X_1 - X_2$. The same method can be applied to any aerial system.

194. Determination of the Velocity of Propagation along an Aerial and a Line.—For many aerial systems this velocity is almost equal to that of light ($c = 3 \times 10^{10}$ cm/sec). For long lines and for wave antennas of the Beverage type, the velocity of propagation v along the line can be appreciably smaller than c. The determination may be carried out with the method of Fig. 327. A high-frequency source is coupled to a single turn in the wave antenna. The frequency is varied for the far end open until a resonance indication is noted on the current meter.

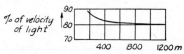

FIG. 328.—Velocity of propagation of waves along a horizontal wave antenna 240m in length and 3m above ground.

This corresponds to the fundamental wave length λ of the line. A further increase in the frequency of the exciter gives another resonance deflection which corresponds to the first higher harmonic distribution along the wire. The frequency f_0, for which the first current maximum is noted, corresponds to the wave length in *free* space which is $\lambda_0 = 4l$, the second current maximum to a wave length $\lambda_0' = \frac{4}{3}l$, the next current maximum to $\lambda_0'' = \frac{4}{5}l$. If λ, λ', λ'', etc., are the corresponding wave lengths due to the actual distributions along the line, $c\lambda_0 = v\lambda = f_0$ for the first current maximum and similar relations for the higher modes. Therefore the velocity v of propagation can be found. The same can also be done with the far end short-circuited to ground. The first maximum current response then happens for $2l$, the next response for l, the next for $\frac{2}{3}l$, etc. The current readings against

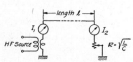

FIG. 329.—Determination of the attenuation along a long line aerial.

the wave length in Fig. 327 indicate experimental results. The heavily drawn curves give the data due to the measurement, while the dotted resonance peaks are computed for the wave propagation along the wire occurring with the velocity c of light. For the open-ended aerial, $\lambda = 1200$ m, λ' = 390 m, $\lambda'' = 192$ m against $\lambda_0 = 4 \times 240 = 960$ m, $\lambda_0' = \frac{4}{3}240 = 320$ m, $\lambda_0'' = \frac{4}{5}240 = 192$ m. This gives the actual velocities of propagation along the line as $v = c\lambda_0/\lambda = \frac{960}{1200} c = 0.8c$, $v' = 0.82c$, and $v'' = 0.87c$. For the aerial short-circuited at the far end $v = \frac{590}{480}c = 0.81c$, etc. Figure 328 gives the results for the actual velocity of propagation in terms of the velocity in empty space.

195. Determination of the Attenuation and Wave-length Constant of a Long Horizontal Aerial and of a Line.—If a long horizontal aerial (such as a wave antenna, Fig. 329) is under consideration, the currents I_1 and I_2 are measured. Since for such a termination no reflections take place at the load resistance R, one has $I_2 = I_1\epsilon^{-\alpha l}$ and the attenuation per unit length is

$$\alpha = \frac{\log_\epsilon \dfrac{I_1}{I_2}}{l} = \frac{2.303 \log_{10} \dfrac{I_1}{I_2}}{l} \tag{14}$$

For double lines and for power lines used for high-frequency work, the circuit of Fig. 325 can be used. The ratio I_1/I_2 is obtained from the ammeter readings corresponding to point P for which $R_2 = \sqrt{L/C}$ and α computed from Eq. (14). Suppose a line $l = 50$ miles long; for a characteristic loading $R = 800\Omega$, $\dfrac{I_1}{I_2} = 2.5$. Then $\alpha = \dfrac{\log_\epsilon 2.5}{50} = \dfrac{0.9163}{50} = 0.0183$ neper attenuation per mile. If all line constants are taken into account; that is, $Z = r + j\omega L = r + jX$ and $Y = g + j\omega C = g + js$ for the impedance along and the admittance across unit length of the line, there are for the corresponding scalar values Z and Y the relations

$r = Z \cos \varphi, g = Y \cos \psi, x = Z \sin \varphi, s = Y \sin \psi$, if $\varphi = \tan^{-1}\dfrac{x}{r}$ and $\psi =$

$\tan^{-1}\dfrac{s}{g}$. For $\theta = 0.5\pi - 0.5(\varphi + \psi)$, there are the complete expressions

$$\left.\begin{array}{l} \alpha = \sqrt{YZ} \sin \theta = \dfrac{\sqrt{rg} \cos 0.5(\varphi + \psi)}{\sqrt{\cos \varphi \cos \psi}} \\[4mm] \beta = \sqrt{YZ} \cos \theta = \dfrac{2\pi f\sqrt{CL} \sin 0.5(\varphi + \psi)}{\sqrt{\sin \varphi \sin \psi}} \end{array}\right\} \tag{15}$$

for the attenuation and wave-length constants per unit length, if r is in ohms, g in mhos, C in farads, L in henries, and f in cycles per second.

196. Surge-impedance Method for the Determination of Capacitance, Inductance, and Resistance of a Long Horizontal Aerial and of a Line.—This method depends primarily upon the determination of the attenuation constant α of the aerial or the line (Sec. 195). By means of Eq. 3, is found the entire resistance for length l from $R_A = 2\alpha l Z_0$, where $Z_0 = \sqrt{L/C}$ is either computed from (2) or found experimentally by means of one of the procedures described in Sec. 192. The velocity of propagation is nearly $v = 1/\sqrt{CL}$ for many high-frequency lines. Comparing $C_A = lC$ and $L_A = lL$ with $c = 1/\sqrt{CL}$ and $Z_0 = \sqrt{L/C}$ gives the total inductance and capacitance of the system of length l from $L_A = Z_0 l/v$ and $C_A = l/(vZ_0)$.

197. Determination of Distributions along Lines and Aerials. Remarks on Aerial Feeders.—One must distinguish between potential (E) and current (I) distributions and at any point of the line. The ratio E/I and the phase is a measure of the impedance beyond that point. For this reason a line terminated by the characteristic impedance $\sqrt{L/C}$

at the far end will have a ratio of E_x/I_x everywhere along the line, that is, for any point a distance x from the far end. The voltage E_x and the corresponding current I_x are then in phase. Using the simplified electrical length $\beta x = 2\pi x/\lambda$ for the high-frequency line for any distance x from the far end which is open, the effective values $E_x = E_m \cos \beta x$ and $I_x = I_m \sin \beta x$ and $Z_x = E_x/I_x = Z_0 \cot \beta x$ are found. To measure the current distribution along the line, a current meter must be moved along the line in such a way that the presence of the meter does not appreciably affect the distributions. It is not practical to cut the line at different places in order to insert the meter so that the current may be measured at such places. The shunt arrangement shown in Fig. 330 or the inductive system shown in the same figure can then be used. For the former, the two pulleys take off a voltage drop across a short line element a, c, and the reading of the meter is proportional to the total current. The

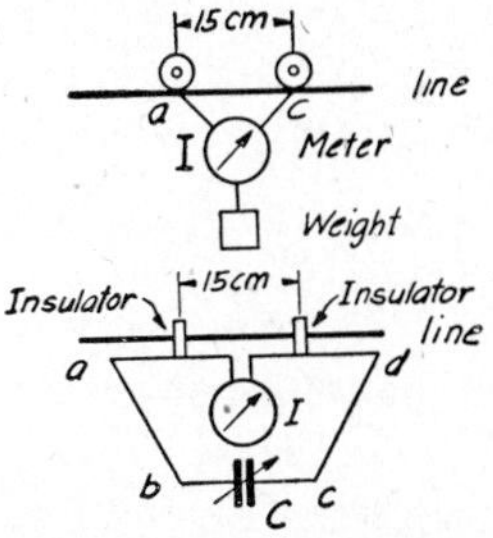

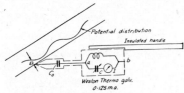

FIG. 330.—Determination of current distribution along lines.

other procedure consists of a pick-up branch a, d which by means of insulators can be moved along and kept a certain distance from the line. In order to adjust the sensitivity, a variable-air condenser C is provided. A more accurate test for the distribution is the voltmeter method shown in Fig. 331. It is due to H. O. Roosenstein[1] and is based upon the fact that at a certain distance from the line the potential falls to zero. The Faraday screen is at this potential. The condenser C_0 of about 3 $\mu\mu f$ is used as a coupling device toward the point of the line where the potential is to be measured. Since the space capacitance of the Faraday cage is large compared with C_0, the potential of the test point is $E_x = I/(\omega C_0)$. The setting of C is chosen such that $\frac{1}{2\pi}\sqrt{CL}$ is larger than the frequency of the line current.

FIG. 331.—Determination of potential distribution.

The meter circuit then acts as a condenser between terminals a and b.

Determinations of line distributions are also of importance when using either single or double lines to feed half wave-length (Hertz) or similar aerial systems[2] (the length of such feeders is then often as long as 300 to 400 m, about 1200 ft, for short-wave work) and aerials whose distributions are artificially changed in order to produce directive and radiation angle effects. Reference is made to Figs. 332 and 333 for the single-feed and parallel-wave feed systems. The single-wire feeder of Fig. 332 should

[1] *Z. Hochfreq.*, **36**, 121, 1930.

[2] EVERITT, W. L., and J. F. BYRNE, *Proc. I.R.E.*, **17**, 1840, 1929; "The Radio Amateurs' Handbook of the American Radio League," Hartford, 1930; C. J. HOULDSON, *Q.S.T.*, **14**, 23, 1930.

not radiate. Therefore, it is necessary that the feeder either has practically a neutralized resultant field (tuned Lecher wire feeder with small spacing) or behaves aperiodically. The latter condition can be fulfilled when the feeder is terminated in its characteristic impedance $\sqrt{L/C}$, for which loading no standing waves can be formed along the feeder. In a double-wire feed system this can be done by using a coupling l_k (Fig. 333) between the end of the feeder and the aerial which matches the radiation resistance against $\sqrt{L/C}$. In Fig. 332, the dotted lines denote the current distributions. When the reading $I_1 > I_2$, the frequency of the tube generator is not properly adjusted and the wave-length distribution is greater than the fundamental required (fundamental of Hertzian dipole requires $AB = \lambda/2$. For $I_1 < I_2$ the opposite is true; that is, the wave length is below the fundamental. When, as in the third case, both readings are equal ($I_1 = I_2$), the generator frequency is correct. The feeder is made aperiodic (I_f distribution constant) by moving P along the aerial AB to a suitable point. The tank circuit with the tap T must be ungrounded; otherwise it would

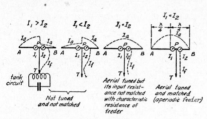

Fig. 332.—Feeding Hertz aerials for short-wave work with a single wire PT ($AB = l$ is Hertz aerial).

be the case of a customary T aerial. For a matched system, the square of the current measured in the feeder multiplied by the effective antenna resistance R_e is the power supplied to the aerial. Since R_e denotes the resistance experienced at P (mostly radiation resistance), this value must be equal to Z_0 of the feeder. Hence, by a suitable location of P, the distribution along the feeder is made uniform and, by the adjustment of the frequency, the aerial AB is made pure resistive. The former is checked by measuring the current distribution along TP and seeing whether it is essentially uniform and the latter by varying f until $I_1 = I_2$ which exists irrespective of the position of P along AB. An approximate test on the fulfillment of both requirements is that the frequency of the tube oscillator should not be materially changed when the connection T is taken off, since the properly loaded feed wire TP, as well as the properly tuned aerial AB, is then purely resistive. Figure 333 shows the parallel-wire feed which may be of either the tuned or aperiodic type. According to Eq. (2), the characteristic resistance of a Lecher wire system is $Z_0 = 276 \log_{10} \frac{2a}{d}$ if a denotes the spacing between the centers of the wires and d the diameter of the conductors. For $Z_0 = 600$ ohms, one has $a = 74.2\ d$. The length of the parallel feed does not matter

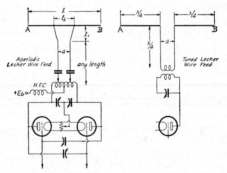

Fig. 333.—Parallel-wire feed of a Hertz aerial AB.

if the coupling length l_k is so that a resistance equal to $Z_0 = \sqrt{L/C}$ is offered. The design formulas for $Z_0 = 600$ ohms are

$$l = pK \qquad\qquad l_k = pK_1 \qquad\qquad l_1 = 0.3p$$

$$p = \begin{cases} \dfrac{150}{f} \text{ for the lengths in meters} \\[2mm] \dfrac{492}{f} \text{ for the lengths in feet} \end{cases} \text{ and } f \text{ in megacycles per second} \Bigg\} \quad (16)$$

since $l = \lambda/2$ and $\lambda^{(m)} f^{(Mc/sec)} = 300$. The factors K and K_1 depend somewhat upon the frequency range. For $f < 3$ Mc/sec $K = 0.96$ and between 3 to 28 Mc/sec $K = 0.95$, above 28 Mc/sec $K = 0.94$. Below 3 Mc/sec $K_1 = 0.25$. Between 3 to 28 Mc/sec $K_1 = 0.24$ and above 28 Mc/sec $K_1 = 0.28$. Hence, if an aerial is to be designed for $f = 3$ Mc/sec and No. 12 A.w.g. wire with a diameter $d = 0.08$ in. is used, then $a = 74.2 \times 0.08 = 5.94$ in. gives a characteristic feeder resistance of $600\,\Omega$. From (16), $l = 0.95 \times {}^{49}2\frac{2}{3} = 156$ ft; $l_k = 0.24 \times {}^{49}2\frac{2}{3} = 39.4$ ft; $l_1 = 0.3 \times {}^{49}2\frac{2}{3} = 49.2$ ft. For the tuned parallel-wire system for which the vertical heights are $\lambda/4$, the spacing a should not be more than about 30 cm (1 ft), so that the fields due to the parallel wires practically cancel each other; that is, the small space-phase difference gives no appreciable loop effects.

198. Determination of Static Antenna Capacitance and Inductance.—In comparison with the effective antenna constants C_e and L_e, the static values C_A and L_A (where for C in farads and L in henries, the natural frequency f in cycles per second), for a quarter wave-length distribution (first mode of oscillation) $f = 1/(4\sqrt{C_A L_A}) = 1/(2\pi\sqrt{C_e L_e})$. If C_e is in microfarads and L_e in

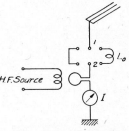

FIG. 334.—Determination of antenna inductance and capacitance.

microhenries, $f = 159.2/\sqrt{C_e L_e}$ kc/sec. The determination of C_A and L_A is as follows. In Fig. 334, a single turn at the ground side, which also contains a thermoelectric-current indicator, is loosely coupled to a tube generator, and with terminals 1 and 2 short-circuited the frequency is varied until for a value f a resonance reading I is noted (for fundamental wave-length $\lambda/4$-distribution). For this condition $C_e = \dfrac{8}{\pi^2} C_A$ and $L_e = 0.5 L_A$ for the capacitance in microfarads and the inductance in microhenries, and $f = 250/\sqrt{C_A L_A}$ kc/sec. For a large coil loading at the grounded side, the current in the aerial decreases almost linearly toward the open end and the potential remains essentially constant. Hence, if a known inductance L_0 in microhenries is inserted and is of a magnitude so that the resonance frequency f_1 of the loaded antenna system is about half the value of f for the unloaded antenna,

$$f_1 = \frac{159.2}{\sqrt{C_e[L_e + L_0]}} = \frac{159.2}{\sqrt{C_A\left[\dfrac{L_A}{3} + L_0\right]}}$$

Hence $f_1 = \dfrac{k}{\sqrt{C_A\left[\dfrac{L_A}{3} + L_0\right]}}$ and $f = \dfrac{k}{\sqrt{\dfrac{4}{\pi^2}C_A L_A}}$ for $k = 159.2$ which gives

the formula

$$L_A = \frac{3\pi^2 f_1^2 L_0}{12f^2 - \pi^2 f_1^2} = \frac{3f_1^2 L_0}{1.215f^2 - f_1^2} \ \mu\text{h} \tag{17}$$

for the static inductance of the aerial. From $f = 250/\sqrt{C_A L_A}$, the static antenna capacitance

$$C_A = \frac{62,500}{f^2 L_A} \ \mu\text{f} \tag{18}$$

is found. In (17) and (18), the frequencies are expressed in kilocycles per second.

Example.—The resonance frequency f is found equal to 438 kc/sec for the unloaded aerial. For a coil loading $L_0 = 448$ μh the resonance frequency becomes $f_1 = 245$ kc/sec, and by means of (17) and (18) it is found that $L_A = 464$ μh and $C_A = 0.0007$ μf. In order to avoid the small error due to the small coil coupling to the high-frequency generator, this coil is dispensed with and the high-frequency generator loosely coupled to a coil $L_0 = L_1$ henries, which is inserted as above between terminals 1 and 2. The resonance frequency is f_1 and given by $f_1 = \dfrac{k}{\sqrt{C_A\left[\dfrac{L_A}{3} + L_1\right]}}$. Next, another loading coil $L_0 = L_2$ is inserted, giving

the resonance frequency $f_2 = \dfrac{k}{\sqrt{C_A\left[\dfrac{L_A}{3} + L_2\right]}}$ where in each case large

coil loading (linear current decrease) is presupposed. The static antenna constants are then computed from

$$L_A = 3\frac{L_1 f_1^2 - L_2 f_2^2}{f_2^2 - f_1^2} \qquad C_A = \frac{k^2}{f_2^2\left[L_2 + \dfrac{L_A}{3}\right]} \tag{19}$$

where $k = 159.2$, the capacitance is in microfarads, the inductances in microhenries, and the frequencies in kilocycles per second.

The static antenna constants can also be determined by means of an impedance bridge, using an audio-frequency current. The capacitance found with this bridge is then equal to C_A and the inductance found at audio frequencies must be multiplied by 3 in order to give the static value L_A of the aerial. The resistance measured at audio frequencies is also to be multiplied by the factor 3 in order to give the static antenna resistance r_A.

A graphical method can also be used to find the static (true) antenna constants. The method is based upon the reactance X_A of an aerial if considered in effect as a long horizontal line given by the expression

$$X_A = -\sqrt{\frac{L_A}{C_A}} \cot\ (\omega\sqrt{C_A L_A})$$

Hence natural oscillations exist for all values of X_A which make

$$\cot\ (\omega\sqrt{C_A L_A}) = 0.$$

If a coil loading $X_0 = \omega L_0$ is inserted at the grounded side, the total reactance $X_0 + X_A$ must become zero for any natural antenna oscillation. The theory and several applications for the determination of C_A and L_A are then as follows:

The method applies to long wire aerials of length l as indicated in Fig. 335. For the coil (L_0) loaded line, the effective reactance of line and loading is $X_e' = j\omega L_0 - j\sqrt{\frac{L}{C}}\cotan\ \Omega = j\sqrt{\frac{L_A}{C_A}}\left\{\frac{\Omega L_0}{L_A} - \cotan\ \Omega\right\}$ where $\Omega = \beta l$ denotes the simplified electrical length $\omega l\sqrt{CL}$ of the line of length l, and C and L the line constants per unit length, and $C_A = lC; L_A = lL$. Since when tuning the reactance X_e' must vanish, $\Omega L_0/L_A = \cotan\ \Omega$. Therefore it is only necessary to draw the cotangent curves (cotan Ω) with y as the ordinate and Ω as abscissa and locate the intersections p, q, r, etc., with the

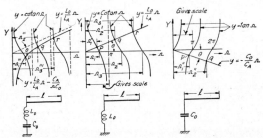

Fig. 335.—Graphical determination of line inductance and capacitance.

ascending line $y = \Omega L_0/L_A$ where L_0 and L_A are fixed and the direction of the line is given by $\theta = \tan^{-1}(L_0/L_A)$. Since Ω_1; Ω_2; Ω_3, etc., denote the states for successive modes of line resonance without loading at the grounded side and Ω_1', Ω_2', Ω_3', etc., for L_0-loading for the fundamental and all higher modes, the ratio of known load inductance to desired static line inductance is $L_0/L_A = (\cotan\ \Omega_1')/\Omega_1' = (\cotan\ \Omega_2')/\Omega_2' = (\cotan\ \Omega_3')/\Omega_3' = \tan\ \theta$. The antenna inductance for resonance for the fundamental line oscillation is computed from $L_A = L_0\Omega_1'\tan\ \Omega_1'$. The scale of the abscissa is given by the cotangent curves, for instance, by π as marked in the figure. The capacitance C_A is found from Eq. (20). The frequency in cycles per second for the fundamental can also be computed from $\Omega_1'/(2\pi\sqrt{C_A L_A})$ with C_A in farads and L_A in henries, although it is more conveniently found by direct measurement. For condenser (C_0) loading, which is also illustrated in Fig. 335, the total reactance is $X_e'' = \frac{1}{(j\omega C_0)} - j\sqrt{\frac{Z}{C}}\cotan\ \Omega = -j\sqrt{\frac{L_A}{C_A}}\left\{\frac{C_A}{(\Omega C_0)} + \cotan\ \Omega\right\}$. Hence, for resonance, the value of x_e'' must vanish again and $\tan\ \Omega = -\Omega C_0/C_A$. Tangent curves, $y =$

tan Ω, are then drawn and the intersection points p and q, etc., found with the slanting line $y = -\Omega C_0/C_A$ with an angle $\theta = \tan^{-1}(C_0/C_A)$. If the condenser-loaded line is tuned to the fundamental mode, the static line capacitance is computed from $C_A = C_0\Omega_1''$ cotan Ω_1''. If series coil (L_0) and condenser (C_0) loading is used to tune the line, the total reactance is $X_e''' = j\left[\omega L_0 - \dfrac{1}{\omega C_0} - \sqrt{\dfrac{L}{C}}\, \text{cotan }\Omega\right] = j\sqrt{\dfrac{L_A}{C_A}}\left\{\dfrac{L_0\Omega}{L_A} - \dfrac{C_A}{C_0\Omega} - \text{cotan }\Omega\right\}$. For resonance $X_e''' = 0$ and cotan $\Omega = \dfrac{\Omega L_0}{L_A} - \dfrac{C_A}{\Omega C_0} = \Omega \tan\theta - \dfrac{C_A}{\Omega C_0}$. Hence, as in Fig. 335, draw the cotangent curves $y = \text{cotan }\Omega$ and find the intersection points p, q, r, etc., with the hyperbola $y = \Omega \tan\theta - \dfrac{C_A}{\Omega C_0}$ with the y-axis and the inclined line $y = \Omega \tan\theta$ as asymptotes.

The equations utilized in the graphical method can also be used for an analytical method.[1] The formulas then are

$$L_A{}^{(\mu h)} = L_0{}^{(\mu h)}\frac{f_1}{f}\frac{\pi}{2}\tan\left(\frac{f_1}{f}90\right); \quad C_A{}^{(\mu f)} = \frac{62{,}500}{f^2 L_A} \tag{20}$$

where f denotes the resonance frequency in kilocycles per second of the unloaded aerial and f_1 the resonance frequency for a coil loading of L_0.

Example.—For no loading $f = 438$ kc/sec. For a loading $L_0 = 345$ μh, the resonance frequency is $f_1 = 266$ kc/sec. Then $\pi f_1/(2f) = 0.953$, $90 f_1/f = 56.3$ deg, and $L_A = 463$ μh; $C_A = 0.0007$ μf.

Another method for finding C_A and L_A is described in the next section in connection with a method which also gives the values of C_e and L_e.

199. Determination of Effective Antenna Capacitance, Inductance, and Resistance.—If the circuit of Fig. 242 is used, the differential system is at first excited with sinusoidal oscillations taken from a tube generator and then with quenched spark-gap oscillations and the system is balanced in each case. For *sinusoidal* excitation the current I in the main branch depends, in the case of resonance only, upon the effective resistance R_2 of the entire system. But for damped oscillations the resonance current I depends upon the decrement δ_1 of the oscillator and the effective decrement δ_2 of the differential system and

$$I = \frac{E_0}{2R_2}\sqrt{\frac{N\delta_2}{f[\delta_1\delta_2 + \delta_1{}^2]}}$$

Hence I depends upon R_2, L_2, C_2 (of secondary for quenched-spark oscillations), the group frequency N of the damped oscillation and the maximum value E_0 of the induced oscillations. The procedure is then as follows:

1. The balance for the sinusoidal excitation gives the settings C_s, L_s and $R_s = R_e$ where R_e denotes the total effective antenna resistance.
2. The differential system is excited with quenched spark-gap oscillations at the same frequency as before and the ratio C_s/L_s is changed until balance again exists.

[1] *Elektrotech. u. Maschinenbau,* Heft 45, 1920.

The settings $C_s' = C_e$ and $L_s' = L_e$ are then the effective antenna capacitance and inductance.

Figure 336 is based upon the same principle.

1. A small coupling coil L is used and, with 1 connected on 2, the frequency of a tube generator varied until resonance is indicated by meter I.

2. Terminal 2 is connected on 3 and 4 on 5, and C_s and L_s are varied until a resonance indication is noted.

3. The setting of R_s is varied until for a value $R_s = R_e$ the same resonance current I as in the aerial flows in the circuit.

4. A quenched spark-gap source is used as the source and the resonance current I_1 noted with the aerial in the circuit.

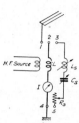

5. The artificial circuit is connected (2 on 3 and 4 on 5) in the measuring system and C_s and L_s are varied until for settings $C_s = C_s'$ and $L_s = L_s'$ the same resonance current I_1 is obtained. This is done by leaving the $R_s = R_e$ setting as before and increasing C_s while decreasing L_s or *vice versa*, since C_eL_e must be equal to C_sL_s and $C_s'L_s' = C_sL_s = C_eL_e$. The settings C_s', L_s', and $R_s = R_e$ are then the effective antenna constants.

Fig. 336.—The equivalent aerial method.

The total effective antenna resistance can also be found by the resistance-variation method as in Fig. 337. For 1 and 2 short-circuited, the resonance current I is noted. A standard resistance R_s is then connected across 1 and 2 and the reduced resonance current I_1 read off, and the effective antenna resistance computed from $R_e = I_1R_s/(I - I_1)$.

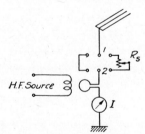 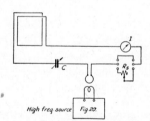

Fig. 337.—Determination of effective antenna resistance.

Fig. 338.—Determination of the effective resistance of a frame aerial.

If a standard resistance is varied until, for a value $R_s = R_1$, $I_1 = I/2$, then $R_1 = R_e$. For very accurate work, the resistance of the meter must be taken into account. The effect of the meter resistance can be made small by coupling a thermogalvanometer loosely to the antenna. In the same manner the effective resistance of a loop aerial is found. The frame is then tuned as in Fig. 338 by means of C. The true as well as the effective antenna[1] constants can also be computed from readings of the unloaded and coil-loaded antenna by means of

$$L_A = \frac{A_1 - A_2}{A_2B_2 - A_1B_1}L_0 \qquad C_A = \frac{62{,}500}{f^2L_A} \qquad (21)$$

[1] *Proc. I. R. E.* **8**, 424, 1920.

where L_A and L_B are in microhenries and C_A in microfarads, if L_0 denotes the loading coil inserted at the ground side, f the resonance frequency in kilocycles per second for the unloaded, and f_1 the resonance frequency for the L_0 loaded aerial. The distribution factors are computed from

$$A_1 = 2.45\frac{f}{f_1}\cdot\frac{\sin^2\left[\frac{f_1}{f}90\right]}{\frac{\pi f_1}{f} + \sin\left\{\left[1 - \frac{f_1}{f}\right]180\right\}} = 2.45\frac{f}{f_1}p \quad B_1 = 0.159\frac{f}{pf_1}$$

$$A_2 = 0.636\frac{f}{f_1}\sin\left[\frac{f_1}{f}90\right] \qquad B_2 = 0.636\frac{f}{f_1}\frac{1 - \cos\left[\frac{f_1}{f}90\right]}{\sin\left[\frac{f_1}{f}90\right]} \tag{22}$$

The effective antenna constants for the coil loading L_0 are $C_e = A_1 C_A$ and $L_e = B_1 L_A$ which differ from the values if no loading exists.

Example.—The resonance frequency for an unloaded aerial was measured as $f = 438$ kc/sec. For loading $L_0 = 246$ μh, the resonance frequency was 295 kc/sec. giving $A_1 = 0.967$, $B_1 = 0.393$;, $A_2 = 0.826$, and $B_2 = 0.56$. Hence,

$$L_A = \frac{0.967 - 0.826}{0.826 \times 0.56 - 0.967 \times 0.393}246 = 413 \text{ μh};$$

$C_A = 0.00079$ μf; $C_e = 0.967 \times 0.00079 = 0.000764$ μf; $L_e = 0.393 \times 413 = 162.5$ μh. If these results are inserted in the formula $f_1 = 159.2/\sqrt{C_e[L_e + L_0]}$ the value of f_1 differs by only about 3.35 per cent from the measured value 295 kc/sec.

200. Determination of Radiation Resistance.—The effective aerial resistance R_e, determined by the methods just described, consists of a useful component which is the radiation resistance R_r of a component which accounts for the losses due to the effective resistance of the aerial wire itself, including the increase of resistance due to eddy currents in ground and surrounding objects. There is also a component which accounts for the dielectric losses in the surrounding medium. At the end of Sec. 134 a method is indicated whereby the different components can be separated if the total resistance R_e is determined experimentally for three different frequencies. Therefore it is possible to find R_r by such a method.

The radiation resistance R_r depends upon the energy flux $W = \frac{1}{4\pi}[\mathcal{E}H]$ of the radiated power and, according to Poynting, this flux is perpendicular to the electric vector $\mathcal{E}$ and magnetic-field vector H. If c denotes the velocity of propagation, and the dielectric constant for air, as well as the magnetic permeability, has the conventional value of unity and $\mathcal{E}_z = cH_y$ if it is assumed that the direction of propagation of the energy is along the x-axis. Therefore it is possible to compute the resistance from $W = \frac{1}{4\pi c}\mathcal{E}^2$ if the electric-field vector $\mathcal{E}$ is measured by means of the voltage induced in a receiving antenna. It can be shown that for a dipole of length l, the radiation energy taken over a sphere of radius ρ is

$$W_r = \frac{2}{3} \frac{l^2}{c} \left[\frac{di}{dt}\right]^2$$

and depends only upon the change of current and length l of the dipole.   Hence, if a current $i = I_m \sin \omega t$ oscillates to and fro along the dipole

$$W_r = \frac{2}{3} \frac{\omega^2 l^2}{c} I_m^2 \cos^2 \omega t$$

showing that the radiated energy is also proportional to the square of the frequency $\omega/(2\pi)$.   The energy radiated from the aerial is equivalent to an increase of aerial resistance and, since for an effective current value I the ratio W_r/I^2 denotes a resistance, the radiation resistance $R_r = \frac{2}{3} \frac{\omega^2 l^2}{c} = \frac{8\pi^2}{3} c \left[\frac{l}{\lambda}\right]^2$ abohms.   For $c = 3 \times 10^{10}$ cm/sec and 1 abohm $= 10^{-9}$ ohm, we find for the dipole $R_r = 80\pi^2 [l/\lambda]^2$ ohms.   The above energy relation holds for the entire sphere about the dipole, and for half of the sphere above ground $40\pi^2 (l/\lambda)^2$ denotes the radiation resistance.   If the ground is considered a fairly good conductor, a vertical dipole of length l can be imagined just as much in the ground as above it and, if h is the vertical height of the conductor above ground, the length l of the imaginary dipole is $2h$ and $R_r = 160\pi^2 [h/\lambda]^2$ ohms, since only the radiation above ground (hemisphere) is of interest.   This formula holds only for the dipole which has a uniform current distribution.   If, instead of h, the effective height h_e of an aerial is used where $h_e = ph$, one has $R_r = 160\pi^2 [h_e/\lambda]^2$ ohms.   But $\lambda f = 3 \times 10^5$ km/sec, where λ is in meters and f in kilocycles per second, and

$$R_r = \begin{cases} 1579 \left[\dfrac{h_e}{\lambda}\right]^2 \\ 1755 \times 10^{-11} h_e^2 f^2 \end{cases} \tag{23}$$

if R_r is in ohms, h_e in meters, and f in kilocycles per second.   For a grounded vertical wire excited (without any loading coil) in the quarter wave-length distribution $p = 2/\pi$; that is, $h_e = 0.636$ times the actual length of the aerial wire, and

$$R_r = 160\pi^2 \left[\frac{\frac{2}{\pi} \frac{\lambda}{4}}{\lambda}\right]^2 = 40 \text{ ohms}$$

If the same wire uses a heavy coil loading for which the current distribution toward the upper end decreases linearly, then $p = 0.5$.   For large horizontal portions of a T aerial $p \cong 1$.   For complicated aerials, the dipole effect must be extended over the entire aerial, and the radiation effect is found by integration which takes into account the radiations in all directions as well as the retardation time.   If this is done for the vertical grounded wire excited in the quarter wave-length distribution, $R_r = 36.6$ ohms instead of 40 ohms as computed above in Eq. (23).   Since the formulas of Eq. (23) are based on fairly good ground the respective numerical constants hold only if this is the case.

From the discussion given above, it is evident that the radiation resistance can be determined if the effective height of an aerial is known. This height can be determined by one of the procedures described in Sec. 201.   The radiation resistance can also be determined by means of the radiated energy (energy flux).   For such measurements the radiated energy is received by another aerial.   It is then of *importance* that neither indirect electromagnetic waves (reflected from the ionized layer) nor the proximity antenna effect (field components of the sender aerials which exist only close to the sender) exist in the region of the receiver. Therefore the measurement is carried on about 5 to 10 wave lengths away from the sender. With the method in Fig. 339 (due to J. Erskine Murray, "Handbook of Wireless Telegraphy," Crosby Lockwood and Son, London), the effective resistance $R_e = R_1$ of the sender is at first determined by one of the procedures described in Sec. 199. The effective resonance currents I_1 and I_2 of the sender and receiver aerial are measured. The aerial of the sender is then lowered to about one-tenth of its normal height and is tuned to the same frequency as before in such a way that the power input $(I_1')^2 R_1' = I_1^2 R_1$ is the same as before if R_1' denotes the new effective aerial resistance of the sender and I_1' the current. The corresponding received current is I_2'. The radiation resistance is then computed from $R_r = I_2^2 R_1[I_1^2 - I_1'^2]/ [I_1^2 I_2'^2 - I_1'^2 I_2^2]$. The efficiency of the sender aerial is then $\eta^\% = 100 R_r/R_1$.

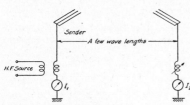

Fig. 339.—Determination of radiation resistance.

Another method is based on the expression

$$W_r = \left\langle \begin{array}{c} 0.0111 d^2 \mathcal{E}^2 \\ 5 \times 10^{12} d^2 H^2 \end{array} \right\rangle \text{watts} \qquad (24)$$

for the radiation energy if $\mathcal{E}$ denotes the effective electric intensity in millivolts per meter and H the effective magnetic-field intensity in gausses at distance d km away from the sender of an aerial of effective height h_e. The values $\mathcal{E}$ and H hold for the equatorial plane. It is an easy matter to derive the above expressions. For the magnetic vector it is as follows: The magnetic field a sufficient distance d cm from the sender aerial is $H = \dfrac{4\pi h_e I}{\lambda d}$ gausses if I is the effective current in amperes measured at the current loop of the sender aerial and distance d is not so far as to show appreciable attenuation. The wave length λ and h_e are in centimeters. For the hemisphere of radius $d_{(cm)}$ there is $W_r = \dfrac{c}{6} H^2 d^2$ ergs/sec where $c = 3 \times 10^{10}$ cm/sec, 1 erg/sec $= 10^{-7}$ watt, and $d_{(cm)} = 10^{-5} d_{(km)}$ confirms the above formula. Knowing the distance d in kilometers and having determined either H in gausses or $\mathcal{E}$ in millivolts per meter the power W_r in watts can be computed from Eq. (24) and the radiation resistance from $R_r = W_r/I^2$ if I denotes the effective aerial current measured at the ground side (current loop).

201. Determination of the Effective Height of Aerials and Its Relation to Radiated Power.—The concept of effective height h_e of an aerial has the advantage that the radiation effect of aerials of different design can be compared at a certain distance. This is important for measurements, since commercial aerials for practical reasons cannot be standardized as to shape and current distribution. Some aerials carry almost uniform current all along the vertical portion, such as is the case for aerials with pronounced flat tops (wide T aerials) and Hertz aerials with aperiodic feeders (Fig. 332), while many others have a nonuniform distribution along the lead-out wire and the aerial extensions at the top. The fields of the different portions are affected by time retardations and may interfere so that the resultant effect at a distant place in space may differ greatly. As a matter of fact, even with comparatively simple senders it may not be the same even in the equatorial plane around a circle with the sender at the center when directive effects present themselves. Therefore, if radiation effects are determined at a certain place, it can be characteristic only for that place, since for a high-angle sender it may be much stronger when observed in an aeroplane and also stronger in the opposite direction to which, for instance, the upper horizontal lead points for an inverted L aerial. The effective height is defined by the relation $Ih_e = \int_0^l I_x dx$ if I denotes the effective current measured at the current loop, l the length of the aerial, and I_x the effective current at any distance x from the ground. Hence, $h_e = \frac{1}{I}\int I_x dx$. The integration must be taken over the entire portion and the retardation time must also be taken into account. The product $I\, h_e$ also known as the "meter-ampere," if the effective height is expressed in meters and the current in amperes, is a measure for the radiated power, since it is a characteristic term in the field-intensity formula for a receiving system of sufficient distance from the sender aerial. However, this must not be so far that indirect electromagnetic waves are received from the ionized layer (at times when refracted waves are possible) and not so far that the arriving wave has suffered appreciable space attenuation. Five to ten wave lengths away is a good distance for such measurements. The field strength at a certain distance d km from the sender is

$$\varepsilon = \left\langle \begin{matrix} 1.256\dfrac{h_e If}{d} \\[2ex] 377 \times 10^3\dfrac{h_e I}{\lambda d} \end{matrix} \right\rangle \ \mu \ \text{volts/m} \tag{25}$$

if f is in kilocycles per second, λ in meters, the effective height h_e of the sender aerial in meters, and the effective current I of the sender in amperes and measured at the current loop. It can be seen that the product $h_e I$ for a fixed distance d and frequency f is a measure for the electric-field intensity ε as well as for the wave energy, since, according to (24), it is proportional to the square of ε. If the distance d is expressed in the same unit as the wave length λ, that is, in meters, the effective height $h_e = h_s$ of a sender aerial, according to Eq. (25), can be computed from

$$h_s = \left\{ \begin{array}{l} 265 \times 10^{-5} \dfrac{\lambda}{I} \dfrac{d}{I} \varepsilon \\[2mm] 796 \dfrac{d}{fI} \varepsilon \end{array} \right\} \quad \text{meter} \qquad (26)$$

The determination of the effective height depends then upon the measurement of ε in microvolts per meter and is carried on the distance d to the receiving aerial in meters (choose d about 5λ m) the sender current I in amperes, and the frequency f in kilocycles per second or the corresponding wave length λ in meters.

The simplest way of determining the effective height h_s is by means of a loop aerial, since the effective height h_r of such an aerial is

$$h_r = 209 \times 10^{-7} A N f$$

if N is the number of turns, A the area of the loop in square meters ($A = a \times h$ if a is the width and h the height of the winding frame), where it is assumed that the width of the loop aerial along the direction of wave propagation is smaller than about one-sixth of the wave length λ in space. If this is not true, Eq. (10) must be used. Hence, if the frequency f is again in kilocycles per second and the corresponding wave length λ in empty space in meters, for the effective height $h_e = h_r$ of the receiving loop,

$$h_r = \left\{ \begin{array}{l} \dfrac{6.28 A N}{\lambda} \\[2mm] 209 \times 10^{-7} A N f \end{array} \right\} \quad \text{meter} \qquad (27)$$

If the loop does not exactly point toward the sender and the vertical plane of the frame makes an angle θ with the vertical plane through sender and receiver stations, the effective height is only $h_r \cos \theta$. If the receiving loop is tuned, its effective resistance $R^{(\text{ohms})}$ only is effective and the resonance current I_r in amperes produces the resonance voltage $E = I_r R = h_r \varepsilon 10^{-6}$ volt. Eliminating ε, in microvolts per meter, from this expression and Eq. (25), one has the identity $\dfrac{1.256 h_s I_s f}{d} = \dfrac{I_r R}{h_r} 10^6$, giving the effective height of the sender aerial

$$h_s = 796 \times 10^3 \dfrac{d\, R\, I_r}{h_r\, f\, I_s} \qquad (28)$$

where h_s and h_r are in meters, I_r and I_s in amperes, d in kilometers, R in ohms, and f in kilocycles per second. Therefore the determination of h_s consists of noting the current I_s at the current loop of the sender aerial, the resonance current I_r of the loop receiver, measuring the sender frequency f, the distance d to the loop, and of computing the value of h_r according to (27). When the received currents are very small, it is better to use the method described in connection with Eq. (26) and measure the field intensity $\mathcal{E}$ by means of an artificial voltage comparator (page 114), using for convenience a receiving loop. This also must be done when the frequency is of such a magnitude that the effective-height formula of (27) no longer holds (is based on fairly good conducting ground and the image effect). Another method determines the effective height of aerials by means of the three-antenna method due to C. Pession.[1] It may also be called the "triangle method." It utilizes the field relation of Eq. (25) together with the resonance voltage $I_2 R_2 = h_2 \mathcal{E} \times 10^{-6}$ volts in a receiving antenna of effective height h_2 if $\mathcal{E}$ is the field strength according to (25) in microvolts per meter. I_2 denotes the resonance current measured at the base and R_2 the effective resistance of the receiving antenna. Eliminating $\mathcal{E}$ again,

$$h_1 h_2 = K \frac{d_{12} R_2 I_2}{f_1 I_1} \tag{29}$$

where h_1 and h_2 are in meters, I_1 and I_2 in amperes, d_{12} in kilometers, R_2 in ohms, and f_1 in kilocycles per second, if $K = 796 \times 10^3$ and d_{12} denotes the distance between the sender aerial of effective height h_1 and the receiver aerial of effective height h_2, and I_1 the effective current measured at the current loop of the sender aerial. Therefore if a third antenna a distance d_{23} to aerial of effective height h_2 is also used and I_2 is now the sender current and I_3 the received resonance current, then

$$h_2 h_3 = K \frac{d_{23} R_3}{f_2} \frac{I_3}{I_2} \tag{30}$$

and, for aerial 3 acting as sender and aerial 1 as tuned receiver,

$$h_3 h_1 = K \frac{d_{31} R_1}{f_3} \frac{I_1}{I_3} \tag{31}$$

From the various measurements, numerical values for $h_1 h_2$, $h_2 h_3$, and $h_3 h_1$ are found and then it is possible to find h_1, h_2, and h_3.

Example.—For the first measurement $d_{12} = 6.67$ km, $I_1 = 18$ amp, $I_2 = 95 \times 10^{-3}$ amp, $R_2 = 12.75$ ohms, $f_1 = 93.7$ kc/sec; hence $h_1 h_2 = 3800$ m^2, $d_{23} = 5.28$ km, $I_2 = 10.6$ and $I_3 = 49 \times 10^{-3}$ amp, $R_3 = 12.9$ ohms, $f_2 = 95.2$ kc/sec; hence $h_2 h_3 = 526$ m^2, $d_{31} = 5.17$ km, $I_3 = 13$ and $I_1 = 24.5 \times 10^{-3}$ amp; hence $h_3 h_1 = 2570$ m^2. The effective heights of the three stations are then $h_1 = 136$ m, $h_2 = 27.9$ m, $h_3 = 18.8$ m.

[1] *Radio Rev.*, **2**, 228, 1921.

CHAPTER XVI

DETERMINATIONS ON WAVE PROPAGATION

Great advances in propagation phenomena have been made in recent years. Skip distances and other extraordinary field-intensity occurrences are better understood, since several investigators have made extensive studies of the ionized layer. Electromagnetic waves at a certain receiver can be elliptically polarized and the polarization at times undergoes changes. The Hertzian rod aerial has been brought to the foreground once more for the study of components of the resultant arriving electromagnetic wave, and tilting coils are used for similar work.

202. Notes on the Electric- and Magnetic-field Intensity of an Electromagnetic Wave in Space.—Several investigators[1] have described methods for the determination of field intensities. As far as ordinary day measurements are concerned (for which indirect rays do not play a part), either receiving antennas or receiving loops can be used, and it does not matter whether the field energy of the arriving wave is expressed in terms of the magnetic- or in terms of the electric-field intensity [Eq. (24), Sec. 200], since ε volts/cm = 300 H gilberts/cm. The equality of ε and H with ε volts/cm = 300 gausses is correct with ground waves (direct waves). But this is generally *not* true when ε_z and H_y values measured with a vertical antenna and a vertical loop pointing toward the sender if the effects of an indirect sky wave are studied. The electric-field intensity of the direct wave a distance d km from the sender antenna is

$$\varepsilon = 1.256 \frac{h_s I_s f}{d} k_A \tag{1}$$

if h_s is the effective height of the sender aerial in meters, I_s the effective sender current measured at the current loop in amperes, f the frequency in kilocycles per second for which the sender is tuned. ε is in microvolts per meter and d is in kilometers. The factor k_A denotes the absorption

[1] Austin, L. W., *Bur. of Standards, Sci. Paper* 159, 1911; *Proc. I.R.E.*, **5**, 239, 1917; H. Barkhausen, *Jahrb. d. drahtl.*, **5**, 261, 1912; F. Braun, *Jahrb. d. drahtl.*, **8**, 132, 212, 1914; R. von Traubenberg, *Jahrb. d. drahtl.*, **14**, 569, 1919; G. Vallauri, *Electrician*, **86**, 249, 1921; H. J. Round and F. C. Lunnon, *J. Inst. Elec. Eng. (London)*, **59**, 865, 1921; M. Guierre, *Radio Rev.*, **2**, 621, 1921; J. Hollingworth, *J. Inst. Elec. Eng. (London)*, **61**, 501, 1923; C. R. Englund, *Proc. I.R.E.*, **11**, 26, 1923; R. Bown, C. Englund, and H. T. Friis, *Proc. I.R.E.*, **11**, 153, 1923; M. Baeumler, *E.N.T.*, **1**, 50, 1924; L. W. Austin and E. B. Judson, *Proc. I.R.E.*, 521, 1924; G. Anders, *E.N.T.*, **2**, 401, 1925; *Standardization Rep.*, *I.R.E.*, 114, 1929; E. Merritt and W. E. Bostwick, *Proc. Nat. Acad. Sci.*, **14**, 884, 1928.

factor. For day transmission this factor is of the form $\epsilon^{-\beta}$ where, for instance, for long waves as used in the Austin transmission experiments,

$$\beta = \frac{kd}{\lambda^p} = k_1 d f^p$$

In many cases for measurements close to the sender the factor, k_A can be put equal to unity. For a tuned loop aerial of N turns a width a and a height h of the frame, there is for the resonance current I_r in microamperes and the effective resistance R of the receiver loop

$$\left.\begin{aligned} \mathcal{E} &= 47{,}700 \frac{I_r R}{f\,a\,h\,N} = 47{,}700 P \\ H &= 1592 \times 10^{-9} P \end{aligned}\right\} \qquad (2)$$

where $\mathcal{E}$ is in microvolts per meter, I_r in microamperes, R in ohms, f in kilocycles per second, a and h in meters, and H in gilberts per centimeter. If a tuned aerial of effective height h_r, effective resistance R, and resonance current I_r measured at the base (current loop) is used as a receiver

$$\mathcal{E} = \frac{I_r R}{h_r} \qquad (3)$$

where $\mathcal{E}$ is in microvolts per meter, I_r in microamperes, R in ohms, and h_r in meters. Now, if it is assumed that the electric-field vector $\mathcal{E}$ of the arriving electromagnetic wave is vertically polarized, a vertical wire aerial will be affected by the entire field intensity. The same is true for a receiving loop whose plane is vertical and points toward the sender aerial. However, if the electric vector $\mathcal{E}$ has a forward tilt, the vertical wire aerial only will be affected by the vertical component of the field vector, while the loop aerial pointing toward the sender picks up the vertical component of $\mathcal{E}$ with its vertical sides, and the horizontal components of $\mathcal{E}$ with its horizontal sides, which means that it receives the resultant field intensity. Therefore a linear aerial (Hertzian rod) can be used to find the wave tilt, since maximum voltage will be induced in it if it is along the field vector and theoretically no voltage if it is perpendicular to $\mathcal{E}$. The latter gives a sharper indication and is therefore commonly used. The loop receiver has, according to Eq. (27) of Sec. 201, the same receiving action in all directions along the plane of the frame, since its effective height is $209 \times 10^{-7} A N f$ and the area A of loop may be a circle, a square, or a rectangle. This is practically true if the lower side of the loop is not too close to ground. But the loop receiver has theoretically no receiving action to waves arriving perpendicular to its plane. Hence, if a loop is with its plane perpendicular to ground and, instead of pointing toward the sender, is also perpendicular to sender-receiver direction, no direct ground wave can be picked up, and so it gives a means for separating the effects of ground and indirect sky wave. As long as the refracted downcoming sky wave which arrives at the loop receiver has an electric-field component which is horizontally polarized, the loop in the mentioned position will be affected by the downcoming wave. The resultant magnetic vector has then a component directed toward the sender.

Unless the received current is of sufficient strength to be read directly on a meter of the receiver aerial, a comparator circuit is used to produce artificially the same effect in the receiver aerial as the arriving wave produces. The artificial voltage is then introduced either by a standard resistance or by a known mutual inductance.

203. Determination of the Absorption Factor of Direct Electromagnetic Waves.—If the transmitter aerial sends out powerful waves and the receiver station is not too far away, a good receiving antenna can be used. Its effective height h_r, as well as h_s of the sender antenna, is first determined by means of a coil receiver which is about 5 wave lengths away. A sensitive microammeter is connected at the base of the receiver antenna and the effective antenna resistance R found (Sec. 199). The meter resistance is also taken into account. The receiving antenna is then tuned to the incoming wave, giving the resonance current I_r in microamperes. The electric-field strength is computed according to (3) by means of $\mathcal{E} = I_r R / h_r$. Since the distance d between the sender and receiver stations is known and the frequency f can be measured, with a knowledge of the sender current in amperes, according to (1) the absorption factor is found from

$$k_A = \frac{\mathcal{E}\, d}{1.256\, h_s I_s f} = 0.796 \frac{I_r\, R\, d}{I_s\, h_s\, h_r\, f} \qquad (4)$$

where $\mathcal{E}$ is in microvolts per meter, I_r in microamperes, R in ohms, d in kilometers, I_s in amperes, h_s and h_r in meters, and f in kilocycles per

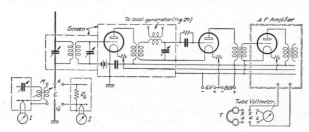

Fig. 340.—Calibration of receivers and determination of field intensity.

second. For stations which are far away so that the received current cannot be read off directly, the method of Fig. 340 can be used. It is then unnecessary that the arriving electromagnetic wave be modulated, since a local heterodyne is employed to produce a suitable beat note (about 1000 cycles/sec) in the telephone receiver. For powerful transoceanic long-wave stations, about three stages of high-frequency amplification using resistance capacitance coupling are used. The method consists of tuning-in the arriving electromagnetic wave and varying the frequency of the local generator until a beat note is heard if the telephone receiver T is connected across the output 5 and 6. A tube voltmeter with terminals 1 and 2 is then connected across 5 and 6 instead of T and the sensitivity changed until a suitable deflection d is noted. This measurement must be carried on with a small standard resistance R_s (about 1 ohm) across AG or the coil L of an air transformer M. If the former is the case, a suitable current I of the same frequency as that of the electromagnetic wave is sent through R_s after the transmitter stops sending, and I is varied until the tube voltmeter gives the same deflection d as before. Since $E = IR_s$ can be computed from the known current I and resistance R_s, the received current I_r is found from E/R if R denotes the effective resistance of the receiving aerial with R_s in the circuit. The small current I is conveniently produced by means of an attenuation box (Fig. 53) and such that $R_s = 1$ ohm is in series with 599 ohms, and the series combination forms the characteristic load resistance of 600 ohms for which the attenuation box has been designed. If the small coupling coil is used during the actual test, R denotes the effective aerial resistance with these few turns at the ground side. After the transmitter stops sending, the known mutual inductance M is varied until the tube voltmeter again gives the deflection d. The voltage E is computed from $2\pi f IM$. If f is in kilocycles per second, I in milliamperes, and M in microhenries, the applied voltage E is in microvolts and for R ohms effective antenna resistance E/R gives the desired received current in microamperes.

Example.—A transoceanic high-power station gave at the Bureau of Standards a received current $I_r = 5.36$ μa. The sender current was $I_s = 380$ amp. The frequency of the carrier wave was 238 kc/sec. The effective height of the sender antenna was $h_s = 150$ m and that of the receiver at Washington, D. C., $h_r = 15$ m, with an effective resistance $R = 85$ ohms. The received electric-field strength was then $\varepsilon = 5.36 \times 85/15 = 30.34$ μvolts/m. Since the transoceanic sender station was at a distance $d = 6650$ km, according to (4) the absorption factor became $k_A = 30.34 \times 6650/(1.256 \times 150 \times 380 \times 23.8) = 0.1185$.

The *equal*-deflection method, and a receiving *antenna* as described above, has the disadvantage that the sender and receiver stations have to experiment together, since the comparator measurement *cannot* be taken unless the transmitter stops sending. For this reason L. W. Austin[1] used the telephone receiver T in order to measure ε as well as k_A, while the transmitter keeps sending. The method is then about 30 per cent accurate, depending very much upon the experimenter. The Morse code which arrives is noted by means of the telephone receiver and the frequency of the local generator is varied until the artificial voltage E which is superimposed gives the same pitch as the arriving signals.

[1] *Loc. cit.*

With a key the voltage E is also impressed by means of a code and such that the artificial code signals occur as much as possible between the signals of the arriving wave. The voltage E is then varied until the same loudness is heard for the actual and artificial code signals. When using a loop receiver as in Fig. 341, a much more accurate method is obtained and the sender station need not stop sending. The loop points toward the sender for the first reading of the tube voltmeter for which the actual wave is picked up. When the artificial voltage E is impressed across the standard resistance R_s (about 1 ohm), located at the middle of the loop, the same is turned at right angles to the direction of the arriving waves. The formula is exactly the same as above except that h_r is computed directly from Eq. (27) of Sec. 201.

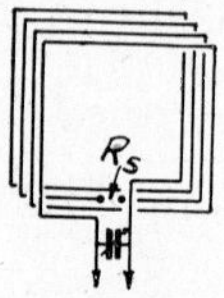

Fig. 341.—Calibration by means of a frame aerial and a known terminal voltage E across a standard resistor R_s.

204. Determination of the Electric-field Intensity.— The methods just described can also be used to find the electric-field intensity ε of a wave. If radiation measurements close to a sender are to be made and sometimes in the broadcast range, the absorption factor k_A, in many cases, can be assumed equal to unity if the measurements are carried on only within a distance range of $d = 2$ to 5 wave lengths. A suitable loop aerial can then be used. It is tuned by means of variable-air condenser at the center of the loop to the particular carrier frequency f and a sensitive thermogalvanometer employed to note the received resonance current I. The effective coil resistance R, including that of a low-resistance heater of the thermogalvanometer, is found by the resistance-variation method and the received field intensity computed from

$$\varepsilon = \frac{IR}{h_e}$$

where

$$h_e = 209 \times 10^{-7} ANf.$$

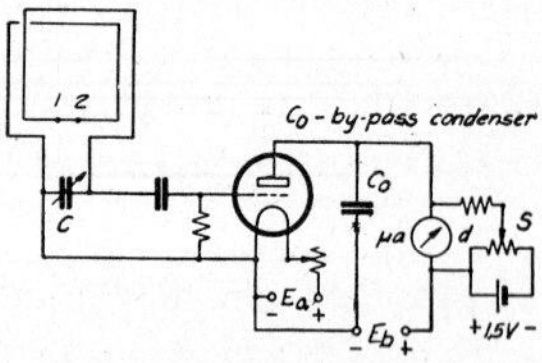

Fig. 342.—Determination of field intensity with a tube voltmeter.

where ε is in microvolts per meter, I in microamperes, R in ohms, and h_e in meters. If the area of the loop is $A = 1m^2$ and $N = 6$ turns are used and the measurements are carried on with a sender rated at 100kc/sec, then $h_e = 209 \times 10^{-7} \times 6 \times 10^3 = 0.1255$ m. The total loop resistance is then in the neighborhood of 20 ohms, and the electric-field intensity $\varepsilon^{(\mu volts/m)} = 159.5 \, I^{(\mu amp)}$. Figure 342 shows an arrangement where the field intensity is determined with a tube voltmeter. The voltmeter is calibrated for the particular frequency range and if the range is too wide, for the particular frequency to which the aerial is tuned (by means of the C setting). The calibration is carried out with the loop and detector-type voltmeter connected under the actual conditions. The calibration is carried on either by means of a known mutual inductance M or with a standard resistance R_s inserted across point 1 and 2.

The field oscillator is indicated in Fig. 343 where L denotes the primary coil and the loop acts as the secondary. The mutual inductance is either computed or measured for a certain relative position of the loop with respect to coil L. The latter can be done as follows: The tube circuit is disconnected and a microammeter inserted in the tuned loop circuit. If I_2 denotes the resonance current, it must be equal to the voltage

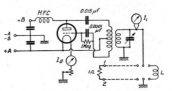

Fig. 343.—Field oscillator.

$2\pi f M I_1$ induced divided by the effective resistance R_2 (including the meter resistance) from which relation

$$M = \frac{I_2 R_2}{6.28 f I_1}$$

The mutual inductance M is in microhenries if I_2 is expressed in microamperes, R_2 in ohms, I_1 in milliamperes, and f in kilocycles per second. The tube branch is connected back to the frame and the primary coil left in position, but the oscillator does not operate. The slider S is moved to such a position that the microammeter gives an arbitrary zero setting (say 5 μa on a 200-μa meter). The tube oscillations are set up and the current I_1 is varied until a suitable deflection $d = d_1$ is noted on the microammeter for the tuned loop. The voltage induced in the loop is then $E_1{}^{(\mu\text{volts})} = 6.28 f^{(\text{kc/sec})} M^{(\mu\text{h})} I_1{}^{(\text{ma})}$, and the deflection d_1 is the calibration point for

$$\mathcal{E} = \frac{E_1}{h_e} = \frac{3 \times 10^5 M I_1}{AN} \tag{5}$$

where $\mathcal{E}$ is in microvolts per meter, E_1 in microvolts, M in microhenries, I_1 in milliamperes, h_e in meters, and A in square meters, where A is

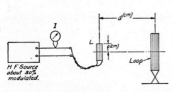

Fig. 344.—Test with a mutual inductance.

the area $h^{(\text{m})} a^{(\text{m})}$ of the loop. The current I_1 is then changed to some other value, giving another deflection $d = d_2$ on the microammeter and $\mathcal{E}$ again computed, and so on, giving the calibration curve of the entire field-intensity set, although it seems more accurate to find the deflection d due to the actual field intensity $\mathcal{E}$ first by directing the loop toward the sender and tuning the loop by means of C and then producing the same deflection by means of the oscillator as just described when the loop is set at right angles with respect to the sender-receiver direction. If the mutual inductance M is computed instead of measured, the calibration of the set is made by the method indicated in Fig. 344. This is the method adopted by the standardization committee of the Institute of Radio Engineers. The loop indicated is then the loop of the field-intensity set shown in Fig. 342, which for a certain sender gives a deflection d. The loop is then turned at right angles with respect to the sender-receiver plane in order to bring the deflection of the indicator back to the arbitrary zero setting and the small coil L is set a certain distance d cm along the common coil axis and the current $I^{(\mu a)}$ varied until the same deflection d is again obtained. If the distance d is large compared with the dimensions of the loop, the field intensity can be computed from

$$\varepsilon = \frac{18{,}850 n \rho^2 I}{\sqrt{[\rho^2 + d^2]^3}} \quad \mu\text{volts/m} \qquad (6)$$

where n is the number of turns of the coupling coil L and ρ the radius of it. If the planes of the small coupling coil L and of the loop are not parallel but make a small angle θ with each other, the above expression must be multiplied by $\cos \theta$ in order to give the correct value for ε. The procedure is exactly the same if one or several stages of high-frequency amplification are to be used between the tuned loop aerial and the tube voltmeter of the field-intensity set. Also in this case it is suggested

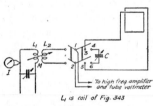

FIG. 345.—Calibration with a mutual inductance.

not to depend upon a calibration but produce at first a deflection by means of the actual field intensity of an arriving electromagnetic wave, if the frame is pointing toward the sender and tuned, and then produce the same deflection by means of the local source, using either formula (5) or (6). The calibration can then also be carried on by the method shown in Fig. 345. This scheme has the inherent advantage that the entire loop circuit cannot act while the calibration is carried on. In the case of all other circuits mentioned above, the loop aerial is always connected during the calibration and certain minimum or other disturbing voltages may be operative even though the loop is at right angles to the direction of the arriving electromagnetic wave. But the disadvantage of the method of Fig. 345 is that the loop circuit and the coil L_2, respectively, across the input terminals 1 and 2 of the high-frequency amplifier of the field-intensity set, may produce different input characteristics of the amplifier. The measurement is as follows: The amplifier is at first connected toward the loop, that is, terminal 1 closed on 3 and 4 and terminal 2 closed on 5 and 6. The loop is turned approximately toward the sender and the loop tuned by means of C. The loop is then turned until practically zero-loop effect is noted on the indicator of the tube voltmeter forming the last stage of the high-frequency amplifier. The loop is then turned at right angles and the resonance deflection d noted. The double-pole switch is connected across the secondary coil L_2, and M and I are varied until the same deflection d is again obtained. For the second deflection the voltage ωIM is impressed on the amplifier, while for the same deflection d obtained with the tuned loop the high-frequency voltage impressed upon the amplifier is $h_e \mathcal{E} S$ if h_e is the effective height of the loop, $S = \omega L/R$ denotes the sharpness of resonance of the loop of the effective inductance L and effective resistance R. Since one and the same deflection d is produced by both voltages, it is found by equating the expressions that the field strength $\mathcal{E} = RMI/(h_e L)$ volts/m if R is in ohms, M and L in henries, I in amperes, and h_e in meters. Introducing the value for the effective height from Eq. (27) of Sec. (201), one can compute the electric-field intensity from

$$\mathcal{E} = 47{,}700 \frac{R\,M\,I}{L\,f\,A\,N} \tag{7}$$

where $\mathcal{E}$ is in microvolts per meter, R in ohms, M and L in microhenries, I in microamperes, f in kilocycles per second, and A in square meters.

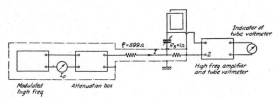

F ıg. 346.—Calibration by means of an attenuation box and a standard resistance R_s.

If the calibration is carried on by means of a standard resistance R_s, the circuit of Fig. 346 can be used where the small current I producing the auxiliary voltage IR_s is computed from the much larger current I_0 passing into the attenuation box. An example of the determination of I is given in Sec. 36. The resistance ρ is chosen such that $\rho + R_s$ is equal to the characteristic load resistance for which the attenuation is designed. It should be noted that the input terminals 1 and 2 are connected to one end and the center of the loop, respectively. Methods using attenuation boxes work satisfactorily up to about the middle broadcast frequencies. For still higher frequencies it seems better to design specially just one section with the proper attenuation giving the desired ratio I_0/I and then to vary I by means of a change in I_0.

For some field-intensity measurements it is of advantage to use the superheterodyne principle for which an intermediate frequency is amplified.

205. Determination of the Height of the Ionized Layer of the Atmosphere.—Three different methods[1] have been used to determine the height

[1] Appleton, E. V., *Proc. Phys. Soc. (London)*, **41**, 43, 1928; *Proc. Roy. Soc. (London)*, A, **126**, 542, 1930; G. Breit and M. A. Tuve, *Phys. Rev.*, **28**, 571, 1926; R. A. Heising, *Proc. I.R.E.*, **16**, 75, 1928; editorial by G. W. Howe, *Exptl. Wireless*, **5**, 657, 1928; J. C. Schelleng, **16**, 1471, 1928; C. W. Kenrick and C. K. Jen, *Proc. I.R.E.*, **17**, 711, 1929; abstract by J. Zenneck, *Z. Hochfreq.*, **36**, 73, 1930; G. Gonbau and J. Zenneck, *Z. Hochfreq.*, **37**, 207, 1931.

of the ionized layer. In Fig. 347, the height of the lower boundary of the layer is *GE*. It could be found from the triangle *SER* if the ionized layer were a good conductor with a definite boundary parallel to the surface of the earth and such that the indirect ray ascends first from the sender *S* along the straight path *SE* and is reflected downward along *E R*. In reality the degree of ionization changes within the layer and the path, after entering the layer, is bent (successively refracted) and follows

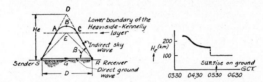

FIG. 347.—Shows different height H_e of the ionized layer.

the curved path *ABC*. Hence *SABCR* is the actual path of an indirect ray. The height *GB* is therefore the actual maximum height for the path, while the height *GD* is the equivalent height, which is confirmed by all three experimental methods used so far. Hence, if the angle β of the downcoming ray is found from an experiment, the equivalent height H_e can be computed from the triangle *SDR*, since the distance *SR = D* is known. E. V. Appleton and M. A. F. Barnett[1] have also used a frequency-variation method (introduced as wave-length change method). G. Breit and M. A. Tuve[2] as well as R. A. Heising[2] have employed the impulse method. In it, the frequency of the sender *S* is constant and

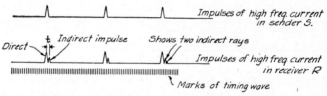

FIG. 348.—Illustration of the impulse method.

impulses (jabs of power) between 0.001 and 0.0016 sec in duration are radiated and the time intervals between the moment at which the direct impulse arrives and the arrival of any impulses along indirect paths are noted. Hence, if about 60 impulses per second are sent out, a long time interval occurs in comparison with the duration of the existence of one impulse. Even if it were assumed that along the actual indirect optical path *SABCR* the velocity of light *c* would also practically exist for the portion *ABC* (which is not the case), the impulse would arrive later at *R* than the effect of the impulse along the direct optical path *SR*. Figure 348 shows the impulses sent out and impulses received if indirect waves

[1] *Loc. cit.*
[2] *Loc. cit.*

are also present. The frequency (or wave-length) variation method is
as follows: In Fig. 349, the direct ray has a length d_1, and the indirect
ray for a single reflection the length d_2. Then $d_2 = d_1\sqrt{1 + \rho^2}$ for
$\rho = 2H/d_1$. The difference in path is $d = d_2 - d_1 = d_1[\sqrt{1 + \rho^2} - 1]$,
and the height H is computed from $H = 0.5\sqrt{d^2 - 2d_1d}$. The difference d in path is found experimentally by the interference-fringe method,
inasmuch as d_1 is known. When the indirect wave arrives
N wave lengths behind the direct wave, $N\lambda = d$. If N
is an integer, the waves steadily reinforce each other, whereas if N is half way between two integers the waves are
steadily in opposite phase and produce fading effects.

Fig. 349.—
Determination of
height H.

Hence, if the frequency f (corresponding to wave length
λ) of the sender is steadily decreased to a value f' (corre-

sponding to length λ'), the number of signal maxima N_m is $d\left[\dfrac{1}{\lambda} - \dfrac{1}{\lambda'}\right]$ or

$N_m = \dfrac{\delta\lambda}{\lambda^2}d$ if the change in λ is very small. Since $\delta\lambda$ and λ are known and
N_m is observed at the receiver end, d can be calculated.

Example.—A change in λ from 385 to 395 m resulted in 7 fringes (maxima);
hence $d = N_m\dfrac{\lambda^2}{\delta\lambda} = 7 \times \dfrac{390^2}{10} = 103$ km.

It is now of importance to see what height is actually measured
with the three procedures. In the angle-of-incidence method the
angle β of the downcoming ray of Fig. 347 is found by experiment.
The equivalent height $H_e = GD$ is obtained by using the formula
$H_e = 0.5D \tan \beta$. In the impulse- and the frequency-variation methods
the different velocities of propagations are taken into account.

For ordinary atmosphere such as for the direct ground wave, the velocity of propagation occurs practically with the velocity $c = 3 \times 10^{10}$ cm/sec of light. But in
the ionized medium with N ions per cubic centimeter of charge q and mass m, for
short waves from which the effect of the earth's magnetic field can be neglected, the

index of refraction $n = \sqrt{1 - \dfrac{Nq^2}{m\pi f^2}} = \dfrac{c}{c'}$, must be taken into consideration, where
for the optical path ABC the value of n is smaller than unity. The quantity c' is
called the phase velocity which is larger than that of light. Hence the upward-
moving sky wave moves with the velocity c from S to A. But as soon as it enters
the layer at A, it meets a certain degree of ionization and higher phase velocity $c' =
c/n$ is effective. As it enters deeper into the layer along the height direction, the
ionization increases and with it the value of c' and the curved or refracted path ABC
results. After emerging from the ionized layer, there is again the velocity c of light
since $n = 1$. Hence if ds denotes an element of the path, the actual path is along

ABC and equal to $\displaystyle\int_{ABC} ds$ but the equivalent path is different. Hence if one thinks of

an infinitely long wave train without modulations in it, the phase velocity on entering at A becomes $c' = c/n$, that is, $>c$, and, upon emerging at C into ordinary atmosphere, the phase velocity will correspond to some path less than $\int_{ABC} ds$. The corresponding path is $\int n\, ds$. The frequency-variation method does *not* depend upon the phase of the arriving wave but upon the *change of* its *phase* as the frequency f of the sender is varied by an amount Δf. But the index n of refraction is a function of f and consequently also the phase velocity c' will be affected by changes Δf, the indirect ray will change its path, and $\int n\, ds$ will also show a correspondingly different value. Now, it is the group velocity $c'' = nc$ with which power (an impulse) is propagated through an ionized medium. But the frequency-variation method consists of noting the number of maxima ΔM for the frequency change Δf due to the interference between direct ground and indirect sky rays. The time which is required to carry energy from the sender S by the path $SABCR$ to receiver R is $\int_{SBR} \dfrac{ds}{c''}$. If the actual path is imagined entirely in air instead of partly (along ABC) in the ionized layer, one has the equivalent path $c \int_{SBR} \dfrac{ds}{c''}$ and it can be shown that for cases where the earth's magnetic field does not materially affect the value of c'' (for very short waves) that the equivalent path $c\int \dfrac{ds}{c''} = \int \dfrac{ds}{n}$. Hence the equivalent path is $SD + DR$ and H_e is the measured height. The same triangle SDR as for the method where H_e is determined by means of angle β is effective. The equivalent height can also be determined by the time difference between direct and indirect wave. For frequencies which are not very high, the group velocity c'' is affected by the magnetic field of the earth. But also in this case the equivalent triangle SDR can be constructed from the path difference of direct and indirect ray and the equivalent path $c\int \dfrac{ds}{c''}$ is then longer than the actual path $\int ds$, and therefore the equivalent height H_e is also larger than the actual height GB. The equivalent path can then differ from $SD + DR$.

If at R of Fig. 347 a loop receiver points toward the sender and it is assumed that the sky wave is reflected at the ground without change in phase and amplitude, the resultant induced voltage in the loop due to both rays is $E_0 \sin \omega t + 2E_1 \sin \omega\left(t - \dfrac{d}{c}\right)$ if d denotes the optical-path difference between the direct ground and indirect sky wave at R. For a square-law detector connected to the loop, a direct-current effect

$$i = k\left[E_0{}^2 + 4E_1{}^2 + 4E_0E_1 \cos \frac{\omega d}{c} \right]$$

will be observed. This would be the reading, if a detector type of tube voltmeter were used and a microammeter balanced to an arbitrary zero setting (for no waves affecting the loop). Hence, if f is gradually changed, the meter will show a series of maxima and minima deflections, depending upon whether $\cos (2\pi f d/c)$ is $+$ or -1. Every time $\omega d/c$ is increased by 2π; that is, fd/c is increased by unity, a new maximum deflection will be observed. For ΔM maxima caused by a frequency change Δf there is

$$\Delta M = \frac{1}{c}\frac{\partial}{\partial f}(fd)\,\Delta f$$

since d is a function of f because the group velocity $c'' = nc$ is a function of f on account of the term n. But

$$\frac{1}{c}\int \frac{\partial}{\partial f}\,(fd) = \int_{SBR} \frac{ds}{c''} - \frac{D}{c}$$

and the equivalent length of the sky wave can be found from

$$c\int \frac{ds}{c''} = D + c\frac{\Delta M}{\Delta f} \tag{8}$$

But

$$c\int_{SBR} \frac{ds}{c''} = \int_{SBR} \frac{ds}{n} = \overline{SD} + \overline{DR}$$

for short waves and

$$\overline{SD} + \overline{DR} = D + 3 \times 10^5 \frac{\Delta M}{\Delta f} \tag{9}$$

where the distances $\overline{SD}$, $\overline{DR}$, and D are in kilometers if the gradual frequency change Δf is expressed in kilocycles per second. Therefore it is only necessary to count the number ΔM of maximum deflections noted on the direct-current meter in the loop circuit while the sender frequency f is gradually changed by a small amount Δf.

If this procedure is compared with the impulse method (Fig. 348), for which the time t at which the sky impulse arrives later than the direct impulse is determined, there is exactly the same relation

$$t = \int_{SBR} \frac{ds}{c''} - \frac{D}{c} \tag{10}$$

where t is in seconds, that is, $\Delta M/\Delta f = t$ and, by multiplying the equation by c,

$$\overline{SD} + \overline{DR} = D + 3 \times 10^5 t \tag{11}$$

where t is in seconds. The distance D km between the sender and receiver station is known and, as in Fig. 350, half of its value is plotted as the base line. Since in the equivalent triangle SDR (shown in Fig. 347), $SD = DR$, the length l_e of the hypotenuse in Fig. 350 is as given in this figure. The dimensions of the triangle are in kilometers if t is in seconds, f in kilocycles per second, and D in kilometers.

For the determination of the equivalent height with either the impulse, the frequency-variation (shift of interference fringes), or the angle-of-incidence (by measuring β or $90 - \beta$) method, it must be understood that it is *impossible*[1] to find the total number of waves in the path.   For instance, in the frequency-variation method, the

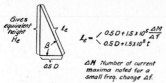

experiment gives the ratio $\Delta M / \Delta f$ only.   Therefore if $p = p_1 - p_0$ denotes the total number p_1 of wave lengths along the indirect path (sky ray) minus the total number p_0 in the direct path (ground ray), from the experiment dp/df is obtained.   Also $p = f(t_1 - t_0)$ where t_1 denotes the time the wave crest (*phase* time) takes to travel over the indirect and t_0 the time to travel over the direct path.   Hence,

FIG. 350.—Equivalent height of ionized layer.

if the length of the direct path is s_0 and that of the indirect path s_1, there is the path difference

$$ s = s_1 - s_0 = c\frac{dp}{df} = c\left[\frac{d(f\,t_1)}{df} - \frac{d(f\,t_0)}{df}\right] $$

where $\dfrac{d(f\,t_1)}{df}$ and $\dfrac{d(f\,t_0)}{df}$ are the *group* times (as *measured* in group-time experiments) along the indirect and direct paths, respectively.   Hence, any time the square-law detector in the coil receiver of Fig. 347 gives another maximum deflection, one wave length has been gained in the sky wave with respect to the number p of waves.   It must be realized, however, that the number p_0 of wave lengths along the direct path also increases when p_1 increases.   Hence, if the number p is integrated from zero frequency up to the highest desired frequency, the difference of wave numbers for the indirect and direct paths is obtained.

The method of J. C. Schelleng,[2] determining the height GB (Fig. 347) of the apex of the actual indirect path, is based on the total number of waves and the triangle construction of Fig. 351 due to P. O.   Pedersen[3] based on the approximation that the wave number along the actual half path SAB is equal to $\dfrac{l}{\lambda} = \dfrac{f\,l}{300}$

where f is expressed in kilocycles per second and l in kilometers.   The approximation holds fairly well for $\beta \leqq 60°$. This method is also based on the empirical relation

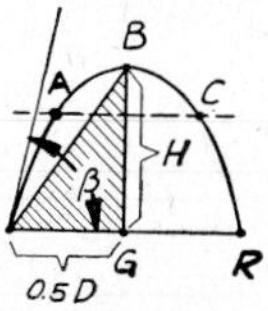

$$ H_e = a + bf \tag{12} $$

H_e being given in kilometers, or some other suitable expression for the equivalent height H_e of the layer where, from experimental data due to Hollingworth, Bown, Martin and Potter, Appleton and Barnett and Heising, the constants a and b came out $a = 80$ km and $b = 0.044$.

FIG.   351.— H — determination $(\overline{SB} = l$ km; in empty space $c = \lambda \cdot f = 300$ km/sec., where λ is in kilometers and f in kilocycles per second).

Since in the actual measurements the *group*-time difference $t_1' - t_0' = t$ appears, one must distinguish between group times t_1' and t_0' and the corresponding phase times for passages along the indirect and direct paths, respectively.   The phase time along the indirect path for a path element s_1 is given by

$$ t_1 = \frac{1}{f}\int\frac{ds_1}{\lambda} = \int\frac{n\,ds_1}{c} = \int\frac{ds_1}{c'} $$

[1] Unless a procedure due to J. C. Schelleng (*loc. cit.*) is employed.

[2] *Loc. cit.*

[3] "Propagation of Radio Waves," Danmarks Naturvidenskabelige Samfund, Copenhagen, 1928, p. 176.

for the index of refraction $n = \sqrt{1 - \dfrac{Nq^2}{m\pi f^2}}$. Since the phase velocity c/p and the group velocity $c'' = nc$, the corresponding *group* time

$$t_1' = \int \frac{ds_1}{c''} = \int \frac{ds_1}{nc}$$

But, according to the discussion given above for both paths, $t_1' - t_0' = \dfrac{dp}{df}$, and for the integration from zero frequency to the highest desired frequency f there is $p = \int_0^f [t_1' - t_0']df = \int_0^f \left\{ \dfrac{d}{df}[p_1 - p_0]df \right.$. The formula for sides $SB = l$ and $\overline{SG} = 0.5D$ that is, half the distance between sender and receiver stations (Fig. 351) becomes

$$l - 0.5D = 0.5p\lambda = \frac{0.5c}{f}\int_0^f [t_1' - t_0']df \tag{13}$$

Since for the triangle (Fig. 350) holding for the equivalent height H_e, the length $l_e = \sqrt{H_e^2 + 0.25D^2}$ and for the shaded triangle (Fig. 351) for the actual height H of the apex of the true indirect path, the term $(l - 0.5D)$ denotes half the path difference between indirect and direct ray, Eq. (13) leads to

$$l - 0.5D = \frac{1}{f}\int_0^f [\sqrt{H_e^2 + 0.25D^2} - 0.5D]df$$

$$= \frac{1}{f}\int_0^f \{\sqrt{[a + bf]^2 + 0.25D^2} - 0.5D\}df$$

since the difference of the two group times t_1' and t_0' with reference to half the path difference is $\dfrac{2}{c}\{\sqrt{H_e^2 + 0.25D^2} - 0.5D\}$. Since $D, f,$ and a and b are known, the hypotenuse l of the shaded triangle of Fig. 351 can be computed from

$$l = 0.5D + \frac{1}{f}\int_0^f \{\sqrt{[a + bf]^2 + 0.25D^2} - 0.5D\}df = 0.5D + Q \tag{14}$$

where $l, D,$ and a are in kilometers, and f in kilocycles per second. The construction for the actual H is carried out with the shaded triangle SBG of Fig. 351 by first plotting the base line $\overline{SG} = 0.5D$ by means of the known distance D km between the sender and receiver stations and finding the height H by means of the hypotenuse $\overline{SB} = l$ computed from Eq. (14).

206. Determination of the Angle of the Downcoming Sky Wave and of the Resultant Wave.—The procedure described in the previous section in connection with Fig. 350 gives two methods for finding the angle β of the downcoming ray, since $0.5D$ denotes half the distance in kilometers between the sender and receiver stations and the length l_e in kilometers can be computed from experiments with the frequency-variation and the impulse methods, respectively. Other procedures utilize a Hertzian rod, a tilting loop, and loop and aerial as receivers.[1]   There are then the formulas

$$\cos \beta = \begin{cases} \dfrac{\mathcal{E}_z - \mathcal{E}_{0z}}{\sqrt{\kappa_e}[\mathcal{E}_x - \mathcal{E}_{0x}]} \text{ determined with Hertzian rod} \\[2ex] \dfrac{\sqrt{\kappa_e}[H_z - H_{0z}]}{H_x - H_{0x}} \text{ with tilting loop} \\[2ex] \dfrac{\mathcal{E}_z - \mathcal{E}_{0z}}{H_y - H_{0y}} \text{ with loop and vertical antenna (does } not \text{ require a knowledge of the conditions of the ground)} \end{cases} \qquad (15)$$

where $\mathcal{E}_z$, $\mathcal{E}_x$, and $\mathcal{E}_y$ are the components of the total electric-field intensity $\mathcal{E}$ of the arriving sky wave with the Z coordinate vertical to ground and the X coordinate in the direction sender to receiver.   The arriving direct wave of resultant electric intensity $\mathcal{E}_0$ generally has the components $\mathcal{E}_{0z}$, $\mathcal{E}_{0x}$, and $\mathcal{E}_{0y}$.   The corresponding H values stand for the magnetic-field intensities and $\sqrt{\kappa_e}$ is the index of refraction of the ground near its surface, and $\kappa_e = \kappa - \dfrac{2j\sigma}{f}$ if κ is the dielectric constant and σ the conductivity of ground.   It may also be regarded as the complex dielectric constant of

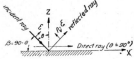

FIG. 352.—Incident, reflected, and direct rays.

ground and is discussed in detail in Sec. 134. If angle β due to the downcoming sky wave is of interest only for the determination of the height of the ionized layer and the determination of the degree of ionization (ionic concentration) at a certain altitude, the determination is carried on far enough away from the sender to make the effect of direct ground wave negligible in the measuring instruments.   For the arrival of both direct and indirect waves, there is the case of Fig. 352 for the XZ plane through the sender and receiver.   Hence, if the receiver is far enough away and the determination is carried on during hours when indirect sky waves are possible, according to (15), $\cos \beta = \mathcal{E}_z/(\mathcal{E}_x\sqrt{\kappa_e})$ is measured with the Hertzian rod.   Generally the downcoming electric vector $\mathcal{E}$ is partially reflected upward again with a somewhat smaller value $\rho_v \mathcal{E}$ if ρ_v denotes the vertical reflection coefficient, and the current induced in the Hertzian rod must be due to both electric-field vectors. The horizontal axis of the rod is set at right angles to the direction of sender to receiver station and the rod turned in a vertical plane until a maximum response is noted in the indicator.   The rod is then along the resultant vector of both fields, and the angle τ which it makes with the vertical to ground is the forward tilt.   The maximum-response position, as a rule, is not so sharp as the position for zero (minimum) effect. Therefore the rod is turned out of this position until a decided minimum effect is observed.   For this location it is perpendicular to the electrical

[1] Such systems have been used by R. L. Smith-Rose and R. H. Barfield, *Proc. Roy. Soc.* (*London*), **110A**, 580, 1926; *Exptl. Wireless*, **4**, 130, 1927.

lines of force of the wave front and the angle it makes with the ground measures the foreward tilt τ, and $\tan \tau = \mathcal{E}_z/\mathcal{E}_x$ if $\mathcal{E}_z$ and $\mathcal{E}_x$ are the vertical and horizontal components of the resultant electric vector. The angle β is then computed from $\cos \beta = \dfrac{\tan \tau}{\sqrt{\kappa_e}}$. Figure 353 shows the loop and antenna method due to Smith-Rose and Barfield[1] which, according to (15), for the reception of the indirect sky wave gives the angle β with the ground by means of formula $\cos \beta = \mathcal{E}_z/H_y$, if $\mathcal{E}_z$ is the vertical component of the sky wave as measured with a *vertical* aerial, while the magnetic component H_y is determined by means of the loop aerial. Since the complex dielectric constant κ_e of ground does not enter the above formula, the nature of ground needs no special consideration. If terminals 1 and 2 are closed on 5 and 6, the vertical triangular loop which points toward the sender is connected to the primary coil L_1 of a goniometer with the secondary L_3 which can be rotated. If terminals 1 and 2 are connected on 3 and 4, the loop terminals are short-circuited and the loop with the rest of the circuit acts as a *vertical* aerial

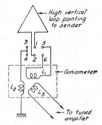

Fig. 353.—Goniometer method.

with a loading coil L_2 as primary of the goniometer. A rocker type of double-pole double-throw switch is used so that 1 and 2 can be readily switched over from the vertical-antenna type to the loop type of receiver, simultaneously changing the angular position of the pick-up coil L_3 which leads at first to a few stages of tuned high-frequency amplification and acts as a field-intensity set. For a certain position of L_3 it will be found that the field-intensity set produces the same deflection on the indicator of the final stage. Since the tangent of the angle which coil L_3 makes for the equal-deflection position with its normal setting is proportional to the current in the two field coils, it must also be proportional to the ratio $\mathcal{E}_z/H_y$. The value of this ratio is found by means of an artificial ground wave (direct wave) of the same frequency for which $\mathcal{E}_z$ and H_y are equal except for the conversion factor c, since $\mathcal{E} = cH$ (see introduction of this chapter). If a tilting loop is used, the axis about which the plane of the frame rotates is horizontal and at right angles to the sender-receiver direction. Hence, if one is far enough away to have only an appreciable downcoming sky wave, Eq. (15) shows that the angle β can be found from $\cos \beta = \dfrac{H_z\sqrt{\kappa_e}}{H_x}$.

If the tilting coil is rotated into such a position that its plane is along the resultant magnetic vector H (minimum effect noted) with vertical and horizontal components H_z and H_x the ratio H_z/H_x can be expressed by $\tan \gamma$ if γ denotes the angle of the plane of the tilting coil with respect to

[1] *Loc. cit.*

the horizontal plane, and β is computed from $\cos \beta = \sqrt{\kappa_e} \tan \gamma$; that is, the property of the ground must be known again.

207. Determination of Ionic Concentration at Different Heights of the Heaviside-Kennelly Layer.—By applying Snell's law ($n \sin \Phi = $ constant),

$$\sin \Phi_0 = \sqrt{1 - \frac{Nq^2}{m\pi f^2}} \cong 1 - \frac{N\,q^2}{2\pi m f^2}$$

and the ionic concentration N for short waves can be computed from

$$N = \frac{6.28 \times 10^{12} m f^2 [1 - \sin \Phi_0]}{q^2} \tag{16}$$

where N denotes the number of ions per cubic centimeter, m and q the mass and charge of the ion, f the frequency in megacycles per second, and Φ_0 the angle of the ascending or descending sky wave with respect to the normal toward the ground.   Thus after knowing the angle of the downcoming ray, it is possible to compute the ionic density.   The angle can also be found from the triangle construction of Fig. 350 or any of the methods described in the previous section.   If it is assumed that electrons are mostly responsible, m and q denote the mass and charge of one electron.   The above formula assumes that the collisions and the earth's magnetic field do not affect the result appreciably, which is true to a fair degree of approximation at frequencies higher than about 3 Mc/sec.   According to T. L. Eckersley[1] and with respect to Fig. 354 for a known height H of the sky ray at its apex the maximum electron density at the apex can be found from

FIG. 354.—Diagram for the determination of electron density in the ionized layer.

$$N = \frac{m\pi f^2}{q^2}[\sin^2 \theta + 2p] \tag{17}$$

where it is assumed that p is small and the gradient of the ionic density is vertical everywhere.   The arc θ must be chosen so that the receiver is not in the dead zone, that is, not within the skip distance.   Again the formula applies to short waves only.

208. Determination of Polarization of Received Electromagnetic Waves and of Fading Effects.—The polarization of the resultant electromagnetic field existing at a receiver system when due to direct and indirect waves is complex, especially during sunset periods.   The phase, as well as the amplitude, of the indirect wave may undergo changes.   The cathode-

[1] *Proc. I.R.E.*, **18**, 106, 1930,

ray tube can then be used to note both amplitude and phase changes. In the method used by E. Merritt[1] and W. E. Bostwick, two vertical loops L_1 and L_2 are employed in such a way that L_1 points toward the sender and the plane of L_2 is perpendicular to the sender-receiver direction. Loop L_1 then picks up the magnetic field of the combined action of the ground wave and the vertically polarized component of the indirect sky wave, whereas L_2 is *not* affected by the direct ground wave and only picks up a signal if the sky wave has a component which is polarized with its electrical vector horizontal. The signals $A \cos \Omega t$ and $B \cos (\Omega t + \theta)$ picked up by loops L_1 and L_2 are heterodyned with $C \cos (\Omega - \omega)t$ by means of a local source whose amplitude C is always larger than either amplitude A or B. After amplification and detection, the variable output voltage from either loop circuit is made to act on the respective deflection quadrants of a cathode-ray oscillograph. The variable voltage due to loop L_1 produces a vibration component of the fluorescent spot along the horizontal and the voltage due to L_2 a variable vertical vibration component. The amplitudes of the vertical and horizontal vibrations are then proportional to the amplitudes of the signals received by the respective loops, and the phase difference shown by the Lissajous figure also gives the phase difference between the original component waves. In the circuit of loop L_1 is found $A \cos \Omega t + C \cos (\Omega - \omega)t = (C - A) \cos (\Omega - \omega)t + 2A \cos 0.5\omega t \cos 0.5(2\Omega - \omega)t$ and in the circuit for loop L_2 is found $B \cos (\Omega t + \theta) + C \cos (\Omega - \omega)t = (C - B) \cos (\Omega - \omega)t + 2B \cos [0.5\omega t + 0.5\theta] \cos [0.5(2\Omega - \omega)t + 0.5\theta]$. Since rectification is used, the amplitude variation has not a beat frequency $0.5\omega/(2\pi)$ as appears in these formulas, but a beat frequency $\omega/2\pi$. The phase difference is θ since rectification cannot change it. If the indirect wave is polarized with the electric vector in the vertical plane, no effect is produced in loop L_2. The Lissajous figure is then a horizontal trace changing slowly in length because of the phase of the two waves. A line of constant length is obtained during the day (for broadcast waves) but, as the sun begins to set, the sky wave appears with most erratic changes and the horizontal trace begins to pulsate and tilts back and forth about the horizontal. In some cases it opens into an ellipse which changes in tilt and area. About ten minutes after sunset the ellipse rotates, changing from ellipse to line and back to ellipse. The method of H. T. Friis also utilizes a cathode-ray oscillograph but depends upon the beating effects of the two received signals, one from the distant and one from a local generator when exposed to two spaced receivers (about one-third wave length apart). The local generator affects both receiving stations. Since the local generator has constant amplitude and fre-

---

[1] MERRITT, E., and W. E. BOSTWICK, *loc. cit.*; H. T. FRIIS, *Proc. I.R.E.*, **16**, 658, 1928.

quency, the beat notes produced in the two receivers give a means of visualizing the amplitude as well as the phase of the wave arriving from the sender. This is true as long as the amplitude does not vary at a greater rate than represented by the beat frequency. Hence, if a beat frequency from 0.5 to 1 kc/sec is chosen, customary normal fading periods from 1 to 10 sec can be readily observed.

The polarization of the indirect wave changes with the frequency, and considerable distortion may be produced in the received signal if selective rotation of the polarization plane[1] over the signal band takes place for a transmission *along* the magnetic field of the earth. The rotation is due to the difference in velocity of propagation of the right- and left-hand circularly polarized components and the rotation varies with the frequency. P. O. Pedersen[2] has given the approximate formula

$$D_0 = \frac{mc}{Nq^2}\frac{\omega^2}{h}10^{-5} \text{ km} \tag{18}$$

for the distance within which the plane of polarization of a short high-frequency wave is rotated through an angle of 360 deg (2π radians). In this formula $c = 3 \times 10^{10}$ cm/sec, $q = 4.77 \times 10^{-10}$ e.s.u., $m = 8.97 \times 10^{-28}$ g, $\omega/2\pi = f$ the frequency in cycles per second, N the number of electrons per cubic centimeter, $h = q/(m\,c)$ times the magnetic field of the earth in gausses. Hence for a distance D of propagation within the electron atmosphere, a rotation angle

$$\theta = \frac{2\pi D}{D_0} = 15{,}920\frac{hq^2DN}{mcf^2} \text{ radians} \tag{19}$$

is obtained, and the rate of change of rotation with frequency is

$$\frac{d\theta}{df} = -7960\frac{h\ q^2DN}{mcf^3} \tag{20}$$

from which the distortion effect can be computed.

209. Notes on the Determination of Direction Effects and Bearing Errors.—The cathode-ray oscillograph can again be used for such work, and vertical and tilting loops (rotating about horizontal axes either along or perpendicular to directions with respect to the sender-receiver direction) can be employed. The Hertzian rod receiver can also be used. Their action is described in Sec. 206.

---

[1] POTTER, R. K., *Proc. I.R.E.*, **18**, 581, 1930.
[2] *Loc. cit.*

CHAPTER XVII

DETERMINATIONS ON PIEZO-ELECTRIC APPARATUS

Piezo-electric quartz elements play an important part if great frequency stability is of interest. Although the crystal holder (proper mounting) and thermostatic temperature control as well as suitable tube circuits are very essential in order to obtain a constant frequency, it is also important that the quartz element be properly oriented with respect to the characteristic axes of the original structure and that no twinning exist. Although some elements oscillate even though cut from twinned portions, it may be stated that the stability cannot be so good as for a plate free from twinning. Only the differential piezo-electric effect can be operative for pronounced twinning.

210. Determination of the Orientation of Quartz Elements and Approximate Design Formulas.—It is customary to work with either

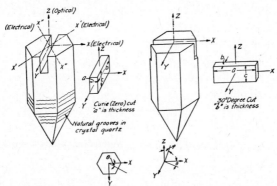

Fig. 355.—Zero and thirty-degree cut piezo-electric quartz elements. (The natural grooves give a means for locating approximately the optical axis if the pyramids are missing.)

Curie or 30-deg cuts, the latter being more convenient for short-wave stabilization (Fig. 355). For either cut, the threefold symmetrical optical axis is parallel to one face. Even though the two end pyramids of a quartz crystal may be practically worn off in some natural crystals, parallel fringes around the crystals always indicate the trend of the optical axis. If a plane is laid through any one of the fringes, the optical axis is perpendicular to the plane. A polariscope is used to find the optical axis more accurately (within about ½ deg). It consists of two nicols which can be crossed by rotating the analyzer with respect to the polarizer. If now a piece of quartz is cut by guess with the end faces

423

perpendicular to the optical axis and the specimen between the two nicols, with its preliminary optic axis along the viewing direction (polarizer to analyzer), the analyser must be turned through a certain angle in order to produce darkness again. The magnitude of the angle depends upon the dimensions of the specimen along the optical axis and the angle which the viewing direction makes with the true optical axis of the specimen. The largest rotation is required if the optical axis and the viewing axis are parallel.

Piezo-electric quartz elements of rectangular slab, disk, and ring shape are used in frequency-stabilization work. Curie and 30-deg cuts are customary. In Fig. 355, a Curie cut element is excited by an electric field acting across faces bc, along the axis X of piezo-electric polarization. Since threefold symmetry exists around the optical Z-axis, the cut can also be made so that the thickness dimension a is along the X' or along the X''-axis. A 30-deg cut crystal is excited across faces ac, that is, along b as thickness dimension. Because of the threefold symmetry, cuts can be parallel to either the XZ plane, the $X'Z$ plane, or the $X''Z$ plane. Usually the fundamental mode of longitudinal vibration is excited in piezo oscillators. For the thickness vibration of a Curie cut, there is the design formula $f_1 = 2870/a$ kc/sec if a is in millimeters. For longitudinal vibration along the Y dimension, $f_2 = 2700/b$ kc/sec if the width b is in millimeters. For plates a coupling frequency f_3 may also occur, which for a square plate ($b = c$) is estimated from $f_3 = 3330/b$ kc/sec if b is in millimeters. If Curie cut disk elements with a thickness a mm and a diameter d mm are used, the three significant fundamental frequencies in kilocycles per second are $f_1 = 2870/a$, $f_2 = 2715/d$, and $f_3 = 3830/d$. For thin 30-deg cut plates of a large area $a\,c$, the thickness vibration is estimated from $f_1 = 1960/b$ kc/sec if b is in millimeters, showing that with a cut of this kind a lower frequency is obtained than with a Curie cut of the same thickness. The other possible longitudinal vibration along the X-axis for a 30-deg cut crystal is $f_2 = 2860/a$ kc/sec if a is in millimeters. For the thickness and Y vibrations in a Curie cut crystal and the width vibrations along the X-axis of a 30-deg crystal, the temperature coefficient of the frequency is negative, since it depends mainly upon the temperature coefficient of Young's modulus in the XY plane. The temperature effects upon the density and the dimension play only a minor part. The average temperature coefficients along the electric axis for Curie and 30-deg cuts vary between -0.002 to -0.0035 per cent, along the Y-axis for Curie cuts between -0.005 to -0.007 per cent, and for Curie cut coupling frequency between -0.004 to -0.007 per cent. Hence, about 20 to 35 cycles variation in 10^6 for each degree centigrade of change for the thickness vibration of Curie cuts and the vibrations along the X-axis for 30-deg cuts. The temperature coefficient of the thickness frequency of a 30-deg cut crystal is usually *positive*.

It varies with the dimension along the X-axis of the plate and also depends upon the temperature. It varies between $+0.01$ to -0.002 per cent. Hence the thickness frequency varies from $+100$ cycles in 10^6 per degree centigrade to -20 cycles, showing that there must be a case for zero-temperature coefficient.

The above formulas for the frequency depending upon the dimensions are the outcome of theoretical analysis and experimental results. Since, for longitudinal vibrations, the frequency is proportional to the square-root value of the elasticity E divided by density ρ, it is evident that the frequency varies if E varies. Hence, if a sphere made of crystal quartz is considered, the elasticity surface produced by all vectors representing the moduli of elasticity is no longer a sphere. The reciprocal of the elasticity surface, according to W. Voigt ("Lehrbuch der Kristallphysik") is given by $1/E = s_{11} \sin^4 \varphi + s_{33} \cos^4 \varphi + (s_{44} + 2s_{13}) \sin^2 \varphi \cos^2 \varphi + 2s_{14} \sin^3 \varphi \cos \varphi$ $\sin 3\theta$ for $s_{11} = 12.7$, $s_{13} = -1.49$, $s_{14} = -4.23$, $s_{33} = 9.8$, $s_{44} = 19.6(10^{-13}$ c.g.s.$)$. Hence in the plane $\perp$ to the X-axis for E, there are the two maxima 13.05 and 10.33 $(10^5$ kg/cm$^2)$ at $\varphi = -48°19'$ and $+11°7'$, respectively, and the two miminum values $E = 10.2$ and $7.06(10^5$ kg/cm$^2)$. The elasticity values for $+71°32'$ and $-48°19'$ confirm the frequency formulas for the two coupling oscillations of a disk in the Curie cut.

211. Test for the Piezo-electric Effect of a Quartz Element.

The quartz element, as in Fig. 356, is placed on a metal electrode which leads to the cathode of a tube, while the upper metal plate rests lightly on the quartz element and is connected to the grid. The galvanometer in the plate branch shows a certain current. If the test piece is a Curie cut and the upper face gives up negative charges upon compression, the plate current I decreases to some value I_1 if the weight is placed on the upper electrode. After a few seconds, the original current I will be noted again. If the weight is taken off, a small current increase occurs. If the piezo-electric element is turned around, only a small deflection occurs when the pressure is applied, but the same large current decrease $I - I_1$ takes place when the pressure is removed. If specimens of the same size are tested, the decrease $I - I_1$ is a measure of the piezo-electric effect. This may be called the "total-surface test." A much more critical test is carried on by using only a small exploring surface instead of the large electrodes and noting the effects at different points of the faces. For a poor piece, the deflections change along the surface, going through zero spots and spots of different polarity.

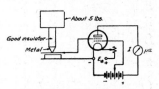

Fig. 356.—Polarity test.

212. The Equivalent Resonator Circuit and Determination of Equivalent Constants of a Quartz Element.

If a piezo-electric quartz element, as in Fig. 357, vibrates longitudinally along the piezo-electric thickness dimension a, one can imagine the crystal as a series combination of inductance L, resistance R, and capacitance C, with a condenser C_0 in multiple accounting for the capacitance of the piezo-electric condenser. The air-gap effect being neglected in this case, the entire network can therefore be

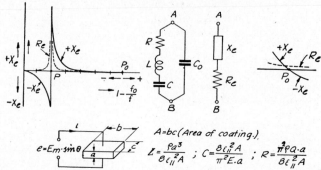

FIG. 357.—Equivalent reactance X_e and resistance R_e of a vibrating quartz plate ($+X_e$ inductive, $-X_e$ capacitive; ρ density of quartz; E modulus of elasticity; ϵ_{11} piezo-electric constant.)

imagined as an effective reactance X_e in series with an effective resistance R_e where

$$R_e = pX\frac{X/p^2R}{1 + mS^2} \qquad X_e = -\frac{X}{p}\frac{mS\left\{mS + \dfrac{X}{pR}\right\} + 1}{1 + m^2S^2} \tag{1}$$

if $p = f/f_0$ denotes the ratio of any frequency f to the resonance frequency f_0 of the voltage acting across the electrodes of the piezo-electric element $m = p - \dfrac{1}{p}$; $S = \dfrac{2\pi f_0 L}{R}$ the sharpness of resonance of the crystal element (alone) and $X = 1/(2\pi f_0 C_0)$ the reactance of the piezo-electric condenser at resonance. Figure 357 gives the effective values of reactance and resistance and shows that the reactance can be positive (inductive) or negative (capacitive). The reactance X_e vanishes at P and P_0. It is the *point P_0* which corresponds to the resonance frequency f_0 of the crystal when operating as an oscillator in spite of the steepness of the X_e characteristic which passes through point P. The reason for this is that the effective resistance R_e has a very high value, and for a crystal connected across the grid and the filament such a high resistance corresponding to point P would prevent oscillations. Hence the point P, corresponding to parallel resonance of the multiple branches C, L, R, and C_0, respectively, does not refer to the frequency f_0 of the oscillation. For point P_0 there is to a good degree of approximation $2\pi f_0 L = 1/(2\pi f_0 C)$, which means a condition corresponding to the mechanical resonance of the piezo-electric quartz element. Strictly speaking, P_0 corresponds to a frequency f' which is somewhat higher than $f_0 = 1/(2\pi\sqrt{CL})$, since $X = 1/(2\pi f_0 C_0)$ acts in parallel with R because $2\pi f_0 L - \dfrac{1}{(2\pi f_0 C)} = 0$. The effective impedance is then

$$\frac{R \, jX}{R + jX} = \frac{RX^2}{R^2 + X^2} + j\frac{R^2 X}{R^2 + X^2} = R_e + jX_e$$

and

$$X_e = \frac{R^2 \, X}{R^2 + X^2}$$

at P_0 is already somewhat capacitive. For an infinitely small value of C_0, one obtains $X_e = 0$, that is, $f' = f_0$ at P_0.

With reference to Fig. 357, the electric-field intensity $\mathcal{E}$ acting for the instantaneous value e of the sinusoidal voltage applied across the electrodes is $\mathcal{E} = e/a$. If now longitudinal mechanical vibrations along the b dimension are considered the piezo-electric stress $Y = \epsilon_{11} \mathcal{E} = \epsilon_{11}e/a$ acts uniformly along the entire length if $\epsilon_{11} = -5.1 \times 10^4$ e.s. c.g.s. units is the piezo-electric constant which plays a part for such mechanical vibrations. Across each area ac there is then a force acY. This force along the entire length then has the same effect as though a force acY were active at each end face but in the opposite direction. Hence the driving force is $F = 2acY = 2c\epsilon_{11}e$. If s denotes the displacement at the ends of the rod, $ds/dt = F/Z_m$, since in the actual mechanical system the driving force F divided by the mechanical impedance $Z_m = \beta + j\left[\alpha\omega - \dfrac{\gamma}{\omega}\right]$ is equal to the velocity $\dfrac{ds}{dt}$ which corresponds to the equivalent electrical relation, driving voltage divided by impedance equal to current. Therefore $ds/dt = 2c\epsilon_{11}e/Z_m$. The total instantaneous current i flowing to the crystal is due to the ordinary dielectric polarization $P_1 = \kappa e/(4\pi a)$ if κ denotes the dielectric constant and the piezo-electric polarization $P_2 = 2\epsilon_{11}s/b$ due to the converse effect, since a strain $2s/b$ is produced because the total displacement is $2s$. Then for the instantaneous current i flowing to the crystal,

$$i = i_1 + i_2 = A\frac{d[P_1 + P_2]}{dt} = \underbrace{\frac{\kappa A}{4\pi a}\frac{de}{dt}}_{\substack{\text{dielectric displace-}\\\text{ment current}}} + \underbrace{\frac{2\epsilon_{11}A}{b}\frac{ds}{dt}}_{\substack{\text{current due to piezo-}\\\text{electric converse effect}}}$$

$$= \frac{\kappa bc}{4\pi a}\frac{de}{dt} + \frac{(2\epsilon_{11}c)^2 e}{Z_m} = C_0\frac{de}{dt} + me$$

Therefore for the effective current value I flowing to the system

$$I = [m + j\omega C_0]E \tag{2}$$

if E is the effective voltage and $m = 4\epsilon^2_{11}c^2/Z_m$ is the motional admittance of the quartz element. For a variable frequency $\omega/2\pi$ its locus is a circle.

Equation (2) can be used to find the impedance E/I of the *mounted* quartz element or its admittance I/E. From the E/I curve (resonance curve) the equivalent electrical constants R, L, and C can be computed. The experimental results give more reliable values than the theoretical formulas, inasmuch as the latter hold for a long rod only. Y. Watanabe[1] gives two methods for this. One procedure is called the "inverted resonance-curve method." The quartz element is connected as in Fig.

[1] *E.N.T.*, **5**, 45, 1928; *Proc. I.R.E.*, **18**, 695, 1930.

358. The effective resistance R_1 of the input coil L_1 is at first determined at a frequency equal to the natural crystal frequency f_0 of interest and L_1 chosen such that C_1 is comparatively large and such that $1/(2\pi\sqrt{C_1L_1})$ is equal to the resonance frequency of the crystal. Since the decrement

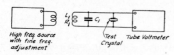

FIG. 358.—Method for finding equivalent constants of an oscillating crystal.

$R_1/(2f_0L_1)$ is large compared with the decrement $R/(2f_0L)$ of the equivalent electrical network of the quartz element, the input circuit $C_1L_1R_1$ remains essentially in resonance, even though the frequency of the oscillator is varied over the small frequency band in order to obtain the sharp resonance curve of the quartz element. The voltage E across the piezo crystal is then

$$E = \frac{E_1}{2\pi j f_0 C_1} \cdot \frac{1}{R_1 + \dfrac{m}{4\pi^2 f_0^2 C_1^2}} \tag{3}$$

if E_1 is the voltage induced in the L_1 coil and is assumed essentially constant. It may be taken constant for the values near the resonance frequency f_0. The reciprocal of the motional admittance m of the vibrating quartz element is $\dfrac{1}{m} = R + j\left[\omega L - \dfrac{1}{\omega C}\right]$ and may be called the "motional impedance." Equation (3) then gives the solution

$$\frac{1}{E} = \frac{j2\pi f_0 C_1}{E_1}\underbrace{\left\{ R_1 + \frac{m}{4\pi^2 f_0^2 C_1^2} \right\}}_{\text{increase of resistance}} =$$

$$\frac{j2\pi f_0 C_1}{E_1}\left\{ R_1 + \frac{1}{4\pi^2 f_0^2 C_1^2}\left[\frac{1}{R + j\left(2\pi f L - \dfrac{1}{2\pi f C} \right)} \right] \right\} = F + G \tag{4}$$

The voltage E is determined by the tube voltmeter, and the above equation shows that the apparent circuit resistance is increased because of the motional impedance $1/m$ of the quartz element. Therefore there is a constant part $F = \dfrac{j\omega_0 l_1}{E_1}R_1$ and a variable part $G = \dfrac{jm}{\omega_0 C_1 E_1}$ as shown in Fig. 359. The variable part has the character of a resonance curve with a maximum value r. If the piezo-electric element vibrates almost at resonance frequency, according to (4), the equivalent circuit resistance is approximately equal to $\dfrac{1}{\omega_0^2 C_1^2 R}$ and, according to Fig. 359, $\dfrac{r}{F}R_1 = \dfrac{1}{\omega_0^2 C_1^2 R}$ and the equivalent resistance is computed from $R = F/(\omega_0^2 C_1^2 R_1\, r)$. Since the logarithmic decre-

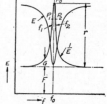

ment $\delta = R/(2f_0L)$ can be found from the resonance curve, the equivalent
inductance is computed from $L = R/(2f_0\delta)$. For points P_1 and P_2, by means
of the parallel-line method giving the corresponding frequencies f_1 and f_2,
the logarithmic decrement $\delta = \pi[f_2 - f_1]/f_0$. The equivalent capacitance,
because of the relation $\omega_0L = 1/(\omega_0C)$, can be computed from $C = 1/(4\pi^2f_0^2L)$. In these formulas C is in farads, L in henries, R in ohms,
and f in cycles per second. The other procedure for finding the equiva-
lent electrical constants of a quartz element employs the substitution
method indicated in Fig. 360. The equivalent series branch CLR of the
vibrating quartz element, in this case, is considered as an equivalent
motional capacitance C_m (positive or negative) in multiple with an equivalent motional conductance G_m. Therefore the motional capacitance
changes its sign when passing through the condition of crystal resonance.

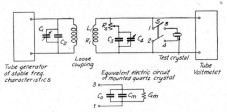

FIG. 360.—Determination of equivalent constants of a vibrating crystal.

In multiple with this combination is the capacitance C_0, which produces
the dielectric displacement current and is practically equal to the measured capacitance of the mounted quartz element when the piezo-electric
element is not vibrating. A tube generator excites the system. C_1
denotes a small vernier condenser so that the frequency f can be varied
very little in the neighborhood of the resonance frequency f_0, and as in
the previous method the small changes $(f_0 - f)$ are determined by means
of a fixed piezo-electric generator of frequency f_0. The beat frequency
$(f_0 - f)$ is made to beat against the audio-frequency note of a variable
beat-frequency generator (Fig. 147) and read off directly on the calibrated
scale of the beat-frequency generator. The measurement is then as
follows:

1. By means of C_1 a frequency f near the resonance frequency f_0 of the crystal is
adjusted.
2. With terminals 1 and 2 closed on 3 and 4 and the standard resistance R_s at
zero value, the small vernier condenser C_4 is varied until for a value C_4 the tube voltmeter gives a maximum response.
3. The switch S is opened and the setting of C_4 increased by an amount $(C_0 + C_m)$,
that is, to a value C_4', for which a somewhat larger maximum response will be noted
on the tube voltmeter.

The standard variable resistance is then gradually cut in until for a
value R_s the same deflection is noted on the tube voltmeter as with the

crystal in the circuit. The difference $C_4' - C_4 = C_0 + C_m$ then gives the capacitance due to the crystal holder and the equivalent motional capacitance C_m of the vibrating quartz element. Since C_0 can be computed from the size of the electrode and the thickness of the quartz element, the motional capacitance is found from $C_m = C_4' - (C_4 + C_0)$. The equivalent motional conductance of the vibrating quartz element is computed from $G_m \cong \omega^2 R_s[C_3 + C_4]^2 \cong \omega^2 R_s C_3{}^2$ where $\omega/2\pi$ is the frequency f in cycles per second, R_s in ohms, and the capacitances C_3 and C_4 expressed in farads. G_m is then in mhos. The exact expression is $G_m = \omega^2 R_s[C_3 + C_4 + C_0 + C_m]^2$. The frequency of the generator is changed to some other value and G_m computed again, and so on. The equivalent constants C, L, and R are again obtained from the experimental curves of Fig. 361, where the frequency f is plotted

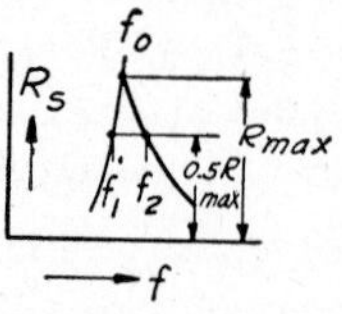

Fig. 361.—Curve for obtaining the equivalent logarithmic decrement of an oscillating crystal.

against the R_s setting where $R_{\max}$ is the value for crystal resonance. As above from $\delta = \pi(f_2 - f_1)/f_0$ the inductance $L = R/(2\delta f_0)$ is obtained if δ is determined from the f_1 and f_2 values for a parallel line drawn a distance $0.5R_{\max}$ above the abscissa. The capacitance is again computed from $C = 1/(\omega_0{}^2 L)$. The resistance R, according to the above approximations, can be computed from $R = 1/(4\pi^2 f_0{}^2 C_3{}^2 R_s)$ if R_s denotes the maximum value $R_{\max}$ for the resonance frequency f_0.

213. Notes on Resonance Curves and the Determination of the Decrement of Vibrating Quartz Elements.—In the preceding section the logarithmic decrement is determined from equivalent resonance curves. In Fig. 362, the resonance curve is taken by means of the potential drop across a high resistance. In Fig. 363, the frequency f of the source is at first chosen close to the natural frequency f_0

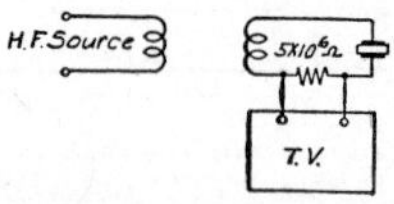

Fig. 362.—System for taking the resonance curve of a crystal.

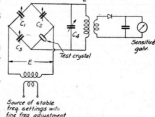

Fig. 363.—Resonance of a vibrating crystal.

of the quartz element about which the resonance curve is to be taken. The bridge is adjusted to balance. A constant voltage E is impressed and the frequency varied, and as f approaches f_0 the sensitive galvanometer gives increasing deflections. After passing the resonance condition $f = f_0$ the deflections decrease again. The output circuit $C_4 L$ is always tuned and has a decrement many times larger than for any piezo-electric vibration and therefore does not give rise to appreciable distortion. The indications of the galvanometer plotted against the frequency give the resonance curve. All these methods require that the voltage be constant; otherwise the curve with a resonance peak cannot be used to determine the decrement. The determination of the decrement from the Bjerkness resonance curve also requires that a *logarithmic* decay take place which, according to the experiments of S. Chaikin,[1] seems to be true for the resonance curves taken for X and Y oscillations experimented with. The main difficulty lies in the fact that δ may be as low as 10^{-4} to 10^{-5} and the resonance curve covers a frequency band of a few cycles only. It is also difficult to avoid any added decrement due to back action. This may be negative (may be the case if amplification is used where the effects in the plate branch are partially reflected into the crystal branch). Since the decrement is small, very many cycles occur before the crystal element stops vibrating, and use can be made of this. Therefore the decrement can be conveniently determined by setting the quartz element into natural vibrations and noting the decay after the initial source has been removed. The logarithmic decrement per cycle is then found by scaling off the amplitudes A_1 and A_n of the same polarity n cycles apart and computing the decrement from

$$\delta = \frac{\log_e (A_1/A_n)}{n} = \frac{2.303 \log_{10} (A_1/A_n)}{r}$$

A procedure of this type was originally suggested by S. Chaikin.[2] It was also used by K. S. Van Dyke (so far unpublished), who used amplifi-

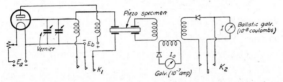

Fig. 364.—Determination of the decrement by means of the ballistic galvanometer.

cation and the records of a cathode-ray oscillograph to visualize dying-off crystal vibrations. Figure 364 gives a procedure of this kind when a tube generator excites the quartz specimen in the desired mode. At a time t_0 the generator is disconnected by means of contact K_1, and the quartz element left free to vibrate out the received energy. During this process, contact can be made after any time t_1 by means of K_2 and the current I noted by the ballistic galvanometer. If i denotes the instantaneous current for a quadratic law, the deflection is proportional to $\int_{t_1}^{t=\infty} i^2 dt$. The process is repeated by choosing another time interval and obtaining another current reading, and so on. The curve $I = k\int_{t_1}^{t=\infty} [\varphi(t)]^2 dt$ for the different values of t_1, giving different values of I noted on the

[1] *Z. Hochfreq.*, **35**, 6, 1930; for decrement measurements see also A. Meissner, *Z. tech. Physik*, **7**, 585, 1926; K. Heegner, *Z. Hochfreq.*, **29**, 177, 1927; E. Giebe and A. Scheibe, *Z. Hochfreq.*, **35**, 165, 1930.

[2] *Loc. cit.*

ballistic galvanometer, gives the decay of amplitude with respect to time if care is taken that the initial amplitude is always the same. This can be satisfied by means of the meter I_0 which must always give the same deflection when K_1 is closed. A rotating device, a Helmholtz pendulum, or the like can be used to operate contacts K_1 and K_2. Because of the square-law detection, the experimental curve gives the factor $\epsilon^{-2\delta t}$ instead of $\epsilon^{-\delta t}$. The accuracy of the method depends upon the accuracy of the I readings and the accuracy with which the time interval

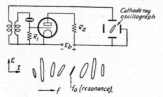

is determined. To ascertain whether a logarithmic decay occurs, log I is plotted against the time interval and a falling straight line obtained for a logarithmic case.

FIG. 365.—Cathode-ray oscillograph for studying piezoelectric oscillations.

214. Dynamic Characteristics of Piezoelectric Vibrations.—Lissajous figures on cathode-ray tubes were used by several investigators to note true crystal excitations.[1] Figure 365 shows the characteristic traces observed if one deflection is proportional to the voltage E and the quadrature deflection proportional to the current through the crystal.

215. Notes on Experiments with Piezo-electric Oscillators.—Such experiments are manifold. If an ordinary three-element tube is used,

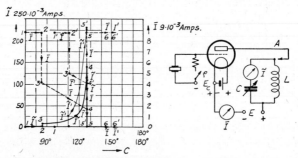

FIG. 366.—For cathode-grid excitation.

one may distinguish between piezo-electric excitation across the filament-grid gap and across the grid-plate gap, respectively. The "pulling in" of piezo-electric oscillations is then as in Figs. 366 and 367. With respect to Fig. 366, the grid leak ρ is at first out of the circuit. The value of C is such that at about 90 deg the oscillation constant CL produces current resonance in the tank circuit if the plate tap is connected on A. The condenser C is at first set for minimum capacitance (0-deg position). A thermoelectric indicator then indicates no oscillation current $\tilde{I}$ and the direct-current meter in the plate branch indicates a steady plate current

---

[1] For publications, reference is made to the papers by Y. Watanabe, *loc. cit.*, and K. S. van Dyke, *Proc. I.R.E.*, **16**, 763, 1928.

$\bar{I}$, depending upon the steady plate potential, the filament current, and the grid charge due to the piezo-electric condenser and the leakage in the tube socket across the filament-grid gap. The setting of C is then gradually increased, until for a certain value (87 deg) piezo-electric oscillations set in. The steady plate current $\bar{I}$ then decreases suddenly to a value at 3 and the oscillation current $\tilde{I}$ has the value at 3 along the $\tilde{I}$ characteristic. For this state, the load impedance in the external plate circuit reacts back through the plate-grid interelectrode capacitance in such a way that the circuit losses of the input branch are compensated. It will be found that the frequency of the oscillations is essentially due to the dimensions of the piezo-electric element (Sec. 210), that the tank circuit CL acts as an inductance at this frequency, and that its natural frequency is above that of the crystal frequency which is excited. A

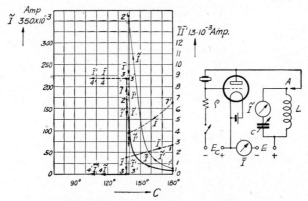

Fig. 367.—For grid-plate excitation.

further increase of the C setting increases the amplitude of the oscillatory current $\tilde{I}$ and decreases the direct-current component $\bar{I}$ of the plate current still more, and almost linearly (3 to 4), until for a C setting corresponding to 4 the oscillation breaks off ($\tilde{I}$ becomes zero and $\bar{I}$ returns to its original normal value). A further increase of the C setting will not bring back the piezo-electric oscillation, since the external plate circuit is then capacitive, for which condition no oscillations are possible. Practically all along the portion 3 to 4, the frequency is that due to the piezo-electric element, except, for C settings close to the break-off point, the frequency is somewhat affected (drawing effect) by the tank circuit. Settings close to this point for which the external impedance of the plate circuit is very high are therefore undesirable for piezo oscillators. The $1'$ $2'$ $3'$ $4'$ $5'$ $6'$ characteristics ($\tilde{I}'$ and $\bar{I}'$) illustrate the experimental results if the grid leak is used. There is then a more efficient oscillator which could be improved still more by using an appropriate grid bias in addition. In a similar way are obtained the $\tilde{I}$, $\bar{I}$ characteristics for no grid leak with the piezo-electric element across the grid and the plate as in Fig. 367. The oscillations are then pulled in from the larger C settings toward the smaller C settings. The I' and $\bar{I}'$ characteristics are obtained for a grid leak ρ. In order to obtain still better efficiency, the plate tap is placed on a suitable point along L. It will be noted that the oscillation breaks off for a C setting of about 128 deg for the grid-filament excitation and at about 138 deg for the grid-plate excitation. The reason for it is that the back feeds are along different paths and that the drawing effect is unsymmetrical, since a rather tight coupling exists between the equivalent piezo-electric circuit of the quartz element and the tank circuit when close to the resonance setting.

CHAPTER XVIII

MISCELLANEOUS MEASUREMENTS AND DATA

Special methods belong to this chapter. Procedures described in the various chapters are used and, as with many high-frequency determinations, a method which may work well in one case may not be at all suitable for another, since the order of the magnitude of the quantity to be determined and the range of frequency play an important part. In the case of grounds, the experimenter must use his own judgment. For many high-frequency measurements a line supplying the high-frequency power must be balanced and grounded at a proper point.

216. Notes on Tests on Special Indicators.—Modern research activities require tests on such apparatus as the photoelectric cell, Kerr cell, and Neon tubes. Experiments on frequency characteristics especially are of importance. For Kerr cell work reference is made to Fig. 368. A discussion with an extended list of references is also given by J. W. Beams.[1]

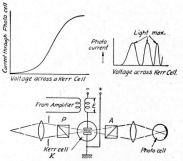

Fig. 368.—Effects in a Kerr cell system (polarizer P and analyzer A are crossed by 90 deg and form with the electric field of the Kerr condenser an angle of 45 deg).

For maximum effect, the plane of the nicol P (the polarizer) is so oriented that the plane of vibration of the light passing through the Kerr condenser K makes an angle of 45 deg. Hence, if the nicol A (the analyzer) is crossed with respect to P, no light reaches the photoelectric cell if no voltage acts across the Kerr cell which is a condenser submerged, for instance, in a liquid of carbon disulphide. But as soon as a voltage acts across K, the carbon disulphide solution becomes double refracting and the component of the light, vibrating parallel to the electric lines of force, must then travel with a different velocity from that of the light which vibrates perpendicular to the lines of force. The result is that elliptically polarized light leaves the Kerr cell and a portion of it can be transmitted through the analyser A to the photoelectric cell. For the refractive indexes n_1 and n_2 of the two beams, the difference φ in phase after emerging from K is $\varphi = 2\pi l(n_1 - n_2)/\lambda = 6.28 l K \mathcal{E}^2$ if K is the Kerr constant, l the length of the light path, $\mathcal{E}$ the electric-field intensity, and λ the wave length of the light. If γ and δ denote the angles which the planes of vibration of the propagated light of A and P make with the $\mathcal{E}$ lines, the light intensity emerging from A is $I = k\left[\cos^2 (\gamma - \delta) - \sin 2\gamma \sin 2\delta \sin^2 \dfrac{\varphi}{2} \right]$ if k is a constant, and if A is crossed with respect to P and the plane of transmission makes an angle of 45 deg with the

[1] *Rev. Sci. Instruments*, **1**, 780, 1930.

$\mathcal{E}$ lines $I = k \sin^2 \dfrac{\varphi}{2} = k \sin^2 (\pi l K \mathcal{E}^2)$ if $\pi l K \mathcal{E}^2$ is in radians. By differentiating this, $dI/d\mathcal{E} = 6.28k\, Kl\mathcal{E} \sin (2\pi l K \mathcal{E}^2)$ is obtained. This means that the rate of change of light intensity varies with $\mathcal{E}$ in such a way that a small alternating voltage e, when superimposed on a steady voltage E as in Fig. 368, can operate the Kerr cell. In this way the light may be interrupted up to 10^9 times/sec.

217. Cathode-ray Tube for Visualizing Atmospheric Disturbances.—

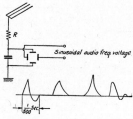

The method of Fig. 369 has been used by E. V. Appleton, Watson Watt, and J. F. Herd.[1] The resistance R makes the receiving antenna aperiodic in order to avoid distortion of the induced voltage due to atmospheric disturbances. Only straight resistance-coupled amplifiers can be used to obtain the true picture of statics (indicated times give only the approximate order for such disturbances). Generally the cathode-ray

Fig. 369.—Study of statics.

tube is connected directly, as in Fig. 369.

218. Determination of Impedance, Reactance, and Resistance of Different Networks.—

In the method of Fig. 370, the unknown impedance Z_x is connected in series with the standard resistances R_1 and R_2 which are alike and variable, so that, as R_1 is cut in, R_2 is cut out by the same amount. The switch S is at first connected on 1 and the current of desired frequency varied until a suitable deflection d is noted on the vacuum-tube

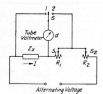

Fig. 370.—Determination of impedance.

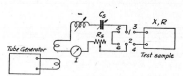

Fig. 371.—Determination of a reactance.

voltmeter. The switch is connected on 2 and the interlocked sliders S_1, S_2 are moved toward the right until the same deflection d is obtained. If R_1 denotes the setting of the resistance to the left, $Z_x = R_1$ ohms. If much larger impendances Z_x are to be determined, a calibrated tube voltmeter is used and the voltages $E_x = IZ_x$ and $E_1 = IR_1$ noted for S on 1 and 2, respectively, and the impedance computed from $Z_x = R_1 E_x/E_1$. Figure 371 shows the method which can be used to determine the reactance X and resistance R of a filter or any other load. The measurement is carried on over the desired frequency band. It uses a tube generator which is powerful enough so that its frequency is unaffected when the measuring system is tuned. Terminals 1 and 2 are connected

[1] *Proc. Roy. Soc. (London)*, A, **103**, 84, 1923.

on 3 and 4 and L and C_s varied with R_s set at zero until the resonance current I flows. If X_1 denotes the reactance $1/(\omega C_1)$ of $C_s = C_1$, X_0 the reactance of the remainder of the system to the left of terminals 1 and 2, and X the reactance due to the test sample, $X_0 + X - X_1 = 0$ where X may be negative or positive. If R_0 denotes the effective resistance of the system to the left of terminals 1 and 2 and R that of the filter, $R_0 + R$ denotes the total circuit resistance and $I[R_0 + R] = E$ the driving voltage producing the resonance current I. Terminals 1 and 2 are now connected on the short 5 and 6 and C_s is varied to some other value C_2, until resonance current flows. The standard resistance is gradually cut in until for a setting R_s the same resonance current I occurs. If the driving voltage E is the same as for the first determination $I[R_0 + R_s] = E$ and R_s expresses the resistance of the test sample directly. If X_2 denotes the reactance $1/(\omega C_2)$, the result is $X_0 - X_2 = 0$. From this $X_0 = X_2$ and if inserted in the reactance expression for the first determination, the reactance of the test sample is formed from

$$X = X_1 - X_2 = \frac{1}{\omega C_1} - \frac{1}{\omega C_2}$$

The reactance X and effective resistance R can also be measured by means of the differential method of Fig. 372. A variable inductance L_s, or a variable condenser C_s, is used as the reactive variable standard, depending upon whether X is positive (inductive) or negative (capacitive). The differential bridge is then balanced by means of the standard reactance X_s and R_s and the setting of X_s and R_s gives R and X directly. If the reactance X to be determined is either too large or too small, a suitable known

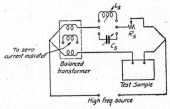

Fig. 372.—Determination of reactance and resistance.

reactance X_0 is connected either in series with X_s or in series with the test sample, whichever makes a balance possible, and the value of X_0 is taken into account in the final result. If the frequency characteristics of ordinary receiving apparatus (also receiving filters) are to be taken, it seems more convenient to apply a constant voltage of adjustable frequency to the input and observe by means of a tube voltmeter across the output terminals of the test sample to what extent the frequency varies the output voltage.

219. Calibration of a Contact Rectifier.—Galena and other contact rectifiers are very convenient means for measuring small high-frequency currents. The calibration can be obtained by means of the method of Fig. 373. If d denotes the deflection of the indicator to be used in connection with the crystal rectifier $I = I_0/\sqrt{d}$ where I_0 is the effective current reading of the high-frequency current. Since it can be assumed that I, for values of R up to 100Ω, is proportional to the value of R, it is

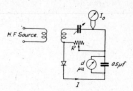

unnecessary to plot the calibration curves for many R values. For the calibration, R is chosen small, for instance, 1 ohm, and I_0 and d are noted. The value of I is then found by the above formula.

Fig. 373.—Calibration of a crystal rectifier.

220. Derivations of Empirical Laws.—The simplest laws are linear functions of the variable; others follow a square or some other law. A portion of an experimental curve can be expressed by an equation of the form

$$y = a + bx + cx^2 + dx^3 + cx^4 + \cdots \tag{1}$$

The quantities y and x are the corresponding ordinates and abscissas of the curve. Just as many points on the curve must be used as there are terms in the above equation. When the points chosen indicate the character of the curve, the equation will be sufficiently accurate. If the experimental characteristic can be determined with the abridged series $y = a + bx + cx^2$, three points of coordinates $(y_1, x_1 \cdots y_2, x_2 \cdots y_3, x_3)$ are needed, and the constants a, b, and c are found from the simultaneous equations $y_1 = a + bx_1 + cx_1^2$; $y_2 = a + bx_2 + cx_2^2$; $y_3 = a + bx_3 + cx_3^2$.

Example.—If an experimental characteristic is to be studied near the intersection with the ordinate axis, such points are used, for instance, as $y_1 = 0.6$, $x_1 = 0$; $y_2 = 4.6$, $x_2 = 1$; and $y_3 = 29.4$, $x_3 = 3$ and $0.6 = a$; $4.6 = a + b + c$; $29.4 = a + 3b + 9c$, giving $b = 1.2$ and $c = 2.8$, and the formula for this portion of the curve is $y = 0.6 + 1.2x + 2.8x^2$, from which it is noted that the square term of x has a great influence.

If this is the case or the characteristic shows pronounced curvature, it is always advisable to consider at least three terms in Eq. (1).

For higher powers of x, the simultaneous equations are conveniently evaluated by means of determinants. For instance, for five coordinate points, there is the system of equations

$$y_1 = a + bx_1 + cx_1^2 + dx_1^3 + ex_1^4$$
$$y_2 = a + bx_2 + cx_2^2 + dx_2^3 + ex_2^4$$
$$\dots\dots\dots\dots\dots\dots\dots\dots\dots\dots\dots$$
$$\dots\dots\dots\dots\dots\dots\dots\dots\dots\dots\dots$$
$$y_5 = a + bx_5 + cx_5^2 + dx_5^3 + ex_5^4$$

with the corresponding determinants

$$\Delta = \begin{vmatrix} 1 & x_1 & x_1^2 & x_1^3 & x_1^4 \\ 1 & x_2 & x_2^2 & x_2^3 & x_2^4 \\ 1 & x_3 & x_3^2 & x_3^3 & x_3^4 \\ 1 & x_4 & x_4^2 & x_4^3 & x_4^4 \\ 1 & x_5 & x_5^2 & x_5^3 & x_5^4 \end{vmatrix} \qquad \Delta_a = \begin{vmatrix} y_1 & x_1 & x_1^2 & x_1^3 & x_1^4 \\ y_2 & x_2 & x_2^2 & x_2^3 & x_2^4 \\ y_3 & x_3 & x_3^2 & x_3^3 & x_3^4 \\ y_4 & x_4 & x_4^2 & x_4^3 & x_4^4 \\ y_5 & x_5 & x_5^2 & x_5^3 & x_5^4 \end{vmatrix}$$

$$\Delta_b = \begin{vmatrix} 1 & y_1 & x_1{}^2 & x_1{}^3 & x_1{}^4 \\ 1 & y_2 & x_2{}^2 & x_2{}^3 & x_2{}^4 \\ 1 & y_3 & x_3{}^2 & x_3{}^3 & x_3{}^4 \\ 1 & y_4 & x_4{}^2 & x_4{}^3 & x_4{}^4 \\ 1 & y_5 & x_5{}^2 & x_5{}^3 & x_5{}^4 \end{vmatrix} \qquad \Delta_c = \begin{vmatrix} 1 & x_1 & y_1 & x_1{}^3 & x_1{}^4 \\ 1 & x_2 & y_2 & x_2{}^3 & x_2{}^4 \\ 1 & x_3 & y_3 & x_3{}^3 & x_3{}^4 \\ 1 & x_4 & y_4 & x_4{}^3 & x_4{}^4 \\ 1 & x_5 & y_5 & x_5{}^3 & x_5{}^4 \end{vmatrix}$$

$$\Delta_d = \begin{vmatrix} 1 & x_1 & x_1{}^2 & y_1 & x_1{}^4 \\ 1 & x_2 & x_2{}^2 & y_2 & x_2{}^4 \\ 1 & x_3 & x_3{}^2 & y_3 & x_3{}^4 \\ 1 & x_4 & x_4{}^2 & y_4 & x_4{}^4 \\ 1 & x_5 & x_5{}^2 & y_5 & x_5{}^4 \end{vmatrix} \qquad \Delta_e = \begin{vmatrix} 1 & x_1 & x_1{}^2 & x_1{}^3 & y_1 \\ 1 & x_2 & x_2{}^2 & x_2{}^3 & y_2 \\ 1 & x_3 & x_3{}^2 & x_3{}^3 & y_3 \\ 1 & x_4 & x_4{}^2 & x_4{}^3 & y_4 \\ 1 & x_5 & x_5{}^2 & x_5{}^3 & y_5 \end{vmatrix}$$

The constants a, b, c, d, and e of the final formula

$$y = a + bx + cx^2 + dx^3 + ex^4$$

are found from the relations

$$a = \frac{\Delta a}{\Delta}; \; b = \frac{\Delta b}{\Delta}; \; c = \frac{\Delta c}{\Delta}; \; d = \frac{\Delta d}{\Delta}; \; e = \frac{\Delta e}{\Delta} \qquad (2)$$

The constants of the polynomial (1) can also be solved graphically. The equation $y = a + bx + cx^2$ may be modified by the addition of another term into $y = a + bx + cx^2 + dx^3$. If the values of x are equidistant (points on the experimental curve chosen such that the difference between consecutive x readings is a constant), it is possible to prove the correctness of the assumption of the last equation. Let the constant difference in the values of x be δ. Then the successive differences in the values of y are

$$\Delta y = [b\delta + c\delta^2 + d\delta^3] + [2c\delta + 3d\delta^2]x + 3d\delta x^2$$
$$\Delta^2 y = [2c\delta^2 + 6d\delta^3] + 6d\delta^2 x$$
$$\Delta^3 y = 6d\delta^3$$

Hence the plot $(x, \Delta^2 y)$ will approximate a straight line and the values of $\Delta^3 y$ are approximately constant. From the equation of the straight line, the constants c and d may be determined and, writing the original equation in the form $y - cx^2 - dx^3 = a + bx$, the plot of $(x, y - cx^2 - dx^3)$ will approximate a straight line, from which the constants a and b may be determined.

This method can also be used in order to find out how many terms are needed in the polynomial (1). For instance for the points:

y	0.0	0.212	0.463	0.772	1.153	1.625	2.207	2.917	3.776	4.798	6.001
x	0.0	0.2	0.4	0.6	0.8	1.0	1.2	1.4	1.6	1.8	2.0

for which the values of x are chosen equidistant. There are the corresponding variable differences between consecutive y values

Table XIV

Formulas	Straight-line equation which holds for all formulas cited	If	Since	Process of plotting	Remarks
(1) $y = ax + b$		$k = a;\ A = b$ $Y = y;\ X = x$	....	Plot x as abscissa, y as ordinate	
(2) $y = ax^2 + b$		$k = a;\ A = b$ $Y = y;\ X = x^2$	$y = a(x^2) + b$	x^2 as abscissa, y as ordinate	
(3) $y = axy + b$		$k = a;\ A = b$ $Y = y;\ X = xy$	$y = a(xy) + b$	xy as abscissa, y as ordinate	
(4) $y = a\dfrac{y}{x} + b$	$\mathbf{Y = kX + A}$ k denotes the slope of straight line and A the intercept on Y-axis	$k = a;\ A = b$ $Y = y;\ X = y/x$	$y = a(y/x) + b$	y/x as abscissa, y as ordinate	
(5) $y = ax^q$		$k = q;\ A = \log a$ $Y = \log y;\ X = \log x$	$(\log y) = q(\log x) + \log a$	$\log x$ as abscissa, $\log y$ as ordinate	$\log = \log_{10}$ ordinary logarithmic paper can be used
(6) $y = ae^{qx}$		$k = 0.4343q;\ A = \log a$ $Y = \log y;\ X = x$	$(\log y) = q \times \log \epsilon + \log a$ $= 0.4343qx + \log a$	x as abscissa, $\log y$ as ordinate	
(7) $y = ax^b + c$		$k = b;\ A = \log a$ $Y = \log (y - c);\ X = \log x$	$[\log (y - c)] = b(\log x) + \log a$	$\log x$ as abscissa, $\log (y - c)$ as ordinate	
(8) $\boldsymbol{y = ae^{bx} + c}$		$k = 0.4343b;\ A = \log a$ $Y = \log (y - c);\ X = x$	$[\log (y - c)] = bx(\log \epsilon) + \log a$ $= 0.4343bx + \log a$	x as abscissa, $\log (y - c)$ as ordinate	

$\Delta y = 0.212; 0.251; 0.309; 0.381; 0.472; 0.582; 0.710; 0.859; 1.002;$ and
$$1.203$$

and the consecutive differences between these values

$\Delta^2 y = 0.039; 0.058; 0.072; 0.091; 0.110; 0.128; 0.149; 0.163;$ and 0.181

and the consecutive differences between these values

$\Delta^3 y = 0.019; 0.014; 0.019; 0.019; 0.018; 0.021; 0.014;$ and 0.018.

Since the third differences are approximately constant and the plot $(x, \Delta^2 y)$ about a straight line, the series $y = a + bx + cx^2 + dx^3$ is sufficient. In this particular case $a = 0$, since the curve passes through the origin.

Moreover, since the equation for a straight line is

$$y = kX + A \tag{3}$$

for the slope k and the intercept A on the y-axis, more complicated characteristics can be written in the above form when certain transformations are used. This is brought out in Table XIV.

The process is as follows: Plot y and x (for instance, voltage against current) on ordinary curve paper. If the experimental series gives a straight line, then there is the characteristic formula (1), which for the voltage-current case must pass through the origin, if Ohm's law holds $(y = ax)$. This is, for example, not true for an electron tube, since the characteristic is not a straight line and does not pass exactly through the origin because of the initial velocities of the electrons. When the characteristic is curved, either the process in Eq. (1) or the cases 2 to 8 of Table XIV can be used. If all of these possibilities do not give approximately a straight line, the following approximation can be tried.

$$\log y = a + bx + cx^2 + dx^3 + ex^4 + \cdots \tag{4}$$

If it is desirable to evaluate solution (6) with the natural logarithm $\log_\epsilon$, a table for the common logarithm $(\log_{10} = \log)$ can be used with the transformation

$$\log_\epsilon N = 2.3026 \log_{10} N$$

Examples:

1. An experimental investigation gave the following values:

x...............	1	2	3	4	5	6	8	9	16
y...............	3	4.25	5.21	6	6.75	7.4	8.55	9	12

The plot on ordinary cross-sectional paper appears regularly curved. A trial with case 5 of Table XIV gives

log x	0.000	0.301	0.477	0.602	0.699	0.778	0.903	0.954	1.204
log y	0.477	0.627	0.717	0.778	0.829	0.869	0.932	0.954	1.079

Plotting now log y and log x as coordinates, practically a straight line is obtained with a slope $k = 0.5$, and the intercept of logarithmic length 0.477 on the ordinate axis. Hence log $y = 0.5$ log $(x) + 0.477$ is the solution which in the exponential form, according to formula (5), reads: $y = 3x^{0.5} = 3\sqrt{x}$, since log $a = 0.477$ corresponds to value 3. The correctness of this result can also be checked by means of any two coordinates (for instance, log $y_1 = 1.079$; log $x_1 = 1.204$ and log $y_2 = 0.717$; log $x_2 = 0.477$) and one has the simultaneous equations $1.079 = 1.2049 + $ log a, and $0.717 = 0.4779 + $ log a.

2. The volt-ampere curve of an electric arc shows a curved negative characteristic when plotted on ordinary cross-sectional paper. But if the power product $E\ I$ is plotted as ordinate against the current I as abscissa, almost a straight line is obtained on ordinary cross-sectional paper. The straight line has the form $E\ I = aI + b$; that is, $Y = kX + A$ for $k = b$, $A = a$, $Y = E$, and $X = 1/I$. Hence the final equation of the static arc characteristic is $E = \dfrac{b}{I} + a$. For any two points of the curve, for instance, $E_1 = 50.25$ volts, $I_1 = 1.96$ amp, and $E_2 = 45$ and $I_2 = 5.97$. Hence, $50.25 = \dfrac{b}{1.96} + a$; $45 = \dfrac{b}{5.97} + a$; and $a = 42.45$; $b = 15.3$. The formula for this portion of the curve is then $E = \dfrac{15.3}{I} + 42.45$.

3. With the grid potential of an electron tube equal to zero, the following values for the anode current I_p and anode e.m.f. E_p were noted:

E_p, volt..............	50	100	200	300	400
I_p, ma...............	2.3	7.5	28.5	63	72.5

The curve with I_p as abscissa and E_p as ordinate has the well-known S-form when drawn on ordinary cross-sectional paper, while it is practically a straight line on logarithm paper. By means of the latter, the expression

$$E_p = 32I_p^{0.55}$$

is obtained. Since it is of more practical importance to have I_p as a function of E_p, this can be obtained from table

log I_p...............	0.356	0.874	1.454	1.799	1.86
log E_p...............	1.699	2.	2.301	2.477	2.602

If the lower portion of the curve is considered, for the coordinate points belonging to it, there is

$$0.356 = 1.699q + \log a$$
$$0.874 = 2q + \log a$$

that is, $q = 1.715$; log $a = -2.556$
$a = 0.00278$

with the equation

$$I_p = 0.00278I_p^{1.715}$$

For the upper portion of the characteristic,

$$\left. \begin{array}{l} 1.454 = 2.301q + \log a \\ 1.799 = 2.477q + \log a \end{array} \right\} \text{that is, } q = 1.96; \log a = -3.061; a = 0.000869$$

$$I_p = 0.000869 E_p^{1.96}$$

4. The graphic representation of an experimental series gives practically a straight line if x is plotted as abscissa and $\log y$ as ordinate. Hence case (6) of Table XIV. The characteristic coordinates are $\log y_1 = 0.845$; $x_1 = 3.892$ and $\log y_2 = 0.623$; $x_2 = 2.87$. Since

$$(\log y) = 0.4343qx + \log a$$

there are the simultaneous equations

$$\left. \begin{array}{l} 0.845 = 0.4343 \cdot 3.892q + \log a \\ 0.623 = 0.4343 \cdot 2.87q + \log a \end{array} \right\} \text{that is, } q = 0.49; \log a = 0.019; a = 1.0278.$$

and the empirical formula

$$y = 1.0278\epsilon^{0.49x}$$

TABLE XV.—MULTIPLY TU OR db BY 0.1151 TO OBTAIN NEPERS AND BY 1.056 TO OBTAIN MILES OF STANDARD CABLE

Number of TU	Power ratio		Number of TU	Power ratio		Number of TU	Power ratio	
	Gain	Loss		Gain	Loss		Gain	Loss
0.1	1.023	0.977	3.6	2.29	0.437	7.1	5.31	0.195
0.2	1.047	0.955	3.7	2.34	0.427	7.2	5.25	0.191
0.3	1.072	0.933	3.8	2.40	0.417	7.3	5.37	0.186
0.4	1.096	0.912	3.9	2.45	0.407	7.4	5.50	0.182
0.5	1.122	0.891	4.0	2.51	0.398	7.5	5.62	0.178
0.6	1.148	0.871	4.1	2.57	0.389	7.6	5.75	0.174
0.7	1.175	0.851	4.2	2.63	0.380	7.7	5.89	0.170
0.8	1.202	0.832	4.3	2.69	0.372	7.8	6.03	0.166
0.9	1.230	0.813	4.4	2.75	0.363	7.9	6.17	0.162
1.0	1.259	0.794	4.5	2.82	0.355	8.0	6.31	0.158
1.1	1.288	0.776	4.6	2.88	0.347	8.1	6.45	0.155
1.2	1.318	0.759	4.7	2.95	0.339	8.2	6.61	0.151
1.3	1.349	0.741	4.8	3.02	0.331	8.3	6.76	0.148
1.4	1.380	0.724	4.9	3.09	0.324	8.4	6.92	0.144
1.5	1.413	0.708	5.0	3.16	0.316	8.5	7.08	0.141
1.6	1.445	0.692	5.1	3.24	0.309	8.6	7.24	0.138
1.7	1.479	0.676	5.2	3.31	0.302	8.7	7.41	0.135
1.8	1.514	0.661	5.3	3.39	0.295	8.8	7.59	0.132
1.9	1.549	0.645	5.4	3.47	0.288	8.9	7.76	0.129
2.0	1.585	0.631	5.5	3.55	0.282	9.0	7.94	0.126
2.1	1.622	0.617	5.6	3.63	0.275	9.1	8.13	0.123
2.2	1.660	0.603	5.7	3.72	0.269	9.2	8.32	0.120
2.3	1.698	0.589	5.8	3.80	0.263	9.3	8.51	0.118
2.4	1.738	0.575	5.9	3.89	0.257	9.4	8.71	0.115
2.5	1.778	0.562	6.0	3.98	0.251	9.5	8.91	0.112
2.6	1.820	0.550	6.1	4.07	0.245	9.6	9.12	0.110
2.7	1.862	0.537	6.2	4.17	0.240	9.7	9.33	0.107
2.8	1.906	0.525	6.3	4.27	0.234	9.8	9.55	0.105
2.9	1.950	0.513	6.4	4.37	0.229	9.9	9.77	0.102
3.0	1.995	0.501	6.5	4.47	0.224	10.0	10.00	0.100
3.1	2.04	0.490	6.6	4.57	0.219	20.0	100.	0.01
3.2	2.09	0.479	6.7	4.68	0.214	30.0	1,000.	0.001
3.3	2.14	0.468	6.8	4.79	0.209	40.0	10,000.	0.0001
3.4	2.19	0.457	6.9	4.90	0.204	50.0	100,000.	0.00001
3.5	2.24	0.447	7.0	5.01	0.200	60.0	1,000,000.	0.000001

TABLE XVI.—AMPLIFICATION RELATION OF POWER RATIO P_2/P_1 TO TU (db)

P_2/P_1	.....	0.01	0.02	0.03	0.04	0.05	0.06	0.07	0.08	0.09	P_2/P_1
1.0	0.00	0.05	0.09	0.13	0.17	0.21	0.26	0.30	0.34	0.38	1.0
1.1	0.42	0.46	0.49	0.53	0.57	0.61	0.65	0.68	0.72	0.76	1.1
1.2	0.79	0.83	0.87	0.90	0.94	0.97	1.01	1.04	1.07	1.11	1.2
1.3	1.14	1.17	1.21	1.24	1.27	1.31	1.34	1.37	1.40	1.43	1.3
1.4	1.47	1.49	1.53	1.56	1.59	1.62	1.65	1.68	1.71	1.73	1.4
1.5	1.76	1.79	1.82	1.85	1.88	1.91	1.93	1.96	1.99	2.02	1.5
1.6	2.04	2.07	2.10	2.12	2.15	2.18	2.20	2.23	2.26	2.28	1.6
1.7	2.31	2.33	2.36	2.38	2.41	2.43	2.46	2.48	2.51	2.53	1.7
1.8	2.56	2.58	2.60	2.63	2.65	2.67	2.70	2.72	2.74	2.77	1.8
1.9	2.79	2.81	2.84	2.86	2.88	2.90	2.92	2.95	2.97	2.99	1.9
2.0	3.01	3.03	3.06	3.08	3.10	3.12	3.14	3.16	3.18	3.20	2.0
2.1	3.22	3.25	3.27	3.29	3.31	3.33	3.35	3.37	3.39	3.41	2.1
2.2	3.43	3.45	3.47	3.49	3.50	3.52	3.54	3.56	3.58	3.60	2.2
2.3	3.62	3.64	3.66	3.68	3.69	3.71	3.73	3.75	3.77	3.79	2.3
2.4	3.80	3.82	3.84	3.86	3.88	3.89	3.91	3.93	3.95	3.96	2.4
2.5	3.98	4.00	4.02	4.03	4.05	4.07	4.08	4.10	4.12	4.14	2.5
2.6	4.15	4.17	4.19	4.20	4.22	4.23	4.25	4.27	4.28	4.30	2.6
2.7	4.32	4.33	4.35	4.36	4.38	4.40	4.41	4.43	4.44	4.46	2.7
2.8	4.47	4.49	4.50	4.52	4.54	4.55	4.57	4.58	4.60	4.61	2.8
2.9	4.63	4.64	4.66	4.68	4.69	4.70	4.71	4.73	4.74	4.76	2.9
3.0	4.77	4.79	4.80	4.82	4.83	4.85	4.86	4.87	4.89	4.90	3.0
3.1	4.92	4.93	4.95	4.96	4.97	4.99	5.00	5.01	5.03	5.04	3.1
3.2	5.05	5.07	5.08	5.10	5.11	5.12	5.13	5.15	5.16	5.17	3.2
3.3	5.19	5.20	5.22	5.23	5.24	5.25	5.26	5.28	5.29	5.30	3.3
3.4	5.32	5.33	5.34	5.36	5.37	5.38	5.39	5.41	5.42	5.43	3.4
3.5	5.44	5.46	5.47	5.48	5.49	5.50	5.52	5.53	5.54	5.55	3.5
3.6	5.57	5.58	5.59	5.60	5.61	5.63	5.64	5.65	5.66	5.67	3.6
3.7	5.68	5.70	5.71	5.72	5.73	5.74	5.75	5.77	5.78	5.79	3.7
3.8	5.80	5.81	5.82	5.83	5.85	5.86	5.87	5.88	5.89	5.90	3.8
3.9	5.91	5.92	5.93	5.95	5.96	5.97	5.98	5.99	6.00	6.01	3.9
4.0	6.02	6.03	6.04	6.06	6.07	6.08	6.09	6.10	6.11	6.12	4.0
4.1	6.13	6.14	6.15	6.16	6.17	6.18	6.19	6.20	6.21	6.22	4.1
4.2	6.24	6.25	6.26	6.27	6.28	6.29	6.30	6.31	6.32	6.33	4.2
4.3	6.34	6.35	6.36	6.37	6.38	6.39	6.40	6.41	6.42	6.43	4.3
4.4	6.44	6.45	6.46	6.47	6.48	6.49	6.50	6.51	6.52	6.53	4.4
4.5	6.53	6.54	6.55	6.56	6.57	6.58	6.59	6.60	6.61	6.62	4.5
4.6	6.63	6.64	6.65	6.66	6.67	6.68	6.69	6.70	6.71	6.71	4.6
4.7	6.72	6.73	6.74	6.75	6.76	6.77	6.78	6.79	6.80	6.81	4.7
4.8	6.81	6.82	6.83	6.84	6.85	6.86	6.87	6.88	6.89	6.90	4.8
4.9	6.90	6.91	6.92	6.93	6.94	6.95	6.96	6.97	6.98	6.99	4.9
5.0	6.99	7.00	7.01	7.02	7.03	7.04	7.04	7.05	7.06	7.07	5.0
5.1	7.08	7.09	7.10	7.10	7.11	7.12	7.13	7.14	7.15	7.15	5.1
5.2	7.16	7.17	7.18	7.19	7.20	7.20	7.21	7.22	7.23	7.24	5.2
5.3	7.25	7.25	7.26	7.27	7.28	7.29	7.29	7.30	7.31	7.32	5.3
5.4	7.33	7.33	7.34	7.35	7.36	7.37	7.37	7.38	7.38	7.39	5.4
P_2/P_1	.....	0.01	0.02	0.03	0.04	0.05	0.06	0.07	0.08	0.09	P_2/P_1

TABLE XVI.—AMPLIFICATION RELATION OF POWER RATIO P_2/P_1 TO TU (db).—
(*Continued*)

P_2/P_1	.....	0.01	0.02	0.03	0.04	0.05	0.06	0.07	0.08	0.09	P_2/P_1
5.5	7.41	7.41	7.42	7.43	7.44	7.45	7.45	7.46	7.47	7.48	5.5
5.6	7.48	7.49	7.50	7.51	7.52	7.52	7.53	7.54	7.55	7.56	5.6
5.7	7.56	7.57	7.58	7.58	7.59	7.60	7.61	7.62	7.62	7.63	5.7
5.8	7.64	7.64	7.65	7.66	7.67	7.67	7.68	7.69	7.70	7.70	5.8
5.9	7.71	7.72	7.73	7.73	7.74	7.75	7.76	7.76	7.77	7.78	5.9
6.0	7.78	7.79	7.80	7.81	7.81	7.82	7.83	7.83	7.84	7.85	6.0
6.1	7.86	7.86	7.87	7.88	7.88	7.89	7.90	7.91	7.91	7.92	6.1
6.2	7.93	7.93	7.94	7.94	7.95	7.96	7.97	7.97	7.98	7.99	6.2
6.3	8.00	8.00	8.01	8.02	8.02	8.03	8.04	8.04	8.05	8.06	6.3
6.4	8.06	8.07	8.08	8.08	8.09	8.10	8.11	8.11	8.12	8.13	6.4
6.5	8.13	8.14	8.14	8.15	8.16	8.16	8.17	8.18	8.18	8.19	6.5
6.6	8.20	8.20	8.21	8.22	8.22	8.23	8.24	8.24	8.25	8.26	6.6
6.7	8.26	8.27	8.28	8.28	8.29	8.30	8.30	8.31	8.31	8.32	6.7
6.8	8.33	8.33	8.34	8.35	8.35	8.36	8.37	8.37	8.38	8.38	6.8
6.9	8.39	8.40	8.40	8.41	8.42	8.42	8.43	8.43	8.44	8.45	6.9
7.0	8.45	8.46	8.47	8.47	8.48	8.48	8.49	8.50	8.50	8.51	7.0
7.1	8.52	8.52	8.53	8.53	8.54	8.55	8.55	8.56	8.56	8.57	7.1
7.2	8.58	8.58	8.59	8.59	8.60	8.61	8.61	8.62	8.62	8.63	7.2
7.3	8.64	8.64	8.65	8.65	8.66	8.67	8.67	8.68	8.68	8.69	7.3
7.4	8.69	8.70	8.71	8.71	8.72	8.72	8.73	8.73	8.74	8.75	7.4
7.5	8.75	8.76	8.76	8.77	8.78	8.78	8.79	8.79	8.80	8.80	7.5
7.6	8.81	8.82	8.82	8.83	8.83	8.84	8.84	8.85	8.86	8.86	7.6
7.7	8.87	8.87	8.88	8.88	8.89	8.90	8.90	8.91	8.91	8.92	7.7
7.8	8.92	8.93	8.93	8.94	8.95	8.95	8.96	8.96	8.97	8.97	7.8
7.9	8.98	8.98	8.99	9.00	9.00	9.01	9.01	9.02	9.02	9.03	7.9
8.0	9.03	9.04	9.04	9.05	9.06	9.06	9.07	9.07	9.08	9.08	8.0
8.1	9.09	9.09	9.10	9.10	9.11	9.11	9.12	9.12	9.13	9.14	8.1
8.2	9.14	9.15	9.15	9.16	9.16	9.17	9.18	9.18	9.19	9.19	8.2
8.3	9.19	9.20	9.20	9.21	9.21	9.22	9.22	9.23	9.23	9.24	8.3
8.4	9.25	9.25	9.26	9.26	9.27	9.27	9.28	9.28	9.29	9.29	8.4
8.5	9.30	9.30	9.31	9.31	9.32	9.32	9.33	9.33	9.34	9.34	8.5
8.6	9.35	9.35	9.36	9.36	9.37	9.37	9.38	9.38	9.39	9.39	8.6
8.7	9.40	9.40	9.41	9.41	9.42	9.42	9.43	9.43	9.44	9.44	8.7
8.8	9.45	9.45	9.46	9.46	9.47	9.47	9.47	9.48	9.49	9.49	8.8
8.9	9.50	9.50	9.51	9.51	9.52	9.52	9.53	9.53	9.53	9.54	8.9
9.0	9.54	9.55	9.55	9.56	9.56	9.57	9.57	9.58	9.58	9.59	9.0
9.1	9.59	9.60	9.60	9.61	9.61	9.62	9.62	9.63	9.63	9.64	9.1
9.2	9.64	9.65	9.65	9.65	9.66	9.66	9.67	9.67	9.68	9.68	9.2
9.3	9.69	9.69	9.70	9.70	9.71	9.71	9.72	9.72	9.72	9.73	9.3
9.4	9.73	9.74	9.74	9.75	9.75	9.76	9.76	9.77	9.77	9.78	9.4
9.5	9.78	9.78	9.79	9.79	9.80	9.80	9.81	9.81	9.82	9.82	9.5
9.6	9.83	9.83	9.83	9.84	9.84	9.85	9.85	9.86	9.86	9.87	9.6
9.7	9.87	9.87	9.88	9.88	9.89	9.89	9.90	9.90	9.91	9.91	9.7
9.8	9.91	9.92	9.92	9.93	9.93	9.94	9.94	9.95	9.95	9.95	9.8
9.9	9.96	9.96	9.97	9.97	9.98	9.98	9.99	9.99	9.99	10.00	9.9
10.0	10.00	10.05	10.09	10.13	10.17	10.21	10.26	10.30	10.34	10.38	10.0
P_2/P_1	.....	0.01	0.02	0.03	0.04	0.05	0.06	0.07	0.08	0.09	P_2/P_1

To add to range multiply $P_2/P_1 \times 10$ and add 10 to TU.

TABLE XVII.—AMPLIFICATION RELATION OF VOLTAGE RATIO E_2/E_1 TO TU (db)

E_2/E_1	.....	0.01	0.02	0.03	0.04	0.05	0.06	0.07	0.08	0.09	E_2/E_1
1.0	.....	0.09	0.17	0.26	0.34	0.42	0.51	0.59	0.67	0.75	1.0
1.1	0.83	0.91	0.98	1.06	1.14	1.21	1.29	1.36	1.44	1.51	1.1
1.2	1.58	1.66	1.73	1.80	1.87	1.94	2.01	2.08	2.14	2.21	1.2
1.3	2.27	2.34	2.41	2.48	2.54	2.61	2.67	2.73	2.80	2.86	1.3
1.4	2.93	2.98	3.05	3.11	3.17	3.23	3.29	3.35	3.41	3.46	1.4
1.5	3.52	3.58	3.64	3.69	3.75	3.81	3.86	3.92	3.97	4.03	1.5
1.6	4.08	4.14	4.19	4.24	4.30	4.35	4.40	4.45	4.51	4.56	1.6
1.7	4.61	4.66	4.71	4.76	4.81	4.86	4.91	4.96	5.01	5.06	1.7
1.8	5.11	5.15	5.20	5.25	5.30	5.34	5.39	5.44	5.48	5.53	1.8
1.9	5.58	5.62	5.67	5.71	5.76	5.80	5.84	5.89	5.93	5.98	1.9
2.0	6.02	6.06	6.11	6.15	6.19	6.24	6.28	6.32	6.36	6.40	2.0
2.1	6.44	6.49	6.53	6.57	6.61	6.65	6.69	6.73	6.77	6.81	2.1
2.2	6.85	6.89	6.93	6.97	7.00	7.04	7.08	7.12	7.16	7.20	2.2
2.3	7.23	7.27	7.31	7.35	7.38	7.42	7.46	7.50	7.53	7.57	2.3
2.4	7.60	7.64	7.68	7.71	7.75	7.78	7.82	7.85	7.89	7.92	2.4
2.5	7.96	7.99	8.03	8.06	8.10	8.13	8.16	8.20	8.23	8.27	2.5
2.6	8.30	8.33	8.37	8.40	8.43	8.46	8.50	8.53	8.56	8.60	2.6
2.7	8.63	8.66	8.69	8.72	8.76	8.79	8.82	8.85	8.88	8.91	2.7
2.8	8.94	8.97	9.00	9.04	9.07	9.10	9.13	9.16	9.19	9.22	2.8
2.9	9.25	9.28	9.31	9.34	9.37	9.40	9.43	9.46	9.48	9.51	2.9
3.0	9.54	9.57	9.60	9.63	9.66	9.69	9.71	9.74	9.77	9.80	3.0
3.1	9.83	9.86	9.89	9.91	9.94	9.97	9.99	10.02	10.05	10.08	3.1
3.2	10.10	10.13	10.16	10.19	10.21	10.24	10.26	10.29	10.31	10.34	3.2
3.3	10.37	10.40	10.43	10.45	10.48	10.50	10.53	10.55	10.58	10.60	3.3
3.4	10.63	10.66	10.68	10.71	10.73	10.76	10.78	10.81	10.83	10.86	3.4
3.5	10.88	10.91	10.93	10.96	10.98	11.00	11.03	11.05	11.08	11.10	3.5
3.6	11.13	11.15	11.18	11.20	11.22	11.25	11.27	11.29	11.32	11.34	3.6
3.7	11.36	11.39	11.41	11.43	11.46	11.48	11.50	11.53	11.55	11.57	3.7
3.8	11.60	11.62	11.64	11.66	11.69	11.71	11.73	11.75	11.78	11.80	3.8
3.9	11.82	11.84	11.86	11.89	11.91	11.93	11.95	11.97	12.00	12.02	3.9
4.0	12.04	12.06	12.08	12.11	12.13	12.15	12.17	12.19	12.21	12.23	4.0
4.1	12.26	12.28	12.30	12.32	12.34	12.36	12.38	12.40	12.42	12.44	4.1
4.2	12.47	12.49	12.51	12.53	12.55	12.57	12.59	12.61	12.63	12.65	4.2
4.3	12.67	12.69	12.71	12.73	12.75	12.77	12.79	12.81	12.83	12.85	4.3
4.4	12.87	12.89	12.91	12.93	12.95	12.97	12.99	13.01	13.02	13.05	4.4
4.5	13.06	13.08	13.10	13.12	13.14	13.16	13.18	13.20	13.21	13.23	4.5
4.6	13.26	13.27	13.29	13.31	13.33	13.35	13.37	13.39	13.41	13.42	4.6
4.7	13.44	13.46	13.48	13.50	13.52	13.53	13.55	13.57	13.59	13.61	4.7
4.8	13.62	13.64	13.66	13.68	13.70	13.72	13.73	13.75	13.77	13.79	4.8
4.9	13.80	13.82	13.84	13.86	13.88	13.90	13.91	13.93	13.95	13.97	4.9
5.0	13.98	14.00	14.01	14.03	14.05	14.07	14.08	14.10	14.12	14.13	5.0
5.1	14.15	14.17	14.19	14.20	14.22	14.24	14.25	14.27	14.29	14.30	5.1
5.2	14.32	14.34	14.36	14.37	14.39	14.40	14.41	14.44	14.45	14.46	5.2
5.3	14.49	14.50	14.52	14.54	14.55	14.57	14.58	14.60	14.62	14.63	5.3
5.4	14.65	14.66	14.68	14.70	14.71	14.73	14.74	14.76	14.78	14.79	5.4
E_2/E_1	.....	0.01	0.02	0.03	0.04	0.05	0.06	0.07	0.08	0.09	E_2/E_1

TABLE XVII.—AMPLIFICATION RELATION OF VOLTAGE RATIO E_2/E_1 TO TU (db).
—(Continued)

E_2/E_1	.....	0.01	0.02	0.03	0.04	0.05	0.06	0.07	0.08	0.09	E_2/E_1
5.5	14.81	14.82	14.84	14.85	14.87	14.89	14.90	14.92	14.94	14.95	5.5
5.6	14.96	14.98	14.99	15.01	15.03	15.04	15.06	15.07	15.09	15.11	5.6
5.7	15.12	15.13	15.15	15.16	15.18	15.19	15.21	15.23	15.24	15.25	5.7
5.8	15.27	15.28	15.30	15.31	15.33	15.34	15.36	15.37	15.39	15.40	5.8
5.9	15.42	15.43	15.45	15.46	15.48	15.49	15.51	15.52	15.53	15.55	5.9
6.0	15.56	15.58	15.59	15.61	15.62	15.63	15.65	15.66	15.68	15.69	6.0
6.1	15.71	15.72	15.73	15.75	15.76	15.78	15.79	15.81	15.82	15.83	6.1
6.2	15.85	15.86	15.87	15.89	15.90	15.92	15.93	15.95	15.96	15.97	6.2
6.3	15.99	16.00	16.01	16.03	16.04	16.05	16.07	16.08	16.10	16.11	6.3
6.4	16.12	16.14	16.15	16.16	16.18	16.19	16.21	16.22	16.23	16.25	6.4
6.5	16.26	16.27	16.28	16.29	16.31	16.32	16.34	16.35	16.36	16.38	6.5
6.6	16.39	16.40	16.41	16.43	16.44	16.46	16.47	16.48	16.49	16.51	6.6
6.7	16.52	16.53	16.55	16.56	16.57	16.59	16.60	16.61	16.62	16.64	6.7
6.8	16.65	16.66	16.68	16.69	16.70	16.71	16.73	16.74	16.75	16.76	6.8
6.9	16.78	16.79	16.80	16.81	16.83	16.84	16.85	16.86	16.87	16.89	6.9
7.0	16.90	16.91	16.93	16.94	16.95	16.96	16.98	16.99	17.00	17.01	7.0
7.1	17.03	17.04	17.05	17.06	17.07	17.09	17.10	17.11	17.12	17.13	7.1
7.2	17.15	17.16	17.17	17.18	17.19	17.21	17.22	17.23	17.24	17.25	7.2
7.3	17.27	17.28	17.29	17.30	17.31	17.33	17.34	17.35	17.36	17.37	7.3
7.4	17.38	17.40	17.41	17.42	17.43	17.44	17.45	17.46	17.48	17.49	7.4
7.5	17.50	17.51	17.52	17.54	17.55	17.56	17.57	17.58	17.59	17.60	7.5
7.6	17.62	17.63	17.64	17.65	17.66	17.67	17.68	17.70	17.71	17.72	7.6
7.7	17.73	17.74	17.75	17.76	17.77	17.79	17.80	17.81	17.82	17.83	7.7
7.8	17.84	17.85	17.86	17.87	17.89	17.90	17.91	17.92	17.93	17.94	7.8
7.9	17.95	17.96	17.97	17.99	18.00	18.01	18.02	18.03	18.04	18.05	7.9
8.0	18.06	18.07	18.08	18.09	18.11	18.12	18.13	18.14	18.15	18.16	8.0
8.1	18.17	18.18	18.19	18.20	18.21	18.22	18.23	18.24	18.25	18.27	8.1
8.2	18.28	18.29	18.30	18.31	18.32	18.33	18.34	18.35	18.36	18.37	8.2
8.3	18.38	18.39	18.40	18.41	18.42	18.43	18.44	18.45	18.46	18.47	8.3
8.4	18.49	18.50	18.51	18.52	18.53	18.54	18.55	18.56	18.57	18.58	8.4
8.5	18.59	18.60	18.61	18.62	18.63	18.64	18.65	18.66	18.67	18.68	8.5
8.6	18.69	18.70	18.71	18.72	18.73	18.74	18.75	18.76	18.77	18.78	8.6
8.7	18.79	18.80	18.81	18.82	18.83	18.84	18.85	18.86	18.87	18.88	8.7
8.8	18.89	18.90	18.91	18.92	18.93	18.94	18.95	18.96	18.97	18.98	8.8
8.9	18.99	19.00	19.01	19.02	19.03	19.04	19.05	19.06	19.06	19.07	8.9
9.0	19.08	19.09	19.10	19.11	19.12	19.13	19.14	19.15	19.16	19.17	9.0
9.1	19.18	19.19	19.20	19.21	19.22	19.23	19.24	19.25	19.26	19.27	9.1
9.2	19.28	19.29	19.29	19.30	19.31	19.32	19.33	19.34	19.35	19.36	9.2
9.3	19.37	19.38	19.39	19.40	19.41	19.42	19.43	19.43	19.44	19.45	9.3
9.4	19.46	19.47	19.48	19.49	19.50	19.51	19.52	19.53	19.54	19.55	9.4
9.5	19.55	19.56	19.57	19.58	19.59	19.60	19.61	19.62	19.63	19.64	9.5
9.6	19.65	19.65	19.66	19.67	19.68	19.69	19.70	19.71	19.72	19.73	9.6
9.7	19.74	19.74	19.75	19.76	19.77	19.78	19.79	19.80	19.81	19.82	9.7
9.8	19.82	19.83	19.84	19.85	19.86	19.87	19.88	19.89	19.90	19.90	9.8
9.9	19.91	19.92	19.93	19.94	19.95	19.96	19.97	19.97	19.98	19.99	9.9
10.0	20.00	20.09	20.17	20.26	20.35	20.42	20.51	20.59	20.67	20.75	10.0
E_2/E_1	.....	0.01	0.02	0.03	0.04	0.05	0.06	0.07	0.08	0.09	E_2/E_1

To add to range multiply $E_2/E_1 \times 10$ and add 20 to TU.   (Numerical example, page 343.)

Table XVIII.—Kilocycles per Second and Wave Length in Meters

The columns can be interchanged so that, for instance, 10-m wave length gives 29,982 kc/sec and 10 kc/sec gives 29,982 m for wave length

kc/sec or m	m or kc/sec	kc/sec or m	m or kc/sec	kc/sec or m	m or kc/sec	kc/sec or m	m or kc/sec	kc/sec or m	m or kc/sec
10	29,982	460	651.8	910	329.5	1,360	220.4	1,810	165.6
20	14,991	470	637.9	920	325.9	1,370	218.8	1,820	164.7
30	9,994	480	624.6	930	322.4	1,380	217.3	1,830	163.8
40	7,496	490	611.9	940	319.0	1,390	215.7	1,840	162.9
50	5,996	500	599.6	950	315.6	1,400	214.2	1,850	162.1
60	4,997	510	587.9	960	312.3	1,410	212.6	1,860	161.2
70	4,283	520	576.6	970	309.1	1,420	211.1	1,870	160.3
80	3,748	530	565.7	980	303.9	1,430	209.7	1,880	159.5
90	3,331	540	555.2	990	302.8	1,440	208.2	1,890	158.6
100	2,998	550	545.1	1,000	299.8	1,450	206.8	1,900	157.8
110	2,726	560	535.4	1,010	296.9	1,460	205.4	1,910	157.0
120	2,499	570	526.0	1,020	293.9	1,470	204.0	1,920	156.2
130	2,306	580	516.9	1,030	291.1	1,480	202.6	1,930	155.3
140	2,142	590	508.2	1,040	288.3	1,490	201.2	1,940	154.5
150	1,999	600	499.7	1,050	285.5	1,500	199.9	1,950	153.8
160	1,874	610	491.5	1,060	282.8	1,510	198.6	1,960	153.0
170	1,764	620	483.6	1,070	280.2	1,520	197.2	1,970	152.2
180	1,666	630	475.9	1,080	277.6	1,530	196.0	1,980	151.4
190	1,578	640	468.5	1,090	275.1	1,540	194.7	1,990	150.7
200	1,499	650	461.3	1,100	272.6	1,550	193.4	2,000	149.9
210	1,428	660	454.3	1,110	270.1	1,560	192.2	2,010	149.2
220	1,363	670	447.5	1,120	267.7	1,570	191.0	2,020	148.4
230	1,304	680	440.9	1,130	265.3	1,580	189.8	2,030	147.7
240	1,249	690	434.5	1,140	263.0	1,590	188.6	2,040	147.0
250	1,199	700	428.3	1,150	260.7	1,600	187.4	2,050	146.3
260	1,153	710	422.3	1,160	258.5	1,610	186.2	2,060	145.5
270	1,110	720	416.4	1,170	256.3	1,620	185.1	2,070	144.8
280	1,071	730	410.7	1,180	254.1	1,630	183.9	2,080	144.1
290	1,034	740	405.2	1,190	252.0	1,640	182.8	2,090	143.5
300	999.4	750	399.8	1,200	249.9	1,650	181.7	2,100	142.8
310	967.2	760	394.5	1,210	247.8	1,660	180.6	2,110	142.1
320	936.9	770	389.4	1,220	245.8	1,670	179.5	2,120	141.4
330	908.6	780	384.4	1,230	243.8	1,680	178.5	2,130	140.8
340	881.8	790	379.5	1,240	241.8	1,690	177.4	2,140	140.1
350	856.6	800	374.8	1,250	239.9	1,700	176.4	2,150	139.5
360	832.8	810	370.2	1,260	238.0	1,710	175.3	2,160	138.8
370	810.3	820	365.6	1,270	236.1	1,720	174.3	2,170	138.1
380	789.0	830	361.2	1,280	234.2	1,730	173.3	2,180	137.5
390	768.8	840	356.9	1,290	232.4	1,740	172.3	2,190	136.9
400	749.6	850	352.7	1,300	230.6	1,750	171.3	2,200	136.3
410	731.3	860	348.6	1,310	228.9	1,760	170.4	2,210	135.7
420	713.9	870	344.6	1,320	227.1	1,770	169.4	2,220	135.1
430	697.3	880	340.7	1,330	225.4	1,780	168.4	2,230	134.4
440	681.4	890	336.9	1,340	223.7	1,790	167.5	2,240	133.8
450	666.3	900	333.1	1,350	222.1	1,800	166.6	2,250	133.3

TABLE XVIII.—KILOCYCLES PER SECOND AND WAVE LENGTH IN METERS.—
(Continued)

kc/sec or m	m or kc/sec	kc/sec or m	m or kc/sec	kc/sec or m	m or kc/sec	kc/sec or m	m or kc/sec	kc/sec or m	m or kc/sec
2,260	132.7	2,710	110.6	3,160	94.88	3,610	83.05	4,060	73.85
2,270	132.1	2,720	110.2	3,170	94.58	3,620	82.82	4,070	73.67
2,280	131.5	2,730	109.8	3,180	94.28	3,630	82.60	4,080	73.49
2,290	130.9	2,740	109.4	3,190	93.99	3,640	82.37	4,090	73.31
2,300	130.4	2,750	109.0	3,200	93.69	3,650	82.14	4,100	73.13
2,310	129.8	2,760	108.6	3,210	93.40	3,660	81.92	4,110	72.95
2,320	129.2	2,770	108.2	3,220	93.11	3,670	81.70	4,120	72.77
2,330	128.7	2,780	107.8	3,230	92.82	3,680	81.47	4,130	72.60
2,340	128.1	2,790	107.5	3,240	92.54	3,690	81.25	4,140	72.42
2,350	127.6	2,800	107.1	3,250	92.25	3,700	81.03	4,150	72.25
2,360	127.0	2,810	106.7	3,260	91.97	3,710	80.81	4,160	72.07
2,370	126.5	2,820	106.3	3,270	91.69	3,720	80.60	4,170	71.90
2,380	126.0	2,830	105.9	3,280	91.41	3,730	80.38	4,180	71.73
2,390	125.4	2,840	105.6	3,290	91.13	3,740	80.17	4,190	71.56
2,400	124.9	2,850	105.2	3,300	90.86	3,750	79.95	4,200	71.39
2,410	124.4	2,860	104.8	3,310	90.58	3,760	79.74	4,210	71.22
2,420	123.9	2,870	104.5	3,320	90.31	3,770	79.53	4,220	71.05
2,430	123.4	2,880	104.1	3,330	90.04	3,780	79.32	4,230	70.88
2,440	122.9	2,890	103.7	3,340	89.77	3,790	79.11	4,240	70.71
2,450	122.4	2,900	103.4	3,350	89.50	3,800	78.90	4,250	70.55
2,460	121.9	2,910	103.0	3,360	89.23	3,810	78.69	4,260	70.38
2,470	121.4	2,920	102.7	3,370	88.97	3,820	78.49	4,270	70.22
2,480	120.9	2,930	102.3	3,380	88.70	3,830	78.28	4,280	70.05
2,490	120.4	2,940	102.0	3,390	88.44	3,840	78.08	4,290	69.89
2,500	119.9	2,950	101.6	3,400	88.18	3,850	77.88	4,300	69.73
2,510	119.5	2,960	101.3	3,410	87.92	3,860	77.67	4,310	69.56
2,520	119.0	2,970	100.9	3,420	87.67	3,870	77.47	4,320	69.40
2,530	118.5	2,980	100.6	3,430	87.41	3,880	77.27	4,330	69.24
2,540	118.0	2,990	100.3	3,440	87.16	3,890	77.07	4,340	69.08
2,550	117.6	3,000	99.94	3,450	86.90	3,900	76.88	4,350	68.92
2,560	117.1	3,010	99.61	3,460	86.65	3,910	76.68	4,360	68.77
2,570	116.7	3,020	99.28	3,470	86.40	3,920	76.48	4,370	68.61
2,580	116.2	3,030	98.95	3,480	86.16	3,930	76.29	4,380	68.45
2,590	115.8	3,040	98.62	3,490	85.91	3,940	76.10	4,390	68.30
2,600	115.3	3,050	98.30	3,500	85.66	3,950	75.90	4,400	68.14
2,610	114.9	3,060	97.98	3,510	85.42	3,960	75.71	4,410	67.99
2,620	114.4	3,070	97.66	3,520	85.18	3,970	75.52	4,420	67.83
2,630	114.0	3,080	97.34	3,530	84.94	3,980	75.33	4,430	67.68
2,640	113.6	3,090	97.03	3,540	84.70	3,990	75.14	4,440	67.53
2,650	113.1	3,100	96.72	3,550	84.46	4,000	74.96	4,450	67.38
2,660	112.7	3,110	96.41	3,560	84.22	4,010	74.77	4,460	67.22
2,670	112.3	3,120	96.10	3,570	83.98	4,020	74.58	4,470	67.07
2,680	111.9	3,130	95.79	3,580	83.75	4,030	74.40	4,480	66.92
2,690	111.5	3,140	95.48	3,590	83.52	4,040	74.21	4,490	66.78
2,700	111.0	3,150	95.18	3,600	83.28	4,050	74.03	4,500	66.63

TABLE XVIII.—KILOCYCLES PER SECOND AND WAVE LENGTH IN METERS.— *(Continued)*

kc/sec or m	m or kc/sec	kc/sec or m	m or kc/sec	kc/sec or m	m or kc/sec	kc/sec or m	m or kc/sec	kc/sec or m	m or kc/sec
4,510	66.48	4,960	60.45	5,410	55.42	5,860	51.16	6,310	47.52
4,520	66.33	4,970	60.33	5,420	55.32	5,870	51.08	6,320	47.44
4,530	66.19	4,980	60.20	5,430	55.22	5,880	50.99	6,330	47.36
4,540	66.04	4,990	60.08	5,440	55.11	5,890	50.90	6,340	47.29
4,550	65.89	5,000	59.96	5,450	55.01	5,900	50.82	6,350	47.22
4,560	65.75	5,010	59.84	5,460	54.91	5,910	50.73	6,360	47.14
4,570	65.61	5,020	59.73	5,470	54.81	5,920	50.65	6,370	47.07
4,580	65.46	5,030	59.61	5,480	54.71	5,930	50.56	6,380	46.99
4,590	65.32	5,040	59.49	5,490	54.61	5,940	50.47	6,390	46.92
4,600	65.18	5,050	59.37	5,500	54.51	5,950	50.39	6,400	46.85
4,610	65.04	5,060	59.25	5,510	54.41	5,960	50.31	6,410	46.77
4,620	64.90	5,070	59.13	5,520	54.32	5,970	50.22	6,420	46.70
4,630	64.76	5,080	59.02	5,530	54.22	5,980	50.14	6,430	46.63
4,640	64.62	5,090	58.90	5,540	54.12	5,990	50.05	6,440	46.56
4,650	64.48	5,100	58.79	5,550	54.02	6,000	49.97	6,450	46.48
4,660	64.34	5,110	58.67	5,560	53.92	6,010	49.89	6,460	46.41
4,670	64.20	5,120	58.56	5,570	53.83	6,020	49.80	6,470	46.34
4,680	64.06	5,130	58.44	5,580	53.73	6,030	49.72	6,480	46.27
4,690	63.93	5,140	58.33	5,590	53.64	6,040	49.64	6,490	46.20
4,700	63.79	5,150	58.22	5,600	53.54	6,050	49.56	6,500	46.13
4,710	63.66	5,160	58.10	5,610	53.44	6,060	49.48	6,510	46.06
4,720	63.52	5,170	57.99	5,620	53.35	6,070	49.39	6,520	45.98
4,730	63.39	5,180	57.88	5,630	53.25	6,080	49.31	6,530	45.91
4,740	63.25	5,190	57.77	5,640	53.16	6,090	49.23	6,540	45.84
4,750	63.12	5,200	57.66	5,650	53.07	6,100	49.15	6,550	45.77
4,760	62.99	5,210	57.55	5,660	52.97	6,110	49.07	6,560	45.70
4,770	62.86	5,220	57.44	5,670	52.88	6,120	48.99	6,570	45.63
4,780	62.72	5,230	57.33	5,680	52.79	6,130	48.91	6,580	45.57
4,790	62.59	5,240	57.22	5,690	52.69	6,140	48.83	6,590	45.50
4,800	62.46	5,250	57.11	5,700	52.60	6,150	48.75	6,600	45.43
4,810	62.33	5,260	57.00	5,710	52.51	6,160	48.67	6,610	45.36
4,820	62.20	5,270	56.89	5,720	52.42	6,170	48.59	6,620	45.29
4,830	62.07	5,280	56.78	5,730	52.32	6,180	48.51	6,630	45.22
4,840	61.95	5,290	56.68	5,740	52.23	6,190	48.44	6,640	45.15
4,850	61.82	5,300	56.57	5,750	52.14	6,200	48.36	6,650	45.09
4,860	61.69	5,310	56.46	5,760	52.05	6,210	48.28	6,660	45.02
4,870	61.56	5,320	56.36	5,770	51.96	6,220	48.20	6,670	44.95
4,880	61.44	5,330	56.25	5,780	51.87	6,230	48.13	6,680	44.88
4,890	61.31	5,340	56.15	5,790	51.78	6,240	48.05	6,690	44.82
4,900	61.19	5,350	56.04	5,800	51.69	6,250	47.97	6,700	44.75
4,910	61.06	5,360	55.94	5,810	51.60	6,260	47.89	6,710	44.68
4,920	60.94	5,370	55.83	5,820	51.52	6,270	47.82	6,720	44.62
4,930	60.82	5,380	55.73	5,830	51.43	6,280	47.74	6,730	44.55
4,940	60.69	5,390	55.63	5,840	51.34	6,290	47.67	6,740	44.48
4,950	60.57	5,400	55.52	5,850	51.25	6,300	47.59	6,750	44.42

TABLE XVIII.—KILOCYCLES PER SECOND AND WAVE LENGTH IN METERS.— (*Continued*)

kc/sec or m	m or kc/sec	kc/sec or m	m or kc/sec	kc/sec or m	m or kc/sec	kc/sec or m	m or kc/sec	kc/sec or m	m or kc/sec
6,760	44.35	7,210	41.58	7,660	39.14	8,110	36.97	8,560	35.03
6,770	44.29	7,220	41.53	7,670	39.09	8,120	36.92	8,570	34.98
6,780	44.22	7,230	41.47	7,680	39.04	8,130	36.88	8,580	34.94
6,790	44.16	7,240	41.41	7,690	38.99	8,140	36.83	8,590	34.90
6,800	44.09	7,250	41.35	7,700	38.94	8,150	36.79	8,600	34.86
6,810	44.03	7,260	41.30	7,710	38.89	8,160	36.74	8,610	34.82
6,820	43.96	7,270	41.24	7,720	38.84	8,170	36.70	8,620	34.78
6,830	43.90	7,280	41.18	7,730	38.79	8,180	36.65	8,630	34.74
6,840	43.83	7,290	41.13	7,740	38.74	8,190	36.61	8,640	34.70
6,850	43.77	7,300	41.07	7,750	38.69	8,200	36.56	8,650	34.66
6,860	43.71	7,310	41.02	7,760	38.64	8,210	36.52	8,660	34.62
6,870	43.64	7,320	40.96	7,770	38.59	8,220	36.47	8,670	34.58
6,880	43.58	7,330	40.90	7,780	38.54	8,230	36.43	8,680	34.54
6,890	43.52	7,340	40.85	7,790	38.49	8,240	36.39	8,690	34.50
6,900	43.45	7,350	40.79	7,800	38.44	8,250	36.34	8,700	34.46
6,910	43.39	7,360	40.74	7,810	38.39	8,260	36.30	8,710	34.42
6,920	43.33	7,370	40.68	7,820	38.34	8,270	36.25	8,720	34.38
6,930	43.26	7,380	40.63	7,830	38.29	8,280	36.21	8,730	34.34
6,940	43.20	7,390	40.57	7,840	38.24	8,290	36.17	8,740	34.30
6,950	43.14	7,400	40.52	7,850	38.19	8,300	36.12	8,750	34.27
6,960	43.08	7,410	40.46	7,860	38.14	8,310	36.08	8,760	34.23
6,970	43.02	7,420	40.41	7,870	38.10	8,320	36.04	8,770	34.19
6,980	42.95	7,430	40.35	7,880	38.05	8,330	35.99	8,780	34.15
6,990	42.89	7,440	40.30	7,890	38.00	8,340	35.95	8,790	34.11
7,000	42.83	7,450	40.24	7,900	37.95	8,350	35.91	8,800	34.07
7,010	42.77	7,460	40.19	7,910	37.90	8,360	35.86	8,810	34.03
7,020	42.71	7,470	40.14	7,920	37.86	8,370	35.82	8,820	33.99
7,030	42.65	7,480	40.08	7,930	37.81	8,380	35.78	8,830	33.95
7,040	42.59	7,490	40.03	7,940	37.76	8,390	35.74	8,840	33.92
7,050	42.53	7,500	39.98	7,950	37.71	8,400	35.69	8,850	33.88
7,060	42.47	7,510	39.92	7,960	37.67	8,410	35.65	8,860	33.84
7,070	42.41	7,520	39.87	7,970	37.62	8,420	35.61	8,870	33.80
7,080	42.35	7,530	39.82	7,980	37.57	8,430	35.57	8,880	33.76
7,090	42.29	7,540	39.76	7,990	37.52	8,440	35.52	8,890	33.73
7,100	42.23	7,550	39.71	8,000	37.48	8,450	35.48	8,900	33.69
7,110	42.17	7,560	39.66	8,010	37.43	8,460	35.44	8,910	33.65
7,120	42.11	7,570	39.61	8,020	37.38	8,470	35.40	8,920	33.61
7,130	42.05	7,580	39.55	8,030	37.34	8,480	35.36	8,930	33.57
7,140	41.99	7,590	39.50	8,040	37.29	8,490	35.31	8,940	33.54
7,150	41.93	7,600	39.45	8,050	37.24	8,500	35.27	8,950	33.50
7,160	41.87	7,610	39.40	8,060	37.20	8,510	35.23	8,960	33.46
7,170	41.82	7,620	39.35	8,070	37.15	8,520	35.19	8,970	33.42
7,180	41.76	7,630	39.29	8,080	37.11	8,530	35.15	8,980	33.39
7,190	41.70	7,640	39.24	8,090	37.06	8,540	35.11	8,990	33.35
7,200	41.64	7,650	39.19	8,100	37.01	8,550	35.07	9,000	33.31

TABLE XVIII.—KILOCYCLES PER SECOND AND WAVE LENGTH IN METERS.— (*Continued*)

kc/sec or m	m or kc/sec	kc/sec or m	m or kc/sec	kc/sec or m	m or kc/sec	kc/sec or m	m or kc/sec	kc/sec or m	m or kc/sec
9,010	33.28	9,210	32.55	9,410	31.86	9,610	31.20	9,810	30.56
9,020	33.24	9,220	32.52	9,420	31.83	9,620	31.17	9,820	30.53
9,030	33.20	9,230	32.48	9,430	31.79	9,630	31.13	9,830	30.50
9,040	33.17	9,240	32.45	9,440	31.76	9,640	31.10	9,840	30.47
9,050	33.13	9,250	32.41	9,450	31.73	9,650	31.07	9,850	30.44
9,060	33.09	9,260	32.38	9,460	31.69	9,660	31.04	9,860	30.41
9,070	33.06	9,270	32.34	9,470	31.66	9,670	31.01	9,870	30.38
9,080	33.02	9,280	32.31	9,480	31.63	9,680	30.97	9,880	30.35
9,090	32.98	9,290	32.27	9,490	31.59	9,690	30.94	9,890	30.32
9,100	32.95	9,300	32.24	9,500	31.56	9,700	30.91	9,900	30.28
9,110	32.91	9,310	32.20	9,510	31.53	9,710	30.88	9,910	30.25
9,120	32.88	9,320	32.17	9,520	31.49	9,720	30.85	9,920	30.22
9,130	32.84	9,330	32.14	9,530	31.46	9,730	30.81	9,930	30.19
9,140	32.80	9,340	32.10	9,540	31.43	9,740	30.78	9,940	30.16
9,150	32.77	9,350	32.07	9,550	31.39	9,750	30.75	9,950	30.13
9,160	32.73	9,360	32.03	9,560	31.36	9,760	30.72	9,960	30.10
9,170	32.70	9,370	32.00	9,570	31.33	9,770	30.69	9,970	30.07
9,180	32.66	9,380	31.96	9,580	31.30	9,780	30.66	9,980	30.04
9,190	32.62	9,390	31.93	9,590	31.26	9,790	30.63	9,990	30.01
9,200	32.59	9,400	31.90	9,600	31.23	9,800	30.59	10,000	29.98

TABLE XIX.—For Wave Length, Frequency and Oscillation Constant

λ = wave length in m
λ^2 = wave length squared
f = cycles per second
CL = oscillation constant
C = capacitance in microfarad
L = inductance in centimeters (1000 cm = 1μh)

λ	λ^2	f	$\sqrt{LC}$	LC
100	10,000	3,000,000	1.68	2.82
110	12,100	2,727,272	1.80	3.24
120	14,400	2,500,000	2.02	4.08
130	16,900	2,307,600	2.18	4.75
140	19,600	2,142,600	2.35	5.52
150	22,500	2,000,000	2.52	6.35
160	25,600	1,874,800	2.68	7.16
170	28,900	1,764,600	2.85	8.12
180	32,400	1,666,600	3.02	9.12
190	36,100	1,578,800	3.19	10.17
200	40,000	1,500,000	3.36	11.29
210	44,100	1,428,400	3.52	12.39
220	48,400	1,363,500	3.69	13.62
230	52,900	1,304,200	3.86	14.90
240	57,600	1,250,000	4.03	16.24
250	62,500	1,200,000	4.19	17.55
260	67,600	1,153,800	4.36	19.01
270	72,900	1,111,000	4.53	20.52
280	78,400	1,071,300	4.70	22.09
290	84,100	1,034,300	4.87	23.72
300	90,000	1,000,000	5.03	25.30
310	96,100	967,700	5.20	27.04
320	102,400	937,400	5.37	28.84
330	108,900	909,100	5.54	30.69
340	115,600	882,300	5.70	32.49
350	122,500	857,100	5.87	34.46
360	129,600	833,300	6.04	36.48
370	136,900	810,800	6.21	38.56
380	144,400	789,400	6.38	40.71
390	152,100	769,200	6.54	42.77
400	160,000	750,000	6.71	45.03
410	168,100	731,700	6.88	47.33
420	176,400	714,300	7.05	49.70
430	184,900	697,700	7.21	51.98
440	193,600	681,800	7.38	54.46
450	202,500	666,700	7.55	57.00
460	211,600	652,200	7.72	59.60
470	220,900	638,300	7.89	62.25

TABLE XIX.—For Wave Length, Frequency and Oscillation Constant.—
(*Continued*)

λ	λ²	f	√LC	LC
480	230,400	625,000	8.05	64.80
490	240,100	612,200	8.22	67.57
500	250,000	600,000	8.39	70.39
510	260,100	588,200	8.56	73.27
520	270,400	576,900	8.72	76.04
530	280,900	566,000	8.89	79.03
540	291,600	555,600	9.06	82.08
550	302,500	545,400	9.23	85.19
560	313,600	535,700	9.40	88.36
570	324,900	526,300	9.56	91.39
580	336,400	517,200	9.73	94.67
590	348,100	508,500	9.90	98.01
600	360,000	500,000	10.07	101.41
610	372,100	491,800	10.23	104.65
620	384,400	483,900	10.40	108.15
630	396,900	476,200	10.57	111.73
640	409,600	486,800	10.74	115.35
650	422,500	461,500	10.90	118.81
660	435,600	454,600	11.07	122.54
670	448,900	447,800	11.24	126.34
680	462,400	441,200	11.41	130.19
690	476,100	434,800	11.58	134.10
700	490,000	428,600	11.74	137.83
710	504,100	422,500	11.91	141.86
720	518,400	416,700	12.08	145.93
730	532,900	411,000	12.25	150.07
740	547,600	405,400	12.41	154.01
750	562,500	400,000	12.58	158.27
760	577,600	394,800	12.75	162.57
770	592,900	389,600	12.92	166.83
780	608,400	384,600	13.09	171.35
790	624,100	379,800	13.25	175.57
800	640,000	375,000	13.42	180.10
810	656,100	370,400	13.59	184.69
820	672,400	365,900	13.76	189.33
830	688,900	361,400	13.93	194.05
840	705,600	357,100	14.09	198.53
850	722,500	352,900	14.26	203.35
860	739,600	348,800	14.43	208.24
870	756,900	344,800	14.60	213.17
880	774,400	340,900	14.76	217.86
890	792,100	337,100	14.93	222.90

TABLE XIX.—For Wave Length, Frequency and Oscillation Constant.— (*Continued*)

λ	λ^2	f	$\sqrt{LC}$	LC
900	810,000	333,300	15.10	228.01
910	828,100	329,700	15.27	233.17
920	846,400	326,100	15.43	238.09
930	864,900	322,600	15.60	243.36
940	883,600	319,100	15.77	248.70
950	902,500	315,800	15.94	254.08
960	921,600	312,500	16.11	259.53
970	940,900	309,300	16.27	264.71
980	960,400	306,100	16.44	270.38
990	980,100	303,000	16.61	275.90
1,000	1,000,000	300,000	16.78	281.57
1,010	1,020,100	297,030	16.94	287.00
1,020	1,040,400	294,120	17.11	292.70
1,030	1,060,900	291,260	17.28	298.60
1,040	1,081,600	288,450	17.45	304.50
1,050	1,102,550	285,710	17.62	310.50
1,060	1,123,600	283,010	17.78	316.10
1,070	1,144,900	280,370	17.95	322.20
1,080	1,166,400	277,780	18.12	328.30
1,090	1,188,100	275,230	18.29	334.50
1,100	1,210,000	272,730	18.45	340.40
1,110	1,232,100	270,270	18.62	346.70
1,120	1,254,400	267,850	18.79	353.10
1,130	1,276,900	265,480	18.96	359.50
1,140	1,299,600	263,150	19.13	366.00
1,150	1,322,500	260,860	19.29	372.10
1,160	1,345,600	258,610	19.46	378.70
1,170	1,368,900	256,400	19.63	385.30
1,180	1,592,400	254,230	19.80	392.10
1,190	1,416,100	252,100	19.97	398.80
1,200	1,440,000	250,000	20.13	405.20
1,210	1,464,100	247,930	20.30	412.10
1,220	1,488,400	245,900	20.47	419.00
1,230	1,512,900	243,900	20.64	426.00
1,240	1,537,600	241,930	20.80	432.60
1,250	1,562,500	240,000	20.97	439.70
1,260	1,587,600	238,090	21.14	446.90
1,270	1,612,900	236,220	21.31	454.10
1,280	1,638,400	234,370	21.47	461.00
1,290	1,664,100	232,560	21.64	468.30
1,300	1,690,000	230,760	21.81	475.70
1,310	1,716,000	229,010	21.98	483.10

TABLE XIX.—FOR WAVE LENGTH, FREQUENCY AND OSCILLATION CONSTANT.—
(Continued)

λ	λ²	f	$\sqrt{LC}$	LC
1,320	1,742,400	227,270	22.15	490.60
1,330	1,768,900	225,560	22.31	497.80
1,340	1,795,600	223,870	22.48	505.30
1,350	1,822,500	222,220	22.65	513.00
1,360	1,849,600	220,590	22.82	520.80
1,370	1,876,900	218,970	22.98	528.10
1,380	1,904,400	217,390	23.15	535.90
1,390	1,932,100	215,830	23.32	543.80
1,400	1,960,000	214,380	23.49	551.80
1,410	1,988,100	212,760	23.66	559.80
1,420	2,016,400	211,260	23.82	567.40
1,430	2,044,900	209,790	23.99	575.50
1,440	2,073,600	208,340	24.16	583.70
1,450	2,102,500	206,900	24.33	591.90
1,460	2,131,600	205,470	24.49	599.80
1,470	2,160,900	204,080	24.66	608.10
1,480	2,190,400	202,700	24.83	616.50
1,490	2,220,100	201,340	25.00	625.00
1,500	2,250,000	200,000	25.17	633.50
1,510	2,280,100	198,680	25.33	641.60
1,520	2,310,400	197,360	25.50	650.20
1,530	2,340,900	196,070	25.67	659.00
1,540	2,371,600	194,800	25.84	667.70
1,550	2,402,500	193,540	26.00	676.00
1,560	2,433,600	192,310	26.17	684.90
1,570	2,464,900	191,060	26.34	693.80
1,580	2,496,400	189,860	26.51	702.80
1,590	2,528,100	188,670	26.68	711.80
1,600	2,560,000	187,500	26.84	720.40
1,610	2,592,100	186,340	27.01	729.50
1,620	2,624,400	185,190	27.18	738.70
1,630	2,656,900	184,050	27.35	748.00
1,640	2,689,600	182,930	27.52	757.30
1,650	2,722,500	181,820	27.68	766.20
1,660	2,755,600	180,730	27.85	775.60
1,670	2,788,900	179,640	28.02	785.20
1,680	2,822,400	178,570	28.19	794.60
1,690	2,856,100	177,510	28.35	803.70
1,700	2,890,000	176,460	28.52	813.40
1,710	2,924,100	175,440	28.69	823.10
1,720	2,958,400	174,420	28.86	832.90
1,730	2,992,900	173,410	29.02	842.20

TABLE XIX.—FOR WAVE LENGTH, FREQUENCY AND OSCILLATION CONSTANT.— *(Continued)*

λ	λ^2	f	$\sqrt{LC}$	LC
1,740	3,026,600	172,410	29.19	852.00
1,750	3,062,500	171,430	29.36	862.00
1,760	3,097,600	170,450	29.53	872.00
1,770	3,132,900	169,490	29.70	882.10
1,780	3,168,400	168,540	29.86	891.60
1,790	3,204,100	167,600	30.03	901.80
1,800	3,240,000	166,670	30.20	912.00
1,810	3,276,100	165,750	30.37	922.30
1,820	3,312,400	164,840	30.54	932.70
1,830	3,348,900	163,940	30.70	942.50
1,840	3,385,600	163,040	30.87	953.00
1,850	3,422,500	162,160	31.04	963.40
1,860	3,459,600	161,290	31.21	974.10
1,870	3,496,900	160,430	31.37	984.10
1,880	3,534,400	159,370	31.54	994.80
1,890	3,572,100	158,730	31.71	1,005.60
1,900	3,610,000	157,890	31.88	1,016.40
1,910	3,648,100	157,060	32.04	1,026.60
1,920	3,686,400	156,240	32.21	1,037.50
1,930	3,724,900	155,440	32.35	1,048.50
1,940	3,763,600	154,630	32.55	1,059.90
1,950	3,802,500	153,840	32.72	1,070.60
1,960	3,841,600	153,060	32.88	1,081.10
1,970	3,880,900	152,280	33.05	1,092.30
1,980	3,920,400	151,510	33.22	1,103.50
1,990	3,960,100	150,750	33.39	1,114.90
2,000	4,000,000	150,000	33.55	1,125.60
2,010	4,040,100	149,250	33.72	1,137.10
2,020	4,080,400	148,520	33.89	1,149.60
2,030	4,120,900	147,780	34.06	1,160.10
2,040	4,166,600	147,060	34.23	1,171.70
2,050	4,202,500	146,340	34.39	1,182.70
2,060	4,243,600	145,630	34.56	1,194.40
2,070	4,284,900	144,930	34.73	1,206.20
2,080	4,326,400	144,230	34.90	1,218.00
2,090	4,368,100	143,540	35.07	1,229.80
2,100	4,410,000	142,850	35.23	1,241.20
2,110	4,452,100	142,180	35.40	1,253.20
2,120	4,494,400	141,510	35.57	1,265.30
2,130	4,536,900	140,840	35.74	1,277.40
2,140	4,579,600	140,180	35.90	1,288.90
2,150	4,622,500	139,540	36.07	1,301.10

TABLE XIX.—FOR WAVE LENGTH, FREQUENCY AND OSCILLATION CONSTANT.—
(*Continued*)

λ	λ²	f	$\sqrt{LC}$	LC
2,160	4,665,600	138,880	36.24	1,313.40
2,170	4,708,900	138,240	36.41	1,325.70
2,180	4,752,400	137,610	36.58	1,338.10
2,190	4,796,100	136,980	36.74	1,349.80
2,200	4,840,000	136,360	36.91	1,362.40
2,210	4,884,100	135,740	37.08	1,374.90
2,220	4,928,400	135,130	37.25	1,387.50
2,230	4,972,900	134,530	37.41	1,399.40
2,240	5,017,600	133,930	37.58	1,412.20
2,250	5,062,500	133,330	37.75	1,425.10
2,260	5,107,600	132,740	37.92	1,438.00
2,270	5,152,900	132,160	38.08	1,450.20
2,280	5,198,400	131,570	38.25	1,463.10
2,290	5,244,100	131,000	38.42	1,476.20
2,300	5,290,000	130,430	38.59	1,489.30
2,310	5,336,100	129,870	38.76	1,502.40
2,320	5,382,400	129,310	38.93	1,515.60
2,330	5,428,900	128,750	39.09	1,528.10
2,340	5,475,600	128,200	39.26	1,541.40
2,350	5,522,500	127,660	39.43	1,554.70
2,360	5,569,600	127,120	39.60	1,568.10
2,370	5,616,900	126,580	39.76	1,580.80
2,380	5,644,400	126,050	39.93	1,594.50
2,390	5,712,100	125,520	40.10	1,608.00
2,400	5,760,000	125,000	40.27	1,621.80
2,410	5,808,100	124,480	40.45	1,636.30
2,420	5,856,400	123,960	40.60	1,648.40
2,430	5,904,900	123,450	40.77	1,662.30
2,440	5,953,600	122,950	40.94	1,676.10
2,450	6,002,500	122,450	41.11	1,690.00
2,460	6,051,600	121,950	41.27	1,703.30
2,470	6,100,900	121,450	41.44	1,717.30
2,480	6,150,400	120,960	41.64	1,731.40
2,490	6,200,100	120,480	41.78	1,745.40
2,500	6,250,000	120,000	41.95	1,759.70
2,510	6,300,100	119,520	42.11	1,773.30
2,520	6,350,400	119,050	42.28	1,787.50
2,530	6,400,900	118,580	42.45	1,802.00
2,540	6,451,600	118,120	42.62	1,816.40
2,550	6,502,500	117,650	42.79	1,831.00
2,560	6,553,600	117,190	42.95	1,844.80
2,570	6,604,900	116,730	43.12	1,859.40

TABLE XIX.—FOR WAVE LENGTH, FREQUENCY AND OSCILLATION CONSTANT.—
(*Continued*)

λ	λ²	f	$\sqrt{LC}$	LC
2,580	6,656,400	116,280	43.29	1,874.00
2,590	6,708,100	115,830	43.46	1,888.70
2,600	6,760,000	115,380	43.62	1,902.60
2,610	6,812,100	114,940	43.79	1,917.50
2,620	6,864,400	114,510	43.96	1,932.30
2,630	6,916,800	114,070	44.13	1,947.40
2,640	6,969,600	113,640	44.29	1,961.60
2,650	7,022,500	113,210	44.46	1,976.60
2,660	7,075,600	112,780	44.63	1,991.70
2,670	7,128,900	112,360	44.80	2,007.00
2,680	7,182,400	111,940	44.97	2,022.30
2,690	7,236,100	111,530	45.13	2,036.60
2,700	7,290,000	111,110	45.30	2,052.00
2,710	7,344,100	110,700	45.47	2,067.40
2,720	7,398,400	110,290	45.64	2,083.00
2,730	7,452,900	109,890	45.80	2,097.70
2,740	7,507,600	109,490	45.97	2,113.10
2,750	7,562,500	109,090	46.14	2,128.90
2,760	7,617,600	108,700	46.31	2,144.70
2,770	7,672,900	108,300	46.47	2,159.50
2,780	7,728,400	107,920	46.64	2,175.20
2,790	7,784,100	107,530	46.81	2,191.10
2,800	7,840,000	107,140	46.98	2,207.00
2,810	7,896,100	106,760	47.15	2,223.00
2,820	7,952,400	106,380	47.32	2,239.20
2,830	8,008,900	106,010	47.48	2,254.40
2,840	8,065,600	105,630	47.65	2,270.60
2,850	8,122,500	105,260	47.82	2,286.90
2,860	8,179,600	104,890	47.99	2,303.10
2,870	8,236,900	104,530	48.15	2,318.50
2,880	8,294,400	104,170	48.32	2,334.90
2,890	8,352,100	103,810	48.49	2,351.30
2,900	8,410,000	103,450	48.66	2,366.30
2,910	8,468,100	103,090	48.83	2,384.30
2,920	8,526,400	102,740	48.99	2,399.00
2,930	8,584,900	102,390	49.16	2,416.70
2,940	8,643,600	102,040	49.33	2,433.60
2,950	8,702,500	101,700	49.50	2,450.30
2,960	8,761,600	101,350	49.66	2,466.10
2,970	8,820,900	101,010	49.83	2,483.00
2,980	8,880,400	100,660	50.00	2,500.00
2,990	8,940,100	100,320	50.17	2,517.00

TABLE XIX.—For Wave Length, Frequency and Oscillation Constant.—
(*Continued*)

λ	λ^2	f	$\sqrt{LC}$	LC
3,000	9,000,000	100,000	50.33	2,533.20
3,025	9,150,625	99,170	50.75	2,575.60
3,050	9,302,500	98,560	51.17	2,618.40
3,075	9,455,625	97,560	51.59	2,661.50
3,100	9,610,000	96,770	52.01	2,705.10
3,125	9,765,625	96,000	52.43	2,748.90
3,150	9,922,500	95,230	52.85	2,793.10
3,175	10,080,625	94,490	53.27	2,837.80
3,200	10,240,000	93,750	53.69	2,882.70
3,225	10,400,625	93,020	54.11	2,927.90
3,250	10,562,500	92,310	54.53	2,973.70
3,275	10,725,625	91,600	54.95	3,019.60
3,300	10,890,000	90,910	55.37	3,065.80
3,325	11,055,625	90,220	55.79	3,112.60
3,350	11,222,500	89,550	56.21	3,159.50
3,375	11,280,625	88,890	56.63	3,207.10
3,400	11,560,000	88,230	57.05	3,254.80
3,425	11,730,625	87,590	57.46	3,301.60
3,450	11,902,500	86,960	57.88	3,350.00
3,475	12,075,625	86,330	58.30	3,398.90
3,500	12,250,000	85,720	58.72	3,448.00
3,525	12,425,625	85,100	59.14	3,497.50
3,550	12,602,500	84,510	59.56	3,547.40
3,575	12,780,625	83,910	59.98	3,597.70
3,600	12,960,000	83,330	60.40	3,648.10
3,625	13,140,625	82,750	60.82	3,699.00
3,650	13,322,500	82,190	61.24	3,750.20
3,675	13,505,625	81,630	61.66	3,802.00
3,700	13,690,000	81,090	62.08	3,853.80
3,725	13,875,625	80,540	62.50	3,906.20
3,750	14,062,500	80,000	62.92	3,958.80
3,775	14,256,025	79,470	63.34	4,012.00
3,800	14,440,000	78,950	63.76	4,065.00
3,825	14,630,625	78,430	64.18	4,119.00
3,850	14,822,500	77,920	64.60	4,173.00
3,875	15,015,625	77,420	65.02	4,228.00
3,900	15,210,000	76,930	65.43	4,281.00
3,925	15,405,625	76,440	65.85	4,336.00

TABLE XIX.—FOR WAVE LENGTH, FREQUENCY AND OSCILLATION CONSTANT.— *(Continued)*

λ	λ^2	f	$\sqrt{LC}$	LC
3,950	15,602,500	75,950	66.27	4,392.00
3,975	15,800,625	75,470	66.69	4,448.00
4,000	16,000,000	75,000	67.11	4,505.00
4,025	16,200,625	74,540	67.53	4,561.00
4,050	16,402,500	74,080	67.95	4,617.00
4,075	16,605,625	73,620	68.37	4,675.00
4,100	16,810,000	73,170	68.79	4,732.00
4,125	17,015,625	72,730	69.21	4,790.00
4,150	17,222,500	72,290	69.63	4,848.00
4,175	17,430,625	71,850	70.05	4,907.00
4,200	17,640,000	71,430	70.47	4,966.00
4,225	17,850,625	71,010	70.89	5,026.00
4,250	18,062,500	70,590	71.31	5,085.00
4,275	18,275,625	70,180	71.73	5,145.00
4,300	18,490,000	69,770	72.15	5,206.00
4,325	18,705,625	69,370	72.57	5,266.00
4,350	18,922,500	68,970	72.99	5,328.00
4,375	19,140,625	68,580	73.40	5,388.00
4,400	19,360,000	68,190	73.83	5,451.00
4,425	19,580,625	67,800	74.24	5,511.00
4,450	19,802,500	67,420	74.66	5,574.00
4,475	20,025,625	67,040	75.08	5,637.00
4,500	20,250,000	66,670	75.50	5,700.00
4,525	20,475,625	66,300	75.92	5,764.00
4,550	20,702,500	65,940	76.34	5,827.00
4,575	20,930,625	65,580	76.76	5,892.00
4,600	21,160,000	65,220	77.18	5,957.00
4,625	21,390,625	64,870	77.60	6,020.00
4,650	21,622,500	64,520	78.02	6,087.00
4,675	21,855,625	64,170	78.44	6,153.00
4,700	22,090,000	63,830	78.86	6,219.00
4,725	22,325,625	62,490	79.28	6,285.00
4,750	22,562,500	63,160	79.70	6,352.00
4,775	22,800,625	62,830	80.12	6,419.00
4,800	23,040,000	62,500	80.53	6,485.00
4,825	23,280,625	62,180	80.95	6,553.00

TABLE XIX.—FOR WAVE LENGTH, FREQUENCY AND OSCILLATION CONSTANT.—
(*Continued*)

λ	λ^2	f	$\sqrt{LC}$	LC
4,850	23,522,500	61,860	81.37	6,621.00
4,875	23,765,625	61,540	81.79	6,690.00
4,900	24,010,000	61,230	82.21	6,759.00
4,925	24,255,625	60,910	82.63	6,828.00
4,950	24,502,500	60,610	83.05	6,897.00
4,975	24,750,625	60,300	83.47	6,967.00
5,000	25,000,000	60,000	83.89	7,038.00

INDEX

Numbers refer to pages.

G